British and International Music Yearbook 2004

Volume Two

Editor: Louise Head

Assistant Editors: Sarah Herbert & Rosemary Woodforth

Thirtieth Edition

Rhinegold Publishing Limited
241 Shaftesbury Avenue
London WC2H 8TF
United Kingdom

Editorial: +44 (0)1789 209280/1 Fax: +44 (0)1789 264009
Book Sales: +44 (0)1832 270333 Fax: +44 (0)1832 275560
Advertising: +44 (0)20 7333 1733 Fax: +44 (0)20 7333 1736
Email: bmyb@rhinegold.co.uk   Website: www.rhinegold.co.uk

First published **2004** in Great Britain by
Rhinegold Publishing Ltd
241 Shaftesbury Avenue
London WC2H 8TF
United Kingdom
tel: +44 (0)20 7333 1700

British Library Cataloguing in Publication Data.
A catalogue record for this book is available from the British Library.

ISBN 1-904226-13-2
ISSN 0306 5928

Front cover:
Design by COLOPHON
Tel: 01491 614499

Printed in Great Britain by The Firary Press, Bridport Road, Dorchester, Dorset DT1 1J

INTRODUCING

THE ♪ MUSIC GROUP

Our Name
A new name ... eight highly respected brands.

Our History
The Music Group brings together the instrument companies that were formerly part of the Boosey & Hawkes Group and represent over 175 years of continuous operation.

Our Products
We are a world leader in the manufacture and distribution of band and orchestral instruments and accessories.

Our Businesses
Twelve manufacturing facilities and a worldwide sales and service network.

Our Goal
To provide the highest quality instruments and accessories, together with an unparalleled service.

www.musicgroup.com

UK:
Besson Musical Instruments Limited
Number 1, Blackmoor Lane,
Croxley Business Park,
Watford, Hertfordshire WD18 8GA
tel: +44 (0)1923 659 500

BESSON
LONDON

BUFFET
Crampon & Cie
A PARIS

Höfner

KEILWERTH
JULIUS
Saxophone

R. Paesold

Rico
international

W. Schreiber

Jakob
WINTER

CEFNOGI CREADIGRWYDD
CYNGOR CELFYDDYDAU CYMRU
THE ARTS COUNCIL OF WALES
SUPPORTING CREATIVITY

All images courtesy of BBC NOW Reso...

THE ARTS COUNCIL OF WALES
SUPPORTING CREATIVITY IN MUSIC

SUCH AS:

Archive of Welsh Traditional Music • BBC National Orchestra of Wales • Beaufort Male Choir • Brecon International Festival of Jazz • Caerphilly County Borough Council • Canolfan Gerdd William Mathias • Cardiff Philharmonic Orchestra • Castell Coch Choral Society • Centre for Performance Research Ltd. • Harlech & Ardudwy Music Society • Chamber Orchestra of Wales • Chepstow Town Band • Clwb Cerdd Dwyfor Music Club • Community Music Wales • Brythoniaid Male Voice Choir • Côr Seiriol • Cwmbach Junior School • Cwpan Aur • Dolgellau Music Club • Early Music Wales • Ensemble Cymru • Fishguard Folk Club • Fishguard Music Festival • Friends of the Classics • Gŵyl Cefni • Gŵyl Werin Pontardawe • Halfpenny Folk Club • Hillbillys • Jubilee Hall, Llangeitho • Lampeter Music Club • Laugharne Festival Committee • Live Music Now Wales • Llanelli Choral Society • Llangollen International Musical Eisteddfod • Llanidloes Music & Arts Club • Llantilio Crosenny Festival • Llantrisant Folk Club • Lower Machen Festival • Machynlleth Tabernacle Trust • Machynlleth and District Music Club • Mase - The Music and Sound Experience • Meibion y Machlud • Merlin Music Society • Mid Wales Opera • MusicFest-Aberystwyth • Music Theatre Wales • Musical Theatre Young Singers of the Year • National Youth Arts Wales • North Wales Bluegrass Music and Dance Festival • North Wales International Music Festival • North Wales Jazz Society • Norwegian Church Arts Centre • Parc and Dare Junior Band • Penywaun Enterprise Partnership • Pontargothi Memorial Hall • Presteigne Festival of Music and the Arts Ltd • Rhyl Music Club • Round The Horn Jazz Society • Royal Buckley Town Band • Ruthin Festival Association • Sesiwn Fawr Dolgellau • Symphonia Cymru • Sound Affairs • St. David's Chamber Orchestra • St. David's Hall • Swansea Festival of Music and the Arts Ltd • The Mold & District Choral Society • The Welsh Chamber Orchestra Ltd. • Torfaen Jazz Society • trac - Music Traditions Wales • Vale of Glamorgan Festival • Welsh Amateur Music Federation • Welsh Jazz Society • Welsh Music Information Centre • Welsh National Opera • Welshpool Music Club • Young Persons Training Orchestras

...AND MANY OTHERS

WWW.CELFCYMRU.ORG.UK WWW.ARTSWALES.ORG.UK

ARIENNIR GAN Y LOTERI
LOTTERY FUNDED

Noddir gan
Lywodraeth Cynulliad Cymru
Sponsored by
Welsh Assembly Government

Lynn Harrell

These new Pirazzi "Evahs" are unique! Beauty of tone – huge dynamic range – warm but brilliant and clear sound – and, of course, a uniform and ease of response.

I have never been so impressed by a company as much as yours. I am a sound man. I have found the ultimate strings.

Lynn Harrell

evah pirazzi
Cello Strings

Please info@pirastro.com contact us

...now available!

SEIT 1798

PIRASTRO®
MUSIKSAITEN

HANDMADE BY PIRASTRO
PIRASTRO GmbH · 63069 OFFENBACH AM MAIN GERMANY · www.pirastro.com

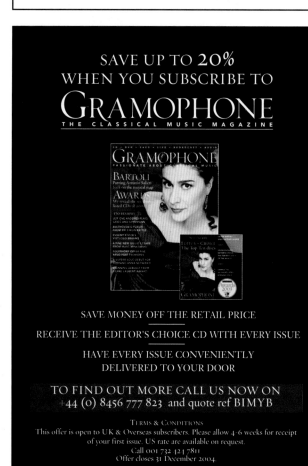

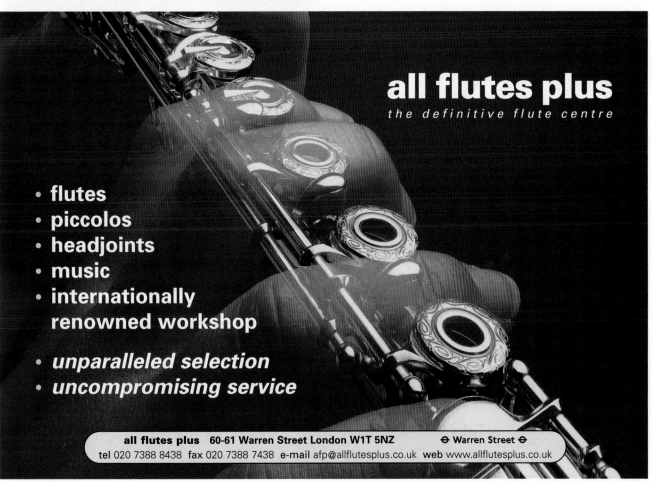

SEYCHELLES ANNUAL INTERNATIONAL FESTIVAL OF CLASSICAL MUSIC

A delectable feast of music at an idyllic venue
Thursday, 27th May to Monday, 14th June 2004 (19 days inclusive)

IN PARTNERSHIP WITH KENYA AIRWAYS AND AIR SEYCHELLES

Joint hosts of the festival: The British High Commissioner and Seychelles Minister of Culture
Co-Musical Directors and Conductors: Brian Wright and Brian Kay, Chorus Master: Roger Humphrey

Performers: Eight international soloists
The International Festival Symphony Orchestra (talented professional players)
The International Festival Chorus (experienced choristers)

CHORAL WORKS : Puccini - Messa di Gloria
Verdi - Requiem Mass
Selection from Opera Choruses - edited by John Rutter
ORCHESTRAL WORKS : Beethoven - Symphony No. 5 in C minor
Bruch - Violin Concerto in E minor
Dvorak - Cello Concerto in B Minor (centenary year)
Mozart - Oboe Concerto in C major
Tchaikovsky - Symphony No. 2 "Little Russian"
Tchaikovsky - Piano Concerto No. 1 in B flat minor

Photo: Angelo Cavalli

Photo: Frank Schneider

HIGHLIGHTS OF THE FESTIVAL

* Grand opening performance of Verdi's Requiem at the Nairobi Sports Amphitheatre *
* Open-air Opera Extravaganza at the Nairobi National Park (large crowd expected) *
* Three-day safari at the famous Treetops/The Ark and Mount Kenya Safari Club *
* Visit to Sweetwaters Game Reserve and photo opportunities with Morani, the pet rhino *
* Official reception at the British High Commissioner's Residence, at Bel'Air, Seychelles *
* Three open-air concerts at Planters House, Plantation Club Resort (under the palm-trees) *
* Three All Soloists Chamber Concerts at Valmer Room, Plantation Club Resort *

THIS SPECIAL OFFER INCLUDES

* Return flight by Kenya Airways, including airport taxes, Heathrow/Nairobi/Seychelles
* 6 nights in five-star accommodation (Lonrho Africa Hotels), two sharing, on full-board basis, including 3-day safari tour of the Aberdare National Park
* 8 nights accommodation, two sharing, on half-board basis at a top resort, in Seychelles
* Transfer: airport/hotel/airport in Kenya and Seychelles
* Tickets to 10 concerts in Nairobi and Seychelles, transportation provided where required
* Quality green souvenir polo-shirt with festival logo

This holiday tour is open to all experienced Choristers (SATB) and prospective Friends of the Seychelles Festival of Classical Music
Please contact Festival Executive Director, Marc Sabadin, on tel: 01268 681565, fax: 01268 478894, e-mail: director@sifocm.co.uk
web-site: www.sifocm.co.uk, for an application form and further information

COST FOR THIS EXCLUSIVE HOLIDAY PACKAGE: £2,000 (basic)
This is indeed a lifetime opportunity that should not be missed!

NB: This tour is covered by a Tour Operator's Insurance, as described under Article 5 of EC Directive 90/314/EEC

Could you help performers back to fitness?

Performers place particular strains on their bodies and even minor injuries can seriously affect their ability to perform. Most problems can be treated by their own GP, but others require specialist help.

The British Association for Performing Arts Medicine (BAPAM) is a registered charity providing free medical assessments for performing artists, including actors, singers, musicians and dancers.

By becoming a member you will help us develop our services so that performers receive the specialist help they need, when they need it.

BAPAM services include:
- Free confidential clinics providing specialist medical assessments.
- A helpline on medical issues for performers.
- A directory of conventional and complementary medical practitioners experienced in working with performers.
- Injury prevention and health-awareness training for performers and students.
- Performing arts medicine training for health practitioners.
- The AMABO (Association of Medical Advisors to British Orchestras) scheme, providing independent medical advice to orchestral musicians.
- Research into health problems affecting performers.

If you would like to support our work by becoming a member or joining our Directory of Practitioners then ring our admin line.
admin: **0845 602 0235**
email: admin@bapam.org.uk
www.bapam.org.uk

If you are a performer you can ring our helpline for more information and to make an appointment:
helpline: **0845 602 0235**
email: clinic@bapam.org.uk
www.bapam.org.uk

Registered Charity: 1083295

British Association for PERFORMING ARTS MEDICINE

caring for performers' health

xvi

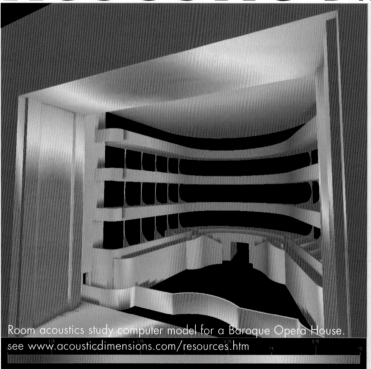

CONTENTS

Volume 1

✦ Performance ✦

Artists and Agents

Competitions

Broadcasting

Venues and Promoters

✦ Indexes ✦

Volume 2

✦ Education ✦

✦ Services ✦

Marketing

Suppliers and Services

Beethoven's Piano Sonatas

A Short Companion

Charles Rosen

Beethoven's piano sonatas form one of the most important collections of works in the whole history of music. In this comprehensive and authoritative guide, Charles Rosen places the works in context and provides an understanding of the formal principles involved in interpreting and performing this unique repertoire, covering such aspects as sonata form, phrasing and tempo, as well as the use of pedal and trills. The book includes a CD of Rosen performing.

"[Readers] will have much to gain from Rosen's admirably wide range of musical reference, and his usual rich mixture of musical wisdom and opinion, both eminently worth having."
—Leon Plantinga, *Times Literary Supplement*

288pp. illustrated with music examples, Hb £20.00

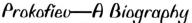

Prokofiev—A Biography

From Russia to the West, 1891–1935

David Nice

"The outstanding merit...of Nice's biography [is the] way that it makes us want to go back to the music, enriched by a deeper engagement with the piquant personality that created it."
—Andrew Clark, *Financial Times*

"[A] balanced life-and-works study that has eluded all previous attempts"
—David Fanning, *BBC Music Magazine*

364pp. 16 illus. Hb £25.00

Notes from the Pianist's Bench

Boris Berman

"an easily digested, reasonably priced introduction to the history of the piano...difficult to beat."
—Pamela Lidiard, *Classical Music*

288pp. 178 musical examples Pb £10.99

Bill Evans

How My Heart Sings

Peter Pettinger

This enthralling book is the first biography in English of Bill Evans, one of the most influential of all jazz pianists.

"marvellous"—Ian Thomson, *The Daily Telegraph*

384pp. 40 illus. Pb £10.99

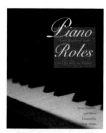

Piano Roles

A New History of the Piano

James Parakilas et al.

Foreword by Noah Adams

"A wonderful mosaic of the history of the piano and the diverse parts it has played in its 300 years of life."—Henry Sheen, *New Statesman*

480pp. 153 b/w + 65 col. illus. Pb £12.50

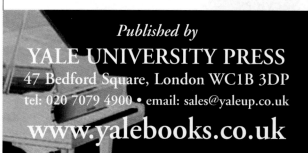

Published by
YALE UNIVERSITY PRESS
47 Bedford Square, London WC1B 3DP
tel: 020 7079 4900 • email: sales@yaleup.co.uk
www.yalebooks.co.uk

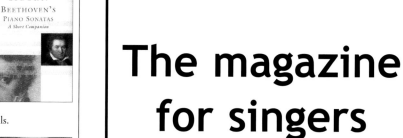

The magazine for singers

First published in 1993

Ten years of *The Singer* magazine

Bi-monthly (6 issues)

Annual UK Subscription prices: £16.00

Please send your orders to:
**Rhinegold Subscriptions,
FREEPOST LON20614,
Peterborough PE8 5BR**
(Cheques payable to
Rhinegold Publishig Ltd)
Tel: **01832 270333**
Fax: **01832 275560**
Email: **subs@rhinegold.co.uk**

www.rhinegold.co.uk

Recording

✦ Organisations ✦

✦ Indexes ✦

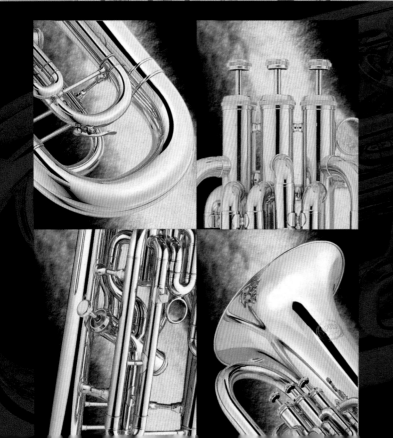

Key and Abbreviations

The geographical scope of the *British and International Music Yearbook* includes England, Scotland, Wales, Northern Ireland, the Isle of Man and the Channel Islands. In lists arranged in alphabetical order of places, London entries are grouped together at the beginning.

The postal address is followed by the full telephone, fax and email numbers. If a telephone number is followed by 'also fax' this indicates the number can also be used as a fax number. In the *British and International Music Yearbook* international telephone numbers are given complete wherever possible, with the UK international access code first, the country code, the local area code, followed by the subscriber's number. (If dialling the number from within the relevant country, the international access code and country code are omitted and a zero is added at the front of the area code.) In the International sections the UK international access code is omitted and replaced with a '+' sign.

In addition to conventional address abbreviations, the following are used throughout the book.

Musical Performance

acc	accompanist	fl	flute	sax	saxophone
bar	baritone	f-pno	fortepiano	sop	soprano
br	brass	gui	guitar	str	string
bs	bass	hn	horn	synth	synthesizer
bs-bar	bass-baritone	hp	harp	tb	tuba
bsn	bassoon	hpd	harpsichord	ten	tenor
cbsn	contrabassoon	inst	instrument, instrumental	timp	timpani
chmbr	chamber	m-sop	mezzo-soprano	tpt	trumpet
cl	clarinet	mus	music, musical	trb	trombone
clvd	clavichord	ob	oboe	va	viola
con	contralto	ob d'am	oboe d'amore	va d'am	viola d'amore
cor	cor anglais	orch	orchestra, orchestral	vc	violoncello
c-ten	counter-tenor	org	organ	vib	vibraphone
db	double-bass	perc	percussion	vn	violin
eh	english horn	picc	piccolo	w/wind	woodwind
ens	ensemble	pno	piano		
euph	euphonium	rcdr	recorder		

Organisations, Orchestras and Halls

ABRSM	Associated Board for the Royal Schools of Music	GSMD	Guildhall School of Music and Drama	RLPO	Royal Liverpool Philharmonic Orchestra
BBCPO	BBC Philharmonic	LCM	London College of Music	RNCM	Royal Northern College of Music
BBCSO	BBC Symphony Orchestra	LPO	London Philharmonic	ROH	Royal Opera House
BBCSSO	BBC Scottish Symphony Orchestra	LSO	London Symphony Orchestra	RPO	Royal Philharmonic Orchestra
BMIC	British Music Information Centre	PO	Philharmonia Orchestra	RSAMD	Royal Scottish Academy of Music and Drama
CBSO	City of Birmingham Symphony Orchestra	QEH	Queen Elizabeth Hall	SMIC	Scottish Music Information Centre
		RAH	Royal Albert Hall	TCL	Trinity College London
		RAM	Royal Academy of Music	WCMD	Welsh College of Music and Drama
ECO	English Chamber Orchestra	RCM	Royal College of Music		
ENO	English National Opera	RFH	Royal Festival Hall	WNO	Welsh National Opera

Positions

admin	administrator	dir	director	mkt	marketing
arr	arranger, arranged by	ed	editor	offr	officer
asst	assistant	exec	executive	sec	secretary
chmn	chairman	gen	general	subs	subscription(s)
cond	conductor	hon	honorary		
co-ord	co-ordinator	mgr	manager, managing		

Other

accs	accessories	jnr	junior	p/t	part time
coll	collection	max	maximum	pw	per week
dept	department	m/class	masterclass	snr	senior
educ	education, educational	mgt	management	tel	telephone number
elec	electronic	min	minimum	u/grad	undergraduate
ext	extension	mkt	marketing	w/day	week day
f/t	full time	ms(s)	manuscript(s)	w/end	weekend
gen	general	mus tech	music technology	w/shop	workshop
gr	grade	pa	per annum	yr	year
hr	hour	p/grad	postgraduate		

xxiv

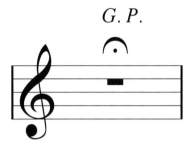

Education

EDUCATION

Choir Schools

The schools listed below provide choristers for cathedral choirs and some parish church choirs. They are primarily independent schools and most are members of the **Choir Schools' Association** (The Minster School, Deangate, York YO1 2JA *tel:* 01904 624900 *fax:* 01904 557232 *email:* info@choirschools.org.uk *website:* www.choirschools.org.uk. Mrs W A Jackson, admin).

Preparatory Schools (age 7-13)

Abbey School. Church St, Tewkesbury, Glos GL20 5PD *tel:* 01684 294460 *fax:* 01684 290797 *email:* info@theabbeyschool.org.uk. G Jones, head; Benjamin Nicholas, dir of mus.

Bramdean School. Richmond Lodge, Leavitree, Exeter, Devon EX1 2QR *tel:* 01392 273387 *fax:* 01392 439330 *email:* bramdeanschool.exeter@virgin.net. Diane Stoneman, head; Tony Connett, dir of mus.

Cathedral Choir School. Whitcliffe Lane, Ripon, N Yorks HG4 2LA *tel:* 01765 602134 *fax:* 01765 608760 *email:* admin@choirschool.demon.co.uk. C R E Pepys, head; A J Bryden, dir of mus.

The Cathedral School (Llandaff). Cardiff Rd, Llandaff, Cardiff CF5 2YH *tel:* 029 2056 3179 *fax:* 029 2056 7752 *email:* hm.sec@thecathedralschool.co.uk. Lindsay Gray, head; Michael Hoeg, dir of mus.

Christ Church Cathedral School. 3 Brewer St, Oxford OX1 1QW *tel:* 01865 242561 *fax:* 01865 202945 *email:* schooloffice@cccs.org.uk. James Smith, head; Paul Miles-Kingston, dir of mus.

Exeter Cathedral School. The Chantry, Palace Gate, Exeter, Devon EX1 1HX *tel:* 01392 255298 *fax:* 01392 422718 *email:* exetercs@aol.com. C J A Helyer, head; S W Tanner, dir of mus.

King's College School. West Rd, Cambridge CB3 9DN *tel:* 01223 365814 *fax:* 01223 461388 *email:* office@kingscam.demon.co.uk. N J Robinson, head; Simon Brown, dir of mus.

King's School Junior School. Ely, Cambs CB7 4DB *tel:* 01353 660730 *fax:* 01353 665281. A G Duncan, head; N Porter-Thaw, dir of mus.

Lanesborough School. Maori Rd, Guildford, Surrey GU1 2EL *tel:* 01483 880650 *fax:* 01483 880651 *email:* office@lanesborough.surrey.sch.uk. K S Crombie, head; S Watts, dir of mus.

Lichfield Cathedral School. The Palace, Lichfield, Staffs WS13 7LH *tel:* 01543 306170 *also fax; email:* lichfield.cathedral.school@cableinet.co.uk. P Allwood, head; R W Dingle, dir of mus.

Lincoln Minster Preparatory School. Hillside, Lindum Terrace, Lincoln LN2 5RW *tel:* 01522 543764 *fax:* 01522 537938 *email:* admin@lincolnminsterschool.co.uk. Karen Maltby, head; Aric Prentice, dir of mus.

The Minster School. Deangate, York YO1 7JA *tel:* 01904 557230 *fax:* 01904 557232 *email:* school@yorkminster.org. Richard Shephard, head; Robert Poyser, dir of mus.

New College School. Savile Rd, Oxford OX1 3UA *tel:* 01865 243657 *also fax.* P F Hindle, head; R W Allen, dir of mus.

Norwich School. 70 The Close, Norwich NR1 4DQ *tel:* 01603 623194 *fax:* 01603 627036 *email:* admissions@norwich-school.org.uk. J B Hawkins, head; Colin Dowdeswell, dir of mus.

The Pilgrims' School. 3 The Close, Winchester, Hants SO23 9LT *tel:* 01962 854189 *fax:* 01962 843610 *email:* pilgrimssecretary@btinternet.com. Rev B A Rees, head; Hilary Webster, dir of mus.

Polwhele House School. Truro, Cornwall TR4 9AE *tel:* 01872 273011 *also fax; email:* polwhele@talk21.com. J Mason, head.

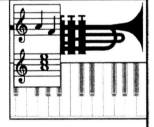

Queen Elizabeth Grammar Junior School. 158 Northgate, Wakefield, W Yorks WF1 3QY *tel:* 01924 373821 *fax:* 01924 231604 *email:* Secretary@queen-elizabeth.wakefld.sch.uk. M M Bisset, head; David Turmeau, dir of mus.

St Edmund's Junior School. Canterbury, Kent CT2 8HU *tel:* 01227 475600 *fax:* 01227 471083 *email:* junsch@stedmunds.org.uk. R G Bacon, head; Ian Sutcliffe, dir of mus.

St Edward's Junior School. Sandfield Park, Liverpool L12 1LF *tel:* 0151 281 2300 *fax:* 0151 281 4900. Sally Carter, head; Brenda Bixter, dir of mus.

St George's School. Windsor Castle, Berks SL4 1QF *tel:* 01753 865553 *fax:* 01753 842093 *email:* headmaster@stgwindsor.co.uk. J R Jones, head; Mrs Y Day, dir of mus.

St John's College School. 73 Grange Rd, Cambridge CB3 9AB *tel:* 01223 353532 *fax:* 01223 315535 *email:* admissions@sjcs.co.uk. K L Jones, head; C Johnson, dir of mus.

St Mary's Preparatory and Choir School. Chart Lane, Reigate, Surrey RH2 7RN *tel:* 01737 244880 *fax:* 01737 221540 *email:* headmaster@reigate-stmarys.org. David Tidmarsh, head; Marian Holmes, dir of mus; John Tobin, master of choristers.

St Paul's Cathedral School. 2 New Change, London EC4M 9AD *tel:* 020 7248 5156 *fax:* 020 7329 6568 *email:* admissions@spcs.london.sch.uk. Andrew Dobbin, head; Mark Williams, school dir of mus.

Salisbury Cathedral School. 1 The Close, Salisbury, Wilts SP1 2EQ *tel:* 01722 555300 *fax:* 01722 410910 *email:* aspire@salisbury.enterprise-plc.com. R M Thackray, head; I M Wicks, dir of mus.

Westminster Abbey Choir School. Dean's Yard, London SW1P 3NY *tel:* 020 7222 6151 *fax:* 020 7222 1548 *email:* headmaster@westminster-abbey.org. Jonathan Milton, head; Simon Bell, mus master.

Independent and Maintained Secondary Schools (age 7-18)

Bristol Cathedral School. College Square, Bristol BS1 5TS *tel:* 0117 929 1872 *fax:* 0117 930 4219 *email:* Headmaster@bristol-cathedral.fsbusiness.co.uk. K J Riley, head; John Seymour, dir of mus.

Chetham's School of Music *see* **Specialist Music Schools.**

Hereford Cathedral School. Old Deanery, Cathedral Close, Hereford HR1 2NG *tel:* 01432 363522 (snr school) *fax:* 01432 363525. H C Tomlinson, head of snr school; T R Lowe, head of prep school; J M Williams, dir of mus.

King's School (Gloucester). Pitt St, Gloucester GL1 2BG *tel:* 01452 337337 *fax:* 01452 337314. Peter Lacey, head; Ian Fox, dir of mus.

King's School (Peterborough). Park Rd, Peterborough, Cambs PE1 2UE *tel:* 01733 751541 *fax:* 01733 751542 *email:* ksp@cwcom.net. G L Longman, head; N C Kerrison, dir of mus.

King's School Rochester. Satis House, Boley Hill, Rochester, Kent ME1 1TE *tel:* 01634 888555 *fax:* 01634 888505 *email:* walker@kings-school-rochester.co.uk. I R Walker, head; G R Williams, dir of mus; R M Sayer, dir of mus, Rochester Cathedral.

King's School (Worcester). College Green, Worcester WR1 2LL *tel:* 01905 721700 *fax:* 01905 721710 *email:* info@ksw.org.uk. T H Keyes, head; D E Brookshaw, dir of mus.

Lincoln Minster School *see* **Preparatory Choir Schools (age 7-13).**

Magdalen College School. Cowley Place, Oxford OX4 1DZ *tel:* 01865 242191 *fax:* 01865 240379 *email:* admissions@mcsoxford.org. A D Halls, head; C J G Ives, org; M N Pearce, dir of mus.

The Minster School. Nottingham Rd, Southwell, Notts NG25 0HG *tel:* 01636 817360 (24-hr hot line) *fax:* 01636 817359. P J Blinston, head; Duncan Lloyd, dir of mus.

Norwich School *see* **Preparatory Choir Schools (age 7-13).**

St Edward's College. Sandfield Park, Liverpool L12 1LF *tel:* 0151 281 1999 ext 225 *fax:* 0151 281 1909. John Waszek, head; John Moseley, dir of mus.

St James' School. 22 Bargate, Grimsby, N E Lincs DN34 4SY *tel:* 01472 503260 *fax:* 01472 503275 *email:* enquiries@saintjamesschool.freeserve.co.uk. Mrs S M Isac, head; Adrian King, dir of mus.

St Mary's Music School. Coates Hall, 25 Grosvenor Cres, Edinburgh EH12 5EL *tel:* 0131 538 7766 *fax:* 0131 467 7289 *email:* info@st-marys-music-school.co.uk. Jennifer Rimer, head; John Grundy, dir of mus.

Wells Cathedral School. Wells, Somerset BA5 2ST *tel:* 01749 834200 *fax:* 01749 834201 *email:* admissions@wells-cathedral-school.com. Elizabeth Cairncross, head; Nick Wilson, head, jnr school; Dorothy Nancekievell, dir of mus.

Roman Catholic Choir Schools

Bramdean School *see* **Preparatory Choir Schools (age 7-13).**

St Edward's Junior School. Sandfield Park, Liverpool L12 1LF *tel:* 0151 281 2300 *fax:* 0151 281 4900. Sally Carter, head; Brenda Bixter, dir of mus; Mervyn Cousins, dir of cathedral mus.

Westminster Cathedral Choir School. Ambrosden Ave, London SW1P 1QH *tel:* 020 7798 9081 *fax:* 020 7630 7209 *email:* office@choirschool.com. J R Brown, head; M Baker, master of mus.

Specialist Music Schools

The schools listed below are especially devoted to the training of musically gifted children. A full list of entry requirements may be found in the *Music Education Yearbook 2003/2004* which is also available from Rhinegold Publishing Ltd.

The BRIT School. 60 The Crescent, Croydon CR0 2HN *tel:* 020 8665 5242 *fax:* 020 8665 8676 *email:* admin@brit.croydon.sch.uk. Nick Williams, principal; David Beer, dir of mus.

Chetham's School of Music. Long Millgate, Manchester M3 1SB *tel:* 0161 834 9644 *fax:* 0161 839 3609 *email:* chets@chethams.com. Mrs C J Moreland, head; Stephen Threlfall, dir of mus.

The City of Edinburgh Music School. Broughton High School, Carrington Rd, Edinburgh EH4 1EG *tel:* 0131 332 7805 *fax:* 0131 343 3296 *email:* musicschool@broughton.edin.sch.uk. Tudor Morris, dir of mus school.

London Oratory School. Seagrave Rd, London SW6 1RX *tel:* 020 7385 0102 *fax:* 020 7381 7676. John McIntosh, headmaster; Lee Ward, head of mus.

Music School of Douglas Academy. Mains Estate, Milngavie, Glasgow G62 7HL *tel:* 0141 956 2281 *fax:* 0141 956 1533. Gordon Wilson, head teacher; Ronald McIntosh, course dir (mus).

Pimlico School. Lupus St, London SW1V 3AT *tel:* 020 7828 0881/7821 1717 *fax:* 020 7931 0549 *email:* pimspecmus@excite.co.uk. Philip Barnard, head; Nigel Rowlands, dir of mus.

Purcell School. Aldenham Rd, Bushey, Herts WD23 2TS *tel:* 01923 331100 *fax:* 01923 331166 *email:* info@purcell-school.org. John Tolputt, head; Quentin Poole, dir of mus.

St Mary's Music School. Coates Hall, 25 Grosvenor Cres, Edinburgh EH12 5EL *tel:* 0131 538 7766 *fax:* 0131 467 7289 *email:* info@st-marys-music-school.co.uk. Jennifer Rimer, head; John Grundy, dir of mus.

Wells Cathedral School. Wells, Somerset BA5 2ST *tel:* 01749 834200 *fax:* 01749 834201 *email:* admissions@wells-cathedral-school.com. Elizabeth Cairncross, head; Dorothy Nancekievill, dir of mus.

Yehudi Menuhin School. Cobham Rd, Stoke d'Abernon, Cobham, Surrey KT11 3QQ *tel:* 01932 864739 *fax:* 01932 864633 *email:* admin@yehudimenuhinschool.co.uk. Nicolas Chisholm, head; Malcolm Singer, dir of mus.

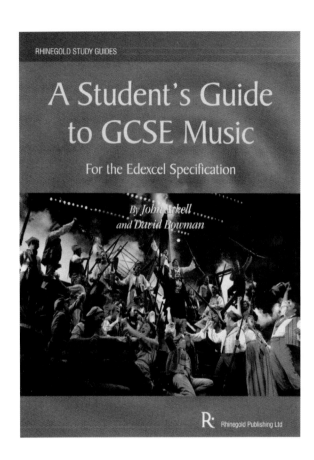
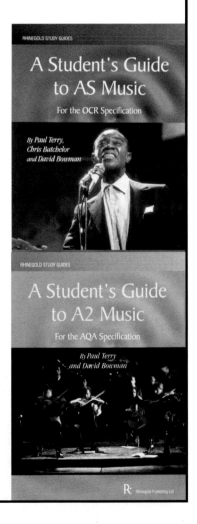

EDUCATING
THE MUSICIANS OF TOMORROW

Do you know a child with a special talent in music?

The UK's five specialist
music schools exist to
provide a unique
world-class education.

Come and visit us

St Mary's Music School,
Coates Hall, 25 Grosvenor Crescent,
Edinburgh EH12 5EL
Tel. 0131 538 7766
www.st-marys-music-school.co.uk

Chethams School of Music,
Long Millgate,
Manchester M3 1SB
Tel. 0161 834 9644
www.chethams.com

The Purcell School,
Aldenham Road,
Bushey, Herts WD23 2TS
Tel. 01923 331100
www.purcell-school.org

Wells Cathedral School,
Wells, Somerset
BA5 2ST
Tel. 01749 834200
www.wells-cathedral-school.com

Yehudi Menuhin School,
Cobham Road, Stoke d'Abernon,
Cobham, Surrey KT11 3QQ
Tel. 01932 864739
www.yehudimenuhinschool.co.uk

Government funding is available for
UK residents providing up to 100% of fees.

Visit the DfES website: www.dfes.gov.uk/mds
for more information about the
music and dance scheme.

NAMDS
National
Association
of Music
and Dance
Schools

Independent Schools Offering Music Scholarships

All the schools listed below offer music scholarships on the basis of musical ability. For full information on scholarships offered and all musical activities see the *Music Education Yearbook 2003/2004,* available from Rhinegold Publishing Ltd.

Abbotsholme School (Co-ed). Rocester, Uttoxeter, Staffs ST14 5BS *tel:* 01889 590217 *fax:* 01889 591001 *email:* admissions@abbots holme.co.uk. Stephen Fairclough, head; Timothy Moon, dir of mus.

Abingdon School (Boys). Abingdon, Oxon OX14 1DE *tel:* 01235 521563 *fax:* 01235 849079. Mark Turner, head; Michael Stinton, dir of mus.

Ackworth School (Co-ed). Ackworth, Pontefract, W Yorks WF7 7LT *tel:* 01977 611401 *fax:* 01977 616225 *email:* Ackworthq@aol.com. Martin Dickinson, head; Richard Ellis, dir of mus.

Aldenham School (Boys). Elstree, Herts WD6 3AJ *tel:* 01923 858122 *fax:* 01923 854410 *email:* admissions@aldenham.com. R S Harman, head; J Wyatt, dir of mus.

Alleyn's School (Co-ed). Townley Rd, Dulwich, London SE22 8SU *tel:* 020 8557 1500 *fax:* 020 8557 1462 *email:* music@alleyns.org.uk. C Diggory, head; A T Kermode, dir of mus.

Ampleforth College (Boys). York YO62 4ER *tel:* 01439 788000 *fax:* 01439 788330 *email:* admiss@ampleforth.org.uk. Revd G F L Chamberlain, head; Ian Little, dir of mus.

Ardingly College (Co-ed). Haywards Heath, W Sussex RH17 6SQ *tel:* 01444 892577 *fax:* 01444 892266 *email:* registrar@ardingly.com. J R Franklin, head; Robert Hammersley, dir of mus.

Ashford School (Girls). East Hill, Ashford, Kent TN24 8PB *tel:* 01233 625171 *fax:* 01233 647185 *email:* registrar@ashfordschool.co.uk. Paula Holloway, headmistress; Maria Young, dir of mus.

Badminton School, Bristol (Girls). Westbury on Trym, Bristol BS9 3BA *tel:* 0117 905 5200 *fax:* 0117 962 8963 *email:* registrar@ badminton.bristol.sch.uk. Mrs J Scarrow, head; W Goodchild, dir of mus.

Bancroft's School (Co-ed). Woodford Green, Essex IG8 0RF *tel:* 020 8505 4821 *fax:* 020 8559 0032 *email:* headmaster@bancrofts.essex.sch.uk. P R Scott, head; R M Bluff, dir of mus.

Barnard Castle School (Co-ed). Barnard Castle, Co Durham DL12 8UN *tel:* 01833 690222 *fax:* 01833 638985 *email:* secretary@barney school.org.uk. M D Featherstone, head; Mark Mawhinney, dir of mus.

Beaconhurst Grange. 52 Kenilworth Rd, Bridge of Allan FK9 4RR *tel:* 01786 832146 *fax:* 01786 833415 *email:* bursar@beaconhurst.com. D R Clegg, head.

Bedales School (Co-ed). Church Rd, Steep, Petersfield, Hants GU32 2DG *tel:* 01730 300100 *fax:* 01730 300500 *email:* admissions@bedales .org.uk. A Hardie, registrar; Keith Budge, head; Nicholas Gleed, dir of mus.

Bedford High School (Girls). Bromham Rd, Bedford MK40 2BS *tel:* 01234 360221 *fax:* 01234 353552 *email:* head@bedfordhigh.co.uk. Mrs G Piotrowska, head; Philip Bond, dir of mus.

Bedford School (Boys). De Parys Ave, Bedford MK40 2TU *tel:* 01234 362200 *fax:* 01234 362283. I P Evans OBE, head; Andrew Morris, dir of mus.

Bedgebury School (Girls). Bedgebury Park, Goudhurst, Cranbrook, Kent TN17 2SH *tel:* 01580 878143 *fax:* 01580 212252 *email:* info@ bedgeburyschool.co.uk. Kate Pusey, dir of mus.

Bedstone College (Co-ed). Bucknell, Shropshire SY7 0BG *tel:* 01547 530303 *fax:* 01547 530740 *email:* admin@bedstone.demon.co.uk. Michael Symonds, head; John Bowen, dir of mus.

Benenden School (Girls). Cranbrook, Kent TN17 4AA *tel:* 01580 240592 *fax:* 01580 240280 *email:* schooloffice@benenden.kent.sch.uk. Mrs C M Oulton, head; Stuart Beer, dir of mus.

Berkhamsted Collegiate School (Co-ed). Castle St, Berkhamsted, Herts HP4 2BB *tel:* 01442 358000 *fax:* 01442 358040 *email:* info@ beschool.org. Peter Hopkins, dir of mus.

Bethany School (Co-ed). Goudhurst, Cranbrook, Kent TN17 1LB *tel:* 01580 213110 *fax:* 01580 211151 *email:* bmskcb@hotmail.com.

N D B Dorey, head; K Brown, dir of mus.

Birkdale School (Boys). Oakholme Rd, Sheffield S10 3DH *tel:* 0114 266 8408 *fax:* 0114 267 1947 *email:* birkdalesc@aol.com. Robert Court, head; Andrew Sanderson, dir of mus.

Bishop's Stortford College (Co-ed). Bishop's Stortford, Herts CM23 2PJ *tel:* 01279 838575 *fax:* 01279 836570. J G Trotman, head; Andrew Bruce, dir of mus.

Blundell's School (Co-ed). Tiverton, Devon EX16 4DN *tel:* 01884 252543 *fax:* 01884 243232 *email:* registrars@blundells.org. J Leigh, head; A H Barlow, dir of mus.

Bootham School (Co-ed). York YO30 7BU *tel:* 01904 623261 *fax:* 01904 652106. Ian M Small, head; Paul Feehan, dir of mus.

Bradfield College (Boys). Reading, Berks RG7 6AU *tel:* 0118 964 4812 *fax:* 0118 964 4811. P J M Roberts, head; A J Copus, dir of mus.

Brentwood School (Co-ed). Ingrave Rd, Brentwood, Essex CM15 8AS *tel:* 01277 243243 *fax:* 01277 243299 *email:* headmaster@ brentwood.essex.sch.uk. J A B Kelsall, head; David Pickthall, dir of mus.

Brighton College (Co-ed). Eastern Rd, Brighton BN2 0AL *tel:* 01273 704200 *fax:* 01273 704204 *email:* admissions@ brightoncollege.demon.co.uk. A F Seldon, head; Richard B Niblett, dir of mus.

Bristol Cathedral School (Boys). College Square, Bristol BS1 5TS *tel:* 0117 929 1872 *fax:* 0117 930 4219 *email:* Headmaster@ bristol-cathedral.fsbusiness.co.uk. K J Riley, head; J H Seymour, dir of mus.

Bristol Grammar School (Co-ed). University Rd, Bristol BS8 1SR *tel:* 0117 973 6006 *fax:* 0117 946 7485 *email:* headmaster@ bgs.bristol.sch.uk. D J Mascord, head; R T Osmond, dir of mus.

The British School of Brussels (Co-ed). Leuvensesteenweg 19, B-3080 Tervuren, Belgium *tel:* 00 32 2 766 0430 *fax:* 00 32 2 767 8070 *email:* admissions@britishschool.be. Tim Willetts, head of inst mus.

Bromley High School GDST (Girls). Blackbrook Lane, Bickley, Bromley, Kent BR1 2TW *tel:* 020 8468 7981 *fax:* 020 8295 1062 *email:* k.rigeway@bro.gdst.net. Mrs L Duggleby, head; Mrs K Ridgeway, dir of mus.

Bromsgrove School (Co-ed). Worcester Rd, Bromsgrove, Worcs B61 7DU *tel:* 01527 579679 *fax:* 01527 576177 *email:* admissions. upper@bromsgrove-school.co.uk. T M Taylor, head; A E Bird, dir of mus.

Bryanston School (Co-ed). Blandford, Dorset DT11 0PX *tel:* 01258 452411 *fax:* 01258 484661 *email:* headmaster@bryanston.co.uk. T D Wheare, head; P B Searle-Barnes, dir of mus.

Burgess Hill School (Girls). Keymer Rd, Burgess Hill, W Sussex RH15 0EG *tel:* 01444 241050 *fax:* 01444 870314 *email:* music@ burgesshill-school.com. Susan Gorham, head; C R B Haslam, dir of mus.

Canford School (Co-ed). Canford Magna, Wimborne, Dorset BH21 3AD *tel:* 01202 841254 *fax:* 01202 881009 *email:* dwarwick@canford.com. J D Lever, head; D A Warwick, dir of mus.

Casterton School (Girls). Kirkby Lonsdale, Carnforth, Lancs LA6 2SG *tel:* 01524 279200 *fax:* 01524 279208 *email:* admissions@ castertonschool.co.uk. A F Thomas, head; D C Chapman, dir of mus.

Caterham School (Co-ed). Harestone Valley Rd, Caterham, Surrey CR3 6YA *tel:* 01883 343028 *fax:* 01883 347795 *email:* enquiries@ caterhamschool.co.uk. R A E Davey, head; J M Gray, dir of mus.

Charterhouse (Boys). Godalming, Surrey GU7 2DX *tel:* 01483 291695/6 *fax:* 01483 291637 *email:* headmaster@charterhouse.org.uk. Revd John Witheridge, head; Robin Wells, dir of mus.

Cheadle Hulme School (Co-ed). Claremont Rd, Cheadle Hulme, Cheadle SK8 6EF *tel:* 0161 488 3330 *fax:* 0161 488 3344. P V Dixon, head; P Dewhurst, dir of mus.

Cheltenham College (Co-ed). Bath Rd, Cheltenham, Glos GL53 7LD *tel:* 01242 513540 *fax:* 01242 265630 *email:* college@ cheltcoll.gloucs.sch.uk. P A Chamberlain, head; G S Busbridge, dir of mus.

The Cheltenham Ladies' College (Girls). Bayshill Rd, Cheltenham, Glos GL50 3EP *tel:* 01242 520691 *fax:* 01242 227882 *email:* registrar@cheltladiescollege.org. Mrs V Tuck, principal; D Hawley, dir of mus.

Chigwell School (Co-ed). Chigwell, Essex IG7 6QF *tel:* 020 8501 5700/5745 (mus dept) *fax:* 020 8500 6232. D F Gibbs, head; Benjamin Charles, dir of mus.

Christ College (Co-ed). Brecon, Powys LD3 8AG *tel:* 01874 615440 (mus dept) *fax:* 01874 615475 *email:* music@christcollegebrecon.com. D P Jones, head; Jonathan T Cooper, dir of mus.

Christ's Hospital Music School (Co-ed). Horsham, W Sussex RH13 7LS *tel:* 01403 247438 *fax:* 01403 276470 *email:* music@

christs-hospital.org.uk. P C D Southern, head; Bruce Grindlay, dir of mus.

City of London Freemen's School (Co-ed). Ashtead Park, Ashtead, Surrey KT21 1ET *tel:* 01372 277933 *fax:* 01372 276165 *email:* headmaster@clfs.surrey.sch.uk. D C Haywood, head; P M Dodds, dir of mus.

City of London School (Boys). Queen Victoria St, London EC4V 3AL *tel:* 020 7489 0291 *fax:* 020 7329 6887. D R Levin, head; M Smedley, dir of mus.

City of London School for Girls (Girls). St Giles' Terrace, Barbican, London EC2Y 8BB *tel:* 020 7628 0841 *fax:* 020 7638 3212 *email:* donnellym@clsg.org.uk. Y A Burne, head; Mrs M Donnelly, dir of mus.

Claremont Fan Court School (Co-ed). Claremont Drive, Esher, Surrey KT10 9LY *tel:* 01372 467841 *fax:* 01372 471109 *email:* admissions@claremont.surrey.sch.uk. Patricia Farrar, principal; Alan Hitchcock, dir of mus.

Clayesmore School (Co-ed). Iwerne Minster, Blandford, Dorset DT11 8LL *tel:* 01747 812122 *fax:* 01747 811343 *email:* music@clayesmore-sch.co.uk. M G Cooke, head; D K Pigot, dir of mus.

Clifton College (Co-ed). Clifton, Bristol BS8 3JH *tel:* 0117 315 7000 *fax:* 0117 315 7101 *email:* admissions@clifton-college.avon.sch.uk. Stephen Spurr, head; James Hills, dir of mus.

Colfe's School (Co-ed). Horn Park Lane, London SE12 8AW *tel:* 020 8852 2283 *fax:* 020 8297 1216. A H Chicken, head; Paul Harrison, dir of mus.

Colston's Collegiate School (Co-ed). Stapleton, Bristol BS16 1BJ *tel:* 0117 965 5207 *fax:* 0117 958 5652. D G Crawford, head; S Bryant, dir of mus.

Colston's Girls' School (Girls). Cheltenham Rd, Bristol BS6 5RD *tel:* 0117 942 4328 *fax:* 0117 942 6933 *email:* admin@colstonsgirls.bristol.sch.uk. Lesley Jones, head; Alistair Mackenzie, dir of mus.

Cranleigh School (Co-ed). Cranleigh, Surrey GU6 8QQ *tel:* 01483 273666 *fax:* 01483 267398 *email:* rgm@cranleigh.org. Guy Waller, head; Richard Mayo, dir of mus.

Croham Hurst (Girls). 79 Croham Rd, South Croydon, Surrey CR2 7YN *tel:* 020 8680 3064 *fax:* 020 8688 1142 *email:* headcroham@aol.com. Miss S Budgen, head; Miss P Stone, dir of mus.

Croydon High School (Girls). Old Farleigh Rd, Selsdon, South Croydon CR2 8YB *tel:* 020 8651 5020 *fax:* 020 8657 5413 *email:* info2@cry.gdst.net. Miss L Ogilvie, head; Mrs J Davies, dir of mus.

Culford School (Co-ed). Bury St Edmunds, Suffolk IP28 6TX *tel:* 01284 728615 *fax:* 01284 728631 *email:* enquiries@culford.co.uk. John Richardson, head; John Humphries, registrar; James Recknell, dir of mus.

Dauntsey's School (Co-ed). W Lavington, nr Devizes, Wilts SN10 4HE *tel:* 01380 814500 *fax:* 01380 814501 *email:* information@dauntseys.wilts.sch.uk. S B Roberts, head; C B Thompson, dir of mus.

Dean Close School (Co-ed). Shelburne Rd, Cheltenham, Glos GL51 6HE *tel:* 01242 258000 *fax:* 01242 258003 *email:* registrar@deanclose.org.uk. Timothy M Hastie-Smith, head; Andrew Cleary, dir of mus.

Denstone College (Co-ed). Uttoxeter, Staffs ST14 5HN *tel:* 01889 590484 *fax:* 01889 591295 *email:* admissions@denstonecollege.org. D M Derbyshire, head; C F McDade, dir of mus.

Dover College (Co-ed). Effingham Cres, Dover, Kent CT17 9RH *tel:* 01304 205969 *fax:* 01304 242208 *email:* registrar@dovercollege.demon.co.uk. H W Blackett, head; Roderick Spencer, dir of mus.

Downe House (Girls). Cold Ash, Hermitage Rd, Thatcham, Berks RG18 9JJ *tel:* 01635 200286 *fax:* 01635 202026. Mrs E McKendrick, head; Anthony Cain, dir of mus.

Downside School (Boys). Stratton on the Fosse, Bath, Somerset BA3 4RJ *tel:* 01761 235100 *fax:* 01761 235105 *email:* cpt@downsidemusic.co.uk. Dom Antony Sutch, head; Chris Tambling, dir of mus.

Dulwich College (Boys). Dulwich Common, London SE21 7LD *tel:* 020 8693 3601/8299 9256/8 *also fax; email:* ashcroftm@dulwich.org.uk. G G Able, master; M Ashcroft, dir of mus.

Dunottar School (Girls). High Trees Rd, Reigate, Surrey RH2 7EL *tel:* 01737 761945 *fax:* 01737 779450 *email:* info@dunottar.surrey.sch.uk. Jeanne Hobson, head; Terry Lamont, dir of mus.

Durham School (Co-ed). Durham City, Co Durham DH1 4SZ *tel:* 0191 386 4783/6572 (mus school) *fax:* 0191 383 1025. N G Kern, head; Roger Muttitt, dir of mus.

Eastbourne College (Co-ed). Old Wish Rd, Eastbourne, E Sussex BN21 4JX *tel:* 01323 452320 *fax:* 01323 452327 *email:* hmsec@eastbourne-college.co.uk. C M P Bush, head; Graham Jones, dir of mus.

Edgbaston High School for Girls (Girls). Westbourne Rd, Birmingham B15 3TS *tel:* 0121 454 5831 *fax:* 0121 454 2363 *email:* registrar@edgbastonhigh.bham.sch.uk. Miss E M Mullenger, head; Miss M Harper, dir of mus.

The Edinburgh Academy (Boys). 42 Henderson Row, Edinburgh EH3 5BL *tel:* 0131 556 4603 *fax:* 0131 624 4994 *email:* rector@ edinburghacademy.org.uk. J V Light, rector; P N Coad, dir of mus.

Ellesmere College (Co-ed). Ellesmere, Shrops SY12 9AB *tel:* 01691 622321 *fax:* 01691 623286 *email:* admin@ellesmere.biblio.net. B J Wignall, head; Julian M Whittaker, dir of mus.

Eltham College (Boys). Grove Park Rd, Mottingham, London SE9 4QF *tel:* 020 8857 1455 *fax:* 020 8857 1913 *email:* mail@ eltham-college.org.uk. P J Henderson, head; Tim Johnson, dir of mus; Norman Levy, asst dir of mus, Tim Garrard, musician in residence.

Emanuel School (Co-ed). Battersea Rise, London SW11 1HS *tel:* 020 8870 4171 *fax:* 020 8877 1424 *email:* jsh@emanuel.org.uk. Anne-Marie Sutcliffe, head; J S Holmes, dir of mus.

Embley Park School (Co-ed). Embley Park, Romsey, Hants SO51 6ZE *tel:* 01794 512206 *fax:* 01794 518737 *email:* embley.park. school@virgin.net. David Chapman, head; Jeffrey Williams, dir of mus.

Epsom College (Co-ed). Epsom, Surrey KT17 4JQ *tel:* 01372 821243 *fax:* 01372 821244 *email:* music@epsomcollege.org.uk. Stephen Borthwick, head; Graeme Lodge, dir of mus.

Eton College (Boys). Music Schools, Windsor, Berks SL4 6EW *tel:* 01753 671000 *fax:* 01753 671159. Anthony Little, head; R Allwood, dir of mus.

Exeter School (Co-ed). Exeter, Devon EX2 4NS *tel:* 01392 258712 *fax:* 01392 498144 *email:* admissions@exeterschool.org.uk. N W Gamble, head; S D Foxall, dir of mus.

Farlington School (Girls). Strood Park, Horsham, Sussex RH12 3PN *tel:* 01403 254967 *fax:* 01403 272258 *email:* office@farlington. w-sussex.sch.uk. P M Mawer, head; Stephen Buckman, dir of mus.

Farnborough Hill (Girls). Farnborough, Hants GU14 8AT *tel:* 01252 545197 *fax:* 01252 513037 *email:* devdir@farnborough.hill.org.uk. Jacqueline Thomas, head; Karen Phillips, dir of mus.

Felsted School (Co-ed). Dunmow, Essex CM6 3JJ *tel:* 01371 822685 (mus school) *fax:* 01371 821179 *email:* musdept@felsted.essex.sch.uk. Stephen Roberts, head; James Lowry, dir of mus.

Fettes College (Co-ed). Carrington Rd, Edinburgh EH4 1QX *tel:* 0131 332 2281 *fax:* 0131 332 3081. Michael Spens, head; David Goodenough, dir of mus.

Forest Girls' School (Girls). Snaresbrook, London E17 3PY *tel:* 020 8521 7477 *fax:* 020 8520 7381. Mrs P Goodman, head; M D Palmer, dir of mus.

Forest School (Boys). Snaresbrook, London E17 3PY *tel:* 020 8520 1744 *fax:* 020 8520 3656. A G Boggis, warden; M D Palmer, dir of mus.

Framlingham College (Co-ed). Framlingham, Suffolk IP13 9EY *tel:* 01728 723789 *fax:* 01728 724546 *email:* registrar@ framcollege.co.uk. G M Randall, head; R Goodrich, dir of mus.

Frensham Heights (Co-ed). Rowledge, Farnham, Surrey GU10 4EA *tel:* 01252 792134 *fax:* 01252 794335 *email:* headmaster@ frensham-heights.org.uk. Peter M de Voil, head; Edwin Rolles, dir of mus.

George Watson's College (Co-ed). Colinton Rd, Edinburgh EH10 5EG *tel:* 0131 447 7931 *fax:* 0131 452 8594 *email:* n.mitchell@gwc.org.uk. G H Edwards, principal; Norman Mitchell, dir of mus (*tel:* 0131 446 6031).

Glenalmond College (Co-ed). Glenalmond, Perthshire PH1 3RY *tel:* 01738 842065 *also fax; email:* registrar@glenalmondcollege.co.uk. Ian Templeton, warden; Robert Gower, dir of mus.

The Godolphin School (Girls). Milford Hill, Salisbury, Wilts SP1 2RA *tel:* 01722 430500 *fax:* 01722 430501 *email:* admissions@ godolphin.wilts.sch.uk. Jill Horsburgh, head; Robin Highcock, dir of mus.

Gordonstoun School (Co-ed). Elgin, Morayshire IV30 5RF *tel:* 01343 837894/5 (mus dept) *fax:* 01343 837808 *email:* gastonn@ gordonstoun.org.uk. M C S-R Pyper, head; Nigel Gaston, dir of mus.

The Gregg School. Townhill Park House, Cutbush Lane, Southampton SO18 2GF *tel:* 023 8047 2133 *fax:* 023 8047 1080 *email:* office@ gregg.southampton.sch.uk. R D Hart, head; D S Bradley, dir of mus.

Gresham's School (Co-ed). Holt, Norfolk NR25 6EA *tel:* 01263 713271 *fax:* 01263 712028 *email:* headmaster@greshams-school.co.uk. Antony Clark, head; Mark Jones, dir of mus.

Guildford High School (Girls). London Rd, Guildford, Surrey GU1 1SJ *tel:* 01483 561440 *fax:* 01483 306516 *email:* registrar@guildford high.surrey.sch.uk. Mrs F J Boulton, head; Graham Thorp, dir of mus.

Haberdashers' Aske's Boys' School (Boys). Butterfly Lane, Elstree, Herts WD6 3AF *tel:* 020 8266 1700 *fax:* 020 8266 1800. P B Hamilton, head; Christopher Muhley, dir of mus.

The Haberdashers' Aske's School for Girls (Girls). Aldenham Rd, Elstree, Herts WD6 3BT *tel:* 020 8266 2300 *fax:* 020 8266 2303

Haberdashers' Monmouth Schools

MUSIC SCHOLARSHIPS and other awards are made at 11+, 13+, and 16+

OUTSTANDING MUSICAL REPUTATION at both schools is based on:

FLOURISHING CHORAL TRADITION
HMSG Chamber Choir finalist at Choral Olympics 2000, and attending 2004.
Choral Society, Trebles Choir and Barbershop.
Performances including;
Handel's Messiah
Carmina Burana at St David's Hall Cardiff with Welsh National Opera
Choral Tours (USA 1998, Italy 2001)

ORCHESTRAS
Including Senior Strings, Symphonic Winds & four String Orchestras.
Orchestra Tours (Paris & Vienna)
String Orchestra our (Italy 2002)

HIGHLY SUCCESSFUL WIND & BRASS BANDS
Finalists for five years in B&H National Wind Band Competition.
(Tour – Barcelona 2001)

HIGH QUALITY CHAMBER MUSIC
Finalists in National Chamber Music Trust Competition for eight consecutive years.
HMSG Harp Trio Winners in 1998

CELEBRITY MASTERCLASSES
Recent ones include:
Jane Glover & Thomas Carroll at Monmouth School
Professor Hugh Bean & Malcolm Golding at HMSG
Rose Consort of Viols

Haberdashers' Monmouth Schools
Enquiries initially to the Admissions Secretary at:
Monmouth School, boys 11-18, boarding & day
Tel: 01600 713143
Haberdasher's Monmouth School for Girls,
Girls aged11-18, boarding & day
Tel: 01600 711104
www.habs-monmouth.org

The Directors of Music are always delighted to meet informally with parents and their children in advance of the Scholarship auditions.

KENT COLLEGE
— CANTERBURY —

This independent co-educational day and boarding school is acquiring a growing reputation in its region for musical excellence.

With a huge variety of concerts each year, a newly completed Music Technology Studio, excellent academic results and even a new Concert Grand Piano, Kent College is an ideal environment in which a musical talent can flourish.

Music scholarships are available at ages 11, 13, and 16.

For details, contact the Director of Music, Stuart McIntosh on 01227 763231

www.kentcollege.com

email: theschool@habsgirls.org.uk. Mrs P Penney, head; Alexander Mitchell, dir of mus.

Haberdashers' Monmouth School for Girls (Girls). Hereford Rd, Monmouth NP25 5XT *tel:* 01600 711100 *fax:* 01600 711233. Brenda Despontin, head; Angela Randles, dir of mus; Karen MacLellan, admissions sec.

Haileybury (Co-ed). Hertford, Herts SG13 7NU *tel:* 01992 463353 *fax:* 01992 470663 *email:* nickjg@haileybury.herts.sch.uk. S A Westley, master; Peter Davis, dir of mus.

Hampton School (Boys). Hanworth Rd, Hampton, Middx TW12 3HD *tel:* 020 8979 5526 *fax:* 020 8941 7368 *email:* music@hampton.richmond.sch.uk. B R Martin, head; Iain Donald, dir of mus.

Harrogate Ladies' College (Girls). Harrogate, Yorks HG1 2QG *tel:* 01423 504543 *fax:* 01423 568893 *email:* enquire@hlc.org.uk. Margaret J Hustler, head; David Andrews, dir of mus.

Harrow School (Boys). Harrow on the Hill, Middx HA1 3HW *tel:* 020 8872 8231 *fax:* 020 8423 3112 *email:* rhw@harrowschool.org.uk. B Lenon, head; R H Walker, dir of mus.

Heathfield School, Ascot (Girls). London Rd, Ascot, Berks SL5 8BQ *tel:* 01344 898342 *fax:* 01344 890689 *email:* info@heathfield.ascot.sch.uk. Helen Wright, head; E F Patterson, dir of mus.

Hereford Cathedral School (Co-ed). Old Deanery, Cathedral Close, Hereford HR1 2NG *tel:* 01432 363522 *fax:* 01432 363525 *email:* enquiry@hcsch.org. H C Tomlinson, head; J M Williams, dir of mus.

Highgate School (Boys). North Rd, London N6 4AY *tel:* 020 8340 1524 *fax:* 020 8340 7674 *email:* office@highgateschool.org.uk. R P Kennedy, head; John March, dir of mus.

Howell's School (Girls). Denbigh, N Wales LL16 3EN *tel:* 01745 813631 *fax:* 01745 814443 *email:* Howells@cix.co.uk. Louise Robinson, principal; Morwen Murray, head of mus.

Hurstpierpoint College (Co-ed). Hassocks, W Sussex BN6 9JS *tel:* 01273 833636 *fax:* 01273 835257 *email:* info@hppc.co.uk. S D A Meek, head; N Houghton, dir of mus.

Hutchesons' Grammar School (Co-ed). 21 Beaton Rd, Glasgow G41 4NW *tel:* 0141 423 2933 *fax:* 0141 424 0251 *email:* rector@hutchesons.org.uk. John G Knowles, head; Edgar Trotter, dir of mus.

Ibstock Place (Co-ed). Clarence Lane, Roehampton, London SW15 5PY *tel:* 020 8876 9991 *fax:* 020 8878 4897. Anna Sylvester-Johnson, head; Gareth Jones, dir of mus.

Ipswich High School for Girls (Girls). Woolverstone, Ipswich IP9 1AZ *tel:* 01473 780201 *fax:* 01473 780985 *email:* admissions@ihs.gdst.net. Miss V C MacCuish, head; Peter Clayton, dir of mus.

Ipswich School (Co-ed). Henley Rd, Ipswich, Suffolk IP1 3SG *tel:* 01473 408300 *fax:* 01473 400058 *email:* registrar@ipswich.suffolk.sch.uk. I G Galbraith, head; A D Leach, dir of mus.

James Allen's Girls' School (Girls). East Dulwich Grove, London SE22 8TE *tel:* 020 8693 1181/7924 9578 *also fax* (mus dept) *fax:* 020 8693 7842 *email:* postmaster@jags.demon.co.uk. Marion Gibbs, head; Rupert Bond, dir of mus.

Kelly College (Co-ed). Tavistock, Devon PL19 0HZ *tel:* 01822 813193 *fax:* 01822 612050 *email:* Registrar@kellycollege.com. M S Steed, head; Andrew Wilson, dir of mus.

Kent College (Co-ed). Canterbury, Kent CT2 9TD *tel:* 01227 763231 *fax:* 01227 764777 *email:* hm@kentcollege.co.uk. G G Carminati, head; S McIntosh, dir of mus.

Kent College Pembury (Girls). Old Church Rd, Pembury, Tunbridge Wells TN2 4AX *tel:* 01892 822006 *fax:* 01892 820221 *email:* Admissions@kentcollege.kent.sch.uk. Anne Upton, head; Jenifer Horbury, dir of mus.

King Edward VI School (Co-ed). Kellett Rd, Southampton SO15 7UQ *tel:* 023 8070 4561 *fax:* 023 8070 5937 *email:* registrar@kes.hants.sch.uk. A J Thould, head; M C Hall, dir of mus.

King Edward's School (Birmingham) (Boys). Edgbaston Park Rd, Birmingham B15 2UA *tel:* 0121 472 1672/471 1640 (mus dept) *fax:* 0121 415 4327 *email:* office@kes.bham.sch.uk. R M Dancey, chief master; M J Monks, dir of mus.

King Edward's School (Godalming) (Co-ed). Witley, Wormley, Godalming, Surrey GU8 5SG *tel:* 01428 683960 (mus dept). P Kerr Fulton-Peebles, head; S C Pedlar, dir of mus.

King Henry VIII School (Co-ed). Warwick Rd, Coventry CV3 6AQ *tel:* 024 7667 3442 *fax:* 024 7667 7102 *email:* info@khviii.com. George D Fisher, head; Richard Hollingdale, dir of mus.

King's College (Co-ed). Taunton, Somerset TA1 3DX *tel:* 01823 328204 *fax:* 01823 328202 *email:* kingscol@aol.com. C D Ramsey, head; C K Holmes, dir of mus.

KING'S COLLEGE SCHOOL

WIMBLEDON COMMON, LONDON SW19 4TT

IAPS 453 boys (7-13)
HMC 773 boys (13-18)
312 in the sixth form

The School has a large and active music department. The Chamber Choir tours extensively in this country and abroad and there is a wide range of orchestras and instrumental groups.

Music Scholarships are offered to talented instrumentalists and singers at 13, subject to audition in February, and a Sixth Form Organ Scholarship is offered for the two years of sixth form.

Boys must be registered for entry to KCS and satisfy the normal entry requirements.

For further information, please contact the Registration Secretary on 020 8255 5352.

KCS, registered charity no. 310024, exists to provide education for children

---

Kent College Pembury

Independent day & boarding school for girls aged 3-18. Christian foundation 1886.

- Music scholarships are available each year for entry at 11+, 13+ and 16+, worth up to 50% of tuition fees.
- Music plays an important part in our school life and scholars play a leading role in the department.
- The department is housed in an attractive, modern, purpose-built centre and is an active, happy place where musical talent thrives.
- Excellent GCSE and A-level results with 100% A & B grades.
- Students regularly go on to read music at university.
- 400-seater state-of-the-art theatre for performing arts.
- Excellent, lively extra-curricular programme including concerts and recitals. Opportunities for inter-school performances.
- 60% of students have individual weekly lessons. Centre for ABRSM examinations. Excellent results throughout full range of grades including diploma level.

For further information, please contact the Director of Music, Mrs J Horbury or the Registrar at Kent College Pembury, Tunbridge Wells, Kent TN2 4AX. Tel: 01892 822006
Email: horburyj@kentcollege.kent.sch.uk or
admissions@kentcollege.kent.sch.uk
www.kent-college.co.uk

INVESTOR IN PEOPLE

Kent College is a registered charity which exists for the education of children. Charity no. 307920.

The King's School *Ely*

A REPUTATION FOR MUSICAL EXCELLENCE

Chapel Choir, Chamber Choir, two orchestras, junior Wind Band and senior Concert Band, instrumental and vocal ensembles. Tours of Czech Republic in 1999, Belgium in 2000, Paris in 2001, Malta in 2002, Thailand in 2003. Every week, 500 individual music lessons given by five full-time and over 20 visiting staff. Junior School music suite. New £1m. senior Music School and Recital Hall opened in 2001.

SCHOLARSHIPS

Up to 50% of fees for excellence and potential in Music (including sixth-form organ scholarship at Ely Cathedral), Art, Drama, Sport and academic work.

ELY CATHEDRAL CHORISTERS

receive generous scholarships (then 33% in the Senior School, to which other awards can be added).

The King's School *Ely*

HMC/IAPS Boys and girls, 2½-18, day and boarding.
Telephone: 01353 660702 Fax: 01353 667485
admissions@kings-ely.cambs.sch.uk
www.kings-ely.cambs.sch.uk
Cambridgeshire CB7 4DB. Charity No. 311440.

KINGSTON GRAMMAR SCHOOL

HMC day school celebrating 25 years of co-education

MUSIC is one of KGS's many strengths. The range of musical experience for its pupils recently has embraced chamber music coaching by a member of the Maggini Quartet to a gospel workshop by Ken Burton.

KGS also offer music scholarships of half fees plus free tuition on one instrument at 11, 13 and 16. String players are particularly welcome.

* Facilities for music, including the 14th century Lovekyn Chapel, are to be enhanced by a new music centre in 2005
* Ensembles include three orchestras, three choirs, Concert Band, Jazz Group and Jazz Quintet
* Concerts, recitals, workshops and a biennial tour
* Second CD shortly to be released

Further details from the Director of Music, Carl Jackson, Kingston Grammar School,
70 London Road, Kingston upon Thames KT2 6PY
Tel: (020) 8939 8832 Fax: (020) 8974 5177
E-mail: musicadmin@kingston-grammar.surrey.sch.uk

For general admissions enquiries, a prospectus or to arrange a visit, telephone the Registrar (020) 8939 8830 or visit our website,
www.kingston-grammar.surrey.sch.uk

A company limited by guarantee, Registered Office as above.
Registered in England No: 3883748 and a Registered Charity No: 1078461

King's College School (Boys). Wimbledon Common, London SW19 4TT *tel:* 020 8255 5300 *fax:* 020 8255 5309 *email:* admissions@kcs.org.uk. A C V Evans, head; J E Millard, dir of mus.

King's School (Bruton) (Co-ed). Bruton, Somerset BA10 0ED *tel:* 01749 814241 *fax:* 01749 813426 *email:* kingshm@kingsbruton. somerset.sch.uk. R I Smyth, head; G E Jenkins, dir of mus.

The King's School, Canterbury (Co-ed). Canterbury, Kent CT1 2ES *tel:* 01227 595556 *also fax* (mus dept) *email:* music@kings-school.co.uk. Revd K H Wilkinson, head; Howard Ionascu, dir of mus.

The King's School, Ely (Co-ed). Ely, Cambs CB7 4DB *tel:* 01353 660700 *fax:* 01353 662187 *email:* music@kings-ely.cambs.sch.uk. R H Youdale, head; G P L Griggs, dir of mus.

King's School (Gloucester) (Co-ed). Pitt St, Gloucester GL1 2BG *tel:* 01452 337337 *fax:* 01452 337314 *email:* hm@thekingsschool.co.uk. Peter Lacey, head; Ian Fox, dir of mus.

The King's School in Macclesfield (Co-ed). Macclesfield, Cheshire SK10 1DA *tel:* 01625 260000 *fax:* 01625 260022 *email:* mail@ kingsmac.co.uk. S Coyne, head; Andrew K Green, dir of mus.

King's School Rochester (Co-ed). Satis House, Boley Hill, Rochester, Kent ME1 1TE *tel:* 01634 888555 *fax:* 01634 888505 *email:* walker@kings-school-rochester.co.uk. I R Walker, head; G R Williams, dir of mus.

King's School (Worcester) (Co-ed). College Green, Worcester, Worcs WR1 2LH *tel:* 01905 721700 *fax:* 01905 721710 *email:* info@ksw.org.uk. T H Keyes, head; D E Brookshaw, dir of mus.

Kingham Hill School (Co-ed). Kingham, Chipping Norton OX7 6TH *tel:* 01608 685999 *fax:* 01608 658658 *email:* secretary@ kingham-hill.oxon.sch.uk. Martin J Morris, head; Robert James, dir of mus.

Kingston Grammar School (Co-ed). 70-72 London Rd, Kingston upon Thames, Surrey KT2 6PY *tel:* 020 8546 5875 *fax:* 020 8974 5177 *email:* registrar@kingston-grammar.surrey.sch.uk. C D Baxter, head; C A Jackson, dir of mus.

Kingswood School (Co-ed). Lansdown Rd, Bath, Somerset BA1 5RG *tel:* 01225 734200 *fax:* 01225 734205 *email:* registrar@ kingswood.bath.sch.uk. Gary Best, head; Richard Dunster-Sigtermans, dir of mus.

The Lady Eleanor Holles School (Girls). Hanworth Rd, Hampton, Middx TW12 3HF *tel:* 020 8979 1601 *fax:* 020 8941 8291 *email:* office@ ladyeleanorholles.richmond.sch.uk. Miss E M Candy, head; Mr Yat Soon Yeo, dir of mus.

Lancing College (Co-ed). Lancing, W Sussex BN15 0RW *tel:* 01273 452213 *fax:* 01273 464720 *email:* lancingmus@aol.com. P M Tinniswood, head; P E Lewis, D N Cox, dirs of mus.

Latymer Upper School (Boys). King St, Hammersmith, London W6 9LR *tel:* 020 8741 1851 *fax:* 020 8748 5212. P J Winter, head; Tony Henwood, dir of mus.

Leeds Girls' High School (Girls). Headingley Lane, Leeds, W Yorks LS6 1BN *tel:* 0113 274 4000 *fax:* 0113 275 2217 *email:* enquiries@lghs.org. Sue Fishburn, head; Katie Staggs, dir of mus.

Leicester Grammar School (Co-ed). 8 Peacock Lane, Leicester LE1 5PX *tel:* 0116 222 0400 *fax:* 0116 291 0505 *email:* tylerk@ leicestergrammar.org.uk. Christopher King, head; David M T Whittle, dir of mus.

Leighton Park School (Co-ed). Shinfield Rd, Reading, Berks RG2 7ED *tel:* 0118 987 9600 *fax:* 0118 987 9625 *email:* info@leightonpark. reading.sch.uk. John Dunston, head; Rosemary Scales, dir of mus.

The Leys School (Co-ed). Cambridge, CB2 2AD *tel:* 01223 508900 *fax:* 01223 505303 *email:* office@theleys.cambs.sch.uk. J C A Barrett, head; Adrian Leang, dir of mus.

Llandovery College (Co-ed). Llandovery, Carmarthenshire SA20 0EE *tel:* 01550 723000 *fax:* 01550 723049 *email:* mail@ LlandoveryCollege.com. Peter A Hogan, head; Emma Lewis, head of mus.

Lomond School (Co-ed). 10 Stafford St, Helensburgh, Argyll and Bute G84 9JX *tel:* 01436 672476 *fax:* 01436 678320 *email:* admin@lomond-school.demon.co.uk. A D Macdonald, head; Anne Lyon, head of mus.

Lord Wandsworth College (Boys). Long Sutton, Hook, Hants RG29 1TB *tel:* 01256 862482 *fax:* 01256 862563 *email:* info@lord-wandsworth. hants.sch.uk. I G Power, head; R J Fitzgerald, head of mus.

Loretto School (Co-ed). Musselburgh, Edinburgh EH21 7RE *tel:* 0131 653 4455 *fax:* 0131 653 4456 *email:* admissions@loretto.com. Michael Mavor, head; Edward Coleman, dir of mus; Fiona Stevenson, admissions dir.

Loughborough Grammar School (Boys). Burton Walks, Loughborough, Leics LE11 2DU *tel:* 01509 233233 *fax:* 01509 218436 *email:* hmpa

Excellence in Music

Boarding and Day School for girls aged 2½ to 18 years.

Junior Exhibitioners at London Colleges - Royal College of Music and Royal Academy.

80% of girls learn a musical instrument.

Excellent reputation for Music at home and abroad - recent concert tours to Australia and USA.

100% A* or A Grades for Music GCSEs in 2001/2002/2003.

3 girls in the top 15 of the UK in A and AS Music Performance 2003.

Music Scholarships available by audition

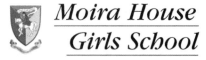

Moira House Girls School

Upper Carlisle Road Eastbourne East Sussex BN20 7TE
Telephone: +44 (0)1323 644144 Fax: +44 (0)1323 649720
E-mail: head@moirahouse.co.uk Website: www.moirahouse.co.uk

Moreton Hall

Independent Boarding and Day School for girls aged 8 – 18

Music Scholarships

- Music scholarships worth up to 50% of full school fees offered at 11+, 13+, 16+
- Auditions by arrangement
- 16 visiting teachers from the top Conservatoires
- Extra tuition available in all instruments and voice
- Students able to make their own CDs in our digital recording studio
- 'A' level Music and Music Technology
- Concert tours in the UK and abroad
- Senior and Junior choir, orchestra, string quartet, string ensemble, wind band, jazz band, vocal ensemble groups

For further information please contact:
Jonathan Forster B.A.,
The Principal,
Moreton Hall, Weston Rhyn, Oswestry, Shropshire,
SY11 3EW
Telephone 01691 776020
Fax 01691 778552
e-mail: forsterj@moretonhall.org

Moreton Hall Educational Trust Limited is a registered charity, number 528409.

OUNDLE SCHOOL
HMC Co-educational Boarding and Day School, 11-18

- Junior scholarships – awards of up to 25% of school fees
- Ten awards of up to 50% at 13+
- Junior organ scholarship
- Sixth form scholarship and senior organ scholarship
- Exhibitions also available
- Eight full time and 35 part time music staff
- Numerous ensembles, wide range of performance opportunities
- Superb facilities, including chapel with frobenius organ
- Regular tours, workshops and masterclasses

The Director of Music is always pleased to meet prospective pupils and parents.
Further details from:
The Music School, Gascoigne Building, North Street
Oundle, Peterborough, PE8 4AS
Tel: 01832 277132
Fax: 01832 277131
e-mail: music@oundle.northants.sch.uk
Website: www.oundleschool.org.uk

@loughboroughgs.demon.co.uk. P B Fisher, head; P J Underwood, dir of mus.

Magdalen College School (Boys). Oxford OX4 1DZ *tel:* 01865 242191 *fax:* 01865 240379 *email:* cdickinson@mcsoxford.org. A D Halls, head; M N Pearce, dir of mus.

Malvern College (Co-ed). College Rd, Malvern, Worcs WR14 3DF *tel:* 01684 581530 (dir of mus)/1 (sec) *fax:* 01684 581617 *email:* ids@malcol.worcs.sch.uk. H C K Carson, head; Iain Sloan, dir of mus.

Malvern Girls' College (Girls). 15 Avenue Rd, Malvern, Worcs WR14 3BA *tel:* 01684 892288 *fax:* 01684 566204 *email:* admin@ mgc.worcs.sch.uk. Philippa M C Leggate, head; M Hamilton, dir of mus.

Marlborough College (Co-ed). Marlborough, Wilts SN8 1PA *tel:* 01672 892300 *fax:* 01672 892307 *email:* mcadmiss@marlboroughcollege. wilts.sch.uk. E J H Gould, master; R W Nelson, dir of mus.

The Mary Erskine School (Girls). Ravelston, Edinburgh EH4 3NT *tel:* 0131 347 5700 *fax:* 0131 347 5799 *email:* schoolsecretary@ esmgc.com. David Gray, principal; Helen Mitchell, head of mus.

The Maynard School (Girls). Exeter EX1 1SJ *tel:* 01392 273417 *fax:* 01392 496199 *email:* office@maynard.co.uk. D West, head; N Horton, dir of mus.

Merchant Taylors' School (Boys). Sandy Lodge, Northwood, Middx HA6 2HT *tel:* 01923 820644 *fax:* 01923 835110 *email:* admissions@ mtsn.org.uk. J R Gabitass, head; Richard Hobson, dir of mus.

Merchiston Castle School (Boys). Colinton, Edinburgh EH13 0PU *tel:* 0131 312 2200 *fax:* 0131 441 6060 *email:* admissions@ merchiston.co.uk. A R Hunter, head; P K Rossiter, dir of mus.

Methodist College (Co-ed). 1 Malone Rd, Belfast BT9 6BY *tel:* 028 9020 5205 *fax:* 028 9020 5230 *email:* school@mcb.rmplc.co.uk. T W Mulryne, head; R McCartney, dir of mus.

Mill Hill School (Co-ed). Mill Hill Village, London NW7 1QS *tel:* 020 8959 1221 *fax:* 020 8906 2614 *email:* registrations@millhill.org.uk. W R Winfield, head; Richard Allain, dir of mus.

Millfield School (Co-ed). Street, Somerset BA16 0YD *tel:* 01458 442291 *fax:* 01458 447276 *email:* admissions@millfield.somerset.sch.uk. P M Johnson, head; R O Knight, dir of mus.

Milton Abbey School (Boys). nr Blandford, Dorset DT11 0BZ *tel:* 01258 880484 *fax:* 01258 881250/194 *email:* rosemarybrinton@milton abbey.co.uk. Jonathan Hughes-D'Aeth, head; John McDonald, dir of mus.

Moira House Girls School (Girls). Upper Carlisle Rd, Eastbourne, Sussex BN20 7TE *tel:* 01323 644144 *fax:* 01323 649720 *email:* head@moirahouse.co.uk. A Harris, head; P Parfitt, dir of mus.

Monkton Combe School (Co-ed). Monkton Combe, nr Bath, Avon BA2 7HG *tel:* 01225 721102 *fax:* 01225 721181 *email:* admissions@ monkton.org.uk. M J Cuthbertson, head; B J Newman, dir of mus.

Monmouth School (Boys). Monmouth NP25 3XP *tel:* 01600 713143 *fax:* 01600 772701 *email:* admissions@monmouth.monm.sch.uk. Tim H P Haynes, head; David Lawson, dir of mus.

Moreton Hall (Girls). Weston Rhyn, Oswestry, Shrops SY11 3EW *tel:* 01691 773671 *fax:* 01691 778552 *email:* jfmhall@aol.com. Jonathan Forster, principal; Mrs C Tilley, head of mus.

The Mount School (Girls). Dalton Terrace, York YO24 4DD *tel:* 01904 667507 *fax:* 01904 667524 *email:* registrar@mount.n-yorks.sch.uk. Diana Gant, head; Derek Chivers, dir of mus.

New Hall School (Girls). Boreham, Chelmsford, Essex CM3 3HS *tel:* 01245 467588 *fax:* 01245 464348 *email:* admin@ newhallschool.co.uk. Mrs K Jeffery, head; A Fardell, dir of mus.

Norwich High School for Girls GDST (Girls). 95 Newmarket Rd, Norwich NR2 2HU *tel:* 01603 453265 *fax:* 01603 259891 *email:* enquire@nor.gdst.net. Mrs V C Bidwell, head; Mrs H Weiland, dir of mus.

Norwich School (Boys). 70 The Close, Norwich NR1 4DD *tel:* 01603 623194 *fax:* 01603 627036 *email:* admissions@norwich-school.org.uk. J B Hawkins, head; Colin Dowdeswell, dir of mus; Miles Quick, asst dir of mus.

Notting Hill and Ealing High School (Girls). 2 Cleveland Rd, Ealing, London W13 8AX *tel:* 020 8799 8400 *fax:* 020 8810 6891. Susan Whitfield, head; Andrew Phillips, dir of mus.

Oakham School (Co-ed). Foundation Office, Chapel Close, Oakham, Rutland LE15 6DT *tel:* 01572 758758 *fax:* 01572 758595 *email:* admissions@oakham.rutland.sch.uk. J A F Spence, head; D N Woodcock, dir of mus.

The Oratory School (Boys). Woodcote, Reading, Berks RG8 0PJ *tel:* 01491 683500 *fax:* 01491 680020 *email:* enquiries@oratory.co.uk. C I Dytor, head; J McNamara, dir of mus.

Oswestry School (Co-ed). Upper Brook St, Oswestry, Shrops SY11 2TL *tel:* 01691 655711 *fax:* 01691 671194 *email:* enquiries@

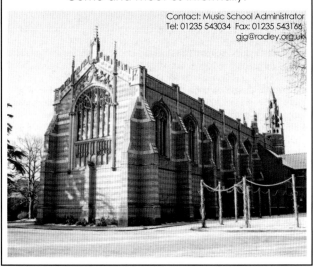

oswestryschool.org.uk. P D Stockdale, head; S J Morris, dir of mus.

Oundle School (Co-ed). Music Dept, The Gascoigne Building, North St, Oundle PE8 4AS *tel:* 01832 277132 *fax:* 01832 277131 *email:* music@oundle.northants.sch.uk. R Townsend, head; Andrew Forbes, dir of mus.

Pangbourne College (Co-ed). Pangbourne, Reading, Berks RG8 8LA *tel:* 0118 984 2101 *fax:* 0118 984 5443. K Greig, head; D C Everhart, dir of mus.

The Perse School (Boys). Music Dept, Hills Rd, Cambridge CB2 2QF *tel:* 01223 568300/283 *fax:* 01223 568293 *email:* office@perse.co.uk; music@perse.co.uk. N Richardson, head; G A Richards, dir of mus.

Pocklington School (Co-ed). West Green, Pocklington, York YO42 2NJ *tel:* 01759 303125 *fax:* 01759 306366 *email:* mainoffice@ pocklington.e-yorks.sch.uk. N Clements, head; M Kettlewell, dir of mus.

Polam Hall School (Girls). Grange Rd, Darlington, Co Durham DL1 5PA *tel:* 01325 463383 *fax:* 01325 383539 *email:* information@ polamhall.com. Mrs H Hamilton, head; Mrs E Sleightholme, dir of mus.

The Portsmouth Grammar School (Co-ed). High St, Portsmouth, Hants PO1 2LN *tel:* 023 9236 0036 *fax:* 023 9236 4256 *email:* admissions@ pgs.org.uk. T R Hands, head; J E C Henderson, dir of mus.

The Princess Helena College (Girls). Preston, Hitchin, Herts SG4 7RT *tel:* 01462 432100 *fax:* 01462 443871 *email:* head@phc.herts.co.uk. A-M Hodgkiss, head; Cynthia Neaum, dir of mus.

Prior Park College (Co-ed). Bath BA2 5AH *tel:* 01225 835353 *fax:* 01225 835753 *email:* admissions@priorpark.co.uk. Giles Mercer, head; Roland Robertson, dir of mus.

Prior's Field School (Girls). Godalming, Surrey GU7 2RH *tel:* 01483 810551 *fax:* 01483 810180 *email:* admin@priorsfield.surrey.sch.uk. Mrs J C Dwyer, head; Miss C Mowat, dir of mus.

The Purcell School (Co-ed). Aldenham Rd, Bushey, Herts WD23 2TS *tel:* 01923 331100 *fax:* 01923 331166 *email:* info@purcell-school.org. John Tolputt, head; Quentin Poole, dir of mus.

Queen Anne's School (Girls). 6 Henley Rd, Caversham, Reading, Berks RG4 6DX *tel:* 0118 918 7300 *fax:* 0118 918 7310 *email:* admis@ queenannes.reading.sch.uk. Mrs D Forbes, head; Miss F Brewitt-Taylor, dir of mus.

Queen Elizabeth's Grammar School (Co-ed). Blackburn, Lancs BB2 6DF *tel:* 01254 686300 *fax:* 01254 692314 *email:* headmaster@

qegs.blackburn.sch.uk. D S Hempsall, head; G R Hill, dir of mus.

Queen Elizabeth's Hospital School (Boys). Berkeley Place, Clifton, Bristol BS8 1JX *tel:* 0117 929 1856 *fax:* 0117 929 3106 *email:* admin@qehbristol.co.uk. S W Holliday, head; Richard Jones, dir of mus.

Queen Ethelburga's College (Co-ed). Thorpe Underwood Hall, Ouseburn, York YO26 9SS *tel:* 0870 742 3300 *fax:* 0870 742 3310 *email:* remember@compuserve.com. P Dass, principal; R Meyer, dir of mus.

Queen Margaret's School (Girls). Escrick Park, York YO19 6EU *tel:* 01904 728261 *fax:* 01904 728150 *email:* enquiries@ qmyork.force9.co.uk. G Chapman, head; M Ward, dir of mus.

Queen Mary's School (Girls). Baldersby Park, Topcliffe, Thirsk, N Yorks YO7 3BZ *tel:* 01845 575000 *fax:* 01845 575001. Margaret and Ian Angus, heads; N Carter, dir of mus.

Queen's College (Taunton) (Co-ed). Trull Rd, Taunton, Somerset TA1 4QS *tel:* 01823 272559 *fax:* 01823 338430 *email:* admissions@ queenscollege.org.uk. Christopher J Alcock, head; Stephen C Bell, dir of mus.

Queenswood School (Girls). Shepherds Way, Brookmans Park, Hatfield, Herts AL9 6NS *tel:* 01707 602500 *fax:* 01707 602597 *email:* registry@queenswood.herts.sch.uk. Clarissa Farr, principal; Stephen Potts, dir of mus; Christos Kokkiner, head of inst mus.

Radley College (Boys). Abingdon, Oxon OX14 2HR *tel:* 01235 543000 *fax:* 01235 543106. Angus McPhail, warden; Stephen Clarke, dir of mus.

Ratcliffe College (Co-ed). Fosse Way, Ratcliffe on the Wreake, Leicester LE7 4SG *tel:* 01509 817000 *fax:* 01509 817004. P Farrar, head; M Jones, dir of mus.

Reading Blue Coat School (Boys). Holme Park, Sonning, Reading RG4 6SU *tel:* 0118 944 1005 *fax:* 0118 944 2690. S J W McArthur, head; Jonathan Bowler, dir of mus.

Red Maids' School (Girls). Westbury on Trym, Bristol BS9 3AW *tel:* 0117 962 2641 *fax:* 0117 962 1687. Stephen J M Browne, dir of mus.

Redland High School for Girls (Girls). Redland Court, Bristol BS6 7EF *tel:* 0117 924 5796 *fax:* 0117 924 1127 *email:* headmistress@ redland.bristol.sch.uk. R A Weeks, head; Nigel Davies, dir of mus.

Reed's School (Boys). Cobham, Surrey KT11 2ES *tel:* 01932 869001 *fax:* 01932 869046 *email:* reedsadmit@compuserve.com. David Jarrett, head; Ian Carnegie, dir of mus.

Rendcomb College (Co-ed). Cirencester, Glos GL7 7HA *tel:* 01285 831213 *fax:* 01285 831331. Gerry Holden, head; David White, dir of mus.

Repton School (Co-ed). Repton, Derbys DE65 6FH *tel:* 01283 559222 *fax:* 01283 559228 *email:* registrar@repton.org.uk. G E Jones, head; Richard Dacey, dir of mus.

Roedean School (Girls). Roedean Way, Brighton BN2 5RQ *tel:* 01273 603181 *fax:* 01273 680791 *email:* admissions@roedean.co.uk. Carolyn Shaw, head; Veronica Fewkes, dir of mus.

Rossall School (Co-ed). Fleetwood, Lancs FY7 8JW *tel:* 01253 774201 *fax:* 01253 772052 *email:* geoffrey.cassidy@virgin.net. Tim Wilbur, head; Geoffrey Cassidy, dir of mus.

Royal Grammar School (Guildford) (Boys). High St, Guildford, Surrey GU1 3BB *tel:* 01483 880600 *fax:* 01483 306127 *email:* bwright@ mail.rgs-guildford.co.uk. Tim Young, head; Peter White, dir of mus.

Royal Grammar School (Worcester) (Co-ed). Upper Tything, Worcester WR1 1HP *tel:* 01905 613391 *fax:* 01905 726892 *email:* office@ rgsw.org.uk. W A Jones, head; A P Wilson, dir of mus.

The Royal High School, GDST (Girls). Lansdown Rd, Bath BA1 5SZ *tel:* 01225 313877 *fax:* 01225 465446 *email:* royalhigh@bat.gdst.net. James Graham-Brown, head; Michael Cockerham, dir of mus.

Royal Hospital School (Co-ed). Ipswich IP9 2RX *tel:* 01473 326200 *fax:* 01473 326213 *email:* music@royalhospitalschool.org. Nicholas Ward, head; Peter Crompton, dir of mus.

Royal Masonic School for Girls (Girls). Rickmansworth Park, Rickmansworth, Herts WD3 4HF *tel:* 01923 773168 *fax:* 01923 896729 *email:* enquiries@royalmasonic.herts.sch.uk. Mrs G Braiden, admissions sec; Leonard J Smith, dir of mus.

Royal Wolverhampton School (Co-ed). Penn Rd, Wolverhampton, W Midlands WV3 0EG *tel:* 01902 341230 *fax:* 01902 344496 *email:* mo@royal.wolverhampton.sch.uk. Mr T J Brooker, head; Mrs C Fellows, dir of mus.

Rydal Penrhos Senior School (Co-ed). Pwllycrochan Ave, Colwyn Bay, N Wales LL29 7BT *tel:* 01492 530155 *fax:* 01492 531872 *email:* info@rydal-penrhos.com. M S James, principal; P J Futcher, dir of mus.

St Albans High School (Girls). 3 Townsend Ave, St Albans, Herts AL1 3SJ *tel:* 01727 853800 *fax:* 01727 792516 *email:* musicdpr@ netscapeonline.co.uk. Mrs C Y Daly, head; Nigel Springthorpe, dir of mus.

St Antony's Leweston School (Girls). Sherborne, Dorset DT9 6EN *tel:* 01963 210691 *fax:* 01963 210786 *email:* st.antony@virgin.net. H MacDonald, head; Rachel Britton, dir of mus.

St Bees School (Co-ed). St Bees, Cumbria CA27 0DS *tel:* 01946 828000 *fax:* 01946 828011 *email:* mailbox@st-bees-school.co.uk. P J Capes, head; H M Turpin, dir of mus.

St Catherine's School (Girls). Bramley, Guildford, Surrey GU5 0DF *tel:* 01483 893363/899646 (mus school) *fax:* 01483 899608/648 (mus school) *email:* schooloffice@st-catherines.surrey.sch.uk; music@ st-catherines.surrey.sch.uk. Mrs A Phillips, head.

St David's College (Co-ed). Llandudno, N Wales LL30 1RD *tel:* 01492 875974 *fax:* 01492 870383 *email:* headmaster@stdavidscollege.co.uk. William Seymour, head; Marion Horley, head of mus.

St Dunstan's College (Co-ed). Stanstead Rd, Catford, London SE6 4TY *tel:* 020 8516 7200/7245 *fax:* 020 8516 7300 *email:* pmg@ stdunstans.org.uk. D I Davies, head; Paul Gobey, dir of mus.

St Edmund's College (Co-ed). Old Hall Green, Ware, Herts SG11 1DS *tel:* 01920 821504 *fax:* 01920 823011 *email:* registrar@ stedmundscollege.org. Mark Loughlin, head; Stephen Oxley, dir of mus.

St Edmund's School (Co-ed). Canterbury CT2 8HU *tel:* 01227 475600 *fax:* 01227 471083 *email:* music@stedmunds.org.uk. A N Ridley, head; I P Sutcliffe, dir of mus.

St Edward's College *see* Choir Schools. (Co-ed).

St Edward's School (Co-ed). Woodstock Rd, Oxford OX2 7NN *tel:* 01865 319200 *fax:* 01865 319202 *email:* Registrar@stedwards.oxon.sch.uk. D Christie, warden; Julian McNamara, dir of mus.

St Elphin's School (Girls). Darley Dale, Matlock, Derbys DE4 2HA *tel:* 01629 733263 *fax:* 01629 733956 *email:* admin@st-elphins.co.uk. Erica Taylor, head; Margaret Garvey, dir of mus.

St Felix and St George's School (Co-ed). Southwold, Suffolk IP18 6SD *tel:* 01502 722175 *fax:* 01502 722641 *email:* thazell@ stfelix.suffolk.sch.uk. Wendy Holland, principal; V Scott, dir of mus.

St George's School, Edgbaston (Co-ed). 31 Calthorpe Rd, Birmingham B15 1RX *tel:* 0121 625 0398 *fax:* 0121 625 3340 *email:* admin@ sgse.co.uk. Miss H Phillips, head; Sarah Russell, dir of mus; Nigel Morley.

St Helen and St Katharine (Girls). Faringdon Rd, Abingdon, Oxon OX14

1BE *tel:* 01235 520173 *fax:* 01235 532934 *email:* info@sthelens.oxon.sch.uk. Cynthia Hall, head; Andrew A Tillett, dir of mus.

St Helen's School (Girls). Eastbury Rd, Northwood, Middx HA6 3AS *tel:* 01923 843210 *fax:* 01923 843211 *email:* mail@sthelensnorthwood.co.uk. Mary Morris, head; Richard Lambert, dir of mus.

St John's School (Boys). Leatherhead, Surrey KT22 8SP *tel:* 01372 385441/71 (mus) *fax:* 01372 386606 *email:* bnoithip@stjohns.surrey.sch.uk. C H Tongue, head; B Noithip, dir of mus.

St Lawrence College (Co-ed). Ramsgate, Kent CT11 7AE *tel:* 01843 592680 *fax:* 01843 851123 *email:* Headmaster.SLC@dial.pipex.com. M Slater, head; S A Clarkson, dir of mus.

St Leonards-Mayfield School (Girls). The Old Palace, Mayfield, E Sussex TN20 6PH *tel:* 01435 874600 *fax:* 01435 872627 *email:* enquiry@stlm.e-sussex.sch.uk. Julia Dalton, head; James Thomas, dir of mus.

St Leonards (Co-ed). St Andrews, Fife KY16 9QJ *tel:* 01334 472126/460506 (mus school) *fax:* 01334 476152 *email:* info@stleonards-fife.org. Mrs W A Bellars, principal; Marilyn Cleobury-Jones, dir of mus.

St Margaret's School for Girls (Girls). 147 Magdalen Rd, Exeter EX2 4TS *tel:* 01392 273197 (head)/491699 (admissions) *fax:* 01392 251402 *email:* mail@stmargarets-school.co.uk. Mrs M D'Albertanson, head; Miranda Ashe, dir of mus.

St Mary's School Ascot (Girls). Ascot, Berks SL5 9JF *tel:* 01344 293607 *fax:* 01344 873281 *email:* rjames@st-marys-ascot.co.uk. Mary Breen, head; Richard James, dir of mus.

St Mary's School (Calne) (Girls). Calne, Wilts SN11 0DF *tel:* 01249 857200 *fax:* 01249 857207 *email:* sms@stmaryscalne.wilts.sch.uk. Mrs C J Shaw, head; Geoffrey Field, dir of mus.

St Mary's School (Gerrards Cross) (Girls). Gerrards Cross, Bucks SL9 8JQ *tel:* 01753 883370 *fax:* 01753 890966 *email:* Headmistress@stmarys-gx.org. Sue Abbott, dir of mus.

St Mary's School (Wantage) (Girls). Wantage, Oxon OX12 8BZ *tel:* 01235 773800 *fax:* 01235 760467 *email:* stmarysw@rmplc.co.uk. Mrs S Sowden, head; Ms F Eagar, dir of mus.

St Mary's Westbrook (Co-ed). Ravenlea Rd, Folkestone, Kent CT20 2JU *tel:* 01303 854006 *fax:* 01303 249901 *email:* hm@st-marys-westbrook.co.uk. Lesley A Watson, head; Anne Johnson, dir of mus.

St Paul's Girls' School (Girls). Brook Green, Hammersmith, London W6 7BS *tel:* 020 7603 2288 *fax:* 020 7602 9932 *email:* admissions@spgs.org. Elizabeth Diggory, high mistress; Julian Grant, dir of mus.

St Paul's School (Boys). Lonsdale Rd, Barnes, London SW13 9JT *tel:* 020 8748 8874 *fax:* 020 8748 9557 *email:* MusDir@stpaulsschool.org.uk. Stephen Baldock, high master; Mark Tatlow, dir of mus.

St Peter's School (Co-ed). York YO30 6AB *tel:* 01904 623213 *fax:* 01904 640973 *email:* enquiries@st-peters.york.sch.uk. A F Trotman, head; Andrew Wright, dir of mus.

St Swithun's School (Girls). Winchester, Hants SO21 1HA *tel:* 01962 835746 (mus dept) *fax:* 01962 835779 *email:* music@stswithuns.co.uk. H L Harvey, head; R Brett, dir of mus.

St Teresa's School (Girls). Effingham Hill, Dorking, Surrey RH5 6ST *tel:* 01372 452037 *fax:* 01372 450311 *email:* kate.nicholson@stteresas.surrey.sch.uk. Mary Prescott, head; Mrs J S Bolton, dir of mus.

School of S. Mary and S. Anne, Abbots Bromley (Girls). Abbots Bromley, Staffs WS15 3BW *tel:* 01283 840232 *fax:* 01283 840988 *email:* info@abbotsbromley.staffs.sch.uk. Mrs M Steel, head; Colin Walker, dir of mus.

Seaford College (Co-ed). Petworth, W Sussex GU28 0NB *tel:* 01798 867392 *fax:* 01798 867606 *email:* seaford@clara.co.uk. T J Mullins, head; David Read, dir of mus.

Sedbergh School and Sedbergh Junior School (Co-ed). Sedbergh, Cumbria LA10 5HG *tel:* 01539 620535 *fax:* 01539 621301 *email:* hm@sedbergh.sch.uk. C H Hirst, head; D M Andrew, dir of mus.

Sevenoaks School (Co-ed). High St, Sevenoaks, Kent TN13 1HU *tel:* 01732 455133/467706 *also fax; fax:* 01732 456143 *email:* regist@cs.soaks.org. C L Ricks, head; Christopher Dyer, dir of mus.

Sherborne School (Boys). Sherborne, Dorset DT9 3AP *tel:* 01935 810518 (mus school) *fax:* 01935 810426 *email:* pce@sherborne.org. Richard Gould; S F Eliot, head; Paul Ellis, dir of mus.

Sherborne School for Girls (Girls). Bradford Rd, Sherborne, Dorset DT9 3QN *tel:* 01935 818287 *fax:* 01935 389445 *email:* enquiry@sherborne.com. Julia Freestone, registrar; John Jenkins, dir of mus.

Shrewsbury School (Boys). Shrewsbury, Shrops SY3 7BA *tel:* 01743 280581 (mus dept) *fax:* 01743 280510 *email:* libby@shrewsbury.org.uk. J W R Goulding, head; John Moore, dir of mus.

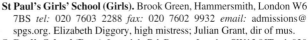

Sibford School (Co-ed). Sibford Ferris, Banbury, Oxon OX15 5QL *tel:* 01295 781200 *fax:* 01295 781204 *email:* sibford.school@ dial.pipex.com. Susan Freestone, head; Matthew Smallwood.

Sidcot School (Co-ed). Winscombe, N Somerset BS25 1PD *tel:* 01934 843102 *fax:* 01934 844181 *email:* admissions@sidcot.org.uk. John Walmsley, head; Timothy Bailey, dir of mus.

Silcoates School (Co-ed). Wrenthorpe, Wakefield, W Yorks WF2 0PD *tel:* 01924 291614 *fax:* 01924 368693. A P Spillane, head; D G Mann, dir of mus.

Sir William Perkins's School (Girls). Guildford Rd, Chertsey, Surrey KT16 9BN *tel:* 01932 562161 *fax:* 01932 570841 *email:* office@ swps.org.uk. Peter Holloway, dir of mus; Jocelyn Slocombe, asst dir; Fiona Taylor.

Solihull School (Boys). Warwick Rd, Solihull, W Midlands B91 3DJ *tel:* 0121 705 4273 *fax:* 0121 711 4439 *email:* admin@solsch.org.uk. J A Claughton, head; Stephen J Perrins, dir of mus.

South Hampstead High School GDST (Girls). 3 Maresfield Gardens, London NW3 5SS *tel:* 020 7435 2899 *fax:* 020 7431 8022 *email:* senior@shhs.gdst.net. Mrs V L Ainley, head; Mr E Kay, dir of mus.

Stewart's Melville College (Boys). Queensferry Rd, Edinburgh EH4 3EZ *tel:* 0131 311 1000 *fax:* 0131 311 1099 *email:* principal@esmgc.com. J N D Gray, principal; Roger Askew, dir of mus.

Stockport Grammar School (Co-ed). Buxton Rd, Stockport, Cheshire SK2 7AF *tel:* 0161 456 9000 *fax:* 0161 419 2407 *email:* sgs@ stockportgrammar.co.uk. I Mellor, head; Jackson Towers, dir of mus.

Stoke College (Co-ed). Stoke-by-Clare, Sudbury, Suffolk CO10 8JE *tel:* 01787 278141 *fax:* 01787 277904 *email:* office@stokecollege.co.uk. John Gibson, head; Adrian Marple, dir of mus.

Stonar School (Girls). Cottles Park, Atworth, Melksham, Wilts SN12 8NT *tel:* 01225 701740/1 *fax:* 01225 790830 *email:* office@stonar.wilts.sch.uk. Mrs C Osborne, head; Nicholas Goodall, dir of mus.

Stonyhurst College (Co-ed). Stonyhurst, Lancs BB7 9PZ *tel:* 01254 827073/093 *fax:* 01254 826370 *email:* admissions@stonyhurst.ac.uk. A J F Aylward, head; R A Highcock, dir of mus.

Stowe School (Boys). Buckingham, Bucks MK18 5EH *tel:* 01280 818264 *fax:* 01280 818181 *email:* jgreen@stowe.co.uk. Anthony Wallersteiner, head; John Cooper Green, dir of mus.

Strathallan School (Co-ed). Forgandenny, Perth PH2 9EG *tel:* 01738 812546 *fax:* 01738 812549 *email:* admissions@strathallan.co.uk. Mr Thompson, head; N R Metcalfe, dir of mus.

Summer Fields (Boys). Mayfield Rd, Oxford OX2 7EN *tel:* 01865 454433 *fax:* 01865 459200 *email:* hmsec@summerfields.org.uk. R Badham-Thornhill, head; Gareth Price, dir of mus.

Sutton Valence School (Co-ed). Sutton Valence, Maidstone, Kent ME17 3HL *tel:* 01622 842281/844092 (mus dept) *fax:* 01622 844093 *email:* sjm@svs.org.uk. J S Davies, head; Simon Marriott, dir of mus.

Taunton School (Co-ed). Taunton, Somerset TA2 6AD *tel:* 01823 349200 *fax:* 01823 349201 *email:* enquiries@tauntonschool.co.uk. J P Whiteley, head; Philip Tyack, dir of mus.

Thetford Grammar School. Bridge St, Thetford IP24 3AF *tel:* 01842 752840 *fax:* 01842 750220 *email:* admin@thetfordgrammarschool. fsnet.co.uk. J R Weeks, head; Mrs J Huntington, dir of mus.

Tonbridge School (Boys). Tonbridge, Kent TN9 1JP *tel:* 01732 365555 *fax:* 01732 770853/363424 *email:* hmsec@tonbridge-school.org. J M Hammond, head; Hilary Davan Wetton, dir of mus.

Tormead School (Girls). Cranley Rd, Guildford, Surrey GU1 2JD *tel:* 01483 575101/796070 (mus office) *fax:* 01483 450592 *email:* head@tormeadschool.org.uk; music@tormeadschool.org.uk. Mrs S E Marks, head; Timothy Ball, dir of mus; Martin Holford, asst dir.

Trent College (Co-ed). Long Eaton, Nottingham, Notts NG10 4AD *tel:* 0115 849 4950 *fax:* 0115 849 4997 *email:* enquiry@ trentcollege.nott.sch.uk. J S Lee, head; P D Redfearn, dir of mus.

Trinity School (Boys). Shirley Park, Croydon CR9 7AT *tel:* 020 8656 9541 *fax:* 020 8655 0522 *email:* music@trinity.croydon.sch.uk. C Tarrant, head; David Swinson, dir of mus.

Truro School (Co-ed). Trennick Lane, Truro, Cornwall TR1 1TH *tel:* 01872 246026 *fax:* 01872 223431 *email:* enquiries@ truro-school.cornwall.sch.uk. P K Smith, head; D J Spedding, dir of mus.

Tudor Hall School (Girls). Wykham Park, Banbury, Oxon OX16 9UR *tel:* 01295 263434 ext 220 *fax:* 01295 253264 *email:* tudorhall@ rmplc.co.uk. Nanette Godfrey, headmistress; Lindsey Lea, dir of mus.

University College School (Boys). Frognal, Hampstead, London NW3 6XH *tel:* 020 7435 2215 *fax:* 020 7433 2111 *email:* senior school@ucsonline.demon.co.uk. K J Durham, head; John Bradbury, dir of mus.

Uppingham School (Co-ed). Uppingham, Rutland, Leics LE15 9QE *tel:* 01572 822267 *fax:* 01572 822792 *email:* dre@uppingham.co.uk. Stephen Winkley, head; David Evans, dir of mus.

Walthamstow Hall (Girls). Sevenoaks, Kent TN13 3UL *tel:* 01732 451334 *fax:* 01732 740439 *email:* registrar@walthamstow.hall.co.uk. Mrs J Milner, head; T J Daniell, dir of mus.

Warwick School (Boys). Myton Rd, Warwick CV34 6PP *tel:* 01926 776400 *fax:* 01926 401259 *email:* enquiries@warwick.warwks.sch.uk. E B Halse, head; Trevor G Barr, dir of mus.

Wellingborough School (Co-ed). Irthlingborough Rd, Wellingborough, Northants NN8 2BX *tel:* 01933 222427 *fax:* 01933 271986. F R Ullmann, head; P R Marshall, dir of mus.

Wellington College (Boys). Crowthorne, Berks RG45 7PU *tel:* 01344 444201 *fax:* 01344 444202 *email:* jdh@wellington-college. berks.scho.uk. A H Munro, head; J D Holloway, dir of mus.

Wentworth College (Girls). College Rd, Bournemouth, Dorset BH5 2DY *tel:* 01202 423266/422584 (mus dept) *fax:* 01202 418030 *email:* wentcolleg@aol.com. Miss S Coe, head; Mary Goodman, dir of mus.

West Buckland School (Co-ed). Barnstaple, Devon EX32 0SX *tel:* 01598 760281/129 (mus dept) *fax:* 01598 760546 *email:* vick@ westbuckland.devon.sch.uk. John Vick, head; Mark Richards, dir of mus.

Westminster School (Boys). 17 Dean's Yard, London SW1P 3PB *tel:* 020 7963 1003 *fax:* 020 7963 1006 *email:* registrar@westminster.org.uk. Tristram Jones-Parry, head; Guy Hopkins, dir of mus.

Westonbirt School (Girls). Tetbury, Glos GL8 8QG *tel:* 01666 880333 *fax:* 01666 880364 *email:* regstrar@westonbirt.gloucs.sch.uk. Mrs M Henderson, head; Malcolm Pike, dir of mus.

Whitford Hall and Dodderhill School. Droitwich Spa WR9 0BE *tel:* 01905 778290 *fax:* 01905 790623 *email:* headmistress@ whitford-dodderhill.worcs.sch.uk. Mrs J M Mumby, head.

Whitgift School (Boys). Haling Park, S Croydon CR2 6YT *tel:* 020 8688 9222 *fax:* 020 8760 0682 *email:* office@whitgift.co.uk. C A Barnett, head; J D Cullen, dir of mus.

Winchester College (Boys). Winchester, Hants SO23 9NA *tel:* 01962 621122 *fax:* 01962 621123 *email:* shcc@wincoll.ac.uk. E N Tate, head; Keith Pusey, master of mus.

Windermere St Anne's School (Co-ed). Windermere, Cumbria LA23 1NW *tel:* 015394 46164 *fax:* 015394 88414 *email:* office@ wsaschool.com. W A Ellis, head; J H McCallum-Hartely, mus dir.

Wispers School for Girls (Girls). High Lane, Haslemere, Surrey GU27 1AD *tel:* 01428 643646 *fax:* 01428 641120 *email:* Head@ wispers.prestel.co.uk. L H Beltran, head; Stephanie Frankland, dir of mus.

Wolverhampton Grammar School (Co-ed). Compton Rd, Wolverhampton WV3 9RB *tel:* 01902 421326 *fax:* 01902 421819 *email:* wgs@wgs.org.uk. Bernard Trafford, head; Andrew Proverbs, dir of mus.

Woodbridge School (Co-ed). Woodbridge, Suffolk IP12 4JH *tel:* 01394 615000 *fax:* 01394 380944 *email:* e-mail@woodbridge.suffolk.sch.uk. Stephen H Cole, head; John R Penny, dir of mus.

Woodhouse Grove School (Co-ed). Apperley Bridge, Bradford BD10 0NR *tel:* 0113 250 2477 *fax:* 0113 250 5290 *email:* enquiries@ woodhousegrove.co.uk. D C Humphreys, head; Mrs J Johnston, dir of mus.

Worksop College (Co-ed). Worksop, Notts S80 3AP *tel:* 01909 537127 *fax:* 01909 537102 *email:* headmaster@worksopcollege.notts.sch.uk. R A Collard, head; P W Boxall, dir of mus.

Worth School (Boys). Paddockhurst Rd, Turners Hill, W Sussex RH10 4SD *tel:* 01342 710200 *fax:* 01342 710201 *email:* school@worth.org.uk. Peter Armstrong, head; Michael Oakley, dir of mus.

Wrekin College (Co-ed). Wellington, Telford, Shrops TF1 3BG *tel:* 01952 242305/223985 (mus dept) *fax:* 01952 240338 *email:* fmurton@ wrekincollege.ac.uk. Stephen G Drew, head; Francis Murton, dir of mus.

Wycliffe College (Co-ed). Stonehouse, Glos GL10 2JQ *tel:* 01453 822432 *fax:* 01453 827634 *email:* senior@wycliffe.co.uk. R A C Collins, head; C G Swain, dir of mus.

Wycombe Abbey School (Girls). High Wycombe, Bucks HP11 1PE *tel:* 01494 520381 *fax:* 01494 473836. Mrs P E Davies, head; M Shepherd, dir of mus.

Yarm School (Co-ed). The Friarage, Yarm, Cleveland TS15 9EJ *tel:* 01642 786023 *fax:* 01642 789216 *email:* dmd@yarm.stockton.sch.uk. D M Dunn, head; Ben Wilson, dir of mus.

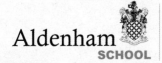

Junior Departments at the Conservatoires

In most cases partial or full local authority funding is available for especially talented children to attend their nearest conservatoire; travelling expenses may also be payable.

Birmingham Conservatoire. Junior School, Paradise Place, Birmingham B3 3HG *tel:* 0121 331 5905 *fax:* 0121 331 5906 *email:* conservatoire. juniors@uce.ac.uk. Timothy English, head of jnr school; David Joyce, str co-ord; Luan Ford, w/wind and br co-ord; Alison Stephen, vocal co-ord; Robert Markham, keyboard co-ord; Lucy Akehurst, young str project co-ord; snr conservatoire staff, CBSO players.

Guildhall School of Music and Drama. Junior School, Barbican, London EC2Y 8DT *tel:* 020 7382 7160 *fax:* 020 7382 7212 *email:* junior@ gsmd.ac.uk. Derek Rodgers, head of jnr school; Alison Mears, head of jnr mus courses; Robert Pell, head of middle school; Robert Porter, head of wind and perc; Mollie Petrie, head of singing; Spencer Down, br co-ord; Timothy Boulton, head of str; Heather Steedman, perc co-ord; Shelagh Sutherland, pno co-ord; Jeffrey Wilson, composition co-ord; Philippa Bunting, str training programme co-ord.

London College of Music and Media at Thames Valley University. Junior College, St Mary's Rd, Ealing, London W5 5RF *tel:* 020 8231 2677 *fax:* 020 8231 2546 *email:* peter.cook@tvu.ac.uk. Peter Cook, dir; Deborah Kemp, head of strs; Daniel Chandler, head of w/wind and br; Jeremy Davis, head of keyboard; Jean Reynolds, head of vocal studies; Martin Vishnick, head of composition; Russell Hepworth-Sawyer, head of mus tech; Fraser Grant, head of drama; Mark Richards, head of academic studies; Edward Stewart, head of gui.

Royal Academy of Music. Junior Academy, Marylebone Rd, London NW1 5HT *tel:* 020 7873 7380 *fax:* 020 7873 7374 *email:* juniors@ ram.ac.uk. Jonathan Willcocks, dir, jnr academy.

Royal College of Music. Junior Dept, Prince Consort Rd, London SW7 2BS *tel:* 020 7591 4334 *fax:* 020 7591 4858 *email:* jd@rcm.ac.uk. Peter Hewitt, dir, jnr dept; Paul Sweetman, acting admin; John Mitchell, orch mgr.

Royal Northern College of Music. The Junior School of Music, 124 Oxford Rd, Manchester M13 9RD *tel:* 0161 273 6283/907 5264 *fax:* 0161 273 7611 *email:* postmaster@fsi.rncm.ac.uk. Karen Humphreys, dir.

Royal Scottish Academy of Music and Drama. Junior Academy of Music, 100 Renfrew St, Glasgow G2 3DB *tel:* 0141 270 8247 *fax:* 0141 353 0372 *email:* a.scott@rsamd.ac.uk. Havilland Willshire, head of jnr academy; Angela Scott, admin.

Royal Welsh College of Music and Drama. Junior Music and Access Studies, Castle Grounds, Cathays Park, Cardiff CF10 3ER *tel:* 029 2039 1365 *fax:* 029 2039 1305 *email:* jmas@rwcmd.ac.uk. Patricia Keir, head of jnr mus and access studies; Sally Craven, admin mgr, jmas.

Trinity College of Music. Junior Dept, King Charles Court, Old Royal Naval College, Greenwich, London SE10 9JF *tel:* 020 8305 4328 *fax:* 020 8305 9328 *email:* mfriend@tcm.ac.uk; cspencer@tcm.ac.uk. Marion Friend, head of jnr dept; Charlotte Spencer, admin and concerts mgr.

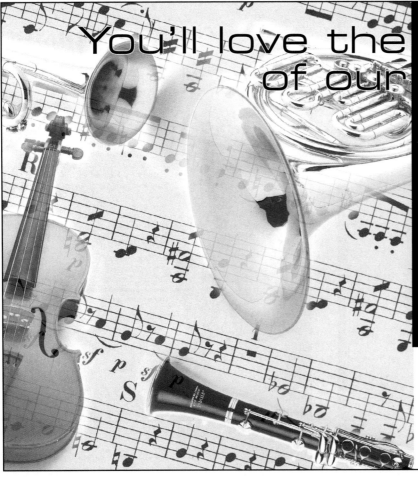

Colleges of Further Education

Aberdeen College. Gordon Centre, Ellon Rd, Bridge of Don, Aberdeen AB23 8LQ *tel:* 01224 706997 *also fax email:* d.carnegie@abcol.ac.uk. Dorothy Carnegie, curriculum mgr.

Accrington and Rossendale College of FE. Rawtenstall Centre, Haslingden Rd, Rawtenstall, Lancs BB4 6RA *tel:* 01254 354202/03/12 *email:* pfinerty@accross.ac.uk; kmatula@accross.ac.uk. Karen Matula, team leader, arts and media dept.

Alton College. Old Odiham Rd, Alton, Hants GU34 2LX *tel:* 01420 592200 *fax:* 01420 592253 *email:* enquiries@altoncollege.ac.uk. Martin Read, head of mus.

The Arts Centre (Liverpool). Liverpool Community College, 9 Myrtle St, Liverpool L7 7JA *tel:* 0151 252 4315/6 *fax:* 0151 252 4401 *email:* anthony.whittaker@liv-coll.ac.uk. Anthony Whittaker, head of mus.

Boston College. Sam Newsom Music Centre, South St, Boston, Lincs PE21 6HT *tel:* 01205 365701 ext 350 *fax:* 01205 311478. Rob Amey, programme leader, performing arts and mus.

Brockenhurst College. Lyndhurst Rd, Brockenhurst, Hants *tel:* 01590 625555 *fax:* 01590 625526 *email:* dcoggins@brock.ac.uk. David Coggins, head of mus.

Bromley College. Rookery Lane, Bromley, Kent BR2 8HE *tel:* 020 8295 7000; 0800 281842 (enquiry hotline) *fax:* 020 8295 7059 *email:* ryoung@bromley.ac.uk. Richard Young, programme mgr.

Broxtowe College. Music and Media Centre, Manor Centre, Church St, Beeston, Notts NG9 1FY *tel:* 0115 917 5252; 0800 281842 (enquiry hotline) *fax:* 0115 917 5200. Dave Sturt, course leader, HND mus performance; Jo Freya, course leader, contemporary popular mus stage 1; Christian Laverick, course leader, contemporary popular mus stage 2/2; Martyn Tite, course leader, contemporary popular mus stage 2/1.

Bury College. Millennium Centre, Market St, Bury, Lancs BL9 0TE *tel:* 0161 280 8404 *fax:* 0161 280 8228 *email:* richard.longden@burycollege.ac.uk. Richard Longden, mus co-ord.

CM. 35 Union St, London SE1 1SD *tel:* 020 7234 0900 *fax:* 020 7403 2611 *email:* everyone@cmonline.org.uk.

Chichester College of Arts, Science and Technology. Creative and Performing Arts, Dept of Music, Westgate Fields, Chichester, W Sussex PO19 1SB *tel:* 01243 786321 *fax:* 01243 775783 *email:* Lisa.Smith@chichester.ac.uk. Gerry Griffith, programme area mgr; Lisa Smith, curriculum team mgr for mus; Glenda Ford, admissions asst.

City College Manchester. City Campus, 34 Whitworth St, Manchester M1 3HB *tel:* 0161 957 1790 *fax:* 0161 945 3854 *email:* admissions@ccm.ac.uk. Martin Moscrop, team leader, mus.

Colchester Institute. Centre for Music and Performance Arts, Sheepen Rd, Colchester, Essex CO3 3LL *tel:* 01206 518777 *fax:* 01206 763041 *email:* info@colch-inst.ac.uk. Bill Tamblyn, dir of centre for mus and performing arts.

Coleg Llandrillo Cymru. Llandudno Rd, Rhos-on-Sea, Colwyn Bay, North Wales LL28 4HZ *tel:* 01492 546666 *fax:* 01492 543052 *email:* a.bettley@llandrillo.ac.uk. Andrew Bettley, head of programme, creative arts.

Cricklade College. Charlton Rd, Andover, Hants SP10 1EJ *tel:* 01264 360000 *fax:* 01264 360010 *email:* jjuszcyk@cricklade.ac.uk. Steve Gower, dir of mus.

Croydon College. Fairfield, College Rd, Croydon CR9 1DX *tel:* 020 8686 5700 ext 3641 *fax:* 020 8760 5880. Jackie Fletcher, programme mgr, performing arts and theatre.

Exeter College. Victoria House, 33-36 Queen St, Exeter EX4 3SR *tel:* 01392 205250/5 *fax:* 01392 205241. Iorwerth Pugh, head of mus.

Fareham College. Bishopsfield Rd, Fareham, Hants PO13 1NH *tel:* 01329 815200 *fax:* 01329 822483 *email:* patrick.ainsworth@fareham.ac.uk. Patrick Ainsworth, programme mgr, performing arts.

Gorseinon College. Belgrave Rd, Swansea SA4 6RD *tel:* 01792 890700/23 *fax:* 01792 898729 *email:* admin@gorseinon.ac.uk. Nick Bennett, principal; Leigh Phillips, head of mus dept; Leslie Ryan, John Quirk, Simon Prothero, Heather James, Tony Small, mus dept.

Great Yarmouth College. Southtown, Great Yarmouth, Norfolk NR31 0ED *tel:* 01493 419223 *email:* f.vettese@gyc.com. F Vettese, team leader; Grant Horsley, mus; Jill Emerson, performing arts.

Harlow College. Velizy Ave, Town Centre, Harlow CM20 1LT *tel:* 01279 868000 *fax:* 01279 868260 *email:* ahopkins@harlow-college.co.uk.

Huddersfield Technical College. New North Rd, Huddersfield HD1 5NN *tel:* 01484 536521 *fax:* 01484 511885 *email:* htcstaff@htcflex8.demon.co.uk. Mark Ellis, programme mgr, mus and performing arts; Rick Cocker, programme mgr, mus tech and popular mus.

Kensington and Chelsea College. Dept for Health and Community, Hortensia Centre, Hortensia Rd, London SW10 0QS *tel:* 020 7573 5233 *fax:* 020 7351 0956. Sally Martin, head of mus.

Kidderminster College. Dept of Community Studies, Hoo Rd, Kidderminster, Worcs DY10 1LX *tel:* 01562 820811 *fax:* 01562 748504 *email:* music@kidderminster.ac.uk. T Bradley, R Fellows, K Rowberry, lecturers in mus; J Bates, lecturer in mus and audio engineering; Pete Ware, lecturer in studio tech/audio engineering; K Gammond, lecturer in mus industry mgt.

Leeds College of Music. 3 Quarry Hill, Leeds LS2 7PD *tel:* 0113 222 3400 *fax:* 0113 243 8798 *email:* enquiries@lcm.ac.uk. Philip Greenwood, head of FE; Ian Smith, programme mgr.

Leicester College. Abbey Annexe, Abbey Park St, Leicester LE1 3WA *tel:* 0116 224 4100 ext 4293; 0800 281842 (enquiry hotline). Andy Richardson, Barry Phillips, stage 2 and 3; Brian Thompson, stage 1 (pre-foundation).

Lewisham College of FE *formerly* **South East London College.** Lewisham Way, London SE4 1UT *tel:* 020 8692 0353 ext 3024. L Newman, programme area leader.

Manchester College of Arts and Technology (MANCAT). Centre for Music and Performance Skills, Lever St, Manchester M1 1FL *tel:* 0800 068 8585 (free course enquiry line) *fax:* 0161 953 2259 *email:* mail@mancat.ac.uk. Anne Bourner, head of mus and performance skills.

Middlesbrough College. Acklam Campus, Hall Drive, Acklam, Middlesbrough, Cleveland TS5 7DY *tel:* 01642 296615/3 *fax:* 01642 296592. Mrs E Round, mus co-ord, lecturer; Barrie Dickinson, popular mus co-ord.

Neath Port Talbot College. Dwr Y Felin Rd, Neath, W Glamorgan SA10 7RF *tel:* 01639 648327 *fax:* 01639 648009 *email:* alan.good@nptc.ac.uk. Alan Good, performing arts programme area leader.

Nelson and Colne College of FE. Scotland Rd, Nelson, Lancs BB9 7YT *tel:* 01282 440200 *fax:* 01282 440274. Mel Simpson, head of creative arts; Rosemary White, section leader in mus; John Catterall, lecturer in mus tech and popular mus; Bill Palmer, lecturer in mus tech.

Newcastle College. School of Music and Performing Arts, Rye Hill Campus, Scotswood Rd, Newcastle upon Tyne NE4 7SA *tel:* 0191 200 4000 *fax:* 0191 200 4729/4675. Vee Wilkinson, dir of school.

North East Surrey College of Technology. Reigate Rd, Ewell, Surrey KT17 3DS *tel:* 020 8394 3245 *fax:* 020 8394 3030 *email:* info@nescot.ac.uk. C Wenley, head of arts media and gen educ; Dawn Samain, admin asst.

North Trafford College. Talbot Rd, Stretford, Manchester M32 0XH *tel:* 0161 886 7070; 0800 281842 (enquiry hotline). Steve Barlowe, snr course tutor.

North Warwickshire and Hinckley College (Hinckley College). Performing Art and Media Centre, London Rd, Hinckley, Leics LE10 1HQ *tel:* 024 7624 3000 ext 3051 *fax:* 01455 633930. Steve Cooper, course leader popular mus/programme area mgr; Ian Wynd, course leader media production; Anita O'Brien, course leader performing arts.

North Warwickshire and Hinckley College (North Warwickshire College). Hinckley Rd, Nuneaton, Warks CV11 6BH *tel:* 024 7624 3000 *fax:* 024 7632 9056 *email:* the.college@nwarks-hinkley.ac.uk. Judith Norden, head of f/t mus studies.

Norwich City College of FE and HE. Ipswich Rd, Norwich NR2 2LJ *tel:* 01603 773288 *fax:* 01603 773301 *email:* dmorgan@ccn.ac.uk. David Morgan, head of dept.

Oldham College. Rochdale Rd, Oldham OL9 6AA *tel:* 0161 785 4070 *fax:* 0161 785 4064 *email:* nick.middleton@oldham.ac.uk. Nick Middleton, head of mus.

Perth College. Faculty of Arts, School of Music and Audio Engineering, Crieff Rd, Perth PH1 2NX *tel:* 01738 621171 *fax:* 01738 440050. Pamela McLean, head of faculty of arts.

Peter Symonds' College. Owens Rd, Winchester, Hants SO22 6RX *tel:* 01962 852764 *fax:* 01962 849372 *email:* abennetts@psc.ac.uk. Anna Bennetts, head of mus, including Hampshire specialist mus course.

Preston College. Park School, Moor Park Ave, Preston, Lancs PR1 6AP *tel:* 01772 225006. Ian Carten, programme co-ord, mus.

Queen Mary's College. Cliddesden Rd, Basingstoke, Hants RG21 3HF *tel:* 01256 417500 *fax:* 01256 417501 *email:* postmaster@qmc.ac.uk. Steve Gallagher, head of performing arts.

Redbridge College. Little Heath, Off Barley Lane, Romford, Essex RM6 4XT *tel:* 020 8548 7400 *fax:* 020 8599 8224 *email:* info@redbridge-college.ac.uk. Pete Herbert, programme area leader.

Redcar and Cleveland College. Corporation Rd, Redcar, Cleveland TS10 1EZ *tel:* 01642 473132 *fax:* 01642 490856. Stephen Colbert, lecturer in mus.

Richmond upon Thames College. Egerton Rd, Twickenham, Middx TW2 7SJ *tel:* 020 8607 8221. Chris Mitchell, Peter Garvey, lecturers in mus; Justin Paterson, Brian Miller, Peter Wilson, lecturers in mus tech.

Rotherham College of Arts and Technology. Eastwood Lane, Rotherham, S Yorks S65 1EG *tel:* 01709 362111 *fax:* 01709 373053 *email:* pgoodwin@rotherham.ac.uk. Peter Goodwin, programme co-ord, popular mus.

Rugby College of FE. Rugby, Warks CV21 3QS *tel:* 01788 338602 *fax:* 01788 338574. Gordon Croft, mus and performing arts co-ord; Kirsty Holt, dir of Rugby mus centre, Warwickshire county mus service.

South Cheshire College. Dane Bank Ave, Crewe, Cheshire CW2 8AB *tel:* 01270 654654 *fax:* 01270 651515. J R Pyatt, head of mus dept.

South Downs College. College Rd, Purbrook Way, Havant, Hants *tel:* 023 9225 7011. Peter Rhodes, head of mus.

Southgate College. High St, Southgate, London N14 6BS *tel:* 020 8886 6521/8982 5087 (direct line) *fax:* 020 8982 5051 *email:* neil.cloake@southgate.ac.uk. Neil Cloake, head of school of performance; Daniel Harding, co-ord jnr arts centre.

Stevenson College, Edinburgh. Bankhead Ave, Edinburgh EH11 4DE *tel:* 0131 535 4621 *fax:* 0131 535 4622 *email:* aguest@stevenson.ac.uk. Alison Guest, curriculum leader mus.

Stratford-upon-Avon College. The Willows, Alcester Rd, Stratford-upon-Avon CV37 9QR *tel:* 01789 266245 *fax:* 01789 267524 *email:* christopherlong@stratford.ac.uk. Chris Long, head of mus; David Coulter, Mike Whitcroft, lecturers.

Strode College. Church Rd, Street, Somerset BA16 0AB *tel:* 01458 844400 *fax:* 01458 844411. Gill Deakin, head of creative arts and design; James Phippen, lecturer in charge of mus.

Taunton's College. Hill Lane, Southampton SO15 5RL *tel:* 023 8051 1811 *fax:* 023 8051 1991 *email:* higginj@tauntons.ac.uk. Jane Higgins, dir of mus; Andy Wild, mus/mus tech.

Tonalis Music Centre. 4 Castle Farm Close, Leighterton, Glos GL8 8UY *tel:* 01666 890460 *fax:* 01666 890460 *email:* tonalis@aol.com. Michael Deason-Barrow, dir.

Wakefield College. School of Music, Thornes Park Centre, Horbury Rd, Wakefield WF2 8QZ *tel:* 01924 789802 *fax:* 01924 789821 *email:* p.feehan@wakcoll.ac.uk. Susan Hirst, head of mus; David Kirtlan, head of popular mus; Nigel Chapman, HNC jazz co-ord.

Walford and North Shropshire College. Shrewsbury Rd, Oswestry, Shrops SY11 4QB *tel:* 01691 688000 *fax:* 01691 688001. Julian Cattley, head of mus.

Warrington Collegiate Institute. Winwick Rd Campus, Warrington, Cheshire WA1 8QA *tel:* 01925 494554; 0800 281842 (enquiry hotline). Martin Lea, course leader; Glen Jackson, snr course tutor (IMF).

West Herts College. Watford Campus, Hempstead Rd, Watford, Herts WD1 3EZ *tel:* 01923 812000/812560 *fax:* 01923 812556. D Morgan, course tutor, mus tech; R Spooner, course tutor, popular mus.

West Kent College. Brook St, Tonbridge, Kent, TN9 2PW *tel:* 01732 358101 ext 4323 *fax:* 01732 771415 *email:* julieparker@wkc.ac.uk. Julie Parker, course leader, ND in popular mus; John Dodd, course leader ND in mus tech.

Westminster Kingsway College. Regents Park Centre, Longford St, London NW1 3HB *tel:* 020 7556 8000 *fax:* 020 7391 6400 *email:* courseinfo@westking.ac.uk. Charlie Round-Turner, popular mus tutor; Sheila Maloney, mus tech tutor; Gary Sieling, AL mus.

Wigan and Leigh College. Leigh Campus, Railway Rd, Leigh, Lancs WN7 4AH *tel:* 01942 761726 *fax:* 01942 761771 *email:* pframpton@wigan-leigh.ac.uk. Peter Frampton, curriculum mgr, performing arts.

Wirral Metropolitan College. Performing Arts and Media, Carlett Park, Eastham, Wirral, Merseyside CH62 0AY *tel:* 0151 551 7583 *fax:* 0151 551 7401 *email:* greg.williams@wmc.ac.uk. Greg Williams, head of school, performing arts.

Worcester College of Technology. Dept of General Education, Deansway, Worcester WR1 2JF *tel:* 01905 725555 *fax:* 01905 28906 *email:* dboothroyd@wortech.ac.uk. David Boothroyd, course dir, HND; Nick Smith, course dir, BTEC Nationals; Jayne Dixon, course tutor, access to mus.

Yale College (Coleg Iâl). Grove Park Rd, Wrexham, Clwyd LL12 7AA *tel:* 01978 311794 ext 2271 *fax:* 01978 291569 *email:* sw@yale.ac.uk; mcs@yale.ac.uk. Paul Croke, principal; Sam Wyse, co-ord for performing arts; Martin Sayer, course team leader, mus.

Yeovil College. Mudford Rd, Yeovil, Somerset BA21 4DR *tel:* 01935 845312 *fax:* 01935 429962 *email:* rosier@yeovil-college.ac.uk. Rosie Russell, head of performing arts.

Music Degrees and Diplomas

The following are generally recognised music qualifications. It should be noted that some refer to institutions which are no longer functioning.

University Degrees

AMusM	*master of musical arts of Nottingham University*	MEd	*master of education*
AMusD	*doctor of musical arts of Nottingham University*	MLitt	*master of letters*
BA	*bachelor of arts*	MMus	*master of music*
BA(QTS)	*bachelor of arts (qualified teacher status)*	MMusRCM	*master of music of the Royal College of Music*
BEd	*bachelor of education*	MPhil	*master of philosophy*
BHum	*bachelor of humanities*	MusB	*bachelor of music*
BMus	*bachelor of music*	MusBac	*bachelor of music*
BPhil	*bachelor of philosophy*	MusD	*doctor of music*
DMus	*doctor of music*	MusDoc	*doctor of music*
DPhil	*doctor of philosophy*	MusM	*master of music*
MA	*master of arts*	PhD	*doctor of philosophy*

Diplomas of Graduate Status

Several institutions have power to grant 'graduate diplomas'. The following selection is of those diplomas most commonly awarded.

DipMusEd (RSAM)	*diploma in musical education of the Royal Scottish Academy of Music and Drama*	GGSM	*graduate of the Guildhall School of Music and Drama*
FRCO	*fellow of the Royal College of Organists*	GLCM	*graduate of the London College of Music*
GBSM	*graduate of the Birmingham School of Music*	GNSM	*graduate of the (former) Northern School of Music*
GCLCM(LightMusic)	*graduate of the City of Leeds College of Music (Light Music)*	GRNCM	*graduate of the Royal Northern College of Music*
		GRSM	*graduate of the Royal Schools of Music*
GDBM	*graduate diploma in Band Musicianship, University of Salford*	GTCL	*graduate of Trinity College of Music*
GDWCMD	*graduate diploma of the Welsh College of Music and Drama*		

Other Diplomas

These are usually awarded for either performing or teaching, and cover a wide range of subjects and instruments. Special qualifications may be additionally designated, eg TD for 'teaching diploma'.

ABCA	*associate of the British College of Accordionists*	DipMusEd	*diploma in musical education (various institutions)*
ABSM	*associate of the Birmingham School of Music*	DipRAM	*recital diploma of the Royal Academy of Music*
ACertCM	*Archbishop's certificate in church music*	DipTMus	*Scottish music teaching diploma*
ADCM	*Archbishop's diploma in church music*	DPLM	*diploma of proficiency in light music of the City of Leeds College of Music*
AGSM	*associate of the Guildhall School of Music and Drama*	DRSAM	*diploma in music of the Royal Scottish Academy of Music and Drama*
ALCM	*associate of the London College of Music*		
AMusLCM	*associate in general musicianship of the London College of Music*	FGCM	*fellowship of the Guild of Church Musicians*
		FLCM	*fellow of the London College of Music*
AMusNCM	*associate in theory of music of the National College of Music*	FNCM	*fellow of the National College of Music*
		FRCO(CHM)	*fellow of the Royal College of Organists, choirmaster's diploma*
AMusTCL	*associate in compositional techniques of Trinity College of Music*	FRMCM	*fellow of the (former) Royal Manchester College of Music*
AMusTS	*associate in general musicianship of the Tonic Sol-Fa College of Music*	FTCL	*fellow of Trinity College of Music*
ANCM	*associate of the National College of Music*	FTSC	*fellow of the Tonic Sol-Fa College of Music*
ANSM	*associate of the (former) Northern School of Music*	FVCM	*fellow of the Victoria College of Music*
ARCM	*associate of the Royal College of Music*	LBCA	*licentiate of the British College of Accordionists*
ARCO	*associate of the Royal College of Organists*	LGSM	*licentiate of the Guildhall School of Music and Drama*
ARCO(CHM)	*associate of the Royal College of Organists, choirmaster's diploma*	LLCM	*licentiate of the London College of Music*
ARMCM	*associate of the (former) Royal Manchester College of Music*	LMusLCM	*licentiate in general musicianship of the London College of Music*
ARNCM	*associate of the Royal Northern College of Music*	LMusNCM	*licentiate in theory of music of the National College of Music*
ATCL	*associate of Trinity College of Music*		
ATSC	*associate of the Tonic Sol-Fa College of music*	LMusTCL	*licentiate in compositional techniques of Trinity College of Music*
AVCM	*associate of the Victoria College of Music*		
DipEd	*diploma in education (various institutions)*		

LMusTSC	*licentiate in general musicianship of the Tonic Sol-Fa College of Music*	LWCMD	*licentiate of the Welsh College of Music and Drama*
LNCM	*licentiate of the National College of Music*	PDBM	*professional diploma in band musicianship, University of Salford*
LRAM	*licentiate of the Royal Academy of Music*	PDBM(PMR)	*professional diploma in band musicianship (popular music with recording), University of Salford*
LRSM	*licentiate of the Royal Schools of Music*		
LTCL	*licentiate of Trinity College of Music*		
LTCL(GMT)	*licentiate in general musicianship (teachers) of Trinity College of Music*	PGCC(Band)	*postgraduate higher certificate in band conducting, University of Salford*
LTSC	*licentiate of the Tonic Sol-Fa College of Music*	PPRNCM	*professional performer of the Royal Northern College of Music*
LVCM	*licentiate of the Victoria College of Music*		

Honorary Awards

These awards are in addition to certain university degrees listed above.

ARAM	*associate of the Royal Academy of Music*	Hon FGSM	*honorary fellow of the Guildhall School of Music and Drama*
ARSCM	*associate of the Royal School of Church Music*	Hon FNCM	*honorary fellow of the National College of Music*
Dmus (Cantuar)	*doctor of music, awarded by the Archbishop of Canterbury*	Hon FRAM	*honorary fellow of the Royal Academy of Music*
FBSM	*fellow of the Birmingham School of Music*	Hon FTCL	*honorary fellow of Trinity College of Music*
FGSM	*fellow of the Guildhall School of Music and Drama*	Hon FTSC	*honorary fellow of the Tonic Sol-Fa College of Music*
FNCM	*fellow of the National College of Music*	Hon GCM	*honorary member of the Guild of Church Musicians*
FNSM	*fellow of the (former) Northern School of Music*	Hon GDBM	*honorary graduate in band musicianship, Salford College of Technology*
FRAM	*fellow of the Royal Academy of Music*		
FRCM	*fellow of the Royal College of Music*	Hon GSM	*honorary member of the Guildhall School of Music and Drama*
FRNCM	*fellow of the Royal Northern College of Music*		
FRSAMD	*fellow of the Royal Scottish Academy of Music and Drama*	Hon LCM	*honorary member of the London College of Music*
		Hon RAM	*honorary member of the Royal Academy of Music*
FRSCM	*fellow of the Royal School of Church Music*	Hon RCM	*honorary member of the Royal College of Music*
FWCMD	*fellow of the Welsh College of Music and Drama*	Hon RSCM	*honorary member of the Royal School of Church Music*
Hon ARAM	*honorary associate of the Royal Academy of Music*	Hon TSC	*honorary member of the Tonic Sol-Fa College of Music*
Hon ARCM	*honorary associate of the Royal College of Music*	Hon VCM	*honorary member of the Victoria College of Music*
Hon FGCM	*honorary fellow of the Guild of Church Musicians*		

Colleges of Higher Education

Application for admission to Colleges of Higher Education must be made through the **Univesities and Colleges Admissions Service (UCAS)**. Applicants who are still at school or college should obtain their application materials from their school or college. Other applicants may obtain application materials from their Local Careers Office, by ordering an application pack from the UCAS website (www.ucas.com) or by contacting UCAS directly (UCAS, Application Requests, Rosehill, New Barn Lane, Cheltenham, Glos GL52 3LZ *tel:* 01242 223707). Applicants who are outside the UK should contact their nearest British Council office. Information about the application process can be found on the UCAS website.

Barnsley College. PO Box 266, Church St, Barnsley, S Yorks S70 2YW *tel:* 01226 730191/216156/475 *fax:* 01226 298514 *email:* s.roberts@barnsley.ac.uk.

Colchester Institute. Centre for Music and Performance Arts, Sheepen Rd, Colchester, Essex CO3 *tel:* 01206 518633/000 *fax:* 01206 518186. Bill Tamblyn, prof and dir; Stephen Bingham, head of strs; Charles Hine, head of w/wind and performance; Jennifer Lilleystone, head of vocal studies; Lesley Young, head of keyboard studies; Alan Bullard, head of composition; Andrew Allen, FdA popular mus course leader; Christopher Phelps, BA course leader; Ian Ray, ND mus course leader; Nick Thompson, teacher in charge, CAMS; Mick Brannan, ND pop mus course leader.

Dartington College of Arts. Music Dept, Totnes, Devon TQ9 6EJ *tel:* 01803 862224 *fax:* 01803 863569 *email:* registry@dartington.ac.uk. Trevor Wiggins, dir of mus; Kevin Thompson, principal; Edward Cowie, dir of research; Frank Denyer, Bob Gilmore, Catherine Laws, Christopher Best, David Prior.

King Alfred's College. Sparkford Rd, Winchester, Hants SO22 4NR *tel:* 01962 841515 *fax:* 01962 842280.

Liverpool Institute for Performing Arts. Mount St, Liverpool L1 9HF *tel:* 0151 330 3000 *fax:* 0151 330 3131 *email:* admissions@hpa.ac.uk. Ian Gardiner, composer in residence; Tim Pike, snr lecturer in mus; Paul Walker, keyboard lecturer; Mark Pearman, songwriting; Martin Isherwood, head of mus; Paul Mitchell-Davidson, lecturer; Sarah Stephenson.

Perth College. Faculty of Arts, School of Music and Audio Engineering, Crieff Rd, Perth PH1 2NX *tel:* 01738 621171 *fax:* 01738 440050. Pamela McLean, head of faculty of arts.

St Martin's College. Lancaster LA1 3JD *tel:* 01524 384234 *fax:* 01524 384593 *email:* r.mcgregor@ucsm.ac.uk. Richard McGregor, principal lecturer in mus; Peter Noke, pianist in residence; Clive Walkely, lecturer (p/t); Hugh Smith.

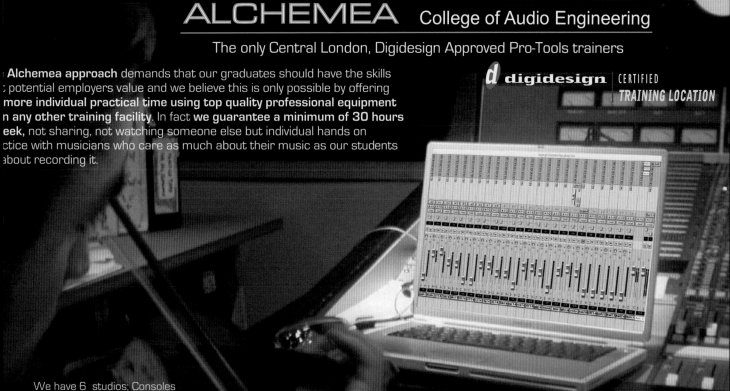

Conservatoires

Applications for places are made directly to the registrar of the establishment concerned who will forward the necessary forms.

Birmingham Conservatoire. Faculty of the University of Central England in Birmingham, Paradise Place, Birmingham B3 3HG *tel:* 0121 331 5901/2 *fax:* 0121 331 5906 *email:* conservatoire@uce.ac.uk. George Caird, prof, principal; Mark Racz, prof, vice-principal; Michael Harris, head of w/wind; Julian Pike, head of vocal studies; Malcolm Wilson, prof, head of keyboard studies; David Purser, head of br; Andrew Downes, prof, head of composition and creative studies; James Strebing, head of perc; David Saint, head of academic studies; Liz Garnett, head of p/grad studies; Peter Johnson, head of research.

Guildhall School of Music and Drama. Silk St, Barbican, London EC2Y 8DT *tel:* 020 7628 2571 *fax:* 020 7256 9438. Genista McIntosh, principal; Damian Cranmer, dir of mus; Bernard Lanskey, asst dir of mus; Richard Jerrom, registrar (admissions); David Takeno, head of strs; Peter Gane, head of wind and perc; Ronan O'Hora, head of keyboard studies; Robin Bowman, head of vocal studies; Yfrah Neaman, head of advanced inst studies; Clive Timms, head of opera studies; Scott Stroman, head of jazz; Sarah Hoskyns, head of mus therapy.

Leeds College of Music. 3 Quarry Hill, Leeds LS2 7PD *tel:* 0113 222 3400 *fax:* 0113 243 8798 *email:* enquiries@lcm.ac.uk. David Hoult, principal; Philip Greenwood, head of FE programmes; Andrew Bates, head of HE programmes; Ted Lee, head of mus inst tech; Lis Parry, head of community educ; David Smith, head of performance.

London College of Music and Media. St Mary's Rd, Ealing, London W5 5RF *tel:* 020 8231 2304 *fax:* 020 8231 2546 *email:* music@tvu.ac.uk. Colin Lawson, pro vice chancellor; Francis Pott, head of research, development and composition; Nick Thompson, head of w/wind, br and perc; Peter Savidge, head of vocal studies; Raphael Terroni, head of keyboard studies; Susanne Stanzeleit, head of strs; Christopher Batchelor, head of mus; Robert Scholl, lecturer, mus; Peter Rudrick, head of BMus Performance/Composition; Simon Zargonski-Thomas, lecturer, mus.

National Opera Studio. Morley College, 61 Westminster Bridge Rd, London SE1 7HT *tel:* 020 7928 6833/7261 9267 *fax:* 020 7928 1810 *email:* Natoperastudio@aol.com. Donald Maxwell, dir; Roy Laughlin, head of mus; Isobel Flinn, head of studies; Hugh Lloyd, admin.

Royal Academy of Music. Marylebone Rd, London NW1 5HT *tel:* 020 7873 7373 *fax:* 020 7873 7374 *email:* registry@ram.ac.uk. Curtis Price, principal; Jonathan Freeman-Attwood, vice-principal, dir of studies; Jeremy Summerly, head of u/grad programmes; Amanda Glauert, head of p/grad programmes; Simon Bainbridge, head of composition; Keith Bragg, head of w/wind; Laurence Cummings, head of historical performance; Christopher Elton, head of keyboard studies; Gerard Presencer, head of jazz; David Strange, head of strs; James Watson, head of br; Dick Walter, head of media and applied mus;, Mark Wildman, head of vocal studies; Iain Ledingham, head of opera.

Royal College of Music. Prince Consort Rd, London SW7 2BS *tel:* 020 7589 3643 *fax:* 020 7589 7740 *email:* info@rcm.ac.uk. Janet Ritterman, dir; Jeremy Cox, dean and deputy dir; Kevin Porter, sec, registrar; Elisabeth Cook, head of u/grad programmes; Darla Crispin, head of p/grad programmes; Graham Caldbeck, head of individual studies; Mark Messenger, head of strs; Neil Mackie, head of vocal studies; Janet Hilton, head of w/wind; Andrew Ball, head of keyboard; Julian Anderson, head of composition; William Mival, head of composition mgt; Peter Bassano, head of br; Kevin Hathway, head of perc; Simon Channing, head of performance planning; Peter Hewitt, dir of jnr dept; Paul Banks, research development fellow.

Royal Northern College of Music. 124 Oxford Rd, Manchester M13 9RD *tel:* 0161 907 5200 *fax:* 0161 273 7611 *email:* David.Young@rncm.ac.uk. Edward Gregson, prof, principal; Colin Beeson, vice-principal; Ronald Woodley, head of p/grad studies and research; Martin Harlow, head of u/grad studies; Adam Gorb, head of composition and contemporary mus; Malcolm Layfield, head of strs; Mark Ray, head of keyboard studies; Alexander Crowe, head of vocal and opera studies; James Gourlay, head of wind and perc; David Young, academic registrar.

Royal Scottish Academy of Music and Drama. 100 Renfrew St, Glasgow G2 3DB *tel:* 0141 332 4101 *fax:* 0141 332 8901 *email:* registry@rsamd.ac.uk. John Wallace, principal; Rita McAllister, dir of mus; Peter Inness, associate dir of mus; Pam Flanagan, head of educ mus; Gordon McPherson, head of composition; Christopher Underwood, head of vocal studies; Philip Jenkins, head of keyboard studies; David Davies, head of orch studies and w/wind; Bryan Allen, head of br; Martin Hughes, head of strs; Timothy Dean, head of opera; Heather Corbett, head of perc; Heather Nicoll, snr tutor, co-ord of w/wind, Brian McNeil, head of Scottish mus.

Royal Welsh College of Music and Drama. Castle Grounds, Cathays Park, Cardiff CF10 3ER *tel:* 029 2039 1363 *fax:* 029 2039 1305 *email:* music.admissions@rwcmd.ac.uk. Jeremy Ward, head of mus; Lucy Robinson, head of academic studies; John Cranmer, BMus course leader; Roger Butler, head of mus tech; Lyn Davies, head of vocal studies; Peter Esswood, head of strs; Richard McMahon, head of keyboard st; John Mills, head of gui; Christopher Mowat, head of br and perc; Andrew Wilson-Dickson, head of early mus; Patricia Keir, head of jnr mus and access studies; Zoë Smith, asst head of mus; John Reynolds, head of w/wind; Howard Williams, head of cond; Alison Levinge, course leader mus therapy; Tim Raymond, head of composition; Meinir Heulyn, hp co-ord; Paula Gardiner, jazz co-ord; Chris Stock, perc co-ord.

Trinity College of Music. King Charles Court, Old Royal Naval College, Greenwich, London SE10 9JF *tel:* 020 8305 4444 *fax:* 020 8309 4444 *email:* ssmith@tcm.ac.uk; info@tcm.ac.uk. Gavin Henderson, principal; Derek Aviss, deputy principal; Roger Pope, warden; Jennifer Barnes, asst principal (academic), dean of studies; Simon Young, asst principal (external relations), head of cond faculty; Anna Jattkowski-Hudson, asst principal (student support services), academic registrar; Daryl Runswick, head of composition faculty; Marian Friend, head of jnr dept; Eleanor Noonan, head of early mus faculty; Douglas Finch, head of keyboard faculty; Linda Hirst, head of vocal faculty; Paul Goodey, head of wind, br and perc faculty; Nicholas Pendlebury, head of str faculty.

Universities

Degree courses in music are offered at the following universities. Applications for admission to undergraduate courses at all of the following, except the Open University, are made through the **Universities and Colleges Admission Service (UCAS)**, Rosehill, New Barn Lane, Cheltenham, Glos GL52 3LZ. Application materials can be obtained from schools, colleges or careers offices in the UK and the British Council in countries outside the UK. They can also be ordered by accessing the UCAS website (www.ucas.com). Information about the application process may be found on the website or by contacting applicant enquiries (*tel:* 01242 227788).

Anglia Polytechnic University (APU). Dept of Music, East Rd, Cambridge CB1 1PT *tel:* 01223 363271 ext 2353 *fax:* 01223 352973 *email:* music@apu.ac.uk. Paul Jackson, head of mus, MA mus course leader; David Crilly, dir of research (mus), admissions tutor; Richard Hoadley, BA mus field leader; Alan Rochford, mus recruitment offr, schools and international adviser; Nicholas Toller, dir of practical studies; Kevin Flanagan, course leader, jazz studies; Helen Odell-Miller, course leader, MA mus therapy.

Bangor, University of Wales. School of Music, College Rd, Bangor, Gwynedd LL57 2DG *tel:* 01248 382181 *fax:* 01248 370297 *email:* mus014@bangor.ac.uk. Robert Pascall, head of school, admissions tutor; Bruce Wood, David Evans, Andrew Lewis, snr lecturers; Wyn Thomas, dir of studies; Suzi Collick, admin.

Bath Spa University College *formerly* **Bath College of HE**. Newton St Loe, Bath BA2 9BN *tel:* 01225 875875 *fax:* 01225 875444. Geoff Smith, head of school of mus and performing arts; Roger Heaton, course dir BA mus; Joseph Hyde, course dir BA creative mus tech; Nick Atkinson, course dir BA creative arts; Matthew Spring, course leader musicology; Joe Bennett, course dir FdMus.

Birmingham University. Dept of Music, Barber Institute of Fine Arts, Edgbaston, Birmingham B15 2TT *tel:* 0121 414 5782 *fax:* 0121 414 5781 *email:* s.miles@bham.ac.uk. John Whenham, head of dept; Jonty Harrison, dir of p/grad studies; Kenneth Hamilton, u/grad admissions tutor.

Bristol University. Dept of Music, Victoria Rooms, Queens Rd, Clifton, Bristol BS8 1SA *tel:* 0117 954 5028 *fax:* 0117 954 5027 *email:* m.e.peirson@bris.ac.uk. Wyndham Thomas, snr lecturer; G Poole, reader in composition; J Cross, reader in musicology, head of dept; W G Jenkins, J Irving, snr lecturers in mus; R Beckles Willson, J Pickard, B Walton, N Farwell, lecturers in mus.

Brunel University. Dept of Performing Arts, Gaskell Building, Uxbridge, Middx UB8 3PH *tel:* 01895 274000 ext 4512 *fax:* 01895 816224 *email:* frank.griffith@brunel.ac.uk (admissions). Laudan Nooshin, BA mus course dir, mus lecturer; Colin Riley, snr tutor, mus lecturer; Frank Griffith, BA admissions tutor, mus lecturer; Sheila McQuattie, mus lecturer; Ben Jarlett, academic related technician, mus lecturer; Helena Mowat-Brown, John Aplin, Peter Cook, p/t mus lecturers.

Buckinghamshire Chilterns University College. Queen Alexandra Rd, High Wycombe, Bucks HP11 2JZ *tel:* 01494 522141.

Cambridge University. University Music School, West Rd, Cambridge CB3 9DP *tel:* 01223 763481 *fax:* 01223 335067 *email:* admin@mus.cam.ac.uk. Roger Parker, prof of mus; Martin Ennis, chmn of faculty board; Sue Round, sec of faculty board; Roger Bowers, Stefano Castelvecchi, Ian Cross, Ruth Davies, Martin Ennis, Iain Fenlon, Marina Frolova-Walker, Robin Holloway, Andrew Jones, Susan Rankin, Dean Sutcliffe, Nicholas Marston.

Canterbury Christ Church University College. Music Dept, North Holmes Rd, Canterbury, Kent CT1 1QU *tel:* 01227 782244 *also fax;*

email: lmrl@cant.ac.uk. Grenville Hancox, head of dept; Roderick Watkins, dir u/grad programmes (BMus/BA); Julian Raphael, dir foundation degree in Popular Music and Technology; Kim Burwell, dir p/grad programme (MMus); John Ludlow, vn consultant; David Campbell, visiting prof of w/wind; David Rees-Williams, jazz pno consultant; Paul Patterson, visiting prof of composition.

Cardiff University. Dept of Music, 31 Corbett Rd, Cardiff CF10 3EB *tel:* 029 2087 4816 *fax:* 029 2087 4379 *email:* music-ucasenq@ cardiff.ac.uk. Robin Stowell, prof and head of dept; Adrian Thomas, Stephen Walsh, John Tyrrell, profs; Anthony Powers, composer in residence; David Wyn Jones, Richard Elfyn Jones, snr lecturers; Timothy Taylor, snr tutor; David Beard, Derek Carew, Kenneth Gloag, David Humphreys, Caroline Rae, Charles Wilson, lecturers.

University College Chichester. Music Dept, Bishop Otter Campus, College Lane, Chichester PO19 6PE *tel:* 01243 816000 *fax:* 01243 816080 *email:* a.robson@ucc.ac.uk. Arthur Robson, Michael Waite, Rod Paton, Ben Hall, Richard Donnelly.

City University. Dept of Music, Northampton Square, London EC1V 0HB *tel:* 020 7040 8284 *fax:* 020 7040 8576 *email:* music@city.ac.uk. Denis Smalley, head of dept; Steve Stanton, BMus/BSc admissions tutor; Jim Grant, Dip/MIT dir; John Richardson, MA dir; Simon Emmerson, research dir; Andrew Pearce, admin; Kathryn McCutcheon, concerts sec.

Coventry University. Performing Arts, Priory St, Coventry CV1 5FB *tel:* 024 7688 7474 *fax:* 024 7688 7497. Sarah Whatley, head of performing arts; Robert Ramskill, course leader; Julian Hellaby, snr lecturer; Robert Godman, lecturer; Paul Leddington-Wright, choir and conducting.

University of Derby. School of Computing and Technology, Kedleston Rd, Derby DE22 1GB *tel:* 01332 591736 *fax:* 01332 597739. Chris Wilson, programme leader, admissions tutor; Richard Hodges, primary subject leader; Michael Brown, lecturer in mus production; John Crossley, lecturer in mus production, subject leader popular mus CSP.

Durham University. Dept of Music, The Music School, Palace Green, Durham DH1 3RL *tel:* 0191 374 3221 *fax:* 0191 374 3219 *email:* karen.scott@durham.ac.uk. Max Paddison, chmn of dept; Michael Spitzer, admissions tutor; Bennett Zon, dir of p/grad studies.

University of East Anglia. School of Music, Norwich NR4 7TJ *tel:* 01603 592452 *fax:* 01603 250454 *email:* mus.admiss@uea.ac.uk. Peter Aston, professorial fellow; David Chadd, head of dept, snr lecturer in mus; Sharon Choa, Simon Waters, Anthony Gritten, Jonathan Impett, lecturers in mus.

University of Edinburgh. School of Arts, Culture and Environment, Music, Alison House, 12 Nicolson Square, Edinburgh EH8 9DF *tel:* 0131 650 2427 *fax:* 0131 650 2425 *email:* music@ed.ac.uk. T N O'Regan, head of dept; N Osborne Reid, prof; E J Harper, reader; J P Kitchen, P W Nelson, T M Turnbull, snr lecturers; M Edwards, E Kelly, D Isaacs, A Roth, lecturers; A M Trewin, ethnomusicology; A Myers, G G O'Brien, organology.

Exeter University. Music Dept, Knightley, Streatham Drive, Exeter, Devon EX4 4PD *tel:* 01392 263810 *fax:* 01392 263815 *email:* music@exeter.ac.uk. Richard Langham Smith, reader; Timothy Jones, lecturer; Alan Street, lecturer and admissions tutor; Peter C Allsop, reader in mus; Paul Morgan, Ian Mitchell, Joe Duddell, p/t lecturers.

Glasgow University. Dept of Music, 14 University Gardens, Glasgow G12 8QH *tel:* 0141 330 4093 *fax:* 0141 330 3518 *email:* secretary@ music.gla.ac.uk. Graham Hair, composition; Marjorie Rycroft, baroque, classical and Scottish mus; Warwick Edwards, medieval, renaissance and Scottish mus; Carola Böhm, mus tech; Nick Fells, electroacoustics, composition; John Butt, head of dept, Bach, baroque, 20th C performance culture; Martin Dixon, philosophy of mus; Bill Sweeney, composition; David Code, Debussy mus, art and literature in 19th C France.

Goldsmiths College. Music Dept, University of London, New Cross, London SE14 6NW *tel:* 020 7919 7640 *fax:* 020 7919 7644 *email:* music@gold.ac.uk. Roger Wibberley, head of dept; John Baily, reader in ethnomusicology; Alexander Ivashkin, dir of Centre for Russian Music; Craig Ayrey, Keith Potter, Anthony Pryer, Roger Redgate, Jill Halstead.

University of Hertfordshire. College Lane, Hatfield, Herts AL10 9AB *tel:* 01707 284441 *fax:* 01707 285098 *email:* A.l.Spence@herts.ac.uk. Howard Burrell, prof of mus and head of dept; Timothy Blinko, associate head of dept; Robert Wright, programme tutor, mus tech and sound design; Martyn Parry, Dave Smith, snr lecturers; Paul Fretwell, programme tutor, composition; Richard Polfreman, research fellow; Gavin Bryars, visiting prof.

The University of Huddersfield. Dept of Music, Queensgate, Huddersfield HD1 3DH *tel:* 01484 472003 *fax:* 01484 472656

UNIVERSITY of GLASGOW

Courses in the Department of Music
(Head of Department: Prof. John Butt)

UNDERGRADUATE DEGREE COURSES
- MA (Master of Arts), 4 years:
  This course is suitable for students with ability in music who are interested in combining its study with other subjects. Music (including performance) can be the main course of study from the third year (Single Honours), or it can be combined with one other subject (Joint Honours)
- BMus (Bachelor of Music), 4 years:
  The BMus is designed for students interested in pursuing a comprehensive course in Music. After a compulsory foundation course in the first year, students can increasingly concentrate on their particular areas of interest such as composition, history, notation or performance
- BEng (Bachelor of Engineering), 4 years:
  This degree provides a unique opportunity to combine musical interests with a thorough study of modern electronics, leading to an accredited engineering qualification

POSTGRADUATE DEGREE COURSES
- MMus (Master of Music), 1 year:
  This course can be taken in one of three specialist areas of study *(Musicology, Composition, Music Technology)*. The course comprises a combination of taught seminar courses and presentation of a thesis or portfolio of compositions

- PhD (Doctor of Philosophy), 3 years:
  This can be taken in *Musicology, Composition, Music Technology* and involves the submission of a thesis (and a project for Music Technology) or a portfolio of compositions

For further information visit our Web Site on http://www.gla.ac.uk/departments/music/

East Coast Music Academy
Grimsby College
Westward Ho,
Grimsby, DN34 5AQ

Tel: 01472 311231
Web: www.ecma.co.uk
e-mail: orientsp@grimsby.ac.uk

HND Music Production
BTEC ND Music Technology
BTEC ND Music Performance

ECMA offers a range of courses that include both HE & FE levels of study based on technology and performance. Students will use industry standard equipment to support their learning. All courses are vocationally based, ECMA has its own student run Record label "LeeryTunes"

Music industry, Media, HE.

HND	2 years	Est. 1996
ND's	2 years	

Interview, industry experience considered,

Course Leader/Contact
Steve Orient 01472 311231

I.P. Co.   N.ENG

---

challenge

MA Music Education

For musicians, music teachers, animateurs or anyone with a deep interest in music. To find out more about studying at a world-renowned centre for music education research please contact:

Lucy Green
Telephone +44 (0)20 7612 6736
Email l.green@ioe.ac.uk
Website www.ioe.ac.uk/masters

Over 100 years of excellence in education

INSTITUTE OF EDUCATION UNIVERSITY OF LONDON

School of Music
Faculty of Art, Design & Music

Study Music at Kingston University!

- exciting courses, undergraduate and masters
- instrumental lessons from top London professionals
- innovative research opportunities
- excellent resources for performance and music technology

BA Mus (Hons) Routes:-	**BA (Hons) Music joint honours**	**Post-graduate Routes:-**
Performance	Music and Drama	Music Performance
Composition	Music and Film Studies	Music Education
Popular Musics		Musicology
Music: Education and Cultural Studies	Music and Art/ Design History	Music Composition
Music: Analysis, Criticism and History	Music and Mathematics	Ethnomusicology
Creative Music Technologies	Music and Internet Computing	Composing for Film and Television
	Music and ICT	Composing for New Media
		Popular Music

Visit the website at www.kingston.ac.uk or contact the Administrator, School of Music, Kingston University, Kingston Hill, Kingston upon Thames, Surrey KT2 7LB.
Tel: 020 8547 7149.
Fax: 020 8547 7349.
E-mail: music.administrator@ kingston.ac.uk

Kingston University London

www.kingston.ac.uk

email: music@hud.ac.uk. Michael Russ, head of dept; James Saunders, admissions offr; John Bryan, dir of u/grad studies; Margaret Lucy Wilkins, composition leader; Michael Clarke, electroacoustic mus leader; Steven Jan, musicology leader; Barrie Webb, performance leader.

Hull University. Dept of Music, Hull University, Hull HU6 7RX *tel:* 01482 465998 *also fax; email:* p.a.muse@hull.ac.uk. Alastair Borthwick, dir of studies; Graham Sadler, reader; Caroline Wood, lecturer; Catherine Dale, snr lecturer; Elaine Goodman, Lee Tsang, lecturers.

Institute of Education, University of London. School of Arts and Humanities, 20 Bedford Way, London WC1H 0AL *tel:* 020 7612 6740 *fax:* 020 7612 6741 *email:* music@ioe.ac.uk. Graham Welch, chair of mus educ, head of school; Keith Swanwick, emeritus prof of mus educ; Lucy Green, reader of mus educ; Rebecca Beckley, Pauline Adams, Penny Davies; Jilly Dolphin, admin; Charles Plummeridge, emeritus reader of mus educ.

Keele University. Dept of Music, Keele University, Keele, Staffs ST5 5BG *tel:* 01782 583295 *also fax; email:* mua09@mus.keele.ac.uk. Alastair Williams, Sohrab Uduman, Barbara Kelly, snr lecturers; Diego Garro, lecturer; Rajmil Fischman, Michael Vaughan, readers; Raymond Fearn, p/t lecturer.

King's College, London. Dept of Music, Strand, London WC2R 2LS *tel:* 020 7848 2029 *fax:* 020 7848 2326 *email:* irene.auerbach@kcl.ac.uk. John Deathridge, mus, mus history; Michael Fend, mus history; Daniel Chua, dir of u/grad studies; George Benjamin, prof of composition; Laurence Dreyfus, prof of performance studies; Cliff Eisen, Daniel Leech-Wilkinson, mus history; Christopher Wintle, mus analysis; Robert Keeley, composition; Silvina Milstein, composition, mus analysis; David Trendell, head of dept mus history, college org; Irene Auerbach, dept sec.

Kingston University. School of Music, Kingston Hill Centre, Kingston on Thames, Surrey KT2 7LB *tel:* 020 8547 7149 *also fax; email:* music.administrator@kingston.ac.uk. Stephen Arnold, prof, head of school of mus; Gloria Toplis, course dir; Kevin Jones, reader; Carol Gartrell, Michael Searby, principal lecturers; Howard Fredrics, Maria Busen-Smith, Caroline Potter, snr lecturers; Ingrid Pearson, dir of mus performance.

Lancaster University. Music Dept, Bailrigg, Lancaster LA1 4YW *tel:* 01524 593772 *fax:* 01524 593939 *email:* music@lancaster.ac.uk. Alan Marsden, head of dept; Rebecca Herissone, u/grad admissions

tutor; Deborah Mawer, p/grad admissions tutor; Roger Bray, prof; Neil Boynton, lecturer; Ed Venn, lecturer.

Leeds Metropolitan University. Faculty of Information and Engineering Systems, City Campus, Leeds LS1 3HE *tel:* 0113 283 5912 *fax:* 0113 283 3110 *email:* s.haigh@lmu.ac.uk. Steve Wilkinson, creative tech scheme leader.

University of Leeds. School of Music, Leeds LS2 9JT *tel:* 0113 343 2583 *fax:* 0113 343 2586 *email:* music@leeds.ac.uk. David Cooper, head of school, prof of mus and tech; Graham Barber, prof of performance studies, dir of p/grad studies; Clive Brown, prof of applied musicology; Philip Wilby, dir of composition studies, MA Music and Liturgy, MMus Composition; Clive McClelland, u/grad admissions tutor; Rachel Cowgill, MMus Musicology co-ord; Annette Davison, MA Film Music Studies co-ord, careers offr; Ewan Stefani, MMus Music Technology co-ord.

Liverpool Hope University College. School of Creative and Performing Arts, Cornerstone, Hope at Everton, Haigh St, Liverpool L3 8QB *tel:* 0151 291 3457 *fax:* 0151 291 3170. Stephen Pratt, dir of mus; Robin Hartwell, David Walters, Mary Black, Ian Sharp, Philip Duffy, Jill Simms.

Liverpool University. Music Dept, PO Box 147, Liverpool L69 7WW *tel:* 0151 794 3096 *fax:* 0151 794 3141 *email:* music@liv.ac.uk. Michael Talbot, head of dept; Robert Orledge, Matthew Fairclough, John Williamson, Sara Cohen, popular mus dirs; Jason Toynbee, James Wishart, head of composition and electronic studio; Tony Shorrocks, head of performance studies.

Manchester Metropolitan University (Crewe and Alsager Faculty). Hassall Rd, Alsager, Cheshire ST7 2HL *tel:* 0161 247 5302 *fax:* 0161 247 6377. Martin Blain, head of mus; Grahame Shrubsole, programme leader for BA Joint Hons Arts.

University of Manchester. Dept of Music, Denmark Rd, Manchester M15 6HY *tel:* 0161 275 4987 *fax:* 0161 275 4994 *email:* lynn.trillo@man.ac.uk. John Casken, prof of mus; David Fallows, prof; Barry Cooper, prof; David Fanning, dept chair; Julie Bray, snr tutor; Crawford Howie, lecturer; Kevin Malone, lecturer, admissions offr; Philip Grange, prof, head of composition, p/grad admissions; James Garratt, lecturer.

Middlesex University. School of Arts - Music, Trent Park Campus, Bramley Rd, London N14 4YZ *tel:* 020 8411 5684 *also fax; email:* b.x.back@mdx.ac.uk. Francois Evans, MA Music/Music

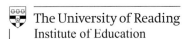

Education; Peter Fribbins, BA Music, BA Music and Arts Management; Stuart Hall, Chris Batchelor, BA Music (Jazz).

Napier University. The Ian Tomlin School of Music, Craighouse Campus, Craighouse Rd, Edinburgh EH10 5LG *tel:* 0131 455 6200 *fax:* 0131 455 6211 *email:* a.butterworth@napier.ac.uk. Anna Butterworth, head of school of mus; Graham Weir, snr lecturer; Nicholas Ashton, Andrew Doig, Michael Harris, Kenneth Dempster, Stephen Davismoon, lecturers; Jim Doyle, technician.

Newcastle University. Dept of Music, Armstrong Building, Newcastle upon Tyne NE1 7RU *tel:* 0191 222 6736 *fax:* 0191 222 5242 *email:* music@ncl.ac.uk. Richard Middleton, head of dept; Ian Biddle, David Clarke, Eric Cross, Agustín Fernández, Magnus Williamson, Matthew Sansom, Goffredo Peastino, Jonathan Clark.

University College Northampton. Music Dept, Avenue Campus, St George's Ave, Northampton NN2 6JD *tel:* 01604 735500 *fax:* 01604 717813 *email:* admissions@northampton.ac.uk. T Williams, L Reim, joint course leaders.

Nottingham University. Dept of Music, University Park, Nottingham NG7 2RD *tel:* 0115 951 4755 *fax:* 0115 951 4756 *email:* sally.britten@nottingham.ac.uk. Robert Adlington, Birtwistle, contemporary mus, analysis; Mervyn Cooke, Britten, jazz, composition, film mus; John Morehen, 16th/17th C church mus, editorial practice; Anthony Pople, analysis, early 20th C mus; Nicholas Sackman, head of dept, composition and contemporary mus; Philip Weller, 18th C opera, 19th and 20th C song; Peter Wright, medieval, renaissance, contemporary.

Open University. Walton Hall, Milton Keynes MK7 6AA *tel:* 01908 274066. Donald Burrows, prof; Trevor Herbert, prof, staff tutor; David Rowland, snr lecturer; J Barrie Jones, David Mateer, Robert Samuels, Robert Philip, Martin Clayton, Patricia Howard, Gabriella Dideriksen, lecturers; Fiona Richards, head of dept; Terence Best, visiting research fellow; Elaine Moohan, staff tutor.

Oxford Brookes University. Music Dept, School of Arts and Humanities, Richard Hamilton Building, Headington, Oxford OX3 0BP *tel:* 01865 484986 *fax:* 01865 484952 *email:* dmgriffiths@brookes.ac.uk. Dai Griffiths, principal lecturer, head of mus; Christina Bashford, snr lecturer in musicology; Paul Dibley, lecturer, studio mgr; Paul Whitty, snr lecturer in composition; Melania Bucciarelli, lecturer in musicology.

Oxford University. Faculty of Music, St Aldate's, Oxford OX1 1DB *tel:* 01865 286264 *fax:* 01865 276128 *email:* academic. secretary@music.ox.ac.uk. Bojan Bujic, reader, fellow of Magdalen College; John Caldwell, prof; Stephen Darlington, org at Christ Church; Peter Franklin, reader, chmn of faculty board; Owen Rees, fellow of Queen's College; Robert Saxton, fellow of Worcester College; Emanuele Senici, fellow of St Hugh's College; Reinhard Strohm, Heather prof of mus.

Queen's University. School of Music, University Rd, Belfast, Northern Ireland BT7 1NN *tel:* 028 9033 5337 *fax:* 028 9033 5053 *email:* music@qub.ac.uk. Jan Smaczny, dir, u/grad admissions; Simon Keefe, p/grad admissions; Michael Alcorn, BSc Mus Tech u/grad admissions.

Reading University. Dept of Music, 35 Upper Redlands Rd, Reading RG1 5JE *tel:* 0118 931 8411 *fax:* 0118 931 8412 *email:* music@reading.ac.uk. Christopher Wilson, head of dept; Jonathan Dunsby, prof; Sophie Fuller, admissions; Laura Tunbridge, lecturer.

Royal Holloway, University of London. Dept of Music, Egham Hill, Egham, Surrey TW20 0EX *tel:* 01784 443532 *fax:* 01784 439441 *email:* music@rhul.ac.uk. John Rink, head of dept; Julie Brown, u/grad admissions; Elizabeth Eva Leach, schools liaison; Katharine Ellis, reader, dir of graduate study; David Charlton, p/grad admissions.

University of Salford. School of Media, Music and Performance, Division of Music, Adelphi, Peru St, Salford, Manchester M3 6EQ *tel:* 0161 295 5000 *fax:* 0161 295 6023. Ron Cook, head of school; Derek Scott, prof of mus; Alan Williams, head of mus division; Robin Dewhurst, head of popular mus; David King, head of performance; Sheila Whiteley, reader in pop mus.

School of Oriental and African Studies. Dept of Music, University of London, Thornhaugh St, Russell Square, London WC1H 0XG *tel:* 020 7898 4680 *fax:* 020 7898 4699 *email:* music@soas.ac.uk. Lucy Durán, admissions tutor (BA), lecturer in African mus; Rachel Harris, lecturer in ethnomusicology; Keith Howard, admissions tutor (MMus), snr lecturer in ethnomusicology; David Hughes, chair of dept, snr lecturer in ethnomusicology; Alexander Knapp, Joe Loss, lecturer in Jewish mus; Richard Widdess, reader in ethnomusicology; Owen Wright, admissions tutor (MPhil/PhD), prof of musicology of the Middle East.

Sheffield University. Dept of Music, Western Bank, Sheffield S10 2TN *tel:* 0114 222 0470 *fax:* 0114 266 8053 *email:* v.r.messenger@

sheffield.ac.uk. Peter Hill, head of dept; A F Bennett, A M Brown, E F Clarke, J W Davidson, M J Hindmarsh, A Moore, G Nicholson, J Stock.

Southampton University. Dept of Music, Highfield, Southampton SO17 1BJ *tel:* 023 8059 3425 *fax:* 023 8059 3197 *email:* musicbox@ soton.ac.uk. David Nicholls, head of dept, prof of mus; Mark Everist, prof of mus; Michael Finnissy, p/t prof of composition; Nicholas Cook, research prof of mus; William Drabkin, reader in mus; Jeanice Brooks, reader in mus, p/grad co-ord; Laurie Stras, lecturer in performance studies; Matthew Head, snr lecturer in mus, admissions tutor; Michael Zev Gordon, composition lecturer; Pete Thomas, p/t lecturer in mus; Peter Collyer, performance co-ord; Paul Cox, head of str studies.

University of Sunderland. School of Arts, Design, Media and Culture, Ashburne House, Ryhope Rd, Sunderland SR2 7EE *tel:* 0191 515 3294 *fax:* 0191 515 3375. Phil Ellis, prof; Judith Hills, principal lecturer; Elizabeth Holden, snr lecturer in mus.

University of Surrey. School of Arts, Dept of Music and Sound Recording, Guildford, Surrey GU2 7XH *tel:* 01483 686500 *fax:* 01483 686501. Dept of Mus: Allan Moore, prof, head of dept, dir of research; Christopher Mark, BMus programme dir; Sebastian Forbes, prof, dir of mus; Stephen Downes, MMus programme dir, BMus admissions offr; Institute of Sound Recording: Dave Fisher, dir of Tonmeister studies; Francis Rumsey, dir of research; Tim Brookes, Tonmeister admissions offr.

University of Surrey Roehampton *formerly* **Roehampton Institute London.** Dept of Music, Southlands College, Roehampton Lane, London SW15 5SL *tel:* 020 8392 3432 *fax:* 020 8392 3435 *email:* music@roehampton.ac.uk. Peter O'Hagan, reader, musicology; Barley Norton, lecturer, ethnomusicology; Claire Taylor-Jay, lecturer, musicology; Alan Stones, snr lecturer, composition, mus tech; Michael Burnett, snr lecturer, educ, ethnomusicology.

Sussex University. Faculty of Music, Falmer, Brighton BN1 9RQ *tel:* 01273 872621 *fax:* 01273 678644 *email:* music@sussex.ac.uk.

Martin Butler, reader in mus; Donald Mitchell, visiting prof in mus; David Osmond-Smith, prof of mus; Nicholas McKay, chair of mus; Björn Heile, doctor of mus; John Croft, lecturer in mus.

Thames Valley University. London College of Music and Media, St Mary's Rd, Ealing, London W5 5RF *tel:* 020 8231 2304 *fax:* 020 8231 2546. Colin Lawson, pro vice-chancellor; Christopher Batchelor, subject head of mus; Francis Pott, head of research, development and composition; Peter Rudnick, head of BMus.

Ulster University. Centre for Creative and Performing Arts, Magee Campus, Londonderry BT48 7JL *tel:* 028 9036 6690 *fax:* 028 9036 6870 *email:* d.hunter1@ulster.ac.uk. D Hunter, head of mus; D Morris, G Nelson.

University of Wolverhampton. School of Sport, Performing Arts and Leisure, Gorway Rd, Walsall WS1 3BD *tel:* 01902 323172 *fax:* 01902 323148. John Pymm, associate dean; Darren Sproston, head of mus; Kevin Stannard, snr lecturer; Anne-Marie Trery, Amanda Bayley, Steven Spencer, Nigel Beer.

University of York. Dept of Music, University of York, York YO10 5DD *tel:* 01904 432446 *fax:* 01904 432450 *email:* music@york.ac.uk. Roger Marsh, head of dept, composition; Nicola LeFanu, composition; Bruce Cole, community mus; Ambrose Field, computer mus, composition, mus educ; Tim Howell, analysis; Nicky Losseff, medieval polyphony, gender and mus, performance; Bill Brooks, reader, composition; Tony Myatt, computer mus composition; John Potter, vocal performance, contemporary mus; Neil Sorrell, world mus, ethnomusicology and composition; Peter Seymour, performance; Jonathan Wainwright, renaissance and early baroque mus.

York St John College. Lord Mayors Walk, York YO31 7EX *tel:* 01904 756771 *fax:* 01904 612512 *email:* d.lancaster@yorksj.ac.uk. David Lancaster, Liz Mellor, snr lecturers in mus; Josephine Peach, snr lecturer in mus p/t; Ralph Bateman, Carol Garbett, Chris Bartram, lecturers in mus p/t.

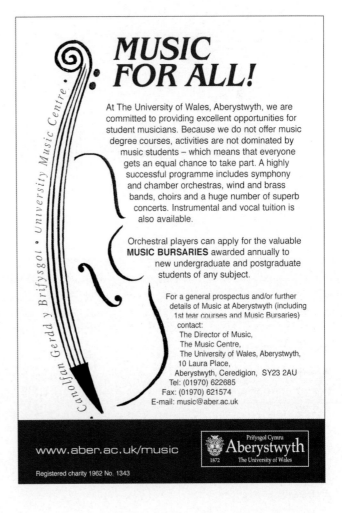

Graded Music Exams
The Associated Board of the Royal Schools of Music

The Associated Board's music exams are available from Grades 1 to 8 for over 35 instruments, practical musicianship and theory of music. As the world's leading provider of music assessments, we set musical standards and bring excellence and innovation to over 600,000 candidates each year in more than 90 countries.

Find out more at www.abrsm.org

ASSOCIATED BOARD
OF THE ROYAL SCHOOLS OF MUSIC

External Examining Institutions

Associated Board of the Royal Schools of Music. 24 Portland Place, London W1B 1LU *tel:* 020 7636 5400 *fax:* 020 7637 0234 *email:* abrsm@abrsm.ac.uk. Richard Morris, chief exec; Philip Mundey, exams dir. *Preparatory test, theory and practical graded exams, professional diplomas; performance assessment for adults. CT ABRSM professional development course for inst and singing teachers.*

Faculty of Church Music. 27 Sutton Park, Blunsdon, Swindon SN26 7BB *tel:* 020 8675 0180. Rev G Gleed, registrar. *Promotion of high standards in church mus. Tuition provided in theoretical subjects and for external mus degrees. Examinations for the grade of Associate, Licentiate and Fellow open to church musicians of any denomination.*

Guild of Church Musicians. St Katharine Cree, 86 Leadenhall St, London EC3A 3DH *tel:* 01883 743168 *fax:* 01883 740570 *email:* JohnMusicsure@aol.com. John Ewington OBE, gen sec; Michael Nicholas, exams sec. *Membership is open to church musicians of all Christian denominations. The Guild administers the exams for the Archbishops' Award in Church Music; Archbishops' Certificate in Music (ACertCM); Fellowship of the Guild of Church Musicians (FGCM).*

Guildhall Examinations Service. 3rd Floor, Milton Court, Moor Lane, London EC2Y 9DZ *tel:* 020 7382 7167 *fax:* 020 7382 7212 *email:* exams@gsmd.ac.uk. Eric Hollis, dir of initial studies; Christopher Poon, business development offr. *Curriculum-based syllabuses and publications supported by the school's Clear Performance Assessment System and its commitment to discipline specific examiners. Graded mus exams accredited by QCA until 2008. Mus performance diplomas now also accredited.*

ICMA. PO Box 134, Witney, Oxon OX29 7FS *tel:* 07000 780728 *also fax;* 08704 599698 (24 hrs) *email:* info@icma-exams.co.uk. Margaret Woolway, registrar. *Diploma and grade exams in all traditional insts, plus electronic org, electronic keyboard, mus tech, composition, conducting, church mus, accordion, gui, rock gui, kit drumming, contemporary vocals, mus theatre, and pop vocals. Regular mus festivals. Examinations are held throughout the yr at times and venues chosen by applicants.*

London College of Music Examinations. Thames Valley University, St Mary's Rd, London W5 5RF *tel:* 020 8231 2364 *fax:* 020 8231 2433 *email:* lcm.exams@tvu.ac.uk. Andrew McBirnie, chief examiner in mus; John Howard, exams mgr. *All insts, singing, mus theatre, duets, ens, theory. Pre-preparatory, steps, leisure play, grs 1-8, DipLCM, ALCM, ALCM(TD), LLCM, LLCM(TD), FLCM (theory, composition, cond), AMusLCM, LMusLCM.*

National College of Music. 4 Duffield Rd, Chelmsford, Essex CM2 9RY *tel:* 01245 354596 *email:* nat.col@btopenworld.com. Eric Hayward, gen sec. *Grs 1-8; bronze, silver and gold medal exams; associate diploma (ANCM), licentiate diploma (LNCM), fellowship diploma (FNCM). All syllabuses approved by the Secretary of State for Examinations in Schools.*

Phillips College. MMI House, 8 Quarry St, Shawforth, Lancs OL12 8HD *tel:* 01706 853664 *fax:* 01706 852282 *email:* examinations@music-services.demon.co.uk. Lord Taylor of Blackburn, president; Lee Longden, dir; Ian Roche, deputy dir. *The examination division of the Cambridge Society of Musicians, offering assessed portfolio certificates, diplomas and advanced diplomas in several subject areas.*

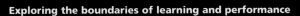

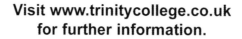

Rockschool/Trinity Graded Examinations for Guitar, Bass, Drums and Popular Piano. 245 Sandycombe Rd, Kew Gardens, Surrey TW9 2EW *tel:* 020 8332 6303 *fax:* 020 8332 6297 *email:* office@ rockschool.co.uk. Simon Pitt, chief exec; Jeremy Ward, dir of academic affairs. *A wholly new exam syllabus for electric gui, bass gui, drums featuring live CD recordings of the exam pieces. Grs Debut - 6 and 8 are available for solo players. Band exams and performance certificates are available at grs 3, 5 and 8. Solo popular pno grs can either be taken on pno or keyboard. The popular pno grade packs include a CD allowing candidates to hear the tunes as well as sample ear-tests. Pre gr 1 exam, Debut, is available for all insts and is an introduction to taking grade exams. Exam centres nationwide. Exams fully accredited by QCA.*

Royal College of Organists. 7 St Andrew Street, London EC4A 3LQ *tel:* 020 7936 3606 *fax:* 020 7353 8244 *email:* admin@rco.org.uk. Gordon Clarke, registrar. *Membership open to any person interested in org and/or choral mus; corporate membership is also available to groups. Those wishing to take any diploma must first apply for membership. ARCO, FRCO. The Choral Directing Diploma (DipCHD) may be taken by any member of the college; the Organ Teaching Diploma (LTRCO) may be taken by those holding ARCO or FRCO. A new Certificate examination (Cert.RCO) has been introduced.*

Royal School of Church Music. Cleveland Lodge, Westhumble, Dorking, Surrey RH5 6BW *tel:* 01306 872800 *fax:* 01306 887260 *email:* education@rscm.com. John Wardle, awards co-ord; Michael O'Conner, warden. *'Voice for Life' scheme including qualifications for singers of all ages and abilities. Forthcoming: HE qualifications in church mus.*

Trinity College London. The International Examinations Board, 89 Albert Embankment, Vauxhall, London SE1 7TP *tel:* 020 7820 6100 *fax:* 020 7820 6161 *email:* music@trinitycollege.co.uk. Mark Stringer, dir of mus, dance, drama and speech exams; Roger Bowers, chief exec. *All qualifications fully accredited by QCA, ACCAC and CCEA. Grs 6, 7 and 8 recognised by UCAS. Practical gr exams in mus for all practical insts and voice from initial to grs 1-8 plus performance only assessments at First Concert and Performers Certificate level. Practical grs in a range of drama and speech subjects including Musical Theatre. Full range of diploma qualifications in performing, teaching individuals and groups, composing, directing, mentoring, examining and adjudicating. National Diplomas in Dance, Acting and Stage Management. Trinity runs Profile, a major continuing professional development programme in association with a range of course providers and associates.*

Victoria College of Music. 9 Staple Inn, London WC1V 7QH *tel:* 020 7405 6483 *also fax; email:* Vcmexams@aol.com. Jeffery Tillett, dir of exams; Sir Malcolm Arnold CBE, hon president; Robin Wood, chief exec. *AVCM, LVCM (teachers and performers), FVCM, AMusVCM, LMusVCM, grs 1-8, jnr bronze, silver and gold medals. All insts including electronic keyboard. Qualifications approved for use in schools and colleges under Section 96 of Learning and Skills Act 2000.*

Specialist Courses

Alexander Technique Training Courses

The **Society of Teachers of the Alexander Technique** can provide a full list of members who teach in the UK. The society can be contacted at Linton House, 39-51 Highgate Rd, London NW5 1RS *tel:* 020 7284 3338 *email:* enquiries@stat.org.uk *website:* www.stat.org.uk.

The Alexander Technique College of Sussex. Unit 3, Hove Business Centre, Fouthill Rd, Hove, E Sussex BN3 6HA *tel:* 01273 562595 *email:* carolyn.nicholls@btinternet.com. C Nicholls, MSTAT, head of training.

Alexander Technique School of Cornwall. 40 Gwithian Towers, Hayle, Cornwall TR27 5BT *tel:* 01736 759526.

Alexander Technique Studio. 6 Ravenslea Rd, Wandsworth Common, London SW12 8SB *tel:* 020 8673 3853. Karen Wentworth, dir.

Bristol Alexander Technique Training School Association. 37 Bellevue Cres, Cliftonwood, Bristol BS8 4TF *tel:* 0117 987 2989 *also fax*; *email:* aliburrows@blueyonder.co.uk. Ali Burrows, head of training.

Centre for the Alexander Technique. 46 Stevenage Rd, London SW6 6HA *tel:* 020 7731 6348 *email:* peter@ribeaux.fsnet.co.uk. P Ribeaux, Mrs E Ribeaux, dirs.

Constructive Teaching Centre. 18 Lansdowne Rd, London W11 3LL *tel:* 020 7727 7222 *fax:* 020 7313 9882 *email:* info@alexandertek.com. W H M Carrington, D M G Carrington, dirs.

Essex Alexander School. 65 Norfolk Rd, Ilford, Essex IG3 8LJ *tel:* 020 8220 1630 *email:* ken_thompson@lineone.net. Ken Thompson, dir; Angela Thompson, head of training.

Headington Alexander Training School. 10 York Rd, Headington, Oxford OX3 8NW *tel:* 01865 765511 *fax:* 01865 454112 *email:* s.c@btinternet.com. Stephen Cooper, dir.

The Highbury Centre for Alexander Technique. 137 Grosvenor Ave, London N5 2NH *tel:* 020 7226 1815 *email:* refia.sacks@virgin.net. R Sacks, dir.

Manchester Alexander Technique Training School (MATTS). c/o 18 Thorne House, Wilmslow Rd, Manchester M14 6DW *tel:* 0161 224 1112 *also fax; email:* williamm@rncm.ac.uk. Malcolm Williamson, head of training.

North London Alexander Technique Teachers Training Centre. 10 Elmcroft Ave, London NW11 0RR *tel:* 020 8455 3938 *also fax*; *email:* jmagidov@btconnect.com. M Magidov, dir.

North of England Teaching Centre for the F M Alexander Technique. Design House, 3 Hanover Ave, Leeds LS3 1BG *tel:* 0113 244 9713 *fax:* 0113 245 8477 *email:* maggie.rakusen@btinternet.com. Margaret Rakusen, dir.

Arts Administration Courses

Anglia Polytechnic University. East Rd, Cambridge CB1 1PT *tel:* 01223 363271 *fax:* 01223 417700 *email:* l.l.charles@apu.ac.uk. Laura Charles, field leader.

Buckinghamshire University College. Wellesbourne Campus, Kingshill Rd, High Wycombe, Bucks HP13 5BB *tel:* 01494 522141 *fax:* 01494 465432 *email:* fmacke01@bcuc.ac.uk. Frazer Mackenzie, head of division, mus & entertainment industry mgt.

City University. Dept of Arts Policy and Management, Frobisher Crescent, Barbican, London EC2Y 8HB *tel:* 020 7477 8751/3 *fax:* 020 7477 8887 *email:* artspol@city.ac.uk. Contact: admissions offr.

Dartington College of Arts. Music Dept, Totnes, Devon TQ9 6EJ *tel:* 01803 861638 *fax:* 01803 866053 *email:* t.warr@dartington.ac.uk. Tracey Warr, development leader, arts and cultural mgt.

The London Institute. 65 Davis St, London W1Y 2DA *tel:* 020 7514 6569 *email:* info@lcp.linst.ac.uk.

Middlesex University. Trent Park, Bramley Rd, London N14 4YZ *tel:* 020 8411 5684 *also fax; email:* b.back@mdx.ac.uk. Julian Mincham, chmn of mus; Peter Fribbins, programme leader; Barbra Back, mus admin.

Royal Welsh College of Music and Drama. Castle Grounds, Cathays Park, Cardiff CF10 3ER *tel:* 029 2039 1328 *fax:* 029 2039 1302 *email:* drama.admissions@rwcmd.ac.uk. Contact: drama admissions offr.

South Bank University. 103 Borough Rd, London SE1 0AA *tel:* 020 7815 7815. Suzy Kerr-Pertic, course dir.

University of Southampton. Dept of Music, Highfield, Southampton SO17 1BJ *tel:* 023 8059 3425 *fax:* 023 8059 3197 *email:* musicbox@soton.ac.uk. Denise Kendall, dept co-ord; Matthew Head, admissions tutor.

University of Surrey Roehampton. Southlands College, 80 Roehampton Lane, London SW15 5SL *tel:* 020 8392 3269 *also fax*; *email:* P.Barrie@roehampton.ac.uk. Peter Reynolds, head of school of arts; Pauline Barrie, programme convener, arts mgt.

University of Sussex. Centre for Continuing Education, Falmer, Brighton BN1 9RG *tel:* 01273 678040 *fax:* 01273 678848 *email:* cce@sussex.ac.uk. Julian Broughton, convener, mus and opera; Janet Summerton, convener, arts and cultural mgt.

University College, Warrington. Padgate Campus, Fearnhead Lane, Warrington WA2 0DB *tel:* 01925 530000 *fax:* 01925 530001 *email:* k.boyle@chester.ac.uk; k.potts@chester.ac.uk. Russell Dyson, leader, Commercial Music Production, Dave Grimshaw, snr lecturer, Radio Production; Stephen Wainwright, leader, TV Production; Phil Potter, snr lecturer, Multimedia Web Production; Peter Winn, lecturer, Performing Arts.

Warwick University. Centre for Cultural Policy Studies, Coventry CV4 7AL *tel:* 024 7652 3020 *fax:* 024 7652 4446. Oliver Bennett, dir, MA cultural policy.

Instrument Making and Repair Courses

Leeds College of Music. 3 Quarry Hill, Leeds LS2 7PD *tel:* 0113 249 2837 *fax:* 0113 243 8798 *email:* enquiries@lcm.ac.uk. Ted Lee, head of mus inst tech; Kevin Wilkes, asst head of mus inst tech.

London Metropolitan University. Sir John Cass Dept of Art Media and Design, 41 Commercial Rd, London E1 1LA *tel:* 020 7320 1000 *fax:* 020 7320 1830 *email:* enqs@lgu.ac.uk (course enquiries and prospectus). Sam Verik, admissions tutor; Allan Seago, Dave Armitage, course organisers.

Merton College. London Rd, Morden, Surrey SM4 5QX *tel:* 020 8408 6478 *fax:* 020 8408 6666 *email:* kgraves@merton.ac.uk. K Graves, course co-ord.

Newark and Sherwood College. School of Violin, Guitar, Woodwind and Piano Technology, Friary Rd, Newark on Trent, Notts NG24 1PB *tel:* 01636 680680 *fax:* 01636 680681 *email:* sgorin@newark.ac.uk. Sam Gorin, curriculum dir; Kerry Boylan, J Lord, G Else, R Summerfield, course tutors.

Royal National College for the Blind. Piano Technology (piano tuning and repairs), College Rd, Hereford HR1 1EB *tel:* 01432 265725 *fax:* 01432 376628 *email:* info@rncb.ac.uk. Philip Kennedy, pno tech programme co-ord.

West Dean College. West Dean, Chichester, W Sussex PO18 0QZ *tel:* 01243 811301 *fax:* 01243 818291 *email:* diplomas@westdean.org.uk. Roger Rose, course tutor.

Professional Development Courses for Private Music Teachers

Associated Board of the Royal Schools of Music. 24 Portland Place, London W1B 1LU *tel:* 020 7467 8257 *fax:* 020 7467 8295 *email:* profdev@abrsm.ac.uk. Richard Crozier, professional development dir.

Bela Bartók Centre for Musicianship. 6 Frognal Court, 158 Finchley Rd, London NW3 5HL *tel:* 020 7435 3685 *email:* agnes.kory@kcl.ac.uk. Agnes Kory, dir.

British Suzuki Institute. 39 High St, Wheathampstead, Herts AL4 8BB *tel:* 01582 832424 *fax:* 01582 834488 *email:* bsi@suzukimusic.force9.co.uk. Landa Melrose, chief exec offr.

European Piano Teachers Association (EPTA) UK. Archpool House, High St, Handcross, W Sussex RH17 6BJ *tel:* 01444 400852 *fax:* 01444 401443 *email:* eptauk@hotmail.com. Heli Ignatius-Fleet, course dir.

Goldsmiths College. Professional and Community Education, University of London, New Cross, London SE14 6NW *tel:* 020 7919 7229 *fax:* 020 7919 7223 *email:* pace@gold.ac.uk. Jeremy Peyton Jones, mus programme co-ord.

University of Reading. International Centre for Research in Music Education, Bulmershe Court, Reading RG6 1HY *tel:* 0118 931 8843/37 *fax:* 0118 931 8834 *email:* mtpp@reading.ac.uk. Nicholas Bannan, course dir.

Psychology for Musical Performance Courses

Psychology for Music Teaching, Learning and Performing. Flat 2, 35 Bush Lane, London EC4R 0AW *tel:* 020 7626 0183 *also fax;* *email:* musicmindmovement@btinternet.com. Lucinda Mackworth-Young, consultant in psychology for musicians.

Recording and Technology Courses

Alchemea College of Audio Engineering. The Windsor Centre, Windsor St, The Angel, Islington, London N1 8QG *tel:* 020 7359 4035 *email:* info@alchemea.com. John Lundsten, principal; Mike Sinnott, mgr; Franz VanDyk, financial dir; Neil Pickles, Christian Huant, principal tutors; Matt McKinley, mus theory tutor; Alex Burak, technical support.

Bangor, University of Wales. School of Music, College Rd, Bangor, Gwynedd LL57 2DG *tel:* 01248 382181 *fax:* 01248 370297 *email:* s.harper@bangor.ac.uk. Robert Pascall, head of school; Sally Harper, snr p/grad tutor.

Bath Spa University College. Newton St Loe, Bath BA2 9BN *tel:* 01225 875875 *fax:* 01225 875444. Joseph Hyde, course dir.

Bournemouth University. Bournemouth Media School, Poole House, Talbot Campus, Fern Barrow, Poole, Dorset BH12 5BB *tel:* 01202 524111/595469. Stephen Deutsch, course dir.

Brunel University. Dept of Performing Arts, Gaskell Building, Brunel University, Uxbridge UB8 3PH *tel:* 01895 274000 ext 4512 *fax:* 01895 816224 *email:* colin.riley@brunel.ac.uk. Colin Riley, mus lecturer; Frank Griffith, BA admissions tutor, mus lecturer; Ben Jarlett, academic-related technician, mus lecturer.

City College Manchester. City Campus, 34 Whitworth St, Manchester M1 3HB *tel:* 0161 957 1790 *fax:* 0161 945 3854 *email:* admissions@ccm.ac.uk. Martin Moscrop, team leader, mus.

City University. Northampton Square, London EC1V 0BH *tel:* 020 7040 8284 *fax:* 020 7040 8576 *email:* music@city.ac.uk. Kathryn McCutcheon, MSc course admin; Jim Grant, course dir.

University of Derby. Kedleston Rd, Derby DE22 1GB *tel:* 01332 591494 *fax:* 01332 597739. Richard Hodges, programme co-ord.

Edinburgh University. Music, Alison House, 12 Nicolson Square, Edinburgh EH8 9DF *tel:* 0131 650 2427 *fax:* 0131 650 2425 *email:* music@ed.ac.uk.

Gateway School of Recording, Music Technology and Music Business Studies. Kingston Hill Centre, Kingston-upon-Thames, Surrey KT2 7LB *tel:* 020 8549 0014 *fax:* 020 8547 7337 *email:* info@gsr.org.uk. Paul Hazel, educ and training mgr.

Glasgow University. Dept of Music, 14 University Gardens, Glasgow G12 8QH *tel:* 0141 330 4093 *fax:* 0141 330 3518 *email:* c.bohm@music.gla.ac.uk. Carola Boehm, lecturer in mus tech.

Goldsmiths College. University of London, Professional and Community Education, New Cross, London SE14 6NW *tel:* 020 7919 7200/7229 *fax:* 020 7919 7223 *email:* pace@gold.ac.uk. Jeremy Peyton Jones, mus programme co-ord.

Keele University. Dept of Music, Keele, Staffs ST5 5BG *tel:* 01782 583295 *also fax; email:* mua09@mus.keele.ac.uk. Michael Vaughan, head of school.

Kidderminster College. Dept of Community Studies, Hoo Rd, Kidderminster, Worcs DY10 1LX *tel:* 01562 820811. T Bradley, lecturer in mus; Jon Bates, lecturer in mus tech; Kevyn Gammond, lecturer in mus industry mgt.

Leeds College of Music. 3 Quarry Hill, Leeds LS2 7PD *tel:* 0113 222 3400 *fax:* 0113 243 8798 *email:* enquiries@lcm.ac.uk. Andrew Bates, head of HE; Dale Perkins, Tony Whyton, asst heads of HE; Elizabeth Dobson, admissions tutor.

London College of Music and Media at Thames Valley University. St Mary's Rd, London W5 5RF *tel:* 020 8231 2304 *fax:* 020 8231 2546. Jolyon Forward, course leader, BA Music Technology; Mark Irwin, course leader, Foundation Degree Music Technology.

London Metropolitan University. Sir John Cass Dept of Art, Media and Design, 41 Commercial Rd, London E1 1LA *tel:* 020 7320 1000 *fax:* 020 7320 1830 *email:* s.verik@lgu.ac.uk. Sam Verik, admissions tutor.

London Metropolitan University, North Campus. School of Computing, Communications Technology and Mathematics, 166-220 Holloway Rd, London N7 8DB *tel:* 020 7133 2161 *fax:* 020 7753 7002 *email:* b.igbavboa@londonmet.ac.uk. B Igbavboa, course admin.

Newcastle College. School of Music and Performing Arts, Rye Hill Campus, Scotswood Rd, Newcastle upon Tyne NE4 7SA *tel:* 0191 200 4211 *fax:* 0191 200 4729 *email:* enquiries@ncl-coll.ac.uk. Vee Wilkinson, dir of school.

Perth College. Faculty of Arts, School of Music and Audio Engineering, Crieff Rd, Perth PH1 2NX *tel:* 01738 621171 *fax:* 01738 440050. Pamela McLean, head of faculty of arts.

Royal National College for the Blind. College Rd, Hereford HR1 1EB *tel:* 01432 265725 *fax:* 01432 376628 *email:* info@rncb.ac.uk. Contact: RNC Registry.

Royal Welsh College of Music and Drama. Castle Grounds, Cathays Park, Cardiff C10 3ER *tel:* 029 2039 1363 *fax:* 029 2039 1305 *email:* butlerra@rwcmd.ac.uk. Roger Butler, head of mus tech; Simon Kilshaw, asst to head; Odilon Marcenaro, recording studio mgr.

SAE Institute. United House, North Rd, Islington, London N7 9DP *tel:* 020 7609 2653 *fax:* 020 7609 6944 *email:* saelondon@sae.edu.

University of Salford. School of Media, Music and Performance - Division of Music, Adelphi, Peru St, Salford, Manchester M3 6EQ *tel:* 0161 295 5000 *fax:* 0161 295 6023. Derek B Scott, prof of mus; Tim Warner, head of mus tech and studio production.

University of Surrey. Dept of Music and Sound Recording, Guildford, Surrey GU2 7XH *tel:* 01483 686500 *fax:* 01483 686501. Dave Fisher, Tonmeister programme dir.

Wakefield College. School of Music, Thornes Park Centre, Horbury Rd, Wakefield WF2 8QZ *tel:* 01924 789874 *fax:* 01924 789821 *email:* s.hirst@wakcoll.ac.uk. Susan Hirst, head of mus; David Kirtlan, BTEC co-ord; Nigel Chapman, HNC jazz co-ord; Jamie Vizard, AS mus tech, Brian Morrell, BTEC First Course in mus.

University of York. Dept of Music, Heslington, York YO10 5DD *tel:* 01904 432430 *fax:* 01904 432450 *email:* music@york.ac.uk. Ambrose Field, mus tech admissions tutor.

Services Schools of Music

Royal Air Force Headquarters Music Services. RAF Uxbridge, Middx UB10 0RZ *tel:* 01895 237144 ext 6383/6345 *fax:* 01895 815224. Sqn Ldr D Compton, dir of mus.

Royal Marines School of Music. HMS Nelson, Queen St, Portsmouth PO1 3HH *tel:* 023 9272 6184 *fax:* 023 9272 5158. Lt-Col C Davis, principal dir of mus.

Royal Military School of Music. Kneller Hall, Twickenham, Middx TW2 7DU *tel:* 020 8898 5533 ext 8625 *fax:* 020 8893 8746. Lt-Col G A Kingston psm, principal dir of mus.

Colleges of Bagpipe Music

The College of Piping. 16-24 Otago St, Glasgow G12 8JH *tel:* 0141 334 3587 *fax:* 0141 587 6068 *email:* college@college-of-piping.co.uk. Robert Wallace, principal; Tom Campbell, mgr.

Royal Scottish Band Association College. 45 Washington St, Glasgow G3 8AZ *tel:* 0141 221 5414 *fax:* 0141 221 1561. Ian Embelton, exec offr.

Scholarships and Grants

The Department of Education and Science publishes leaflets on state scholarships. The **Musicians Benevolent Fund** publishes annually the *Handbook of Music Awards and Scholarships*, available from 16 Ogle St, London W1W 6JA *tel:* 020 7636 4481.

The Directory of Grant-Making Trusts (published by CAF) and the *Arts Funding Guide* (published by DSC) are available from the Directory of Social Change, 24 Stephenson Way, London NW1 2DP *tel:* 020 7209 5151 *email:* books@dsc.org.uk. *The Grants Register* is published by Macmillan and is available from Macmillan Distribution, Brunel Road, Houndmills, Basingstoke, Hants RG21 6XS *tel:* 01256 302699. Scholarships tenable at UK universities by overseas students at undergraduate, graduate and postdoctoral levels are contained in *International Awards,* which is available from Publications Sales, Association of Commonwealth Universities, 36 Gordon Square, London WC1H 0PF *tel:* 020 7380 6700 *email*: acusales@acu.ac.uk.

Unless otherwise stated, scholarships for study and research are available to British and Commonwealth students only. For details of low-interest loans towards the purchase of instruments, apply to The Secretary, **Loan Fund for Musical Instruments**, 16 Ogle Street, London W1W 6JA *tel:* 020 7436 4816. There is also a **Loan Scheme for Musical Instruments** (for students under 25, mainly string instruments); enquiries to Liz Clark or Clare Talbot, Benslow Musical Instrument Loan Scheme, Little Benslow Hills, Benslow Lane, Hitchin, Herts SG4 9RB *tel:* 01462 420748 *fax:* 01462 440171 *email:* loanscheme@benslow.org *website:* www.benslow.org.

Abbado European Young Musicians Trust. Speechly Bircham, 6 St Andrew Street, London EC4A 3LX *tel:* 020 7427 6400 *fax:* 020 7427 6600 *email:* john.hughes@speechlys.com. Contact: J V Hughes. *Loans (usually interest free) to assist young instrumentalists in buying suitable insts. Applications to be supported with details of specific inst. Available for those aged 30 or under.*

Alfreda Hodgson Bursary/Raymond Fox Bursary. c/o Making Music (formerly NFMS), 7-15 Rosebery Ave, London EC1R 4SP *tel:* 0870 872 3300 *fax:* 0870 872 3400 *email:* kate@makingmusic.org.uk. Kate Fearnley, award admin. *Award in alternate yrs for singers and instrumentalists respectively as part of the Richard and Dorothy Green Award for Young Concert Artists in association with Making Music. Applications are invited from EU citizens aged up to 32 (singers) or up to 28 (instrumentalists) who are at the beginning of their professional careers in mus and normally resident in the UK. Bursaries consist of c £400 to be spent on a specific course of training. Candidates should contact the administrator for details of applying and for the deadline.*

Allcard Grants. The Worshipful Company of Musicians, 6th Floor, 2 London Wall Buildings, London EC2M 5PP *tel:* 020 7496 8980 *fax:* 020 7588 3633 *email:* deputyclark@wcom.org.uk. Mrs M Alford, deputy clerk. *Singers, str players, pno accompanists and (in exceptional circumstances) wind players; for three p/grad scholarships of £3000 for an advanced course of performance study within the EU. Applications only through the heads of conservatoires or university mus depts. Applicants must have studied for at least 3 consecutive yrs at a British college or conservatoire. Nominations by 30 Apr, final selection by audition and interview in May/Jun.*

Awards for Advanced Study in Music. Arts Council of Wales, 9 Museum Place, Cardiff CF10 3NX *tel:* 029 2037 6500 *fax:* 029 2022 1447 *email:* information@ccc-acw.org.uk. Simon Lovell-Jones, snr arts development offr (mus). *Applications for funding for study (not f/t) under the Professional Development Scheme are received by the Arts Council of Wales. Awards have been made to musicians under 28, born in Wales; also open to those now permanently resident in Wales and normally having lived there for 2 yrs. Applications by 1 Mar annually. Award up to £5000.*

Awards for Young Musicians. PO Box 2097, Wickford SS12 0QZ *tel:* 01268 571887 *fax:* 01268 571972 *email:* awards@a-y-m.org.uk. Bridget Sime, dir. *Awards (£100-2000) to outstanding young instrumentalists aged 5-18. Applications by end Jan 2004, accompanied by a letter from a teacher or mus establishment and evidence of financial need. Send SAE for application form.*

Belfast Classical Music Bursaries. 56 Oakhurst Ave, Blacks Rd, Dunmurry, Belfast BT10 0PE *tel:* 028 9062 6269 *fax:* 028 9062 6269 *email:* angelafeeney@belfastmusicbursary.org. Una Downey, admin; Angela Feeney, artistic dir. *Open to all classical musicians born on the island of Ireland, aged 17-23 (inst) and 18-26 (vocal) on 15 Feb. Closing date*

7 Feb; application fee £12. Prize £10,000; BBC studio recordings; lunchtime concerts in Belfast plus concerts in Munich, Bordeux, Brussels.

Bob Harding Bursary for Young Conductors. c/o 152 West St, Havant, Hants PO9 1LP *tel:* 023 9248 3228. Peter Craddock, mus dir. *Opportunity for young cond to assist in and observe rehearsals and concerts of the Havant Symphony Orchestra throughout a season. Must be under 30, on an advanced conducting course and resident in UK. Travel and subsistence grant up to £350. Selection by audition; open to candidates nominated by London mus colleges. Applications by Jun annually.*

Professor Charles Leggett Trust. c/o Musicians Benevolent Fund, 16 Ogle St, London W1W 6JA *tel:* 020 7636 4481 *fax:* 020 7637 4307 *email:* education@mbf.org.uk. Contact: educ admin. *Awards of up to £5000 for outstanding p/grad wind and br players aged under 25. Closing date in Feb for auditions in Apr. In collaboration with MBF Music Education Awards.*

The Countess of Munster Musical Trust. Wormley Hill, Godalming, Surrey GU8 5SG *tel:* 01428 685427 *fax:* 01428 685064 *email:* munstertrust@compuserve.com. Gillian Ure, sec. *Tuition and maintenance grants for UK and Commonwealth students, tenable at home or abroad. Ages 18-24 (instrumentalists), 18-27 (singers). Excludes conductors. Interest-free loans available for inst purchase to young professional musicians aged under 28. Applications by mid-Feb, auditions Apr-Jun.*

Craxton Memorial Trust. 15 Cambridge Rd, Uxbridge, Middx UB8 1BQ *email:* info@craxtonmemorialtrust.org.uk. Jane Craxton, hon sec. *Biennial awards worth £300-700 for outstanding young pianists and instrumentalists (excluding org, perc and hpd) aged 17-24 and of any nationality. Send SAE for application form. Application fee £5. Next awards spring 2005, closing date 31 Jan 2005.*

Denis Matthews Trust Scholarships for Pianists. 10 Russell Rd, Moseley, Birmingham B13 8RD *tel:* 0121 449 3055 *fax:* 0121 449 3055 *email:* peter.bevan9@btopenworld.com. Beryl Chempin, Piano Faculty, Birmingham Conservatoire. *Annual scholarships to student pianists (aged 18-30 and of any nationality), except 1st yrs at Birmingham Conservatoire. Two u/grad scholarships and one or two p/grad scholarships are awarded.*

Miss E B Wrightson's Charitable Trust. Swangles Farm, Cold Christmas, Herts SG12 7SP *email:* norahhickman@henryhickman.com. Norah Hickman, admin. *Awards for young musicians: ages 8-18 are given priority and support not normally given to u/grads and p/grads. Awards vary from £100-1500; grants made either as one-off payments or reviewable annually. Applications considered regularly.*

ESTA Nannie Jamieson Nutshell Fund. 6 Ember Lane, Esher, Surrey KT10 8ER *tel:* 020 8398 4691 *email:* sylvia.palmer@virgin.net. European String Teachers Association, British Branch. *Modest bursaries awarded annually for students and teachers of str insts (ESTA* *members) for help to attend w/shops, conferences and teaching courses. Applications by 1 Jul.*

Emanuel Hurwitz Award for UK Violinists. Beeches, Well Hill, Chelsfield, Kent BR6 7PR *tel:* 01959 532299 *fax:* 01959 532299. Martyn Jones, admin. *Annual awards open to all UK students, as well as those studying in the UK, aged 25 or under. Applications by 1 Feb, auditions in Apr. Registration fee £15 to be accompanied by SAE.*

Emanuel Hurwitz Chamber Music Charitable Trust. 44 Church Cres, London N3 1BJ. Miriam Keogh, founder, admin. *Bursaries for str players to further their studies in chmbr mus; college/university fees will not be paid, although there is some help available with p/grad fees only at RAM, RCM, RNCM, and Guildhall. UK citizens only. Applications will only be accepted in writing with SAE. References and CVs essential. Applications by 1 Jun. Awards £300-500.*

Emily English Scholarship. c/o Musicians Benevolent Fund, 16 Ogle St, London W1W 6JA *tel:* 020 7637 4481 *fax:* 020 7637 4307 *email:* education@mbf.org.uk. Contact: educ admin. *Award of £5000 to assist an outstanding p/grad violinist aged under 25. Closing date in Feb for auditions in Apr. In collaboration with MBF Music Education Awards.*

The Emmy Destinn Foundation. PO Box 33164, London NW3 4BW *email:* edf@destinn.com. *The Emmy Destinn Foundation dedicated to upholding the legacy of the Czech diva by supporting young singers in the early stages of their careers. Small bursary available for singers studying Czech opera.*

Eric Thompson Trust. c/o The Royal Philharmonic Society, 10 Stratford Place, London W1C 1BA *tel:* 020 7491 8110 *fax:* 020 7493 7463 *email:* ett@royalphilharmonicsociety.org.uk. *The trust provides modest grants to young professional organists. Preference will be given to assistance with specific projects rather than continuing academic tuition. Applications considered twice yearly. Closing dates 31 Dec and 30 Jun. Johannes Klais org scholarship: a scholarship to enable a young organist to visit the Klais w/shops in Bonn, Germany, for a short introductory course in org building and tuning, and to have lessons with a leading German organist. This will normally take place in Nov. It is awarded annually and applicants should be f/t org students studying in the UK or Ireland who will be under 25 at the time of taking up the award. The application letter should include date of birth and full details of training and career so far, with written references from 2 organists of standing. It should also include a brief outline of how such a visit might benefit their future career. Applications will be reviewed at the trustees' Jul meeting and should be received by 30 Jun.*

Francis Chagrin Fund. c/o spnm, 4th Floor, St Margarets House, 18-20 Southwark St, London SE1 1TJ *tel:* 020 7407 1640 *fax:* 020 7403 7652 *email:* spnm@spnm.org.uk. Jo-Anne Naish, admin. *Grants available towards cost of reproducing performance materials of unperformed works by British composers and composers resident in Britain of any age (pieces must have scheduled date for performance). Applications considered monthly; max £250.*

The Guilhermina Suggia Gift for Cello. c/o Musicians Benevolent Fund, 16 Ogle St, London W1W 6JA *tel:* 020 7636 4481 *fax:* 020 7637 4307 *email:* education@mbf.org.uk. Contact: educ admin. *Award of £3000 to assist exceptionally talented vc students of any nationality aged under 21, plus other discretionary awards.*

H J C Stevens Organ Scholarship. St Bride's Church, Fleet St, London EC4Y 8AU *tel:* 020 7427 0133 *fax:* 020 7583 4867 *email:* info@stbrides.com. Robert Jones, mus dir. *Award to 2nd or 3rd yr org student at London mus college or university; p/grad student applications also considered.*

Harriet Cohen Memorial Music Awards Trust. c/o Rubenstein Phillips, 19 Buckingham St, London WC2N 6EF *tel:* 020 7925 2244 *fax:* 020 7925 2256. John Rubinstein, admin trustee. *Discretionary annual awards to max £1500 made to British performers, composers, academics or singers aged 18-30 of outstanding excellence and promise. Nominations by 8 mus institutions by invitation only. No individual applications will be considered. Candidates will be auditioned and interviewed.*

Hattori Foundation For Young Musicians. 72e Leopold Rd, London SW19 7JQ *tel:* 020 8944 5319 *fax:* 020 8946 6970 *email:* admin@hattorifoundation.org.uk. Sarah Hallam, admin. *Awards up to £6000. Aims to assist exceptionally talented instrumentalists (aged 15-20 and 21-27) to pursue a solo career. Also awards to ens with average age under 27. Awards are not for tuition fees in f/t study courses or inst purchase. Open to British nationals and foreign nationals studying in the UK. Applications by 30 Apr for snrs and at any time for jnrs.*

Hinrichsen Foundation. 10-12 Baches St, London N1 6DN. Lesley Adamson, admin. *Awards only in the areas of contemporary composition and its performance, and musicological research. Costs of degree and study courses, recordings and the purchase of insts and equipment*

excluded. Preference shown to UK applicants. Applications by 1 Jan, 1 Apr, 1 Jun, 1 Sep (subject to change).

Holst Foundation. 43 Alderbrook Rd, London SW12 8AD *tel:* 020 8673 4215 *fax:* 020 7228 2358. *Funds available to applicants of any age, primarily for the performance of mus by contemporary composers. No application form but guidelines available.*

Ian Fleming Musical Theatre Awards. c/o Musicians Benevolent Fund, 16 Ogle St, London W1W 6JA *tel:* 020 7636 4481 *fax:* 020 7637 4307 *email:* education@mbf.org.uk. *Awards of up to £4000 are made to outstanding candidates under 28 intending to take a p/grad mus theatre course in 2004/5. Closing date 22 Apr 2004 for auditions in May.*

Sir James Caird's Travelling Scholarships Trust. Thorntons Solicitors, 50 Castle St, Dundee DD1 3RU *tel:* 01382 229111 *fax:* 01382 202288 *email:* afmcdonald@thorntonsws.co.uk. A F McDonald, admin and sec; M Black, admin and sec. *Grants and scholarships of up to £3500 available to Scottish p/grad students studying away from home. Scholarships are tenable for 1 yr but may be renewed for up to 2 further yrs. Wiseman Prize (£600) for best performance and Joseph Bloch LRAM Prize (£200) for best str player. Auditions in Mar or Apr in London and Glasgow, applications by 31 Jan.*

The James Pantyfedwen Foundation. 9 Market St, Aberystwyth SY23 1DL *tel:* 01970 612806 *fax:* 01970 612806 *email:* pantyfedwen@btinternet.com. Richard Morgan, exec sec. *For Welsh students requiring support for approved courses, excluding private study. Applications by 31 Jul annually.*

Sir John Cass's Foundation. 31 Jewry St, London EC3N 2EY *tel:* 020 7480 5884 *fax:* 020 7488 2519. R M Foley, trust admin. *Helps individuals and organisations that will benefit the under 25s in the inner London area. Can help p/grad students with fees but not insts. Will not fund performances. Candidates must have upper second or first class degree.*

John E Mortimer Awards. Beeches, Well Hill, Chelsfield, Kent BR6 7PR *tel:* 01959 532299 *fax:* 01959 532299. Martyn Jones, admin. *5-10 awards open to all UK students, as well as those studying in the UK, aged 25 or under. Applications by 1 Feb, auditions in Apr. Registration fee £15 to be accompanied by SAE.*

Julius Isserlis Scholarship. Royal Philharmonic Society, 10 Stratford Place, London W1C 1BA *tel:* 020 7491 8110 *fax:* 020 7493 7463 *email:* admin@royalphilharmonicsociety.org.uk. Rosemary Johnson, gen admin. *Scholarship worth £25,000 over two yrs to fund study abroad. Awarded biennially by competition in selected performing categories to students aged 15-25 (of any nationality) permanently resident in the UK. Next scholarship Jun 2005. Entry by Mar, fee £20.*

June Allison Award for Woodwind. Philharmonia Orchestra/Martin Musical Scholarship Fund, Beeches, Well Hill, Chelsfield, Kent BR6 7PR *tel:* 01959 532299 *fax:* 01959 532299. Martyn Jones, admin. *Offered annually for outstanding w/wind performers. Award also includes recital in La Dolce Musica Series. Applications by 1 Feb for award the following yr; auditions in Apr. Application fee £15. Send SAE for application form.*

Lady Marga Alexander Award (Cellists). Philharmonia Orchestra/Martin Musical Scholarship Fund, Beeches, Well Hill, Chelsfield, Kent BR9 7PR *tel:* 01959 532299 *fax:* 01959 532299. Martyn Jones, admin. *Award for £1000.*

Lake District Summer Music Trust. Stricklandgate House, 92 Stricklandgate, Kendal, Cumbria LA9 4PU *tel:* 0845 644 2505 *fax:* 0845 644 2506 *email:* info@ldsm.org.uk. Sir John Manduell, chmn; Andrew Lucas, admin. *Bursaries and scholarships to help students receive specialist inst and chmbr mus training at Lake District Summer Music International Summer School (conservatoire and young professional level) and Young String Venture (ages 6-18) (see Summer Schools). 2003 awards amounted to over £10,000.*

Loan Fund for Musical Instruments. 16 Ogle St, London W1W 6JA *tel:* 020 7436 4816 *fax:* 020 7637 4307. Marjorie Dickinson, sec. *Low-interest loans to talented young professional musicians (aged under 36) towards the purchase of fine insts. Further details and application form available from the secretary.*

MBF Awards for Accompanists and Repetiteurs. c/o Musicians Benevolent Fund, 16 Ogle St, London W1W 6JA *tel:* 020 7636 4481 *fax:* 020 7637 4307 *email:* education@mbf.org.uk. Contact: educ admin. *Annual awards for accompanists aged under 27 and repetiteurs aged under 30. Individual awards up to £4000. Closing date 7 May 2004.*

MBF Awards for Under 18s. c/o Musicians Benevolent Fund, 16 Ogle St, London W1W 6JA *tel:* 020 7636 4481 *fax:* 020 7637 4307 *email:* education@mbf.org.uk. Contact: educ admin. *Up to £1000 towards fees, inst purchase or private lessons, for musicians under 18 who achieved distinction in their most recent exam and are in financial need. Closing date 25 Jun 2004.*

MBF Music Education Awards. c/o Musicians Benevolent Fund, 16 Ogle St, London W1W 6JA *tel:* 020 7636 4481 *fax:* 020 7637 4307 *email:* education@mbf.org.uk. Contact: educ admin. *Awards for p/grad study and help with inst purchase to outstanding young musicians. Open to instrumentalists aged under 25, female singers under 27, male singers under 28. Must be British or Irish or resident in UK for three yrs. Closing date 11 Feb for auditions 29 Mar-2 Apr 2004. Awards £1000-3500.*

Maisie Lewis Young Artists Fund. The Worshipful Company of Musicians, 6th Floor, 2 London Wall Buildings, London EC2M 5PP *tel:* 020 7496 8980 *fax:* 020 7588 3633 *email:* deputyclerk@ wcom.org.uk. Margaret Alford, admin. *Assists singers (under 32) and instrumentalists (under 27) of British residency to gain experience on the concert platform. Application forms available autumn for next yr. Award: concert.*

Manoug Parikian Award. c/o Musicians Benevolent Fund, 16 Ogle St, London W1W 6JA *tel:* 020 7636 4481 *fax:* 020 7637 4307 *email:* education@mbf.org.uk. Contact: educ admin. *Award to assist an exceptional young vn student aged under 21 of any nationality. Award up to £3000, plus other discretionary awards.*

The Mario Lanza Educational Foundation. 20 Feversham Close, Shoreham on Sea, Sussex. William Earl, chmn. *Various awards for students who are engaged in a f/t course of classical singing at a college or conservatoire. Age 18 and over.*

Michael James Music Trust. 4 Onslow Gardens, Rowlands Hill, Wimborne, Dorset BH21 2QG *tel:* 01202 842103. Contact: admin trustees. *Aims to advance educ in mus, particularly that performed in a Christian setting. Annual awards to young organists and choral scholars, with other instrumentalists considered when funds are available. Applications by 30 Apr. Age limit: 30.*

Michael Tippett Musical Foundation. 50 Broadway, London SW1H 0BL. Gwyn Rhydderch, sec. *Foundation has suspended its grant-making activities until further notice, owing to financial constraints.*

The Miriam Licette/Maggie Teyte Awards. 20 Beaumont St, London W1G 6DG *tel:* 020 7935 8810 *fax:* 07092 269247 *email:* felicityg@ teyte.co.uk. Felicity Guinness, admin. *Female singers, aged 30 and under either in f/t educ or within 1st yr of entering professional career. Maggie Teyte Prize Competition: prize of £2000 together with a recital, presented in association with the Friends of Covent Garden for the ROH. Miriam Licette Scholarship of £3000 for advanced study, with guaranteed audition for Musicians' Company Concerts (Maisie Lewis Young Artists' Fund) held at the Wigmore Hall. More than one scholarship may be awarded at the discretion of the adjudicating panel. Megan Foster Prize (£1000) is awarded to an accompanist under the age of 30 taking part in the awards. Awards annually in Jan/Feb, applications by 1 Dec. Registration fee £18.*

Muriel Taylor Scholarship. The Warehouse, 13 Theed St, London SE1 8ST *tel:* 020 7928 9251 *fax:* 020 7928 9252 *email:* murieltaylor@ lfo.co.uk. Kate Beresford, sec. *£3500 awarded annually to cellist aged 17-23 for advanced study. Send SAE for further details. Application fee £10.*

The Music Sound Foundation. c/o 27 Wrights Lane, London W8 5SW *tel:* 020 7795 7000 *fax:* 020 7795 7296 *email:* orrj@emigroup.com. Janie Orr, admin. *Charitable trust dedicated to improving mus educ. Bursary scheme for mus students, funds administered annually through 6 colleges: RSAMD, Glasgow; WCMD, Cardiff; RAM, London; University of Liverpool (Institute of Popular Music); Birmingham Conservatoire; Drumtech (Drum and Percussion School).*

Myra Hess Trust. c/o Musicians Benevolent Fund, 16 Ogle St, London W1W 6JA *tel:* 020 7636 4481 *fax:* 020 7637 4307 *email:* education@mbf.org.uk. Contact: educ admin. *Limited number of awards towards p/grad fees, cost of inst or recital debut for exceptional young str players and pianists aged 20-27 beginning their performing careers. Closing date 20 May 2004. Individual awards £1000-3000.*

National Opera Studio. 2 Chapel Yard, Wandsworth High St, London SW18 4HZ *tel:* 020 8874 8811 *fax:* 020 8875 0404 *email:* info@ natoperastudio.org.uk. Donald Maxwell, dir; Roy Laughlin, head of mus; Isobel Flinn, head of studio; Hugh Lloyd, admin. *One-yr master course of intensive training for 12 singers and 3 repetiteurs. Scholarships given to trainees mainly to cover course fees. Audition fee £45. Applications by previous. Nov*

Neath Opera Group Bursary. 36 Cherry Grove, Sketty, Swansea SA2 8AT *tel:* 01792 411225 *fax:* 01792 541536 *email:* cjandbj@ ntlworld.com. Clive John, mus dir. *Annual award made to Welsh-born singing student in f/t educ.*

The Nelly Ben-Or Scholarship Trust. 23 Rofant Rd, Northwood, Middx HA6 3BD *tel:* 01923 822268 *fax:* 01923 822268 *email:* roger. clynes@virgin.net. Roger Clynes, hon sec; Sir Colin Davis, patron. *Scholarships and grants for talented and deserving young performers from any country, to enable them to advance their mus training by attending courses on pno-playing incorporating the Alexander Technique, given by Nelly Ben-Or (see* **Summer Schools***). Completed application form (with audio tape or CD and written references) to be submitted to the hon sec by 1 May for the Jul course in London.*

The Nicholas Danby Scholarship. The Nicholas Danby Trust, 72 Wandsworth Common Westside, London SW18 2ED *tel:* 020 8874 2757 *fax:* 020 8874 2757 *email:* secretary@ndanbytrust.freeserve.co.uk. Robert Vincent, James O'Donnell, Patrick Russill, Catherine Ennis, John Ramsey, Mary Danby Calvert, Hal Danby, trustees. *Up to £5000 pa to be awarded biennially, to an org student of outstanding promise for p/grad conservatoire study outside their home tradition. Open to org students from UK mus colleges for study elsewhere in Europe, and to org students from other European conservatoires for study in UK. Closing date for applications 31 May.*

Oppenheim-John Downes Memorial Trust. Reference SBS, 50 Broadway, Westminster, London SW1H 0BL *tel:* 020 7227 7000 *fax:* 020 7222 3480 *email:* hamishfrost@bdb-law.co.uk. Sarah Stowell, trustee. *Makes awards each Dec to deserving artists who are unable to pursue their vocation by reason of their poverty. Awards restricted to persons who are natural-born British subjects, of parents both of whom are British subjects (section 34 of the Race Relations Act applies). Age range 30+. Closing date for applications 15 Oct.*

Peter Whittingham Award for Jazz. c/o Musicians Benevolent Fund, 16 Ogle St, London W1W 6JA *tel:* 020 7636 4481 *fax:* 020 7637 4307 *email:* education@mbf.org.uk. Contact: educ admin. *Annual award of £4000 open to individuals under 26 for projects in cutting edge jazz. Applications for course fees not accepted. Application fee £10.*

Peter Whittingham Award for Song Creation. c/o Musicians Benevolent Fund, 16 Ogle St, London W1W 6JA *tel:* 020 7636 4481 *fax:* 020 7637 4307 *email:* education@mbf.org.uk. Contact: educ admin. *Annual award of £4000 available to songwriters under 26 for a project to be taken independently or with others. Project may be in recording, compostion or performance and must be in the field of creative songwriting. Only u/grad students on popular mus courses at selected universities may apply and must be nominated by head of course.*

Philharmonia Orchestra/Martin Musical Scholarship Fund. Beeches, Well Hill, Chelsfield, Kent BR6 7PR *tel:* 01959 532299 *fax:* 01959 532299. Martyn Jones, admin. *Annual awards for instrumentalists aged 25 and under. Funds mainly p/grad mus students, both tuition and maintenance. Orch insts. Preference to UK citizens. Students may study abroad; foreign students in UK may also apply. Younger applicants are occasionally awarded prizes. Applications by 1 Feb, auditions Apr. Application fee £15. Please send SAE.*

Philharmonia Orchestra/Total Ensemble Award. Philharmonia Orchestra/Martin Musical Scholarship Fund, Beeches, Well Hill, Chelsfield, Kent BR9 7PR *tel:* 01959 532299 *fax:* 01959 532299. Martyn Jones, admin. *An award of £6000 will be given to a small ens aged 28 and under (3-8 performers). Total Fina Elf will endeavor to 'adopt' the ens and provide them with performing platforms across the country. Closing date for applications 15 Dec, auditions Feb.*

Philharmonia Trust/Total Outreach Award. Philharmonia Orchestra/Martin Musical Scholarship Fund, Beeches, Well Hill, Chelsfield, Kent BR6 7PR *tel:* 01959 532299 *fax:* 01959 532299. Martyn Jones, admin. *Award of £5000 to an ens aged 28 or under, interested in educ work. Application fee £15. Closing dated for applications 15 Dec, auditions Feb.*

Pocklington Apprenticeship Trust. RB of Kensington and Chelsea, Room 250, Town Hall, Hornton St, London W8 7NX *tel:* 020 7361 2239 *fax:* 020 7361 2764 *email:* voluntary.organisations@rbkc.gov.uk. Contact: funding programmes admin. *Small educ awards for young people aged 21 and under in financial need, born and/or living in the Royal Borough for 10 yrs. Max grant awarded £300.*

RPS Emily Anderson Prize. c/o Musicians Benevolent Fund, 16 Ogle St, London W1W 6JA *tel:* 020 7636 4481 *fax:* 020 7637 4307 *email:* education@mbf.org.uk. Contact: educ admin. *Open to violinists of any nationality aged under 21. In collaboration with the Manoug Parikian Award. Prize £2500 offered by The Royal Philharmonic Society.*

Reginald Conway Memorial Award for String Instrumentalists. Beeches, Well Hill, Chelsfield, Kent BR6 7PR *tel:* 01959 532299

fax: 01959 532299. Martyn Jones, admin. *Annual awards open to all UK students, as well as those studying in the UK, aged 25 and under. Applications by 1 Feb, auditions Apr. Registration fee £15 to be accompanied by SAE.*

The Ricci Foundation. PO Box 124, Harrow, Middx HA2 8ZQ *email:* info@riccifoundation.org. John Rubenstein, trustee, chmn. *Established in honour of the violinist Ruggiero Ricci. For violinists and pianists aged 16-28, awards of up to £2000. Closing date for applications Oct. Entry fee £10.*

Sir Richard Stapley Educational Trust. North St Farmhouse, Sheldwich, nr Faversham, Kent ME13 0LN *email:* admin@stapleytrust.org. Contact: admin. *Grants of £300-1000. For graduates aged 24 and over on 1 Oct of the proposed academic yr, with a first or upper-second class degree studying for higher degrees at a university in the UK, or courses considered to be equivalent to a higher degree by the university or conservatoire, and who are not in receipt of substantial local authority, research council, British Academy or other similar public bodies awards. Applicants must already be resident in the UK at the time of application. Send large SAE for application form. Applications to arrive before 31 Mar, with academic reference. Applicants will be notified during Jun.*

Royal College of Organists. 7 St Andrew Street, Holborn, London EC4A 3LQ *tel:* 020 7936 3606 *fax:* 020 7353 8244 *email:* admin@rco.org.uk. Gordon Clarke, registrar. *A number of trusts available to organists who are members of the College (non-members considered in exceptional circumstances). No age limit. Awards £150-1200. Closing date for applications 30 Apr.*

Royal Hospital Church Music Scholarship. The Organist, 22 West Rd, Royal Hospital, Chelsea, London SW3 4NL *tel:* 020 7730 7395 *fax:* 020 7881 5463 *email:* iancurror@chelsea-pensioners.org.uk. Ian Curror, org. *Annual scholarship (£3500) providing an aspiring young church musician (org) with an opportunity to receive practical guidance, support and experience. Designed for young organists, aged 18-27, preferably students in HE living within easy reach of central London. Tenable for one academic yr (Sep-Jul). Closing date for applications 31 Mar. Auditions and interviews May.*

The Rushworth Trust. Liverpool CSS, 14 Castle St, Liverpool L2 0NJ *tel:* 0151 236 7728 *fax:* 0151 258 1153. Contact: Marjorie Staunton. *One-off grants of up to £300 for the support and promotion of mus activities and training within 60 miles of Liverpool Town Hall. Incorporates The A K Holland Fund and the H A Thew Fund.*

Ryan Davies Memorial Awards. 1 Squire Court, The Marina, Swansea SA1 3XB *tel:* 01792 301500 *fax:* 01792 301500. Michael Evans, sec. *Awards of £500-2000 to assist young Welsh p/grads aged 16-30 in mus and drama. Applications by 30 May.*

St Martin-in-the-Fields Organ and Choral Scholarships. 6 St Martin's Place, Trafalgar Square, London WC2N 4JJ *tel:* 020 7766 1111 *fax:* 020 7839 5163. Nicholas Danks, dir of mus. *Grants scholarships to 8 student choral scholars together with an org scholar each yr. These challenging, high-profile scholarships draw on the rich repertory of Anglican church mus and provide valuable experience within a busy mus dept. Open to f/t or p/t students and are ideal for those wishing to gain mus experience during a gap yr. There is a good financial reward of £1250, reflecting the required commitment. Applicants should have a good level of sight-reading and an understanding of Anglican Chant is desirable. Both male and female altos are invited to apply. To apply send current CV with names/addresses of 2 referees together with a covering letter.*

Schools Music Association Founder's Fund. 71 Margaret Rd, New Barnet, Herts EN4 9NT *email:* maxwellpryce@educamus. free-online.co.uk. Maxwell Pryce MBE, hon sec, chief exec. *Small awards made to help with purchase costs of mus insts and summer schools available to British school pupils and students in FE and HE, aged 18 and under. On-going courses cannot be funded.*

Scottish Arts Council Funding. Scottish Arts Council, 12 Manor Place, Edinburgh EH3 7DD *tel:* 0131 226 6051 *fax:* 0131 225 9833 *email:* helen.jamieson@scottisharts.org.uk. Contact: help desk (tel: 0845 603 6000). *The Scottish Arts Council has reviewed its funding processes. Information can be found in the Guide to Funds booklet available from the help desk and on website.*

Scottish International Education Trust. 22 Manor Place, Edinburgh EH3 7DS *tel:* 0131 225 1113 *fax:* 0131 225 1113 *email:* siet@ukonline.co.uk. E C Davison, dir. *Grants to promote individual Scottish talent or for educ projects contributing to the quality of life in Scotland. Over school-age. Applications in writing to above address.*

Sophie's Silver Lining Fund. 17 Silver St, Chacombe, Banbury, Oxon OX17 2JR *tel:* 01295 711155 *email:* TheLarges@aol.com. Cherry and Stephen Large, trustees. *For needy acting and singing students at recognised drama schools or mus colleges/conservatoires. Closing date for applications Aug 2004. Award £200-1000.*

Sybil Tutton Awards. c/o Musicians Benevolent Fund, 16 Ogle St, London W1W 6JA *tel:* 020 7636 4481 *fax:* 020 7637 4307 *email:* education@ mbf.org.uk. Contact: educ admin. *Awards to assist exceptionally talented opera students aged under 30 with the cost of training on a recognised course at p/grad level. Closing date 14 May 2004 for auditions in Jun. Must be British or resident in UK for three yrs. Awards £1500-3000.*

Sydney Perry Foundation Awards. Philharmonia Orchestra/Martin Musical Scholarship Fund, Beeches, Well Hill, Chelsfield, Kent BR6 7PR *tel:* 01959 532299 *fax:* 01959 532299. Martyn Jones, admin. *Specifically for p/grad study. 5-10 scholarships awarded annually. Applications by 1 Feb for award the following yr; auditions in Apr. Application fee £15. Send SAE for application form.*

Tait Memorial Trust. 4/80 Elm Park Gardens, London SW10 9PD *tel:* 020 7351 0561 *fax:* 020 7349 0531 *email:* islabaring@compuserve.com. Isla Baring, chmn. *Awards for p/grad performance opportunities and general help in the furtherance of the careers of Australian musicians and performing artists resident in the UK. Apply (include SAE) with tape, full CV and 2 references by 31 Mar. Awarded in May.*

Thalben-Ball Memorial Awards. St Michael's Vestry, Cornhill, London EC3V 9DS *tel:* 01737 244604; 07799 641699 *fax:* 01737 244604 *email:* jonathanrennert@hotmail.com. Jonathan Rennert, trustee, hon sec. *Annual grants ranging from £100-4000 for young organists and church musicians (not child choristers or adult singers) of any nationality studying in the UK. Age limit usually 26. Applications by 1 Apr annually. Funds also available for annual scholarship for org scholar at St Michael's Church, Cornhill, London. No application form or fee; write in confidence to the hon sec, giving brief details of past experience, names/telephone numbers of 2 referees, plans for the coming academic yr and financial position. Decisions usually made during autumn.*

Sir Thomas Beecham Trust. Castle House, 15 Earsham St, Bungay, Suffolk NR35 1AE *tel:* 01986 892111. Lady Beecham, trustee. *Scholarships, tenable for 3 yrs, established in partnership with certain universities. Available to 1st-yr students studying for a mus degree and nominated by the university.*

Sir Thomas White's Educational Foundation. General Charities City of Coventry, Old Bablake, Hill St, Coventry CV1 4AN *tel:* 024 7622 2769 *fax:* 024 7622 2769. *Mus scholarship, tenable in a HE institution approved by Trustees. For students with local connections only. Ages 18-25. Advertised annually in local press.*

Tillett Trust. Courtyard House, Neopardy, Crediton, Devon EX17 5EP *tel:* 01363 777844 *fax:* 01363 777845 *email:* tilletttrust@tiscali.co.uk. Katie Avey, admin. *Limited financial assistance given to individual young classical musicians of exceptional talent, usually aged under 30, to help them achieve performing opportunities in the earlier stages of their professional solo careers. Must be British or residing f/t in British Isles. Applicants must have completed all their formal educ, including u/grad and p/grad courses. Awards normally in £200-1000 range. No application forms available but write giving full CV, two references, demo tape/CD and budget. Funds not available for the purchase of insts, funding commissions or commercial recordings.*

Trevor Snoad Award. Philharmonia Orchestra/Martin Musical Scholarship Fund, Beeches, Well Hill, Chelsfield, Kent BR6 7PR *tel:* 01959 532299 *fax:* 01959 532299. Martyn Jones, admin. *Open to outstanding va player aged 25 and under of p/grad standard. Preference given to UK citizens. Award of £500 pays for tuition fees and/or maintenance. Auditions held in London. Application forms available early summer. Applications by 1 Feb annually. Auditions Apr. Application fee £15, send with SAE.*

The Tunnell Trust for Young Musicians. 4 Royal Terrace, Edinburgh EH7 5AB *tel:* 020 8241 9330 *fax:* 020 8241 9330 *email:* tunnelltrust@ aol.com. Jonathan Tunnell, artistic dir. *Awards in form of paid engagements in conjunction with Scottish mus societies to young professional inst chmbr ens (max 8 players). Preference given to British-based groups aged 27 or under. Application forms supported by tapes. Applications by end Jun each yr for following season.*

W T Best Memorial Scholarship. Worshipful Company of Musicians, 6th Floor, 2 London Wall Buildings, London EC2M 5PP *tel:* 020 7496 8980 *fax:* 020 7588 3633 *email:* deputyclerk@wcom.org.uk. Mrs M Alford, deputy clerk. *Provides financial assistance (£4000 pa for a maximum of 3 yrs) to an org scholar, aged 18-25, showing exceptional promise. Nominations from certain professors or principals of mus colleges. Next available in 2005.*

William Cox Memorial Fund for Young Singers (The Cox Trust). Badger Bungalow, 41 Findon Ave, Witton Gilbert, Durham DH7 6RF. Antony Elton, hon admin, hon trustee. *Grants to help very talented advanced students of professional solo singing to purchase scores, etc. For ages 19-29 inclusive. Trustees normally meet spring and autumn. Awards at discretion of trustees and dependent on resources. Enquiries* *and applications by post only; those not sending SAE may be ignored. No application fee.*

Wingate Scholarships. 20-22 Stukeley St, London WC2B 5LR *email:* clark@wingate.org.uk. Faith Clark, admin. *Awards of up to £10,000 pa (max £30,000 over 3 yrs) made to people undertaking original work in almost any field and to outstanding musicians for advanced training. Open to citizens of the UK, Commonwealth, Ireland or Israel, and to EU citizens who have been resident in the UK for at least 3 yrs. All applicants must be aged 24 or over on 1 Sep and resident in British Isles during period of application. Applications by 1 Feb. Shortlisted candidates auditioned/interviewed in London during May and results announced in Jun. Total award available £6,500. Send A4 SAE for forms or available to download from website after 15 Sep.*

Worshipful Company of Musicians. 6th Floor, 2 London Wall Buildings, London EC2M 5PP *tel:* 020 7496 8980 *fax:* 020 7588 3633 *email:* deputyclerk@wcom.org.uk. Mrs M Alford, deputy clerk. *Busenhart-Morgan-Evans award. 1 award for p/grad study £4500. Closing date for applications 30 Apr. Applicants must have consecutive*

study for at least 3 yrs at a British college or conservatoire. Nominations must come from principals or heads of mus.

Yamaha Music Foundation of Europe. Yamaha-Kemble Music (UK) Ltd, Sherbourne Drive, Tilbrook, Milton Keynes MK7 8BL *tel:* 01908 369235 *fax:* 01908 368872 *email:* ian.frankland@yamaha-music.co.uk. Ian Frankland, mkt asst. *3 scholarships of £2000 awarded annually to UK and international student performers on f/t courses at UK conservatoires, universities and tertiary educ colleges. Mus disciplines rotate annually. 2004: strs (vn, va, vc, db). Initial round takes place previous Dec, final round in Feb. Open to those aged under 25. Contact for application form. Closing date previous Nov.*

Youth Music. 1 America St, London SE1 0NE *tel:* 020 7902 1060 *fax:* 020 7902 1061 *email:* info@youthmusic.org.uk. *Funding programmes to reach young people, aged 18 and under, who have limited access to mus-making opportunities. Grants of up to £20,000 are available for not-for-profit organisations to support children and young people in mus-making of all styles and genres.*

Scholarships for Study Abroad

Organisations

It is advisable to contact the Embassy or High Commission in Britain of the country in which you wish to study. The organisations below can provide information on opportunities in certain countries.

Czech Ministry of Culture. Foreign Relations Dept, Milady Horákové 139 160 41, Praha 6 CZ-118 11, Czech Republic *tel:* 00 420 2 5708 5294 *fax:* 00 420 2 2432 4282 *email:* renata.romanova@mkcr.cz. Renata Romanova, British desk offr. *Czech artists, agents or representatives may seek support directly (in accordance with the grant system) from the Ministry of Culture of the Czech Republic. The Ministry of Culture liaises with the Embassy's Cultural Dept.*

Embassy of Brazil. 32 Green St, London W1K 7AT *tel:* 020 7399 9000/1/2/3/4 *fax:* 020 7399 9100 *email:* ffortuna@inforlondres.org.uk. Luis Felipe Fortuna, head of cultural section. *All requests for support should be addressed to the head of the Cultural Section at the Brazilian Embassy, which has a budget for support towards Brazilian cultural activity in the UK. The type and level of support is determined by each application. Proposals should be presented in writing or by fax, and interviews will be arranged where appropriate. The cultural section of the Embassy can advise on sponsorship opportunities. It is essential that* such requests be presented at least six months before the intended date of the recital or concert.

Embassy of Venezuela. Bolívar Hall, 54 Grafton Way, London W1T 5DL *tel:* 020 7388 5788 *fax:* 020 7383 4857 *email:* embvenuk-ccm@dial.pipex.com. Gloria Carnevali, cultural attaché. *UK promoters seeking advice or support for projects should contact the Cultural Centre, which can liaise with the relevant Ministry in Venezuela. The Cultural Centre has a small budget to supplement some of the costs of projects involving the presentation of Venezuelan arts in the UK.*

German Academic Exchange Service (DAAD). 34 Belgrave Square, London SW1X 8QB *tel:* 020 7235 1736 *fax:* 020 7235 9602 *email:* info@daad.org.uk. *Offers scholarships to p/grad students based at UK institutions of HE to study in Germany.*

The Italian Cultural Institute. The Bursary Dept, 39 Belgrave Square, London SW1X 8NX *tel:* 020 7235 1461 *fax:* 020 7235 4618 *email:* ici@italcultur.org.uk. *Courses at art academies and mus conservatoires. A final diploma in mus or art is required. (BA level)*

Scholarships

Arts Council of Wales. 9 Museum Place, Cardiff CF10 3NX *tel:* 029 2037 6500 *minicom:* 029 2039 0027 *fax:* 029 2022 1447 *email:* simon.lovelljones@artswales.org.uk. Simon Lovell-Jones, snr arts development offr - mus. *Details of the Professional Development and Training schemes and all other funding schemes run by the Arts Council Wales can be downloaded from the website or sent from contact details given above.*

Banff Centre Scholarships. The Banff Centre, Office of the Registrar, Box 1020, Station 28, 107 Tunnel Mountain Drive, Banff, Alberta T1L 1H5, Canada *tel:* 00 1 403 762 6180 *fax:* 00 1 403 762 6345 *email:* arts_info@banffcentre.ca. Jane Bateman, enquiries/information offr. *The Banff Centre is a place for artists. Dedicated to life-long learning and professional career development in the arts, the year-round continuing educ facility serves as site and catalyst for creative activity and experience. Scholarships available to UK musicians as a contribution towards fees. Please see website for closing date for applications.*

Brandon University Graduate Assistantships. School of Music, Brandon University, Brandon, Manitoba R7A 6A9, Canada *tel:* 00 1 204 727 7343 *fax:* 00 1 204 728 6839 *email:* music@brandonu.ca. *4-6 awards annually with value up to $C6500, tenable at Brandon University for one year. For study leading to Master of Music degree. Applications by 1 May.*

ESTA Nannie Jamieson Nutshell Fund. 6 Ember Lane, Esher, Surrey KT10 8ER *tel:* 020 8398 4691 *email:* sylvia.palmer@virgin.net. Sylvia Palmer, hon sec; Marian Seymour, ESTA admin. *European String Teachers Association, British Branch. Modest bursaries awarded annually for students and teachers of str insts (ESTA members) for help to attend w/shops, conferences and short courses on str teaching. May be used for study abroad. For ESTA membership apply to Marion Seymour 020 8940 4640.*

Emanuel Hurwitz Chamber Music Charitable Trust. 44 Church Cres, London N3 1BJ. Miriam Keogh, founder, admin. *Bursaries for str players to further their studies in chmbr mus at home or abroad; college/university fees will not be paid although there is some help available with p/grad fees only at RAM, RCM, RNCM and Guildhall. Applications will only be accepted in writing with SAE. Applications by 1 Jun. UK citizens only. References and CVs are essential.*

Fulbright Awards. Fulbright Commission, Fulbright House, 62 Doughty St, London WC1N 2JZ *tel:* 020 7539 4409 *fax:* 020 7404 6834 *email:* cnormantaylor@fulbright.co.uk. Contact: British programme mgr. *Scholarships for 1st year of p/grad academic study and research in the US. Any discipline, must have or expect a 2:1 degree, be an EU citizen normally resident in the UK and be able to demonstrate initiative and participation in extra curricular activities; deadline for submission of application forms is early Nov. Benefits include tuition fees and maintenance allowance. Distinguished scholar awards available to established or potential leaders in any field for a min of 10 months* lecturing or research in the US. Applicants must be EU citizens normally resident in the UK. Application forms should be submitted by 12 Mar. Benefits include £15,000 and health insurance. Also Fulbright Chester Schirmer Fellowship in Music Composition, to enable a young British composer to spend time in the US extending his/her artistic experience and developing an international reputation. Benefits include up to £12,000 pro rata (min stay 4 months), plus round-trip travel, deadline 26 March. Further information and application forms for any of the above can be obtained by visiting the Commission's website or send an A4 SAE (for 42p) to British Programme Manager, stating clearly the award for which details are required.

Ian Fleming Charitable Trust Music Education Awards. c/o Musicians Benevolent Fund, 16 Ogle St, London W1W 6JA *tel:* 020 7636 4481 *fax:* 020 7637 4307 *email:* education@mbf.org.uk. Contact: educ admin. *Awards for p/grad study and help with inst purchase to outstanding young musicians beginning their career. Open to those aged under 25 (instrumentalists), 27 (female singers), 28 (male singers). Auditions Apr, in collaboration with MBF Music Education Awards.*

Julius Isserlis Scholarship. Royal Philharmonic Society, 10 Stratford Place, London W1C 1BA *tel:* 020 7491 8110 *fax:* 020 7493 7463 *email:* admin@royalphilharmonicsociety.org.uk. Rosemary Johnson, gen admin. *Awarded biennially by competition to students aged 15-25, of any nationality, permanently resident in the UK. Selected performing categories. For study abroad. Value £25,000 over 2 years. Entry fee £20. Jun 2005.*

Philharmonia Orchestra/Martin Musical Scholarship Fund. Beeches, Well Hill, Chelsfield, Kent BR6 7PR *tel:* 01959 532299 *fax:* 01959 532299. Martyn Jones, admin. *Annual awards for instrumentalists aged 25 and under to study in UK or abroad. Fund aims to assist exceptional talent with specialist and advanced study and to help bridge the gap between study and fully-professional status. Not open to organists, singers, conductors, composers or academic students. Includes tuition fees and subsistence grants. Application fee £15 (returnable if not offered an audition) which covers all the awards within the PO/MMSF. Selection of candidates is by audition. Auditions held in Apr. Applications by 1 Feb. Awards payable from 1 May. Send SAE.*

Nadia and Lili Boulanger International Foundation. 25 Ave des Gobelins, Paris F-75013, France *tel:* 00 33 1 47 07 05 93 *fax:* 00 33 1 45 35 09 43 *email:* contact@fondation-boulanger.com. Alexandra Laederich, sec. *Scholarships are awarded to musicians of all nationalities studying in France and to scholars who propose research into the history or theory of mus who have shown ability for mus achievement and creativity. Open to those aged 20-35. Application form available on request.*

The Nicholas Danby Trust. 72 Wandsworth Common Westside, London SW18 2ED *tel:* 020 8874 2757 *fax:* 020 8874 2757 *email:* secretary@ndanbytrust.freeserve.co.uk. Margaret Danby, sec and treasurer. *Biennial award of up to £5000 pa (up to 2 years) for org student of outstanding promise, for p/grad conservatoire org study outside their home tradition. Open to UK org students for study in Europe and for org students from other European countries for study in the UK. Also helps successful candidates to establish concert careers.*

Scottish Arts Council. 12 Manor Place, Edinburgh EH3 7DD *tel:* 0845 603 6000 *fax:* 0131 225 9833 *email:* helen.jamieson@scottisharts.org.uk. Contact: Help Desk. *The Scottish Arts Council has reviewed its funding process; information on funding can be found on its website and in its Guide to Funds booklet available from the Help Desk.*

Trevor Snoad Award (Viola). Philharmonia Orchestra/Martin Musical Scholarship, Beeches, Well Hill, Chelsfield, Kent BR6 7PR *tel:* 01959 532299 *fax:* 01959 532299. Martyn Jones, admin. *Open to outstanding va player aged 25 and under of p/grad standard. Preference given to UK citizens. Award of £500 pays for tuition fees and/or maintenance. Auditions held in London. Application forms available early summer. Applications by 1 Feb annually. Auditions Apr. Application fee £15, send with SAE.*

Winston Churchill Memorial Trust. 15 Queen's Gate Terrace, London SW7 5PR *tel:* 020 7584 9315 *fax:* 020 7581 0410 *email:* office@wcmt.org.uk. Ms S Matthews, mgr; Nigel Sudborough. *Travelling fellowships in arts subjects, not necessarily mus. Applications Jun-Oct. Open categories on occasion. The trust will support projects that encourage personal development and benefit the community. The Fellowship Scheme does not cover attending courses, academic studies, student grants or gap year projects.*

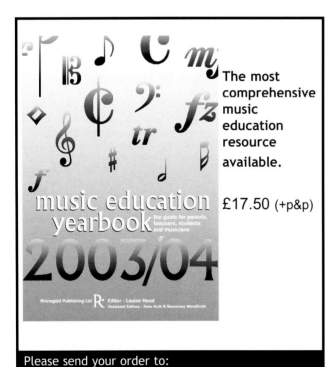

Youth Orchestras and Bands

This section is divided into lists of orchestras, wind bands and brass bands. Each list is subdivided under international, national, and regional and local headings. This subdivision is based upon the method and scope of the audition procedure, and from where the majority of players are drawn. Other orchestras which hold annual courses, but who do not audition and whose personnel change every year are listed under **Summer Schools and Short Courses**. School, music college and university groups are not listed unless membership of the group is open to external applicants. Details of county youth orchestras administered by local education authorities and which are not listed here can be obtained from the Local Music Education Adviser.

An asterisk indicates membership of the **National Association of Youth Orchestras**, Central Hall, West Tollcross, Edinburgh EH3 9BP *tel:* 0131 221 1927 *fax:* 0131 229 2921 *email:* admin@nayo.org.uk *website:* www.nayo.org.uk, which draws its members from amongst both independent and LEA-run orchestras.

Youth Orchestras

International

European Union Baroque Orchestra. Hordley, Wootton, Woodstock OX20 1EP *tel:* 01993 812111 *fax:* 01993 812911 *email:* info@eubo.org.uk. Lars Ulrik Mortensen, mus dir; Paul James, gen admin; Emma Wilkinson, mgr.

European Union Youth Orchestra. 65 Sloane St, London SW1X 9SH *tel:* 020 7235 7671 *fax:* 020 7235 7370 *email:* info@euyo.org.uk. Vladimir Ashkenazy, mus dir; Joy Bryer, sec gen; Huw Humphreys, gen mgr.

National

Britten-Pears Orchestra and Britten-Pears Baroque Orchestra. Britten-Pears Young Artist Programme, Snape Maltings Concert Hall, Saxmundham, Suffolk IP17 1SP *tel:* 01728 688671 *fax:* 01728 688171 *email:* britten-pears@aldeburgh.co.uk. Andrew Comben, dir; Caroline Newton, admin; Charlotte Penton-Smith, m/class co-ord; Polly Brown, asst.

* **Camerata Scotland.** NYOS, 13 Somerset Place, Glasgow G3 7JT *tel:* 0141 332 8311 *fax:* 0141 332 3915 *email:* info@nyos.co.uk. Richard Chester, dir; Joanna Slade, asst admin.

ESO Children's, Intermediate and Youth Orchestras. The Old Hop Store, Three Counties Showground, Welland, Malvern WR13 6SP *tel:* 01684 560696 *fax:* 01684 560656 *email:* info@eso.co.uk. William

Boughton, artistic/mus dir; Alison King, head of finance and admin; Kate Hodson, admin.

* **European Vacation Chamber Orchestras.** Ashley House, Ure Bank, Ripon, N Yorks HG4 1JG *tel:* 01765 602856 *email:* mail@vaco.net. Xenophon Kelsey, mus dir; Jane Lomax, admin.

Guildhall School of Music & Drama, Junior Guildhall Symphony Orchestra. Junior School, Guildhall School of Music & Drama, Silk St, Barbican, London EC2Y 8DT *tel:* 020 7382 7160 *fax:* 020 7382 7212 *email:* junior@gsmd.ac.uk. Derek Rodgers, head.

Jewish Youth Orchestra of Great Britain. 5 Bradby House, Carlton Hill, London NW8 9XE *tel:* 020 7624 1756. Sidney Fixman, dir of mus.

The London Philharmonic Youth Orchestra. 89 Albert Embankment, London SE1 7TP *tel:* 020 7840 4202 *fax:* 020 7840 4201. Maria Smith, educ, youth orch admin.

* **London Schools Symphony Orchestra.** Centre for Young Musicians, 61 Westminster Bridge Rd, London SE1 7HT *tel:* 020 7928 3844 *fax:* 020 7928 3454 *email:* peter@cymlondon.demon.co.uk. Peter Ash, artistic dir, LSSO.

Methodist Association of Youth Clubs Orchestra and Singers. 25 Marylebone Rd, London NW1 5JR *tel:* 020 7467 5208 *fax:* 020 7467 5281 *email:* saundersr@methodistchurch.org.uk. Rachel Saunders, mus dir.

NISA (National ISCis Strings Academy). Stud Farm Cottage, Stratford St Andrew, Saxmundham, Suffolk IP17 1LW *tel:* 01728 605917 *fax:* 01728 602679 *email:* director@nisastrings.org. Viviane Ronchetti, mus dir; Sir Neville Marriner CBE, principal patron; Levon Parikian, cond.

* **National Children's Orchestra.** 84a Elm Tree Rd, Locking, Weston-Super-Mare BS24 8EH *tel:* 01934 820254 *fax:* 01934 820257 *email:* admin@nco.org.uk.

national musicians symphony orchestra. 11 Gunnersbury Ave, London W5 3NJ *tel:* 020 8993 3135 *fax:* 020 8993 2635 *email:* admin@nmso.org.uk. James Blair, artistic dir, principal cond.

National Youth Jazz Orchestra of Great Britain. 11 Victor Rd, Harrow, Middx HA2 6PT *tel:* 020 8863 2717 *fax:* 020 8863 8685 *email:* bill.ashton@virgin.net. Bill Ashton, mus dir.

* **The National Youth Jazz Orchestra of Scotland.** NYOS, 13 Somerset Place, Glasgow G3 7JT *tel:* 0141 332 8311 *fax:* 0141 332 3915 *email:* info@nyos.co.uk. Richard Chester, dir; Pippa Heath, jazz co-ord.

National Youth Jazz Orchestra of Wales. Ty Cerdd, 15 Mount Stuart Square, Cardiff CF10 5DP *tel:* 029 2046 5700 *fax:* 029 2046 2733 *email:* nyjow@tycerdd.org. John Quirk, mus dir; Keith Griffin, dir.

* **National Youth Orchestra of Great Britain.** 32 Old School House, Britannia Rd, Bristol BS15 8DB *tel:* 0117 960 0477 *fax:* 0117 960 0376 *email:* info@nyo.org.uk. Jonathan Vaughan, dir; Nina Camilleri, dir of development; Andrea Robins, company mgr; Shaun Parker, corporate development mgr; Amelia Clarke, development offr; Sophie Lomax,

publicity offr; Jo Philpott, educ and outreach offr; Morag Vockins, orch admin.

* **The National Youth Orchestra of Scotland.** NYOS, 13 Somerset Place, Glasgow G3 7JT *tel:* 0141 332 8311 *fax:* 0141 332 3915 *email:* info@nyos.co.uk. Richard Chester, dir.

* **National Youth Orchestra of Wales.** Welsh Joint Education Committee, 245 Western Ave, Cardiff CF5 2YX *tel:* 029 2026 5047 *fax:* 029 2026 5014 *email:* beryl.jones@wjec.co.uk. Beryl Jones, admin; Pauline Crossley, expressive arts offr.

National Youth Sinfonia. Homecroft, Sun Lane, Harpenden, Herts AL5 4GJ *tel:* 01582 713333 *fax:* 01582 767343 *email:* info@musicale.co.uk. Gillian Johnston, mus dir; David Johnston, admin; Melanie Ragge, associate dir.

* **National Youth String Orchestra of Scotland and Training School.** Scottish Amateur Music Association, 18 Craigton Cres, Alva, Clackmannanshire FK12 5DS *tel:* 01259 760249 *email:* secretary@sama.org.uk. Margaret Simpson, hon sec; Mark Duncan, mus dir.

National Youth Symphonic Brass Ensemble of Wales. Ty Cerdd, 15 Mount Stuart Square, Cardiff CF10 5DP *tel:* 029 2046 5700 *fax:* 029 2046 2733 *email:* wamf@tycerdd.org. James Watson, mus dir; Keith Griffin, dir.

* **National Youth Wind Orchestra of Great Britain.** 51 Highlands, Tadmarton Park, Banbury, Oxon OX15 5SR *tel:* 01295 721020 *fax:* 01295 721020 *email:* kit@nywo.org.uk. Kit Shepherd, dir.

National Youth Wind Orchestra of Wales. Ty Cerdd, 15 Mount Stuart Square, Cardiff CF10 5DP *tel:* 029 2046 5700 *fax:* 029 2046 2733 *email:* wamf@tycerdd.org. Keith Griffin; Frank Renton, mus dir.

Pro Corda (The National School For Young Chamber Music Players). Leiston Abbey House, Theberton Rd, Leiston, Suffolk IP16 4TB *tel:* 01728 831354 *fax:* 01728 832500 *email:* mail@procorda.fsbusiness.co.uk. Sir Colin Davies, president; Ioan Davies, dir of mus; Mrs M Crump, admin.

* **Rehearsal Orchestra.** 60-62 Clapham Rd, London SW9 0JJ *tel:* 020 7820 9994 *email:* admin@rehearsal-orchestra.org. Amanda Lockhart Knight, admin; Levon Parikian, artistic dir; Harry Legge OBE, founder.

Royal College of Music Junior Dept Symphony Orchestra. Junior Dept, Royal College of Music, Prince Consort Rd, London SW7 2BS *tel:* 020 7591 4334 *fax:* 020 7591 4858 *email:* jd@rcm.ac.uk. Peter Hewitt, dir, jnr dept; Richard Dickins, cond; John Mitchell, orch mgr.

* **Royal Scottish Academy of Music and Drama Junior Academy Orchestra.** Junior Academy, Royal Scottish Academy of Music and Drama, 100 Renfrew St, Glasgow G2 3DB *tel:* 0141 332 4101 *fax:* 0141 353 0372 *email:* a.scott@rsamd.ac.uk. Havilland Willshire, head of jnr academy; Angela Scott, admin.

* **Vacation Chamber Orchestras.** Ashley House, Ure Bank, Ripon, N Yorks HG4 1JG *tel:* 01765 602856 *email:* mail@vaco.net. Xenophon Kelsey, mus dir; Jane Lomax, admin.

Regional and Local

* **Bedfordshire County Youth Orchestras.** Bedfordshire Music, Floor 6, County Hall, Cauldwell St, Bedford MK42 9AP *tel:* 01234 408177 *fax:* 01234 408182 *email:* morrisa@bedfordshire.gov.uk. Nigel Mainard, head of Bedfordshire Music.

Berkshire Youth Orchestra. Berkshire Young Musicians Trust, Stoneham Court, 100 Cockney Hill, Reading RG19 4NU *tel:* 0118 901 2354 *fax:* 0118 901 2351 *email:* davidmarcou@bymt.org.uk. Robert Roscoe, cond.

Bodmin College Jazz Orchestra. Lostwithiel Rd, Bodmin, Cornwall PL31 1DD *tel:* 01208 72114 *fax:* 01208 261036. Adrian Evans, dir of mus.

* **Bromley Youth Chamber Orchestra.** Bromley Youth Music Trust, Southborough Lane, Bromley, Kent BR2 8AA *tel:* 020 8467 1566 *fax:* 020 8468 7595 *email:* mawson@bymt.co.uk. Jonathan Josephs, head of str teaching, Bromley Youth Music Trust.

* **Bromley Youth Symphony Orchestra.** Bromley Youth Music Centre, Southborough Lane, Bromley, Kent BR2 8AA *tel:* 020 8467 1566 *fax:* 020 8468 7595 *email:* mawson@bymt.co.uk. Peter M Mawson, principal.

* **Cambridgeshire and Peterborough County Youth Orchestra.** CIMA, Ermine St North, The Old School, Papworth Everard, Cambs CB3 8RH *tel:* 01480 831695 *fax:* 01480 831696 *email:* peter.britton@cambridgeshire.gov.uk. Peter Britton, dir.

Capriccio Young String Ensemble. 9 Harboro Rd, Sale, Cheshire M33 5AE *tel:* 0161 973 0392 *email:* delythw@onetel.net.uk. Stephen Wilkinson, cond.

* **Cardiff County and Vale of Glamorgan Youth Orchestra.** The Friary Centre, The Friary, Cardiff CF10 3FA *tel:* 029 2064 0950/1 *fax:* 029 2066 6593 *email:* music@ccvgmusicservice.com. Eric Phillips, mus dir;

Stuart Burrows, president.

* **Cheshire Youth Orchestra.** Woodford Lodge Professional Centre, Woodford Lane West, Winsford, Cheshire CW7 4EH *tel:* 01606 814339 *fax:* 01606 814301 *email:* cortena@cheshire.gov.uk. Laura Jellicoe, mus dir; Alison Corten, mus mgr.

* **City of Coventry Youth Symphony Orchestra.** 3rd Floor, Queens House, Queens Rd, Coventry CV1 3EG *tel:* 024 7653 2455 *fax:* 024 7653 2522 *email:* office.covpas@virgin.net. Brian Chappell, dir.

* **City of Hull Youth Symphony Orchestra and Youth Jazz Orchestra.** The Albemarle Music Centre, Ferensway, Hull HU2 8LZ *tel:* 01482 223941 *fax:* 01482 320565. Chris Maynard, head of mus service; June Pitts, head of inst teaching; Laurence Rugg, mus service co-ord; Niall McEwen, head of br and w/wind.

* **City of Sheffield Youth Orchestra.** The Cottage, Park Head, Birds Edge, Huddersfield HD8 8XW *tel:* 01484 606114 *fax:* 01484 606114 *email:* e.woodhead@ntlworld.com. Edward Woodhead, dir; Christopher Gayford, cond.

* **Colchester Youth Chamber Orchestra.** Weltevreden, Mount Pleasant, Hundon, nr Sudbury, Suffolk CO10 8DW *tel:* 01440 786337 *fax:* 01440 786337. George Reynolds, mus dir; Edna Robson, hon sec.

* **Cornwall Youth Orchestra and Cornwall Youth Wind Orchestra.** c/o The Music Service, Dalvenie House, County Hall, Truro TR1 3AY *tel:* 01872 323476 *fax:* 01872 323849 *email:* ibowden@cornwall.gov.uk. Janet Elston, extra curricular co-ord.

Derbyshire City & County Youth Orchestra. Advisory and Inspection Service, John Hadfield House, Dale Rd, Matlock DE4 3RD *tel:* 01629 580000 ext 2771 *fax:* 01629 585466 *email:* Philip.King@education.derbyshire.gov.uk. Philip King, adviser; Peter Stark, guest cond.

* **Dorset - Youth Orchestras and Ensembles.** Dorset Music Service, Unit 5, New Fields Business Park, Stinsford Rd, Poole BH17 0NF *tel:* 01202 678233 *fax:* 01202 679381 *email:* dorsetmusicservice@dorset-cc.gov.uk. David Kenyon, head of service; Stephanie Sainsbury, office mgr.

* **Dudley Schools' Symphony Orchestra.** Dudley Music Centre, Lawnwood Rd, Wordsley, Stourbridge DY8 5PQ *tel:* 01384 813865 *fax:* 01384 813866 *email:* dmusicservs.ed@mbc.dudley.gov.uk. Gerald Johnson, head of Dudley Performing Arts; Keith Horsfall, snr mgr Dudley Performing Arts.

* **Dundee Schools' Symphony Orchestra.** Dundee City Council, Gardyne Rd, Dundee DD5 1NY *tel:* 01382 462857 *fax:* 01382 462862 *email:* charlie.maynes@dundeecity.gov.uk. Charles Maynes, dir.

* **Ealing Youth Orchestra.** 9 Woodstock Rd, Chiswick, London W4 1DS *tel:* 020 8747 3272 *email:* chair@eyo.org.uk. Janet King, chmn; Mark Forkgen, mus dir.

East Sussex String Chamber Orchestra. East Sussex Music Service, Watergate Lane, Lewes BN7 1UQ *tel:* 01273 472336 *fax:* 01273 486396 *email:* music.service@eastsussexcc.gov.uk. Phillip Scott; Christopher Hirons, dir.

* **East Sussex Youth Orchestra.** East Sussex Music Service, Watergate Lane, Lewes BN7 1UQ *tel:* 01273 472336 *fax:* 01273 486396 *email:* music.service@eastsussexcc.gov.uk. Phillip Scott, dir; Colin Metters, cond; Colin Moore, co-ord.

* **Edinburgh Youth Orchestra.** 92 St Alban's Rd, Edinburgh EH9 2PG *tel:* 0131 667 4648 *fax:* 0131 662 9169 *email:* marjory@ednet.co.uk. Marjory Dougal, admin; En Shao, artistic dir.

Enfield Young Symphony Orchestra. Enfield Arts Support Service, Aylward School, Windmill Rd, Edmonton, London N18 1NB *tel:* 020 8807 8881 *fax:* 020 8807 8213 *email:* info@enfieldartssupportservice.org.uk. Kim Hember, orch mgr; Stephen Block, cond.

* **Fife Youth Orchestra.** Auchterderran Centre, Woodend Rd, Cardenden KY5 0NE *tel:* 01592 414659 *fax:* 01592 414641 *email:* graeme.wilson@fife.gov.uk. Graeme Wilson, mus services mgr, Education Service.

Folkestra North. Folkworks, The Sage Gateshead, PO Box 254, Gateshead NE8 2YR *tel:* 0191 443 4666 *fax:* 0191 443 4550 *email:* gillian.walsh@musicnorth.org. Gillian Walsh, youth ensembles co-ord, The Sage, Gateshead; Kathryn Tickell, artistic dir and main tutor.

Four Counties Youth Orchestra. c/o ESIS, G5, Treforest Industrial Estate, Pontypridd CF37 5YL *tel:* 01443 845402 *fax:* 01443 842639 *email:* esis@aol.com. Kevin Adams, mus adviser.

Gloucestershire Youth Jazz Orchestra. c/o Colwell Arts Centre, Derby Rd, Glos GL1 4AD *tel:* 01452 330300 *fax:* 01452 541303 *email:* gyjo1@aol.com. Tony Sheppard, mus dir, head of br tuition, Gloucestershire Music Service.

Goldsmiths' Youth Orchestra. PACE, Goldsmiths College, University of London, Lewisham Way, London SE14 6NW *tel:* 020 7919 7171 *fax:* 020 7919 7223. Elinor Corp, cond.

* **Grimsby, Cleethorpes and District Youth Orchestra.** 102 Woodhall Drive, Waltham, Grimsby DN37 0UT *tel:* 01472 827661 *email:* sue.parr@gcdyo.org.uk. Mrs S Parr, sec; Leo Solomon, chmn.

Hallé Youth Orchestra. Hallé Concerts Society, The Bridgewater Hall, Manchester M1 5HA *tel:* 0161 907 9031 *fax:* 0161 237 7028 *email:* hyo@halle.co.uk. Naomi Elliot-Newman, youth orch admin; Edward Gardner, cond.

* **Hampshire County Youth Orchestra.** Hampshire Music Centre, Bereweeke Rd, Winchester, Hants SO22 6AJ *tel:* 01962 861502 *fax:* 01962 863690 *email:* nicholas.wilks@hants.gov.uk. Nicholas Wilks, staff cond; Carl Clausen, asst cond; Shirley Taylor, snr mgr.

Jordan Junior Strings. 17 Meadow Cottages, Little Kingshill, Great Missenden, Bucks HP16 0DX *tel:* 01494 862861 *email:* bonnerfamily@jjstrings.fsnet.co.uk. Elaine Bonner, dir.

Mendip Music Centre. Bath and North East Somerset Music Service, PO Box 25, Riverside, Keynsham, Bristol BS31 1DN *tel:* 01225 395388. Andrew Foister, head of centre.

* **Midland Youth Orchestra.** Registered Office, 3 Armour Close, Burbage, Hinckley, Leics LE10 2QW *tel:* 01455 890528 *fax:* 01455 612288 (chmn) *email:* info@mlyo.org.uk. Stephen Williams, chmn; Anthony Bradbury, mus dir; Philip Garner, hon sec (tel: 01527 402090).

Milton Keynes Music Centre Symphony Orchestra. Milton Keynes Music Centre, Stantonbury Campus, Stantonbury, Milton Keynes MK14 6BN *tel:* 01908 324448 *fax:* 01908 224201 *email:* music@milton-keynes.gov.uk.

North Norfolk Youth Orchestra. 1 Oak Villas, East Ruston, Stalham, Norfolk NR12 9JG *tel:* 01692 650093 *email:* Barry.Bryant@btinternet.com. Barry Bryant, dir; Norman Moor, associate cond; Alan Morris, associate cond.

Northamptonshire County Youth Orchestra. Northamptonshire County Music and Performing Arts, 125-129 Kettering Rd, Northampton NN1 4AZ *tel:* 01604 637117 *fax:* 01604 603070 *email:* musicservice@northamptonshire.gov.uk. Peter Dunkley, cond, head of mus and performing arts service.

Nottingham Youth String Orchestra. 2 Trinity Cottages, Stapleford Woods, Lincs LN6 9LE *tel:* 01522 789245 *fax:* 01522 789245 *email:* admin@nctmusic.org. Paul Redfearn, cond; Angela Kay, cond.

* **Perth Youth Orchestra.** Byres Croft, Main Rd, Guildtown, Perth PH2 6BS *tel:* 01821 640431. Mrs D Lindsay, hon sec.

Ripon Youth String Ensemble. Ashley House, Ure Bank, Ripon, N Yorks HG4 1JG *tel:* 01765 602856 *email:* mail@vaco.net. Xenophon Kelsey, mus dir.

Solihull Youth Concert Orchestra. Lyndon Music Centre, Daylesford Rd, Solihull, W Midlands B92 8ES *tel:* 0121 743 2483 *fax:* 0121 743 5682. Joyce Rothschild, mus inspector; Tim Low, head of mus service; Richard Hart, asst head of service.

* **South East Surrey Area Youth Orchestra.** Surrey County Arts East, Longmead Adult Education Centre, Holland Close, Redhill, Surrey RH1 1HT *tel:* 01737 778890 *fax:* 01737 780380 *email:* musarts@sympa.org.uk. Michael Hensor, head of mus centre.

* **Southampton Youth Orchestra.** Southampton Music Service, 5th Floor Frobisher House, Nelson Gate, Southampton SO15 1BZ *tel:* 023 8083 3648 *fax:* 023 8083 3324 *email:* P.Litchfield@southampton.gov.uk.

* **Stoneleigh Youth Orchestra.** 52 Manor Rd, Teddington, Middx TW11 8AB *tel:* 020 8943 2661 *fax:* 020 8977 4653 *email:* christineblake@tinyworld.co.uk. Christine Blake, admin; Adrian Brown, mus dir.

* **Strathclyde Youth Jazz Orchestra.** Dept of Applied Arts, University of Strathclyde, Jordanhill Campus, 76 Southbrae Drive, Glasgow G13 1PP *tel:* 0141 950 3476 *fax:* 0141 950 3314 *email:* mark.sheridan@strath.ac.uk. Stewart Forbes, mus dir; Mark Sheridan, research, development.

String Quartets From Scratch, Birmingham. c/o 110 Willow Ave, Edgbaston, Birmingham B17 8HE *tel:* 0121 429 8894. Mary Cohen, creative dir/project leader.

* **Suffolk Youth Orchestra.** County Music Service, Northgate Arts Centre, Sidegate Lane West, Ipswich, Suffolk IP4 3DF *tel:* 01473 281866 *fax:* 01473 286068 *email:* count.musicservice@educ.suffolkcc.gov.uk. Philip Shaw, county adviser for mus, cond.

Thames Vale Youth Orchestra. 39 Leckford Rd, Oxford OX2 6HY *tel:* 01865 514855 *email:* info@tvyo.co.uk. Ian Wylie, chmn; Michael Stinton, dir of mus.

* **Ulster Youth Orchestra.** 109/113 Royal Ave, Belfast BT1 1FF *tel:* 028 9027 8287 *fax:* 028 9027 8297 *email:* uyo@nireland.com. Paula McHugh, gen mgr.

Wakefield Youth Symphony Orchestra. Manygates Music Centre, Manygates Lane, Wakefield *tel:* 01924 303306 *email:* vjennings@wakefield.gov.uk. V J Jennings, head of inst mus service.

Warrington and District Youth Orchestra. 266 Manchester Rd, Warrington WA1 3RB *tel:* 01925 490527. R Green, chmn.

* **Warwickshire County Youth Orchestra.** CMS, County Education Office, 22 Northgate St, Warwick CV34 4SP *tel:* 01926 412803 *fax:* 01926 412803 *email:* rayhutchinson@warwickshire.gov.uk. Ray Hutchinson, head of youth mus.

* **West of England Schools' Symphony Orchestra.** North Somerset Music Service, Station Rd, Congresbury BS49 5DX *tel:* 01934 832395 *fax:* 01934 877461 *email:* music-service@n-somerset.gov.uk. Emma Frost, co-ord of orchs.

West Norfolk Jubilee Youth Music Association. The Dairies, Stoney Rd, Roydon, King's Lynn, Norfolk *tel:* 01485 600792. S Corbett, sec; Jo Kemp, head of orch; Richard Hall, head of band.

* **West Wiltshire Youth Orchestra.** Wiltshire Music Centre, Ashley Rd, Bradford-on-Avon, Wilts BA15 1DZ *tel:* 01225 860116/0 *fax:* 01225 860117. James Monckton, mus dir.

Weston Youth Orchestra. 39 Stanhope Rd, Weston-Super-Mare BS23 4LR *tel:* 01934 412019 *fax:* 01934 641649 *email:* SFPHIL1605@aol.com. Dennis Cole, cond; Mrs S Philpott, admin.

* **Wirral Schools' Orchestras.** Education Centre, Acre Lane, Bromborough, Wirral CH62 7BZ *tel:* 0151 346 6507 *fax:* 0151 346 6657 *email:* philchapman@yahoo.com. Philip Chapman, dir, head of str teaching.

York Area Schools Symphony Orchestra. York Arts Service, Mill House, North St, York YO1 6JD *tel:* 01904 554660 *fax:* 01904 554661. Alison Goffin, head of mus; Gill Cooper, mgr of performing arts service; Sharon Hudson, head of centres.

* **Young Sinfonia.** The Sage Gateshead, PO Box 254, Gateshead NE8 2YR *tel:* 0191 443 4589 *fax:* 0191 443 4550 *email:* marion.wilson@musicnorth.org. Marion Wilson, admin.

Wind Bands

National

National Children's Wind Orchestra of Great Britain. Homecroft, Sun Lane, Harpenden, Herts AL5 2GJ *tel:* 01582 713333 *fax:* 01582 767343 *email:* info@musicale.co.uk. Gillian Johnston, mus dir; David Johnston, mus dir; Caroline Marriott, admin.

* **National Youth Wind Ensemble and Wind Band of Scotland.** Scottish Amateur Music Association, 18 Craigton Cres, Alva, Clackmannanshire FK12 5DS *tel:* 01259 760249 *email:* secretary@sama.org.uk. Margaret Simpson, hon sec; Charles Maynes, mus dir.

National Youth Wind Ensemble. Homecroft, Sun Lane, Harpenden, Herts AL5 4GJ *tel:* 01582 713333 *fax:* 01582 767343 *email:* info@musicale.co.uk. Gillian Johnston, dir; David Johnston, dir; Caroline Marriott, admin; Melanie Ragge, associate dir; Phillip Scott, cond.

Regional and Local

* **Barnet Schools' Wind Orchestra.** Music Office, Building 5, North London Business Park, Oakleigh Rd South, London N11 1NP *tel:* 020 8359 6310. James Williams MBE, mus dir, cond.

* **Bedfordshire County Bands.** Bedfordshire Music, Floor 6, County Hall, Cauldwell St, Bedford MK42 9AP *tel:* 01234 408177 *fax:* 01234 408182 *email:* mainarn@bedfordshire.gov.uk. Nigel Mainard, head of Bedfordshire Music.

Berkshire Youth Wind Orchestra. Berkshire Young Musicians Trust, Stoneham Court, 100 Cockney Hill, Reading RG30 4EZ *tel:* 0118 901 2354 *fax:* 0118 901 2351 *email:* charleshenwood@bymt.org.uk. Charles Henwood, cond.

* **Bromley Youth Concert Band.** Bromley Youth Music Centre, Southborough Lane, Bromley BR2 8AA *tel:* 020 8467 1566 *fax:* 020 8468 7595 *email:* mawson@bymt.co.uk. Peter Mawson, cond, principal Bromley Youth Music Trust.

* **Cardiff County and Vale of Glamorgan Youth Wind Band.** The Friary Centre, The Friary, Cardiff CF10 3FA *tel:* 029 2064 0950/1 *fax:* 029 2066 6593 *email:* music@ccvgmusicservice.com. Sean O'Neill, mus dir; Iau Provis, admin; Harry Fowler.

* **City of Hull Youth Symphonic Wind Band.** The Albemarle Music Centre, Ferensway, Hull HU2 8LZ *tel:* 01482 223941 *fax:* 01482 320565 *email:* chrismaynard@kuhmusicservice.karoo.co.uk. Chris Maynard, head of mus service; June Pitts, head of inst teaching; Niall McEwen, head of br and w/wind; Laurence Rugg, mus curriculum co-ord.

Derbyshire City & County Youth Wind Band. Advisory and Inspection Service, Dale Rd, Matlock DE4 3RD *tel:* 01629 580000 ext 2771 *fax:* 01629 585466 *email:* Philip.King@education.derbyshire.gov.uk. Philip King, adviser; Peter Lacey, cond; plus guest conductors.

Dorset Youth Wind Orchestra and Concert Band. Dorset Music Service, Unit 5, New Fields Business Park, Stinsford Rd, Poole, Dorset BH17 0NF *tel:* 01202 678233 *fax:* 01202 679381 *email:* dorsetmusicservice@dorsetcc.gov.uk. David Kenyon, head of service; Stephanie Sainsbury, office mgr.

East Bedfordshire Youth Concert Band. 7 The Hill, Blunham, Beds MK44 3NG *tel:* 01767 640707 *fax:* 01767 640707. Jim Hibbert.

East Sussex Wind Orchestra. East Sussex Music Service, Watergate Lane, Lewes BN7 1UQ *tel:* 01273 472336 *fax:* 01273 486396 *email:* music.service@eastsussexcc.gov.uk. Phillip Scott, dir; David Johnston, cond.

Enfield Youth Wind Band. Enfield Arts Support Service, Windmill Rd, Edmonton, London N18 1NB *tel:* 020 8807 8881 *fax:* 020 8807 8213 *email:* mea.jenkins@enfieldartssupportservice.org.uk. Mea Jenkins, activities co-ord.

* **Fife Youth Concert Band.** Auchterderran Centre, Woodend Rd, Cardenden KY5 0NE *tel:* 01592 414659 *fax:* 01592 414641 *email:* graeme.wilson@fife.gov.uk. Graeme Wilson, music services mgr, Education Service.

Four Counties Youth Wind Band. Education and Leisure Services, Sunnyside, Bridgend CF31 4AR *tel:* 01656 642658 *fax:* 01656 642646. David Hughes, cond.

* **Hampshire County Youth Wind Orchestra.** Hampshire Music Centre, Bereweeke Rd, Winchester SO22 6AJ *tel:* 01962 861502 *fax:* 01962 863690 *email:* nicholas.wilks@hants.gov.uk. Shirley Taylor, snr mgr; David Woodgates, cond; Carl Clausen, admin.

Harrogate and Skipton Area Schools' Concert Band. 3 Royd Place, Cononley, Keighley, W Yorks BD20 8JT *tel:* 01535 636823 *email:* bentierney@tiscali.co.uk. Bernard G Tierney, dir of mus.

High Wycombe Music Centre Concert Band. Millbrook School, Mill End Rd, High Wycombe, Bucks *tel:* 01494 445947 *fax:* 01494 442773 *email:* hwmusic@buckscc.gov.uk. Andy Rogers, cond.

Highbury Area Band. 30 Gains Rd, Southsea, Hants PO4 0PL *tel:* 023 9275 6912 *email:* Tim@tedwards98.freeserve.co.uk. T D Edwards, chmn; Mrs B Boyer, mgr; S Tanner, mus dir.

Highland Schools Wind Band. Music Dept, Culloden Academy, Keppoch Rd, Inverness IV2 7JZ *tel:* 01463 790851 *fax:* 01463 790061. Brian Mitchell.

Isle of Wight Youth Concert Band. 9 Elm Close, Ryde, Isle of Wight PO33 1ED *tel:* 01983 565675 *fax:* 01983 565675. Martyn Stroud, mus dir.

Kent Music School. Astley House, Hastings Rd, Maidstone, Kent ME15 7SG *tel:* 01622 358430 *email:* gstandley@kentmusicschool.org. Graham Standley, dir.

Mancunian Winds. Zion Arts Centre, Stretford Rd, Manchester M15 5ZA *tel:* 0161 226 4411/22 *fax:* 0161 226 1010 *email:* music-service@manchester.gov.uk. Allan Jones, head of mus service.

Milton Keynes Music Centre Wind Orchestra. Milton Keynes Music Service, Stantonbury Campus, Stantonbury, Milton Keynes MK14 6BN *tel:* 01908 324448 *fax:* 01908 225271 *email:* music@milton-keynes.gov.uk.

North Tyneside Concert Band. Harmonic Sounds, 9 Beverley Rd, Whitley Bay, N Tyneside NE25 8JH *tel:* 0191 251 8237 *email:* foymint@breathemail.net. R Harrison, cond.

Northamptonshire County Youth Concert Band. Northamptonshire County Music Service, 125-129 Kettering Rd, Northampton NN1 4AZ *tel:* 01604 637117 *fax:* 01604 603070 *email:* musicservice@northamptonshire.gov.uk. Peter Smalley, cond; Peter Dunkley, head of mus and performing arts service.

Shrewsbury Concert Band. 9 Greyfriars Rd, Longden Coleham, Shrewsbury SY3 7EN *tel:* 01743 367482 *fax:* 01743 340412 *email:* general@shrewsburyconcertband.co.uk. Ken Lumley, cond.

Solihull Youth Wind Ensemble. Lyndon Music Centre, Daylesford Rd, Solihull, W Midlands B92 8EJ *tel:* 0121 743 2483 *fax:* 0121 743 5682 *email:* messages@solmus.fsnet.co.uk. Tim Low, head of mus service; Richard Hart, asst head of service.

* **South East Surrey Area Wind Band.** Surrey County Arts East, Longmead Community Learning Centre, Holland Close, Redhill, Surrey RH1 1HT *tel:* 01737 778890 *fax:* 01737 780380 *email:* sca.east@surreycc.gov.uk. Michael Hensor, head of centre.

South Norfolk Youth Symphonic Band. 2 Warren Way, Tacolneston, Norwich NR16 1DH *tel:* 01953 788142 *fax:* 01953 788142 *email:* geraldaward@yahoo.co.uk. Gerald Ward, hon sec.

* **Suffolk Youth Wind Band.** County Music Service, Northgate Arts Centre, Sidegate Lane West, Ipswich, Suffolk IP4 3DF *tel:* 01473 281866 *fax:* 01473 286068 *email:* county.musicservice@educ.suffolkcc.gov.uk. Philip Shaw, county adviser for mus; Sue Taylor, cond.

* **Surrey County Youth Wind Orchestra.** Surrey County Arts North, The Oast House, 36 Kingston Rd, Staines TW18 4LN *tel:* 01932 794584 *fax:* 01932 794588 *email:* hugh.craig@surreycc.gov.uk. Hugh Craig, cond.

Trafford Youth Concert Band and Wind Band. 11 Drayton Grove, Timperley, Cheshire WA15 7PZ *tel:* 0161 904 0511 *email:* enquiry@tyo.org.uk. Anthony Houghton, cond.

* **Warwickshire County Youth Wind Band.** CMS, 22 Northgate St, Warwick CV34 4SP *tel:* 01926 412803 *fax:* 01926 412803 *email:* cms@warwickshire.gov.uk. Jim Norden, dir; Ray Hutchinson, head of youth mus.

* **West of England Schools' Symphonic Wind Band.** North Somerset Music Service, Station Rd, Congresbury BS49 5DX *tel:* 01934 832395 *fax:* 01934 877461 *email:* music.service@n-somerset.gov.uk. Emma Frost, co-ord of orchs.

* **West Kent Youth Wind Band.** Kent Music School, Astley House, Hastings Rd, Maidstone, Kent ME15 7SG *tel:* 01622 691212 *email:* admin@kentmusicschool.org. Ruth Summers, area mgr, Tonbridge.

* **Wirral Schools' Concert Band.** Wirral Education Centre, Acre Lane, Bromborough, Wirral CH62 7BZ *tel:* 0151 346 6507 *fax:* 0151 346 6657 *email:* wsms@wirral.gov.uk. Miss G Horne, Wirral Schools Music Service teacher.

York Area Schools' Senior Concert Band. City of York Council Arts Service, Mill House, North St, York YO1 6JD *tel:* 01904 554660 *fax:* 01904 554660. Alison Goffin, head of mus; Gill Cooper, head of arts; Sharon Hudson, head of centres.

Brass Bands

National

* **National Youth Brass Band of Great Britain.** 2 The Coppice, Impington, Cambridge CB4 9PP *tel:* 01223 234090; 07710 505689 *fax:* 01223 234090 *email:* nybbgb@bandstand.demon.co.uk. Philip Biggs, admin; Elgar Howarth, artistic dir.

* **National Youth Brass Band of Scotland.** Scottish Amateur Music Association, 18 Craigton Cres, Alva, Clackmannanshire FK12 5DS *tel:* 01259 760249 *email:* secretary@sama.org.uk. Margaret Simpson, hon sec; Neil Cross, mus dir.

National Youth Brass Band of Wales. c/o Welsh Amateur Music Federation, Ty Cerdd, 15 Mount Stuart Square, Cardiff CF10 5DP *tel:* 029 2046 5700 *fax:* 029 2046 2733 *email:* nybbw@tycerdd.org. Keith Griffin, dir; Edward Gregson, president; Robert Childs, mus adviser.

Regional and Local

Berkshire Youth Brass Band. Berkshire Young Musicians Trust, Stoneham Court, 100 Cockney Hill, Reading RG30 4EZ *tel:* 0118 901 2354 *fax:* 0118 901 2351 *email:* clarehawkins@bymt.org.uk. Paul Chappell, cond.

* **Cardiff County and Vale of Glamorgan Symphonic Brass.** The Friary Centre, The Friary, Cardiff CF10 3FA *tel:* 029 2064 0950/1 *fax:* 029 2066 6593 *email:* music@ccvgmusicservice.com. Matthew Thistlewood, mus dir.

* **Cardiff County and Vale of Glamorgan Youth Brass Band.** The Friary Centre, The Friary, Cardiff CF10 3FA *tel:* 029 2064 0950/1 *fax:* 029 2066 6593 *email:* music@ccvgmusicservice.com. Keith Griffin, mus dir; Adrian Dinsmore, asst dir.

* **Cheshire Youth Brass Band.** Music Team, Woodford Lodge Professional Centre, Woodford Lane West, Winsford, Cheshire CW7 4EH *tel:* 01606 814340 *fax:* 01606 814301 *email:* lancashired@cheshire.gov.uk. David Lancashire, mgr.

* **City of Hull Youth Brass Band.** The Albemarle Music Centre, Ferensway, Hull HU2 8LZ *tel:* 01482 223941 *fax:* 01482 320565 *email:* chrismaynard@kuhmusic.karoo.co.uk. Chris Maynard, head of mus service; June Pitts, head of inst teaching; Niall McEwen, head of br and w/wind.

Dobcross Youth Band. 42 Sandy Lane, Dobcross, Oldham, Lancs OL3 5AG *tel:* 01457 870895. Jenny Wood, sec.

East Riding Youth Brass Band. South Cattleholmes, Wansford, Driffield, E Riding of Yorks YO25 8NW *tel:* 01377 254293. Mrs M A Buckton, sec.

East Sussex Brass Band. East Sussex Music Service, Watergate Lane, Lewes BN7 1UQ *tel:* 01273 472336 *fax:* 01273 486396 *email:* music.service@eastsussexcc.gov.uk. Phillip Scott, co-ord.

Greater Gwent Youth Brass Band. Gwent Music Support Service, Melfort Rd, Newport, S Wales NP20 3FP *tel:* 01633 223196 *fax:* 01633 252051 *email:* gwent.music@newport.gov.uk. Contact: Alun F Williams.

Guildhall School of Music and Drama Junior Guildhall Brass Band. Junior School, Silk St, Barbican, London EC2Y 8DT *tel:* 020 7382 7160 *fax:* 020 7382 7212 *email:* junior@gsmd.ac.uk. Derek Rodgers, head; Spencer Down, cond.

Hathern Youth Band. 10 St Peters Ave, Hathern, Loughborough, Leics LE12 5JL *tel:* 01509 842813. Mrs M Spencer, sec.

Northamptonshire County Youth Brass Band. Northamptonshire County Music Service, 125-129 Kettering Rd, Northampton NN1 4AZ *tel:* 01604 637117 *fax:* 01604 603070 *email:* musicservice@northamptonshire.gov.uk. Adele Sellers-Peck, cond; Peter Dunkley, head of mus and performing arts service.

Poynton Youth Brass Band. 21 Hollymount Gardens, Offerton, Stockport, Cheshire SK2 7NE *tel:* 0161 487 1989 *fax:* 0161 487 1989 *email:* enquiries@poyntonyouthband.org.uk. F Cox, sec.

Ratby Co-operative Youth Band. 5 Nook Close, Ratby, nr Leicester LE6 0JW *tel:* 0116 238 6749 *email:* m.pounder@rdplus.net. M Pounder, sec.

Stantonbury Brass Band. Milton Keynes Music Service, Stantonbury Campus, Stantonbury, Milton Keynes MK14 6BN *tel:* 01908 324448 *fax:* 01908 225271 *email:* music@milton-keynes.gov.uk. Alan Jenkin, mus dir.

Stockport Schools' Senior, Intermediate and Junior Bands. 16 Palmerston Rd, Woodsmoor, Stockport SK2 7EA *tel:* 0161 456 4748 *email:* ssbb@ssbb.freeserve.co.uk. Jane Simpson, admin.

Wakefield Metropolitan Band. Band Room 1-2, Manygates Adult Education Centre, Manygates Lane, Wakefield WF2 7DK *tel:* 01924 253059 *fax:* 01924 240824 *email:* richard.stevens3@virgin.net. R A Stevens, sec.

* **Wirral Schools' Brass Band.** Professional Development Centre, Acre Lane, Bromborough, Wirral CH62 7BZ *tel:* 0151 346 6654 *fax:* 0151 346 6657 *email:* AMBrass1@aol.com. A Milnes, head of br teaching.

Youth Choirs

The Youth Choirs listed below are divided under national, regional and local headings, depending on the method and scope of the audition procedure and from where the majority of performers are drawn. A list of **Youth Opera and Music Theatre** companies appears at the end of the section.

National

British Methodist Youth Choir. 35 Westwood Rd, Sutton Coldfield, W Midlands B73 6UP *tel:* 0121 605 8766 *fax:* 0121 605 8766 *email:* gilbert.jones@blueyonder.co.uk. Gilbert Jones, admin; Ashley Thompson, cond.

National Children's Choir of Great Britain. PO Box 1628, Andover, Hants SP10 1NU *tel:* 01264 365966 *fax:* 01264 365966 *email:* cojack@theknappcottage.fsnet.co.uk. Lissa Gray, mus dir; Jacky Crowhurst, admin.

National Youth Choirs of Great Britain. PO Box 67, Holmfirth, Huddersfield, W Yorks HD9 3YT *tel:* 01484 687023 *fax:* 01484 687023 *email:* office@nycgb.net. Mark Anyan, gen admin; Carl Browning, gen sec; Mike Brewer OBE, mus dir; Deborah Catterall, mus dir, training and regional choirs.

National Youth Choir of Scotland. The Mitchell Library, 201 North St, Glasgow G3 7DN *tel:* 0141 287 2856 *fax:* 0141 287 2858 *email:* admin@nycos.co.uk. Ruth Townsend, admin; Christopher Bell, artistic dir, cond; Ian Mills, gen mgr.

National Youth Choir of Wales. Welsh Amateur Music Federation, Ty Cerdd, 15 Mount Stuart Square, Cardiff CF10 5DP *tel:* 029 2046 5700 *fax:* 029 2046 2733 *email:* nycw@tycerdd.org. Keith Griffin, dir; Bryn Terfel, president; David Rowland, cond.

The Rodolfus Choir. The Shepherd's Cottage, Great Shelford, Cambridge CB2 5JX *tel:* 01223 845685 *fax:* 01223 841980 *email:* r.allwood@etoncollege.org.uk. Ralph Allwood, cond; Lydia Smallwood, admin.

Vacation Chamber Choirs. Ashley House, Ure Bank, Ripon, N Yorks HG4 1JG *tel:* 01765 602856 *email:* mail@vaco.net. Xenophon Kelsey, mus dir; Jane Lomax, admin.

Regional and Local

Alicia Bardsley Singers. 22 Greek St, Stockport SK3 8AB *tel:* 0161 429 7413 *fax:* 0161 429 7413 *email:* ab22@supanet.com. V Gill, admin; Alicia Bardsley, cond.

Berkshire Boys' Choir. Berkshire Young Musicians Trust, Stoneham Court, 100 Cockney Hill, Reading, Berks RG30 4EZ *tel:* 0118 901 2364 (cond)/2354 (admin) *fax:* 0118 901 2351 *email:* gilliandibden@bymt.org.uk. Gillian Dibden, head of voice and choral mus.

Berkshire Girls' Choir. Berkshire Young Musicians Trust, Stoneham Court, 100 Cockney Hill, Reading, Berks RG30 4EZ *tel:* 0118 901 2364 (cond)/2354 (admin) *fax:* 0118 901 2351 *email:* gilliandibden@bymt.org.uk. Gillian Dibden, head of voice and choral mus.

Berkshire Youth Choir. Berkshire Young Musicians Trust, Stoneham Court, 100 Cockney Hill, Reading, Berks RG30 4EZ *tel:* 0118 901 2364 (cond)/2354 (admin) *fax:* 0118 901 2351 *email:* gilliandibden@bymt.org.uk. Gillian Dibden, head of voice and choral mus.

The Bradford Choristers. 8 Moorcroft, Eldwick, nr Bingley, Yorks BD16 3DR *tel:* 01274 774758 *email:* a.foster@btinternet.com. Ann Foster, sec; Richard Darke, mus dir.

The Bromley Boy Singers. 15 Goddington Lane, Orpington, Kent BR6 9DR *tel:* 01689 896971 *fax:* 01689 608123 *email:* richardapsley@lineone.net. Richard Apsley, dir; Colin Nash, chmn; Sue Smith, sec.

Bromley Youth Choir. Bromley Youth Music Trust, Bromley Youth Music Centre, Southborough Lane, Bromley, Kent BR2 8AA *tel:* 020 8467 1566 *fax:* 020 8468 7595 *email:* mawson@bymt.co.uk. Jane Werry, cond BYCC, BYSC; Lesley Cooper, cond BYJC, BYGC; Tom Scratchley, dir of choral studies.

Cantamus. c/o Camerata, 4 Margaret Rd, Birmingham B17 0EU *tel:* 0121 426 6208 *fax:* 0121 608 0676. Sheila Haslam, sec; Pamela Cook MBE, dir.

Cantate Youth Choir. The Latton Bush Centre, Southern Way, Harlow, Essex CM18 7BL *tel:* 01279 304746 *fax:* 01279 304746 *email:* info@cantateyouthchoir.org.uk. Michael Kibblewhite, mus dir; Dawn Helder, gen mgr.

Cantores Novae. 269 Dobcroft Rd, Sheffield S11 9LG *tel:* 0114 235 0993 *fax:* 0114 235 1883 *email:* vpvoices@btinternet.com. Vivien Pike, cond.

Capital Arts Boys' Treble Choir. 225 Shurland Ave, East Barnet, Herts EN4 8DG *tel:* 020 8449 2342 *fax:* 020 8449 2342 *email:* capitalartstheatre@o2.co.uk. Kathleen Shanks, mus dir.

Capital Arts Children's Choir. 225 Shurland Ave, E Barnet, Herts EN4 8DG *tel:* 020 8449 2342 *fax:* 020 8449 2342 *email:* capitalartstheatre@o2.co.uk. Kathleen Shanks, mus dir.

Cardiff County and Vale of Glamorgan Youth Choir. The Friary Centre, The Friary, Cardiff CF10 3FA *tel:* 029 2064 0950/1 *fax:* 029 2066 6593 *email:* music@ccvgmusicservice.com. Jan Richards, mus dir.

Chelmer Young Singers (7-11). 25 Burton Place, Chelmer Village, Chelmsford, Essex CM2 6TY *tel:* 01245 464762; 07719 420622 *email:* baritone@do-re-mi.co.uk. Owain Jones, cond.

Chelmer Youth Choir (12-20). 25 Burton Place, Chelmer Village, Chelmsford, Essex CM2 6TY *tel:* 01245 464762; 07719 420622 *email:* baritone@do-re-mi.co.uk. Owain Jones, cond.

Cheshire Youth Choir. The Professional Centre, Woodford Lane West, Winsford, Cheshire CW7 4EH *tel:* 01606 814339 *fax:* 01606 814301 *email:* cortena@cheshire.gov.uk. Shirley Court, dir; Alison Corten, mgr.

Chester Music Society Junior Choirs. c/o 5 Kennedy Close, Newton, Chester CH2 2PL *tel:* 01244 351003 *fax:* 01244 401902 *email:* chesterchoirs@hotmail.com. Pat Dayananda, admin.

Children's Voices of Enfield and Children's Younger Voices. 20 Brycedale Cres, Southgate, London N14 7EY *tel:* 020 8882 0630 *fax:* 020 8882 0630. June Keyte, cond.

City of Birmingham Symphony Youth Chorus. CBSO Centre, Berkley St, Birmingham B1 2LF *tel:* 0121 616 6500 *fax:* 0121 616 6518 *email:* bc@cbso.co.uk. Shirley Court, cond; Baz Chapman, chorus mgr; Simon Halsey, chorus dir.

City of Birmingham Young Voices. CBSO Centre, Berkley St, Birmingham B1 2LF *tel:* 0121 616 6500 *fax:* 0121 616 6518 *email:* bc@cbso.co.uk. David Lawrence, cond; Baz Chapman, chorus mgr; Simon Halsey, chorus dir.

Ealing Youth Choir. 12 Bennetts Ave, Greenford, Middx UB6 8AU *tel:* 020 8632 1854 *fax:* 020 8632 1854 *email:* paulayres@clara.net. John Compton, chmn; Paul Ayres, cond.

East Sussex Youth Choirs. East Sussex Music Service, Mountfield Rd, Lewes BN7 2XH *tel:* 01273 472336 *fax:* 01273 486396 *email:* music.service@eastsussexcc.gov.uk. Phillip Scott, dir.

Farnham Youth Choirs. 21 Firgrove Hill, Farnham, Surrey GU9 8LH *tel:* 01252 717173 *fax:* 01252 717173 *email:* fyc@which.net. David Victor-Smith MBE, dir; Catherine Watts, associate cond.

Fife Youth Choir (Sing, Sing, Sing). Auchterderran Centre, Woodend Rd, Cardenden KY5 0NE *tel:* 01592 414659 *fax:* 01592 414641 *email:* graeme.wilson@fife.gov.uk. Graeme Wilson, mus services mgr, educ service.

Finchley Children's Music Group. 76 St James's Lane, London N10 3DF *tel:* 020 8444 8418 *fax:* 020 8444 8418 *email:* info@fcmg.org.uk. Ruth Gates, admin; Grace Rossiter, mus dir.

Folkestra North. Folkworks, The Sage Gateshead, PO Box 254, Gateshead NE8 2YR *tel:* 0191 443 4666 *fax:* 0191 443 4550 *email:* gillian.walsh@musicnorth.org. Gillian Walsh, youth ens co-ord, The Sage, Gateshead.

Four Counties Youth Choir. c/o Caerphilly County Borough Council, Caerphilly Music and Arts Service, Coed Cae Ddu Rd, Pontllanfraith, Blackwood NP12 2DA *tel:* 01495 228948 *fax:* 01495 227058 *email:* ellerk@caerphilly.gov.uk. Keith Ellerington, cond.

Guildford Chorale. St Catherine's School, Bramley, Guildford, Surrey *tel:* 01483 899646 *fax:* 01483 899648 *email:* schooloffice@st-catherines.surrey.sch.uk. Kerry Beaumont, co-cond, admin.

Hallé Youth Choir. The Bridgewater Hall, Manchester M1 5HA *tel:* 0161 907 9031 *fax:* 0161 237 7028 *email:* hyc@halle.co.uk. Naomi Elliot-Newman, choral admin; James Burton, choral dir.

Hampshire County Children's Choir and Boys Choir. c/o Hampshire Music Service, Bereweeke Rd, Winchester, Hants SO22 6AJ *tel:* 01962 861502 *fax:* 01962 863690 *email:* kathy.moore@hants.gov.uk. Lissa Gray, mus dir.

Hampshire County Youth Choir. Hampshire Music Service, Bereweeke Rd, Winchester, Hants SO22 6AJ *tel:* 01962 861502 *fax:* 01962 863690 *email:* kathy.moore@hants.gov.uk. Keith Clark, mus dir, cond.

Hywel Girls' Choir and Hywel Boy Singers. 6 Harries Ave, Llanelli, Carmarthenshire SA15 3LF *tel:* 01554 772979 *fax:* 01554 772979 *email:* JeremyWilliamsUSA@PhotosoundUSA.com. John Hywel Williams MBE, mus dir; Lady Mary Mansel Lewis OBE, president; Stuart Burrows, vice-president.

Ipswich Girls' Choir. County Music Service, Northgate Arts Centre, Sidegate Lane West, Ipswich, Suffolk IP4 3DF *tel:* 01473 281866 *fax:* 01473 286068 *email:* Sue.Taylor@educ.suffolkcc.gov.uk. Sue Taylor, snr county mus tutor.

Jewish Youth Choir. PO Box 232, Harrow, Middx HA1 2NN *tel:* 020 8909 2445 *fax:* 020 8909 1030 *email:* jewishmusic@jmi.org.uk. Vivienne Bellos, mus dir.

Kent County Junior Choir. Kent Music School, Astley House, Hastings Rd, Maidstone ME15 7SG *tel:* 01622 358403 *fax:* 01622 358417 *email:* pevans@kentmusicschool.org. Andrew Larner, mus dir; Phil Evans, mgr.

Kent County Junior Singers. Kent Music School, Astley House, Hastings Rd, Maidstone ME15 7SG *tel:* 01622 358403 *fax:* 01622 358417 *email:* pevans@kentmusicschool.org. Andrew Larner, mus dir; Phil Evans, mgr.

Kent Youth Chamber Choir. Kent Music School, Astley House, Hastings Rd, Maidstone ME15 7SG *tel:* 01622 358403 *fax:* 01622 358417 *email:* pevans@kentmusicschool.org. Andrew Larner, mus dir; Phil Evans, mgr.

Kent Youth Choir. Kent Music School, Astley House, Hastings Rd, Maidstone ME15 7SG *tel:* 01622 358403 *fax:* 01622 358417 *email:* pevans@kentmusicschool.org. Andrew Larner, mus dir; Phil Evans, mgr.

Kent Youth Singers. Kent Music School, Astley House, Hastings Rd, Maidstone ME15 7SG *tel:* 01622 358403 *fax:* 01622 358417 *email:* admin@kentmusicschool.org. Andrew Larner, mus dir; Phil Evans, mgr.

Kingsway Music Centre. Kingsway, Bishop Auckland, Durham DL14 1JT *tel:* 01388 608421 *fax:* 01388 663250 *email:* jan.wilson@durham.gov.uk. Jan Wilson, acting head of service; Hilary Ions, cond.

The Manchester Boys' Choir. Zion Arts Centre, Stretford Rd, Manchester M15 5ZA *tel:* 0161 226 4411 *fax:* 0161 226 1010 *email:* music-service@manchester.gov.uk. Jeffrey Wynn Davies, dir; Fiona Clucas, admin.

Manchester Boys' Chorus. Zion Arts Centre, Stretford Rd, Manchester M15 5ZA *tel:* 0161 226 4411 *fax:* 0161 226 1010 *email:* music-service@manchester.gov.uk. Jeffrey Wynn Davies, dir; Fiona Clucas, admin.

Manchester Girls Choir. Manchester Music Service, Zion Arts Centre, Stretford Rd, Manchester M15 5ZA *tel:* 0161 226 4411/22. Delia Maunder, dir; Allan Jones, head of Manchester Music Service.

Manx Youth Choir. Music Centre, Lord St, Douglas, Isle of Man IM1 1LE *tel:* 01624 686555 *fax:* 01624 686557 *email:* musiccentre@doe.gov.im. Graham Kirkland, dir.

Maureen Hunter Singers. 14 Vine Close, Cottingham, E Yorks HU16 5RF *tel:* 01482 843344 *fax:* 01482 843344. J Graham Hunter, mgr.

Methodist Association Youth Club Orchestra and Singers. 25 Marylebone Rd, London NW1 5JR *tel:* 020 7467 5208 *fax:* 020 7467 5281 *email:* saundersr@methodistchurch.org.uk. Rachel Saunders, dir.

New London Children's Choir. 76 Brent St, London NW4 2ES *tel:* 020 8202 8123 *fax:* 020 8203 4134 *email:* reynaldo@angkor.demon.co.uk. Ronald Corp, cond.

Northants County Youth Choirs. c/o Music and Performing Arts Service, 125-129 Kettering Rd, Northampton NN1 4AZ *tel:* 01604 637117 *fax:* 01604 603070 *email:* musicservice@northamptonshire.gov.uk. Peter Dunkley, head of mus and performing arts service.

Nottingham Boys' Voices. 4a Claude St, Dunkirk NG7 2LB *tel:* 0115 9147633 *email:* admin@nctmusic.org. Robin Crawford, cond; Angela Kay, cond.

Nottingham Youth Chamber Choir. 2 Trinity Cottages, Stapleford Woods, Lincs LN6 9LE *tel:* 01522 789245 *fax:* 01522 789245 *email:* admin@nctmusic.org. Jane McDouall, cond; Angela Kay, cond.

Philharmonic Youth and Training Choirs. Royal Liverpool Philharmonic, Hope St, Liverpool L1 9BP *tel:* 0151 210 2895/1952 *fax:* 0151 210 2902 *email:* lynne.dawson@liverpoolphil.com. Lynne Dawson, admin; Simon Emery, mus dir.

Royal Scottish National Orchestra Junior Chorus. 73 Claremont St, Glasgow G3 7JB *tel:* 0141 225 3553 *fax:* 0141 221 4317 *email:* chorus@rsno.org.uk. Christopher Bell, chorus master; Jenny McKay, chorus mgr.

Southend Boys' Choir. PO Box 6, Civic Centre, Southend on Sea, Essex *tel:* 01702 215436 *fax:* 01702 215631 *email:* rogerhumphrey@southend.gov.uk. Roger Humphrey, cond.

Southend Girls' Choir. PO Box 6, Civic Centre, Southend on Sea, Essex *tel:* 01702 215436 *fax:* 01702 215631 *email:* Rosemarypennington@southend.gov.uk. Roger Humphrey, cond.

Stockport Youth Choirs and The Maia Singers. 23 Buttermere Rd, Gatley, Cheadle, Cheshire SK8 4RH *tel:* 0161 428 5456 *fax:* 0161 428 5456 *email:* john.pomphrey@ukgateway.net. John Pomphrey, dir; Lynda Whitney, admin.

Suffolk Jubilee Choir. County Music Service, Northgate Arts Centre, Sidegate Lane West, Ipswich, Suffolk IP4 3DF *tel:* 01473 281866 *fax:* 01473 286068 *email:* Philip.Shaw@educ.suffolkcc.gov.uk. Philip Shaw, county adviser for mus.

Vivace Girls' Choir. c/o 7 Park Lane, Charvil, Reading RG10 9TR *tel:* 0118 934 0589 *email:* suzannenewman@amserve.net. Miss S Newman, mus dir.

The Voice Squad. Fish and Bell Management, PO Box 175, Bury St Edmunds, Suffolk IP31 3TZ *tel:* 01359 271925 *fax:* 01359 271925 *email:* voice.squad@virgin.net. Birgitta Kenyon, dir.

Wenhaston Girls Choir. Brampton School, Southwold Rd, Brampton, Suffolk NR34 8DW *tel:* 01502 575287 *fax:* 01502 575287 *email:* wenhaston_girlschoir@yahoo.co.uk. Mrs Lloyd, sec.

Youth Opera and Music Theatre

British Youth Opera. c/o South Bank University, 103 Borough Rd, London SE1 0AA *tel:* 020 7815 6090 *fax:* 020 7815 6094 *email:* info@byo.org.uk. Timothy Dean, artistic dir; Judith Butler, gen mgr; Stuart Barker, artistic admin.

Music Box Children's Opera Group. 88 Belmont Rd, St Andrews, Bristol BS6 5AU *tel:* 0117 942 3775 *fax:* 0117 942 3526 *email:* markrlawrence@onetel.net.uk. Mark Lawrence, mus dir; Kate Hargreaves, sec (tel: 0117 924 5601).

Saturday Live! ENO Baylis, English National Opera, The ENO Works, 40 Pitfield St, London N1 6EU *tel:* 020 7935 9501 (direct line Saturday Live!); 020 7739 5808 (ENO Baylis) *fax:* 020 7729 8928 (ENO Baylis) *email:* baylis@eno.org. Kath Sparks, admin; Alix Griffiths, (temporary) projects offr.

Organisations for Young Performers

The organisations listed below exist to promote excellence in performance for school-age musicians and singers.

Allianz Cornhill Musical Insurance Youth Orchestra Awards. NAYO, Central Hall, West Tollcross, Edinburgh EH3 9BP *tel:* 0131 221 1927 *fax:* 0131 229 2921 *email:* admin@nayo.org.uk. Carol Main, dir. *5 awards of £500 each will be made to youth orchs within NAYO's membership towards a project to enhance the orchs' activities. Deadline for applications Apr. Previous winners may reapply after an interval of one year.*

Benslow Musical Instrument Loan Scheme. Little Benslow Hills, Benslow Lane, Hitchin, Herts SG4 9RB *tel:* 01462 420748 *fax:* 01462 440171 *email:* loanscheme@benslow.org. Liz Clark, mgr; Clare Talbot, development co-ord. *Applicants must be in f/t educ and a recommendation from inst teacher is required. Age range 5-25. Loans of insts only, not financial. No application fee, annual hire charge, some bursaries available. Application forms can be downloaded from website or sent on request.*

British Choral Institute. 1 Bazehill Rd, Rottingdean, Brighton BN2 7DB *tel:* 01273 300894 *fax:* 01273 308394 *email:* BritChorInst@fastnet.co.uk. Roy Wales, dir; Christine Wales, admin. *National organisation established as an advisory, promotional, educ and training body for choral singers, conds, choral administrators and organisers from all sectors of the choral community with a special emphasis on developing international choral projects.*

English Folk Dance and Song Society. Cecil Sharp House, 2 Regent's Park Rd, London NW1 7AY *tel:* 020 7485 2206 ext 17 *fax:* 020 7284 0534 *email:* info@efdss.org. *The society aims to promote and develop folk traditions. Written and recorded resources for sale plus INSET courses available for teachers. Free cat available.*

Essex Young Musicians' Trust. Loom House, Royal Square, Dedham, Essex CO7 6AA *tel:* 01206 322938 *fax:* 01206 322938. Judith A Fowle, founding trustee. *Aims to give young musicians in Essex access to mus educ and experience as a member of one of the county youth orchs. Full fee and tour bursaries plus occasional discretionary awards available.*

London String Quartet Foundation. 110 Gloucester Ave, London NW1 8HX *tel:* 020 7483 2681 *fax:* 020 7586 5343 *email:* info@playquartet.com. Sarah Gordon, admin. *Educ programme for young str quartets. Schools programme for underpriviledged children plus summer schools and short courses. (See also London String Quartet Week in Festivals section)*

Music for Youth. 102 Point Pleasant, London SW18 1PP *tel:* 020 8870 9624 *fax:* 020 8870 9935 *email:* mfy@mfy.org.uk. Larry Westland CBE, exec dir. *National charity dedicated to keeping youth mus alive through a series of festivals and concerts for young musicians.*

National Association of Choirs. Fig Tree House, 9 The Green, Glinton, Peterborough PE6 7JN *tel:* 01733 252464 *fax:* 01733 252464 *email:* petefig@aol.com. Peter Marshall, gen sec. *NAC caters exclusively for choirs, providing a wide range of services such as liaison with festivals, insurance, charitable status applications, mus discount, mus loan scheme. Choirs benefit from being placed in groups for local and combined choir activities.*

National Association of Youth Orchestras (NAYO). Central Hall, West Tollcross, Edinburgh EH3 9BP *tel:* 0131 221 1927 *fax:* 0131 229 2921 *email:* admin@nayo.org.uk. Carol Main, dir. *Has members from independent and LEA-run orchs and ens. Organises the Festival of British Youth Orchestras in Edinburgh and Glasgow, European Youth Music Week, Allianz Cornhill Musical Insurance Youth Orchestra Awards, Allianz Cornhill Musical Insurance Conducting Prize and Schott Musik International Youth Orchestra Award. Organises various Silver Baton award schemes in association with business sponsors. Publishes a newsletter 'Full Orchestra' three times pa. Also the Marion Semple Weir library of chmbr mus, free hire to members; the 'Directory of Youth and Student Orchestras'; Youth Orchestras Tour Guide; and the NAYO website which is updated monthly.*

The Princes Trust. 18 Park Square East, London NW1 4LH *tel:* 01746 787240 *email:* carolfra@princes-trust.org.uk. Susie O'Hagen, programme standards and development - Sound Live.

Sing for Pleasure. Unit 10a, Nortonthorpe Mills, Wakefield Rd, Scissett, Huddersfield HD8 9LA *tel:* 0800 018 4164 *fax:* 0800 018 4164 *email:* admin@singforpleasure.org.uk. Michelle Eastham, office mgr. *Singing and cond; day, w/end and summer schools for all ages. INSET singing days in schools. Graded choral cond training. Publications of adult and children's song books.*

youngchoirs.net (British Federation of Young Choirs). Devonshire House, Devonshire Square, Loughborough, Leics LE11 3DW *tel:* 01509 211664 *fax:* 01509 260630 *email:* admin@youngchoirs.net. Malcolm Goldring, chief exec; Eleri Bristow, admin. *Choral events for young people and training courses for teachers, conds and singers. 600 members (choirs, organisations and individuals). Choral animateurs all over UK.*

Youth Music. 1 America St, London SE1 0NE *tel:* 020 7902 1060 *fax:* 020 7902 1061 *email:* info@youthmusic.org.uk. *Funding programmes to reach young people, aged 18 and under, who have limited access to mus-making opportunities. Grants of up to £20,000 are available for not-for-profit organisations to support children and young people in mus-making of all styles and genres. See also Scholarships and Grants and Associations sections.*

Festivals for Young Performers

Aberdeen International Youth Festival. Linksfield Community Centre, 520 King St, Aberdeen AB24 5SS *tel:* 01224 494400 *fax:* 01224 494114 *email:* admin@aiyf.org. Stephen Stenning, chief exec; Jenny Phillips, admin. *Classical, symphony, chmbr, choir, jazz, mus theatre, dance and drama. International youth groups, mainly amateur, but some professional input.*

The Festival of British Youth Orchestras in Edinburgh and Glasgow. NAYO, Central Hall, West Tollcross, Edinburgh EH3 9BP *tel:* 0131 221 1927 *fax:* 0131 229 2921 *email:* admin@nayo.org.uk. Carol Main, dir. *14 Aug-5 Sep 2004. Celebrating its 25th anniversary in 2004, the festival involves 2500 young musicians in 60 concerts from a wide range of youth orchs and ens. RSAMD box office tel: 0141 332 5057.*

National Festival of Music for Youth. Music For Youth, 102 Point Pleasant, London SW18 1PP *tel:* 020 8870 9624 *fax:* 020 8870 9935 *email:* mfy@mfy.org.uk. Larry Westland CBE, exec dir; Samantha Weitzel, festival dir. *Festival involves 40,000 young musicians, including youth orchs, chmbr groups, br bands, choirs, jazz and swing bands, steel bands, rock and roll, electronic and folk mus. See Music for Youth Schools Prom.*

Music for Youth Schools Prom. Music for Youth, 102 Point Pleasant, London SW18 1PP *tel:* 020 8870 9624 *fax:* 020 8870 9935 *email:* mfy@mfy.org.uk. Larry Westland CBE, exec dir; Alexandra Williams, events dir. *Some of the UK's best youth mus groups perform at the Royal Albert Hall during 3 nights in Nov, following their participation in the National Festival of Music for Youth.*

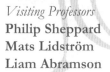

UK Summer Schools and Short Courses

Courses held in the holidays, at weekends and in the evenings are listed here with the address for applications and the venue (if different from the first address). The **Benslow Music Trust** (*see entry below*) maintains a permanent short-term residential centre and presents courses throughout the year for amateur musicians of all types and standards.

A detailed list of music courses held throughout the year can be found in the February issue of *Music Teacher* and in a supplement published in a January issue of *Classical Music*. Both magazines are available from Rhinegold Publishing Ltd. **City & Guilds** (1 Giltspur Street, London EC1A 9DD *tel:* 020 7294 2850 *email:* timetolearn@city-and-guilds.co.uk *website:* www.timetolearn.org.uk) produces a bi-annual directory '*Time to Learn*' detailing a wide range of residential courses, day schools and study tours abroad.

Aberdeen International Youth Festival. Linksfield Community Centre, 520 King St, Aberdeen AB24 5SS *tel:* 01224 494400 *fax:* 01224 494114 *email:* splore@btconnect.com. Jenny Phillips, admin; Dave Francis, course dir; Stephen Stenning, chief exec. *25 Jul-2 Aug 2004; closing date for applications 13 Jun. Open to those aged 16-25. Scottish traditional mus with a core focus on mus of N E Scotland - individual tuition, ens work, composition and arrangement, w/shops and m/classes, and work with musicians from other countries, part of the Aberdeen International Youth Festival. Fees: £200 full board; £100 non-residential. Bursaries available.*

Abingdon Summer School for Solo Singers. Pencots, Northmoor, Oxon OX29 5AX *tel:* 01865 300884 *fax:* 01865 300884 *email:* herfords@connectfree.co.uk. Henry Herford, dir; Lindsay John, admin; Robin Bowman, dir. *1-8 Aug 2004, apply by mid-May. Open to those aged 18+. Held at Abingdon School, Oxon. Course includes w/shops in the performance of opera, oratorio and song; classes in movement and Alexander Technique; evening concerts by participants and m/classes with distinguished visiting soloists.*

Alston Hall College. Alston Lane, Longridge, Preston, Lancs PR3 3BP *tel:* 01772 784661 *fax:* 01772 785835 *email:* alston.hall@ed.lancscc.gov.uk. Graham Wilkinson, principal. *Open to those aged 19+. Courses include mus appreciation, chmbr mus, choral singing, viol, sax and rcdr playing w/shops. Fees: w/ends from £103; day courses from £19.50.*

The Amadeus Chorus and Orchestra Summer School. 14 Yew Tree Ave, Northenden, Manchester M22 4GY *tel:* 07957 257716 *fax:* 0161 902 0224 *email:* macamadeus@ukonline.co.uk. Philip Mackenzie, dir; Odaline de la Martinez, president. *18-20 Jul 2004. For players aged 18-30, min gr 8 (higher for wind, br and perc). Also places for 4 conds (u/grads). Held in Somerset. Repertoire includes Berlioz 'Symphonic Fantastique' and Poulenc 'Organ Concerto'. Fees: £109 (half-price bursaries are available).*

Association of British Choral Directors (ABCD). 15 Granville Way, Sherborne, Dorset DT9 4AS *tel:* 01935 389482 *fax:* 0870 128 4085 *email:* rachel.greaves@abcd.org.uk. Rachel Greaves, gen sec. *27-29 Aug 2004. 19th Annual Convention at Exeter University. Wide range of w/shops and seminars for choral dirs and trainers of all levels. Non-members welcome. Also Pre-Convention Conducting Course 26-27 Aug; and Young Choral Conductors' Convention 27-29 Aug for those aged 17-22 who do not earn their living from choral conducting. Fees: on application.*

Bass-Fest. The British and International Bass Forum, PO Box 151, Aldershot, Hants GU12 6YQ *tel:* 01252 319610 *fax:* 01252 319610 *email:* doublebass@tiscali.co.uk. David Heyes, dir. *4-8 Apr 2004. Open to db players of all abilities aged 11+. A convention/course held at the Purcell School. Involves quartet coaching, individual lessons, bass orch, improvisation, m/class, orch technique, recitals, warm-ups, 'All Stars' concert, mus and CD shop, etc. Emphasis on enjoyment and informality. 4 tutors from 4 countries. Fees: from c £160 (non-residential); £225 (residential).*

Bath Spa University College Summer School Programme. Newton Park, Newton St Loe, Bath BA2 9BN *tel:* 01225 875522 *fax:* 01225 875495 *email:* e.ginn@bathspa.ac.uk. Emmanuelle Ginn, bookings admin. *Jul-Aug. Open to those aged 16+ of any standard. Creative mus tech summer schools including Digidesign ProTools, Emagic guide to Logic Audio, Korg Pro Workstation. Also gui summer schools including classical, contemporary, composition, rhythm, advanced fingerstyle, rock, jazz, blues and world mus and composing for TV. Fees: from £180 tuition for w/end courses.*

Beauchamp House Holiday Music and Drama Courses. Churcham, Gloucester GL2 8AA *tel:* 01452 312661 *fax:* 01452 312661 *email:* mouflon@breathemail.net. Anna McDade, course mgr; Caroline and Alan Lumsden, dirs. *Courses throughout school holidays. For beginners up to gr 8 and above, aged 7+. 3-day and 1-week w/shops for children, including orch courses (jnr, intermediate, snr str and advanced chmbr), jazz, international mus theatre week, jnr choir, gr 5 theory, jnr str, wind and br. Also early mus week, jazz and chmbr mus course for adults. Mostly residential. Fees: £70-335 p/week.*

Beechwood Easter Guitar Course. Elizabeth's Cottage, The Green, Leigh, Tonbridge, Kent TN11 8QW *tel:* 01732 832459 *email:* ray@lizcot.demon.co.uk. Raymond Love, course dir. *Apr, applications by Mar. Open to those aged 16+. 4-day residential course for classical gui; solo and ens playing. Emphasis on ens playing and concerts. Fees: £170-190.*

Bela Bartók Centre for Musicianship. 6 Frognal Court, 158 Finchley Rd, London NW3 5HL *tel:* 020 7435 3685 *email:* agnes.kory@kcl.ac.uk. Agnes Kory, dir. *Ages 2-adult. Professional, amateur and children's classes focus on comprehensive mus educ including the Kodály system, Sary system, history, analysis and performance skills. Regular classes and occasional intensive holiday courses. Summer course for chmbr mus, Jul, London. Fees: £180. Also running history of mus summer courses abroad (Budapest, Bayreuth, St Petersburg). Fees: various. See also entry in* **Specialist Courses**.

Benslow Music Trust. Little Benslow Hills, off Benslow Lane, Hitchin, Herts SG4 9RB *tel:* 01462 459446 *fax:* 01462 440171 *email:* info@benslow.org. Katarina Söderberg, mus admin; Julie Green, registrar; David Matthews, dir of mus. *Courses throughout yr including summer. Beginners-advanced, according to each course specification. Residential w/end, midweek and week-long courses for students, teachers and amateur musicians, aged 16+. Annual programme of over 100 different courses includes many for chmbr mus (str, wind, pno, mixed), orch, rcdr, choral, early mus, hp, big band, sax, etc. All directed and coached by leading professional musicians who, on selected courses, give public recitals in the Benslow Concerts Series. Limited number of bursaries available for those in financial need. Brochure with full details on request. Fees: from £100.*

Bingham String Quartet Chamber Music Weekends. 6 Munsons Lane, Feltwell, Norfolk IP26 4DE *tel:* 01842 828424 *fax:* 01842 828424 *email:* courses@binghamquartet.net. Brenda Stewart. *18-19, 25-26 Jul 2004. Open to all ages and abilities. Formed quartets preferred though not essential. 18-19 Jul at The Gateway Arts Centre, Shrewsbury; and 25-26 Jul at Edmund de Moundeford School, Feltwell, Norfolk. Non-residential, accommodation list available on request. Fees: £60 adults; £40 students.*

Birkbeck College Faculty of Continuing Education. 26 Russell Square, London WC1B 5DQ *tel:* 020 7631 6660 *fax:* 020 7631 6686 *email:* j.gough@bbk.ac.uk. Jane Gough, programme mgr. *Jan-Jul 2004. No formal entry requirements, but you should be able to read mus, and have knowledge of basic mus terms. Varied programme of mus courses, covering both the history of mus and various genres.*

Bochmann String Courses. BMCC, The Barns, Village Farm, Ford, Cheltenham, Glos GL54 5RU *tel:* 01386 584539 *fax:* 01386 584839 *email:* bochmann@ukonline.co.uk. Gina Bochmann, admin; Michael Bochmann, dir. *For students, p/grads and young professionals aged 18+. For str ens and solo vn with or without pno. Courses throughout the yr. Dates and duration arranged according to mutual convenience. Main tutor: Michael Bochmann, leader of Bochmann String Quartet, English String and Symphony Orchestras.*

Border Marches Early Music Forum. 13 Courtnay Rise, Hereford HR1 1BP *tel:* 01432 341154 *email:* hannah@thedavies.f9.co.uk. Hannah Davies, chair; Emma Wheelock, newsheet ed (tel: 01600 740412). *Feb, Apr, May, Jun, Sep, Oct. Medieval to baroque vocal and inst day w/shops held on Sat/Sun in Herts and surrounding Border Marches region. Fees: £10 (members); £12 (non-members).*

The Borenstein Music Festival. Flat 5, Welldon Court, 2a Welldon Cres, Harrow HA1 1QS *tel:* 020 8427 4568; 07956 852736 *fax:* 020 8427 4568 *email:* admin@borenstein.org.uk. Nimrod Borenstein, dir; Laura Borenstein, co-dir. *Summer 2004. Auditions Mar at Royal Academy of Music. Gr 7/8 standard or above. Central London summer festival including youth orch course with solo opportunities see also entry in* **UK Competitions**. *Fees: £20 admin with application, £180 course.*

Brass Band Summer School. 2 The Coppice, Impington, Cambridge CB4 9PP *tel:* 01223 234090; 07710 505689 *fax:* 01223 234090 *email:* philipbiggs@bandstand.demon.co.uk. Philip Biggs, admin. *Aug, applications by Mar. All ages and standards welcome. Held at Bromsgrove School, Worcs. Fees: from £280.*

The British Kodály Academy. c/o 13 Midmoor Rd, London SW19 4JD *tel:* 020 8971 2062 *fax:* 020 8946 6561 *email:* BKAhelp@aol.com. Celia Cviic, treasurer and courses sec; Mary Place, summer school sec. *Aug. Summer school at the University of Leicester studying the Kodály approach to musicianship, classroom techniques and choral conducting. Also adult diploma courses, certificates in Kodály mus educ certified by the University of Surrey, Roehampton, w/end courses, w/shops and INSET throughout the UK. Special courses for singers and choral conds. Tutors from Hungary and the UK. Musicianship courses, 4 levels, London, Manchester, Bedford and Winchester. Most courses accredited by TCL.*

British Suzuki Institute. 39 High St, Wheathampstead, Herts AL4 8BB *tel:* 01582 832424 *fax:* 01582 834488 *email:* bsi@suzukimusic.force9.co.uk. Landa Melrose, chief exec offr. *Week-long, w/end and day courses and w/shops throughout the summer for vn, va, fl, rcdr, and pno. All age groups. Residential and non-residential.*

British Youth Opera. c/o South Bank University, 103 Borough Rd, London SE1 0AA *tel:* 020 7815 6090 *fax:* 020 7815 6094 *email:* info@byo.org.uk. Timothy Dean, artistic dir; Judith Butler, gen mgr; Stuart Barker, artistic admin. *Summer season mid-Jul to mid-Sep, auditions from Nov. Open to singers and instrumentalists aged 18-30 who live or study in the UK. Summer season comprises two full scale opera productions, rehearsed over six weeks, and performed at the Queen Elizabeth Hall, London. Also yr round programme of w/shops and m/classes. Fees: no fees for successful candidates.*

Britten-Pears Young Artist Programme. Snape Maltings Concert Hall, Saxmundham, Suffolk IP17 1SP *tel:* 01728 688671 *fax:* 01728 688171 *email:* britten-pears@aldeburgh.co.uk. Andrew Comben, head of artist development; Caroline Newton, admin; Charlotte Penton-Smith, m/class co-ord; Polly Brown, school asst. *Apr-Nov. Open to advanced students and professional instrumentalists and singers; entry by audition (Nov-Feb). 10-day residential m/class courses for singers and instrumentalists, also opera course, Britten-Pears Orchestra and Britten-Pears Baroque Orchestra. Please contact for course details. Fees: vary.*

Bromley Arts Council. Ripley Arts Centre, 24 Sundridge Ave, Bromley, Kent BR1 2PX *tel:* 020 8464 5816 *fax:* 020 8464 5816 *email:* enquiries@bromleyarts.com. Thelma Richardson, admin. *Diverse range of practical and theoretical arts and educ courses.*

Bryanston International Summer School. London Suzuki Group, 96 Farm Lane, London SW6 1QH *tel:* 020 7386 8006 *fax:* 020 7386 8006 *email:* lsg@suzukimusic.net. Nicholas Pullinger, admin. *15-22 Aug 2004 tbc, closing date for applications 15 May. Open to those aged 5-17. Individual and group lessons for Suzuki vn, va, vc and pno students. Four levels of orch, chmbr mus, multi-keyboard, choirs, Dalcroze, Kodály and theory. Residential. BSI teacher training. Fees: £340-410; parents £375. Non-residential and observer rates available.*

Burton Manor. Burton, Neston, Cheshire CH64 5SJ *tel:* 0151 336 5172 *fax:* 0151 336 6586 *email:* enquiry@burtonmanor.com. Janet Hooper, course admin. *Residential courses: 23-25 Jan 2004, A Raven with Peacock's Feathers - the enigma of an unfinished work, tutor Julian Williamson. 21-22 Feb 2004, Rhapsody for the Jazz Age, tutor Chris Hoes. 2-4 Apr 2004, from Tallis to Tavener - celebrating 50 yrs of British mus, tutor John Hursey. 11-13 Jun 2004, Classical Guitar Workshop, entry requirements: gr 4 standard, tutors John and Cobie Mills. 10-12 Sep 2004, Singing for Pleasure, tutor Rona Campbell. Fees: on request.*

Cadenza International Music Summer School. 3 Park Terrace, Glasgow G3 6BY *tel:* 0141 333 0357 *email:* John.Thwaites@rsamd.ac.uk. John Thwaites, course dir. *One week in Jul, applications by Jun. Open to those aged 11+. Individual tuition, coaching in chmbr mus, str orch, str and pno, and performances. Staff mostly Menuhin/Purcell Schools, RCM, GSMD, RAM. Residential in London area, Dante Quartet in residence. Fees: £430.*

Cambridge Early Music Summer Schools. Trinity Hall, Cambridge CB2 1TJ *tel:* 01223 847330 *fax:* 01223 847330 *email:* info@cemss.org. Selene Mills, admin. *7-14 Aug, baroque mus with The Parley of Instruments. 14-21 Aug, vocal ens mus with Trio Mediaeval and John Potter. 21-28 Aug 2004, renaissance mus with Musica Antiqua of London. Applications by Jun; open to those aged 16+. Week-long courses in baroque, renaissance and medieval mus for professional and amateur players and singers. Tutors have also included Sirinu and The Hilliard Ensemble. Fees: £615 (residential); £575 (non-residential) tbc.*

Cambridge School of Music. Maple House, Westley Waterless, nr Newmarket, Suffolk CB8 0RQ *tel:* 01638 508577 *fax:* 01638 508578 *email:* info@cambridgemusic.press.co.uk. Mrs Barker, course dir. *9-15 Aug 2004. Residential orch course for gr 1-5 with chmbr mus and choir. Full programme including leisure activities. Fees: £325 wilth 10% discount for subsequent family members.*

Cambridge Violin Makers. 70a Hartington Grove, Cambridge CB1 7UB *tel:* 01223 411071 *fax:* 01223 561736 *email:* chris@makeviolins.com. Juliet Barker, organiser; Christopher Beament, organiser. *Weeks from 13 Jul-6 Sep. Entry requirements: patience and perseverance. Vn making for amateurs. 20 places on each course. Fees: £185 p/week (tuition only); materials from £75; accommodation from £80 p/week.*

Canford Summer School of Music. 5 Bushey Close, Old Barn Lane, Kenley, Surrey CR8 5AU *tel:* 020 8660 4766 *fax:* 020 8668 5273 *email:* canfordsummersch@aol.com. Malcolm Binney, mus dir. *26 Jul-16 Aug 2004, applications by early Jul. Open to those aged 16+. Orch, wind band and choral conducting, Sibelius software course, chmbr mus for w/wind and str, composition, jazz, m/class for pno, pno accompaniment and voice, wind orch, choirs, opera, orchs, str orch, perc. Fees: c £380 p/week.*

Centre For Young Musicians. Morley College, 61 Westminster Bridge Rd, London SE1 7HT *tel:* 020 7928 3844 *fax:* 020 7928 3454 *email:* info@cymlondon.demon.co.uk. Victoria Sweetman, admin. *Courses in school holidays. School age children of all standards. 4-5 day courses at venues around London. Courses include: London Youth Wind Band, beginners' strs, snr str ens, intermediate str ens, jnr w/wind, jnr strs, jnr rcdrs, jnr guis, jnr perc, jnr musicianship, jnr br. London Schools Concert Band. Fees: published in brochure.*

The Chalemie Summer School of Early Music, Dance and Commedia. 3 Thornhill Square, London N1 1BQ *tel:* 020 7700 4293 *fax:* 020 7700 5877 *email:* chalemie@thorn.demon.co.uk. Barbara Segal, summer school organiser. *25-30 Jul 2004. Open to all ages. Held at Headington School, Oxford. Mus, dance and commedia from 17th/18th C. Fees: £315.*

Chamber Music Holidays and Festivals. 57 Chatsworth Rd, Bournemouth, Dorset BH8 8SL *tel:* 01202 528328 *fax:* 01202 524081 *email:* info@cmhf.co.uk. Vivienne Pittendrigh. *Intermediate advanced. Bangkok and Chiang Mai, Thailand, 15-29 Feb; Prague Spring Festival, 14-22/26 May; Prague International String Quartet Festival, 29 Aug-9 Sep; Venice and Asolo, 11-18 Sep; Divertimenti in Corfu, 21 Sep-5 Oct 2004. Holidays for chmbr mus players and listeners. Scheduled playing with coaching, concerts, operas and various festival activities in historically and scenically interesting places. Fees: on application.*

Chamber Music International. 30 Knoll Court, Farquhar Rd, London SE19 1SP *tel:* 020 8766 0399; 07970 850057 *fax:* 020 8766 0399 *email:* charlotte@chambermusicintl.org. Charlotte Tomlinson, artistic dir. *Late Aug 2004, closing date 1 Apr. Week-long course for advanced instrumentalists and composers aged 16+. Pre-formed groups for pno/wind and pno/strs. Scholarships available.*

Chamber Music at Pocklington. 18 Latchingdon Court, 26 Forest Rd, London E17 6JT *tel:* 01582 834101 *fax:* 01582 834102 *email:* pocklingtonmusic@yahoo.co.uk; clairealtman@hotmail.com. James Chambers, admin (tel: 020 8521 3641, email: james.chambers@btinternet.com). *Early Jul 2004 tbc, applications by mid Jun. All ages, gr 7 and above, other by arrangement. Residential course for str, w/wind and pno. M/classes and intensive coaching for students of all ages (individuals and ens welcome). Teaching focuses on individual development together with exploring the 'how to' of chmbr mus. Special feature of course is the high proportion of or tuition, which is given by distinguished artists, accliamed as soloists in their own right. Informal and friendly atmosphere. Spacious accommodation, professional catering, indoor heated swimming pool plus other activities. Fees: residential and non-residential rates available.*

Charterhouse Summer School of Music. Music Office, Charterhouse, Godalming, Surrey GU7 2DX *tel:* 01483 291696. Robin Wells, dir of mus. *Jul, applications by 1 Apr. Open to those aged 18+. Symphony, str and chmbr orchs, chmbr mus, gui, accompaniment, solo and choral singing, org. Fees: on application.*

Chetham's International Summer School and Festival for Pianists. Chetham's School of Music, Long Millgate, Manchester M3 1SB *tel:* 0161 834 9644 *fax:* 0161 839 3609 *email:* murraymclachlan@chethams.com. Murray McLachlan, artistic dir. *26 Aug-2 Sep 2004. Open to all ages from gr 6 to concert standard. Residential course with 2 concerts every evening. Lectures, m/classes and one-to-one teaching*

from an outstanding team of performers and teachers. Over 100 state-of-the-art practice rooms available all day to participants. Performance opportunities. Limited number of scholarships available. Also jazz, composition and improvisation courses. Fees: £150-450; daily observer rate £20.

Choral Singing for Enjoyment. British Choral Institute, 1 Bazehill Rd, Rottingdean, Brighton BN2 7DB *tel:* 01273 300894 *fax:* 01273 308394 *email:* BritChorInst@fastnet.co.uk. Roy Wales, dir. *18-20 Jun 2004. Enthusiastic singers with some sight-reading ability. W/end course at West Dean College, Chichester, for choral singers. Fees: £187 (full board and tuition); £117 (non-residential).*

City College Manchester. City Campus, 34 Whitworth St, Manchester M1 3HB *tel:* 0161 957 1790 *fax:* 0161 945 3854 *email:* admissions@ccm.ac.uk. Martin Moscrop, team leader, mus. *Also at: Abraham Moss Centre, Crescent Rd, Crumpsall, Manchester M8 5FU. Introduction to MIDI sequencing; Introduction to Sound Recording; Introduction to DJ'ing; Get into Entertainment. All week-long courses.*

The City Lit. Music Dept, 16 Stukeley St, off Drury Lane, London WC2B 5LJ *tel:* 020 7430 0546 *fax:* 020 7405 3347 *email:* music@citylit.ac.uk. Janet Obi-Keller, head of mus. *Open to those aged 18+. Adult educ courses from beginner to advanced level in inst and vocal studies, opera, musicianship, various ens in both jazz and classical styles. Appreciation and mus tech. Students may join throughout academic yr subject to vacancies and appropriate level. Fees: average £3.25-4.50 per hour.*

The Clarinet Summer School. Liverpool Hope, Hope at Everton, The Cornerstone, Haigh St, Liverpool L3 8QB *tel:* 0151 291 3284/3457 *fax:* 0151 291 3170 *email:* walterd@hope.ac.uk. David Walters, learning and teaching fellow; Andrew Roberts, (Leblanc). *Jul, applications by Jun. Open to those of gr 6 standard and above; no age limit. M/classes and chmbr groups with UK's leading players.*

Clifford Benson International Summer School. 76 Quarry Hill Rd, Tonbridge, Kent TN9 2PE *tel:* 01732 364204 *fax:* 01732 364204 *email:* dilysbenson@tinyworld.co.uk; clifford@bensonmusic.free-online.co.uk. Dilys Benson, course admin; Clifford Benson, tutor. *Aug. Gr 8+ ABRSM (or equivalent). For solo pno and chmbr groups with pno. Held at Frensham Heights School, Farnham, Surrey. Fees: £295 performer, £195 auditor; £175 shared room, £195 single room.*

Coleg Harlech WEA. Harlech, Gwynedd LL46 2PU *tel:* 01766 781900 *fax:* 01766 780169 *email:* info@harlech.ac.uk. Debbie Gardner. *8-15 Aug 2004. For ages 16+. Orch mus summer school. Fees: £290; students £180.*

Colourstrings/Colourkeys Course for Teachers. The Szilvay Foundation, PO Box 764a, Surbiton, Surrey KT5 9XP *tel:* 020 8330 7500 *fax:* 020 8330 7500 *email:* colourstrings@compuserve.com. Pat Wislocki, dir; Deborah Harris, dir. *Aug (summer school). Annual residential/day courses including mus kindergarten and primary school mus (ages 4-7), pre-instrumental mus, vn, vc, fl, mini-bass, pno and gui teaching methods. Kodály-based, using relative sol-fa to train the inner ear prior to learning an inst and continuing this approach in inst tuition. Musicianship and Dalcroze Eurhythmics classes included.*

Conducting Course with the Amadeus Orchestra. 14 Yew Tree Ave, Manchester M22 4GX *tel:* 0161 902 0224. Odaline de la Martinez; Philip Mackenzie. *18-24 Jul 2004. Auditions in Apr. Held in Somerset. Lessons and m/classes with full symphony orch for u/grad and p/grad conds. Fees: £460.*

Conspiracy of Flutes No. 10. 41 Devon Ave, Twickenham TW2 6PN *tel:* 020 8241 7572 *fax:* 020 8241 7572 *email:* julie.flute@blueyonder.co.uk. Julie Wright. *Aug Bank holiday. Adults, any age. A booster course for adult flautists of all levels, directed by Julie Wright and Atarah Ben-Tovim MBE.*

Cosmic Hippo Jazz. The New House, Sandy Balls Estate, Godshill, Hants SP6 2LA *tel:* 01425 650770 *email:* hippotrain@btinternet.com. Derek and Alison Ayling. *25-27 Jun 2004. Good knowledge of own inst, chords and scales. Jazz w/shop, every midsummer Solistice w/end, for 2 days. Fees: £75 (including all meals and tuition - B&B not included).*

Dalcroze Society UK (Inc). 100 Elborough St, London SW18 5DL *tel:* 020 8870 1986 *fax:* 020 8870 1986 *email:* admin@dalcroze.org.uk. Jane Rivers, admin. *1-8 Aug 2004 tbc. Summer course of mus educ through movement for adults.*

Dartington International Summer School. The Barn, Dartington Hall, Totnes, Devon TQ9 6DE *tel:* 01803 847077/80 *fax:* 01803 847087 *email:* info@dartingtonsummerschool.co.uk. Gavin Henderson, artistic dir; Lisa Warren Clark, mgr; Sam McCaffrey, registrar; Sophie Bradford, admin. *Jul-Aug 2004. All ages and standards. Summer course with opportunity for advanced tuition and m/classes, informal*

mus-making, plus concerts, talks, etc. Composer in residence; mus theatre, masque and opera. Fees: £225-800 p/week.

Dillington House. Ilminster, Somerset TA19 9DT *tel:* 01460 52427 *fax:* 01460 52433 *email:* dillington@somerset.gov.uk. Geoff Hewitt, programme mgr; Wayne Bennett, gen mgr. *Open to adults of all ages. W/end residential courses throughout the yr: gui summer school, str quartet and rcdr w/ends, mus appreciation. Free brochure available.*

Dolmetsch Summer School. Heartsease, Grayswood Rd, Haslemere, Surrey GU27 2BS *tel:* 01428 643235/651473 *fax:* 0870 056 0190 *email:* brian@dolmetsch.com. Dr Blood, course sec. *19-25 Jul 2004. For any age group. Held at Fresham Heights, Rowledge, Farnham, Surrey. Rcdr; also optional classes for viols, chmbr orch, classroom techniques, choir and rcdr orch. Fees: £590/510 (residential); £285 (non-residential).*

Double Bass Summer School. 7 St Clair Drive, Worcester Park, Surrey KT4 8UG *tel:* 020 8330 3188 *fax:* 020 8330 3188 *email:* emerypc@dialstart.net. P W Emery, hon sec. *Aug, applications by 1 Aug. Separate courses for beginners, intermediate and advanced db players aged 8-25. Ens playing, m/classes, technique classes and chmbr mus. Fees: £250.*

ESO Children's and Intermediate Orchestras. English Symphony Orchestra, The Old Hop Store, Three Counties Showground, Welland, Malvern, Worcester WR13 6SP *tel:* 01684 560696 *fax:* 01684 560656 *email:* info@eso.co.uk. Kate Hodson, admin. *Children's: 13-16 Mar, 10-11 Jul; Intermediate: 21-22 Feb, 8-9 May 2004. Children's: ages 7-11, gr 1-3, open entry. Intermediate: ages 10-16, gr 4-6, open entry. 3 w/end courses pa per orch held in Malvern, Worcs. Fees: £56 per w/end, £10 new membership fee; 20% discount for 2 or more in family.*

ESO Youth Orchestra Course. English Symphony Orchestra, The Old Hop Store, Three Counties Showground, Welland, Malvern, Worcester WR13 6SP *tel:* 01684 560696 *fax:* 01684 560656 *email:* info@eso.co.uk. Kate Hodson, admin. *Oct 2004. Entry by audition. Open to those of gr 8 and above standard. 'Side-by-side' project, Malvern, Worcs. All inclusive 4-day residential course. Student sits next to professional for rehearsals and concert.*

The Earnley Concourse. Earnley, Chichester, W Sussex PO20 7JL *tel:* 01243 670392 *fax:* 01243 670832 *email:* info@earnley.co.uk. Contact: booking sec. *For ages 16+. W/end and week-long study courses featuring mus history, chmbr and singers' w/shops. Fees: c £175 (w/end); c £475 (week) inclusive of accommodation, meals and tuition.*

East Anglia Summer Music School. c/o Opera da Camera, 7 Meadow Rd, New Costessey, Norwich NR5 0NF *tel:* 01603 744584 *email:* c.l.thornton@virgin.net; davies.jw@ukf.net. Jeffrey Davies, organiser and dir. *Aug, applications by 1 Jul. For ages 17+, intermediate to advanced. Residential and w/end classes at the University of East Anglia, covering concert repertoire, opera and technique. M/classes, opera w/shops and w/shops for singers and accompanists. Fees: £155 (residential); £90 (non-residential) per w/end.*

Eastbourne Singing Weekends. Pelham Cottage, 120 Wish Hill, Willingdon, E Sussex BN20 9HL *tel:* 01323 509035 *fax:* 01323 509035 *email:* sarabande@btclick.com. Liza Hobbs, tutor; Soo-Bee Lee, tutor; Su Shanson, admin. *8-10 Aug 2004. Open to those aged 17+. Intensive w/end for a small number of solo singers (professional and amateur) covering all aspects of performing opera, oratorio, song and mus theatre. B&B by arrangement. Fees: £125.*

Edrom Chamber Music Course (Strings and Piano). 20 Hillway, London N6 6QA *tel:* 020 8340 0897 *fax:* 020 8341 5292 *email:* info@p-lynex.co.uk. Penelope Lynex, dir. *24-31 Jul 2004. Closing date 27 May. For professional and amateur adults and young people, intermediate and advanced. Held at Winton House, East Lothian. Fees: £395 (residential), £210 (non-residential).*

Elizabeth College (Guernsey) Summer Orchestral Course. Champs Verts, Le Mauxmarquis, St Andrews, Guernsey *tel:* 01481 238346 *fax:* 01481 233085 *email:* ccottam@champsverts.demon.co.uk. Charles Cottam, admin. *Aug, applications by 1 Jul. Open to those aged 9-19 of gr 5 and above standard. All orch and wind insts; 3 orchs, 3 bands. Fees: £150 including accommodation.*

English Folk Dance and Song Society. Cecil Sharp House, 2 Regent's Park Rd, London NW1 7AY *tel:* 020 7485 2206 ext 17 *email:* diana@efdss.org. Contact: national educ mgr. *INSET courses available for teachers. Educ publications for folk dance traditions of England, books, CDs, tapes, videos. Cat available by post or online.*

English Song Weekend. Musicair Ltd, 88 Albany Rd, Hersham, Surrey KT12 5QQ *tel:* 01932 244038 *fax:* 01932 889186 *email:* georgina@musicair.demon.co.uk. Georgina Colwell, tutor. *4-6 Jun 2004. Open to all standards. A feast of English song. Solo singing in m/classes; an in-depth look at particular composers by visiting experts; duets, madrigals. Takes place at Halsway Manor, Somerset. Theme:*

1934, a year to remember; the deaths of Delius, Elgar and Holst, a chance to look afresh at these composers. Fees: £199 including tuition and accommodation.

Eton Choral Courses. Eton College, Windsor, Berks SL4 6DW *tel:* 01753 671124 *fax:* 01753 671265 *email:* ceri.davies@etoncollege.org.uk. Ralph Allwood, dir; Ceri Davies, admin. *Jul-Aug, applications by Apr. Open to those aged 16-20. 5 courses held at Eton College and other venues. Fees: tbc.*

European Piano Teachers' Association UK (EPTA UK) Ltd. Archpool House, High St, Handcross, W Sussex RH17 6BJ *tel:* 01444 400852 *fax:* 01444 401443 *email:* eptauk@hotmail.com. Sally Course, admin; Frank Martin, chmn; Heli Ignatius-Fleet, course dir. *Jan-Jun 2004, 12 Sun, apply by previous Nov. Piano Pedagogy Course, alternate Suns, at London College of Music and Media. All aspects of pno teaching covered. For practising pno teachers, those about to start teaching and students preparing for pno diplomas. Fees: £510, £420 members. Open to those aged 18+. Also annual residential conference, Bath Spa University, 9-11 Jul 2004. Short course in collaboration with the Benslow Trust: Pianism for Teaching Pianist, 16-18 Jan 2004.*

European String Teachers' Association (ESTA). 105 Perryfield Way, Richmond, Surrey TW10 7SN *tel:* 020 8940 4640 *fax:* 020 8940 4300 *email:* marionseymour@compuserve.com. Marion Seymour, admin. *22-27 Aug 2004, closing date 30 Jun. Open to teachers, players and students aged 18+ of bowed str insts interested in honing their playing and teaching skills. Fees: available on request. Bursaries available for members.*

European Vacation Chamber Orchestras. Ashley House, Ripon, N Yorks HG4 1JG *tel:* 01765 602856 *email:* mail@vaco.net. Xenophon Kelsey, mus dir; Jane Lomax, admin. *Open to students aged 16-24 with gr 8+. Residential course every summer for advanced players from Europe, involving 3 days rehearsals and 4 public concerts. Expert professional coaching. Fees: £125/200 euros.*

European Youth Summer Music. Festivals House, 198 Park Lane, Macclesfield, Cheshire SK11 6UD *tel:* 01625 428297 *fax:* 01625 503229 *email:* jacqui@festivals.demon.co.uk. Liz Whitehead, course organiser. *24-31 Jul 2004. Age 11-21, gr 4+ standard. Summer orch course for young musicians. Also opportunities for jazz, big band, mus theatre and chmbr mus.*

Fantasia Music School. 5 Aspen Way, Middleton on Sea, W Sussex PO22 6PW *tel:* 01243 586068. Mrs M Sutton, admin. *Aug 2004. Open to those aged 6-18. 4 summer courses held at Dorset House School, nr Arundel for young musicians. Residential and day.*

Fife Summer Jazz Course. Arts Development, The Tower Block, Auchterderran Centre, Woodend Rd, Cardenden KY5 0NE *tel:* 01592 414714 *fax:* 01592 414727 *email:* arts.development@fife.gov.uk. Anne Chalk, support services offr. *Jul, applications by Jun. For all ages. Jazz Course directed by Richard Michael. Aims to improve and develop standards of playing, public performance and improvisation. Fees: £40-240.*

Flutewise Residential Courses. 9 Beaconsfield Rd, Portslade, E Sussex BN41 1XA *tel:* 01273 702367 *fax:* 01273 888864 *email:* mail@flutewise.com. Liz Goodwin, admin; Christine Mead, admin. *Easter and Oct half term. For fl players aged 7-adult. Adult only and teacher course before Easter. Fees: from £150 (members); £200 (non-members).*

Folkworks Adult Summer School. The Sage Gateshead, PO Box 254, Gateshead NE8 2YR *tel:* 0191 443 4666 *fax:* 0191 443 4550/1 *email:* folkworks@musicnorth.org. David Oliver, head of folk participation programmes. *26-31 Jul 2004. Open to those aged 20+. Annual summer school in traditional mus, song and dance in Durham. W/shops for a range of individual insts as well as mixed ens. Performance opportunities at the Durham Gathering Festival. Course fee covers tuition only; camping and B&B available locally. Fees: 2003: £135.*

Folkworks Youth Summer School. The Sage Gateshead, PO Box 254, Gateshead NE8 2YR *tel:* 0191 443 4666 *fax:* 0191 443 4550/1 *email:* folkworks@musicnorth.org. David Oliver, head of folk participation programmes. *26-31 Jul 2004. Open to those aged 12-25. Annual summer school in traditional mus, song and dance in Durham. W/shops for a range of individual insts as well as mixed ens. Performance opportunities at Durham Gathering Festival. Residential and non-residential places available. Fees: 2003: £220 (residential), £160 (non-residential with meals).*

Glamorgan Summer School. The Summer School Office, University of Glamorgan, Pontypridd, S Wales CF37 1DL *tel:* 01443 482828 *fax:* 01443 483393 *email:* summerschool@glam.ac.uk. Gill Giles, events mgr. *26 Jul-6 Aug 2004. Open to those aged 18+. Jazz and electronic mus summer schools, including Music Producers m/classes,*

held at University of Glamorgan, Treforest, Pontypridd. Fees: please contact for further information.

Glasgow University. Dept of Adult and Continuing Education, St Andrew's Building, Eldon St, Glasgow G3 6LP *tel:* 0141 330 1842 *fax:* 0141 330 3525 *email:* enquiry@educ.gla.ac.uk. R Hamilton, co-ord, continuing educ programme. *For those aged 18+. Joint study days with Scottish Opera. Also mus appreciation and theory, popular mus culture, 8, 10 and 20-week courses from Oct. Fees: from £57 (subject to revision) for 10-week courses.*

Gloucestershire Choral Weekend. Cotswold House, Naunton, Cheltenham, Glos GL54 3AA *tel:* 01451 850796. Cedric Virgin, organiser; Gregory Rose, mus dir. *16-18 Apr 2004. No age limit. Study of 8 choral works for mixed voices; held at the Royal Agricultural College, Cirencester, Glos. 81 singers attended in 2003. Fees: £115.75 (residential); £73.75 (non-residential), prices include meals, hire of mus and tuition.*

Gloucestershire Summer Orchestral Course. Colwell Centre for Arts in Education, Derby Rd, Gloucester GL1 4AD *tel:* 01452 330300 *fax:* 01452 541303 *email:* admin@colwellarts.co.uk. Brenda Whitwell, office mgr. *26 Jul-1 Aug 2004. Min age 8, min gr 1 (jnr course) and gr 5 and above (snr course). Residential orch summer course held in Cheltenham.*

Goldsmiths College. Professional and Community Education, University of London, New Cross, London SE14 6NW *tel:* 020 7919 7200/7229 *fax:* 020 7919 7223 *email:* pace@gold.ac.uk. Jeremy Peyton Jones, mus programme co-ord. *P/t and w/end courses throughout the yr in a wide variety of styles and at a range of levels from beginners to advanced standard. Open to those aged 18+. Certificate courses giving access to HE. Professional development courses for musicians and mus teachers. Courses include mus theory, mus history and analysis, composition and arranging, jazz and pop, gospel singing, mus tech, mus therapy, world mus, inst and vocal classes, jazz and classical ens. Certificate courses in Music Workshop Skills, Music Teaching to Adults, Music Studies, Jazz and Popular Music.*

The Great Grimsby Weekend Masterclass for Solo Singers. 71 Lansdowne Ave, Grimsby DN32 0BX *tel:* 01472 310818. Adele Dixon. *6-8 Feb 2004. Lead by soprano Alison Pearce and pianist David Murray.*

Guildhall Summer School. Guildhall School of Music and Drama, Barbican, Silk St, London EC2Y 8DT *tel:* 01702 714733 (answerphone) *email:* hswain@gsmd.ac.uk. Heather Swain, mgr. *Mid-Jul 2004. Open to those aged 10-70. Jazz, rock, studio mus summer school. Fees: £80 (intro to jazz w/end); £280 (jazz, rock and studio 1 week); £280 (recording engineering course); £100 (advanced jazz w/end); £75 (singers w/end course). Small rise in fees possible 2004.*

H F Holidays Ltd. Imperial House, Edgware Rd, London NW9 5AL *tel:* 020 8905 9558/9388 (24-hr brochure line) *fax:* 020 8205 0506 *email:* info@hfholidays.co.uk. Christine Helps, PR mgr; Sam McGeary, sales and mkt exec. *Various dates. Wide variety of mus-making and appreciation holidays with expert tuition throughout the yr. Open to all standards from beginners to the more experienced. Courses include The Building Blocks of Music, Composers of Gloucestershire, Choral Singing, Gilbert and Sullivan, Singing for Pleasure.*

Hawkwood Short Courses. Hawkwood Residential College, Painswick Old Rd, Stroud, Glos GL6 7QW *tel:* 01453 759034 *fax:* 01453 764607 *email:* info@hawkwoodcollege.co.uk. *Skill level can be discussed with organisers. W/end courses for str, fl, chmbr mus, mus appreciation. Summer orch week (wind and str). Various w/end and mid-week courses throughout yr. Hawkwood chmbr orch for str, w/wind and br players of moderate ability. Baroque chmbr mus w/end, open to all str, keyboard and w/wind players and singers.*

Hereford International Summer School. 27 Avondale, Newport, Shropshire TF10 7LS *tel:* 01952 812284 *fax:* 01952 812284 *email:* hiss@blueyonder.co.uk. Biff Patterson, admin. *14-21 Aug 2004, closing date 31 Jul. For ages 12+. Courses for choral singers, choral conducting, solo singers, pno performance, young pianists, adult pianists, pno accompaniment and composition. Fees: £300-500 (depending on accommodation).*

Higham Hall College. Bassenthwaite Lake, Cockermouth, Cumbria CA13 9SH *tel:* 017687 76276 *fax:* 017687 76013 *email:* admin@highamhall.com. Alex Alexandre, principal. *For ages 18+. Various courses throughout the yr: jazz w/shop; chmbr mus for str quartets; mus appreciation; rcdr ens; wind quartet/quintet w/end; pno playing m/classes. Fees: from £130.*

Holiday Music. 34 Stanton Rd, London SW20 8RJ *tel:* 020 8947 5538 *fax:* 020 8947 5538. Muriel Levin, dir. *Courses in Apr and Aug. 'Piano Plus' day and residential courses for pianists and others (str, w/wind, vocal) aged 15+. Recitals, w/shops. Apr 2004: 'Holiday Music in*

Sussex'. Aug 2004: 'Summer Music at Wells', for pno, strs, w/wind and includes creative improvisation and dance sessions.

Hylands House Opera Summer School. Hylands Park, London Rd, Widford, Chelmsford, Essex CM2 8WQ *tel:* 01245 496800 *fax:* 01245 496804 *email:* linda.palmer@chelmsfordbc.gov.uk; alison.day@chelmsfordbc.gov.uk. Linda Palmer, Hylands House mgr; Alison Day, support offr. *Jul. For those between amateur and professional, all ages. Audition tape required. W/shops and m/classes including auditioned m/class. Fees: tbc.*

Incorporated Association of Organists Festival and Summer Congress. 17 Woodland Rd, Northfield, Birmingham B31 2HU *tel:* 0121 475 4408 *fax:* 0121 475 4408 *email:* w.j.stormont@btinternet.com. John Stormont, hon gen sec; Simon Lindley, president. *23-27 Jul 2004, applications by May. Open to all who study or enjoy org mus. Annual summer congress held in Hampshire/south coast for 2004, over a long w/end. Includes recitals, lectures and m/classes. Fees: bursaries available for f/t students.*

Incorporated Society of Musicians (ISM). 10 Stratford Place, London W1C 1AA *tel:* 020 7629 4413 *fax:* 020 7408 1538 *email:* membership@ism.org. Neil Hoyle, chief exec. *Conferences of special interest to school and private teachers, performers and composers. Also w/shops, seminars, lecture recitals at various regional centres. Open to non-members.*

The Inner Voice. The White House, Aston Hill, Aston Rowant, Watlington, Oxon OX49 5SG *tel:* 01844 351561 *fax:* 01844 354891 *email:* elisabeth@innervoice.demon.co.uk. Elisabeth Wingfield; Ali Gordon-Creed. *Courses designed to help performers free themselves of problems associated with nerves, lack of self-confidence and the inner critic. Training enables performers to use their potential more effectively and reduce the negative effects of stress. Also, psychology for musical performance courses in England and Italy for teachers, students, professional singers and musicians.*

International Guitar Festival. at Bath Spa University College, Newton Park, Newton St Loe, Bath BA2 9BN *tel:* 01225 875522 *fax:* 01225 875495 *email:* e.ginn@bathspa.ac.uk. Emmanuelle Ginn, bookings admin. *Jul-Aug. Annual 3-week festival with international concert programme and week-long summer schools. Top performers and teachers in all styles of gui: classical, rock, jazz and blues. Also drum school and creative mus tech courses for Korg workstation, Digidesign ProTools and Emagic guide to Logic Audio, composing for computer games. All levels welcome from age 16. Fees: from £180 per w/end (tuition fees only).*

International Musicians Seminar. IMS, Prussia Cove, 32 Grafton Square, London SW4 0DB *tel:* 020 7720 9020 *fax:* 020 7720 9033 *email:* rosie@i-m-s.org.uk. Rosanna Yeatman, admin. *Mar-Apr, applications by Dec. For advanced str players, pianists and chmbr ens aged 16-30. M/classes in Cornwall given by eminent musicians (Steven Isserlis, Ralph Kirshbaum, Andras Schiff). Fees: £650 per 10-day course.*

International Saxophone Summer School. Jonathan Myall Music, 46 South End, Croydon CR0 1DP *tel:* 020 8662 8400 *fax:* 020 8662 8409 *email:* admin@summermusic.org.uk. Contact: course admin. *24-30 Jul 2004. Open to all ages and abilities. Participants explore the potential of the sax in a wide range of mus settings, from classical solo performance to jazz and improvised mus. W/shops, m/classes and informal concerts. Tutors: Rob Buckland and Andy Scott. Form/brochure available on request. Fees: £475 full board; part week possible, please contact. £85 deposit to accompany application.*

International Society for Study of Tension in Performance (ISSTIP). c/o 28 Emperor's Gate, London SW7 4HS *tel:* 020 7373 7307 *fax:* 020 7373 5440 *email:* carogrindea@yahoo.com. Carola Grindea, chmn, London Performing Arts Clinic. *Annual 1-day w/shops and seminars open to non-members. Special courses to train therapists by arrangement. Performing Arts and Media Clinic, Wed at LCMM. Also course for 'Music Medicine Therapists'. Fees: non-members £495; members £450; students £250.*

Islington Arts Factory. 2 Parkhurst Rd, London N7 0SF *tel:* 020 7607 0561 *fax:* 020 7700 7229 *email:* IAF@islingtonartsfactory.fsnet.co.uk. Licy Clayden, office mgr. *Dates vary. Open to all aged 8+. Arts centre offering courses and w/shops for adults and children. Vocal classes. Fees: from £30 per 3-month term. Waged/concession rate.*

Jackdaws Educational Trust. Bridge House, Great Elm, nr Frome, Somerset BA11 3NY *tel:* 01373 812383 *fax:* 01373 812083 *email:* music@jackdaws.org. Maureen Lehane Wishart, mus dir. *Courses from Apr-Oct 2004. Jackdaws aim is to bring classical mus of the highest standard to people of all ages, abilities and backgrounds, and to give to all the opportunity to discover that the deepest pleasure in mus comes from understanding and therefore hard work. The attraction of the Trust's setting is highly conducive to promoting this thoughtful attitude*

to mus. Residential courses are offered every w/end for singers and instrumentalists of all levels. All courses are taught by top-class tutors. Fees: £130 plus B&B at £19.50 per person per night.

Jazz Academy. c/o 12 Castle St, Berkhamsted, Herts HP4 2BQ *tel:* 01442 864989; 01892 541464 *fax:* 01442 384493. Michael Garrick, dir. *Open to all. Piano People, Easter; Summer Jazz, Aug; Xmas Swing, Dec 2004. Fees: on application.*

Jazz Courses. 58 Pond Bank, Blisworth, Northants NN7 3EL *tel:* 01604 858192 *email:* owen-iris@bryceo.fsnet.co.uk. Iris Bryce; Owen Bryce, tutor. *Apr, Jul, Nov. Various jazz courses, including Let's Play Jazz, Launde Abbey Jazz Course, All Saints (St Albans) Jazz Course and Alison House (Cromford, Derby) Jazz Course. Fees: £115-130.*

Jewish Music Summer School. Jewish Music Institute (JMI), SOAS, University of London, Russell Square, London WC1H 0XG *tel:* 020 7898 4308 *fax:* 020 7898 4309 *email:* jewishmusic@jmi.org.uk. Geraldine Auerbach MBE, dir. *Jul-Aug. Interest in singing or playing Jewish mus. Beginner to professional Summer academy to learn aspects of Jewish mus from choral to Klezmer mus and Yiddish song. Weekly modules, w/shops, m/classes and performances.*

Just Flutes at Woldingham. Jonathan Myall Music, 46 South End, Croydon CR0 1DP *tel:* 020 8662 8400 *fax:* 020 8662 84049 *email:* admin@summermusic.org.uk. Contact: course admin. *24-30 Jul 2004. Open to all ages and abillities. Tutors: Clare Southworth, Helen Brew, Michael Cox, Ian Clarke, Louise Matthew, Gary Woolf and Tim Carey (tbc). Application form/brochure available on request. Fees: £475 full board; part week possible, please contact. £85 deposit to accompany application.*

Kato Havas One-Day Workshop for Strings. 72 Victoria Rd, Oxford OX2 7QE *tel:* 01865 514094 *fax:* 01865 514094. Kato Havas, sec. *Jul. Release of Tension and Stage Fright in Performance, held at St Edmund Hall, Oxford. Fees: £12 (Khana members); £30 (non-members).*

Keele Summer Schools. Centre for Continuing and Professional Education, Keele University, Keele, Staffs ST5 5BG *tel:* 01782 583436 *fax:* 01782 583248 *email:* ada12@cpe.keele.ac.uk. Helen McGarry, course sec. *14-21 Aug 2004, applications by May. For amateurs, students and teachers aged 18+. Chamber Music Summer School.*

Kenneth van Barthold Intensive Piano Workshop. Arvensis, Stour Lane, Stour Row, Shaftesbury, Dorset SP7 0QJ *tel:* 01747 838318 *fax:* 01747 838318 *email:* Kvanbarthold@aol.com. Kenneth van Barthold. *Aug 2004. 2 tutors for 12 students, 12 practice rooms, recording facilities, final public recitals on Steinway concert grand. Presented in association with the University of Edinburgh Music dept.*

Knuston Hall. Irchester, Wellingborough, Northants NN29 7EU *tel:* 01933 312104 *fax:* 01933 357596 *email:* enquiries@knustonhall.org.uk. Eamonn Flanagan, centre mgr. *Various week and w/end adult residential courses throughout yr. Fees: w/ends from £116-128.*

The Kodály Institute of Britain. 133 Queen's Gate, London SW7 5LE *tel:* 020 7823 7371 *fax:* 020 7584 7691. Mary Skone-Roberts, admin. *Adult, willingness to sing. 1-yr p/t courses in musicianship according to the Kodály Principles at 3 levels: elementary, intermediate, advanced. Begins late Sep in London and is credit bearing for Trinity College LTCL (Mus Ed) Cert and Dip. Courses acknowledged by the Liszt Academy of Music, Budapest.*

LMFL. Park View, Alveston Rd, Old Down, S Glos BS32 4PH *tel:* 01454 419504 *fax:* 01454 419504 *email:* mail@lmfl.com. Arlette Herrenschmidt-Moller, organiser; J-Luc Borsarello, artistic dir. *Jul. Gr 7 and above. 7th Musical Summer School of Frensham Heights. Classical and jazz, inst and vocal mus course, one-to-one tuition. M/classes in accordion, vc, vn, va, db, ob, fl, picc, cl, bs-cl, rcdr, hp, pno, sax and br. Composition course, conducting course. Chmbr mus, orch, choir. English, French, German, Italian and Russian taught as foreign languages in situ. Fees: £600 day students; £940 full board.*

Lacock Summer School. Cantax House, Lacock, Chippenham, Wilts SN15 2JZ *tel:* 01249 730468 *fax:* 01249 730468 *email:* avdb@cantax.freeserve.co.uk. Andrew van der Beek. *18-23 Jul, 25-30 Jul 2004. For singers and players of renaissance and baroque insts. All ages. Fees: £310, £210 (aged 25 and under).*

Lake District Summer Music International Summer School. Stricklandgate House, 92 Stricklandgate, Kendal, Cumbria LA9 4PU *tel:* 0845 644 2505 *fax:* 0845 644 2506 *email:* info@ldsm.org.uk. Christopher Rowland, summer schools dir; Andrew Lucas, admin. *31 Jul-11 Aug 2004 tbc. For ens, str players and pianists at conservatoire*

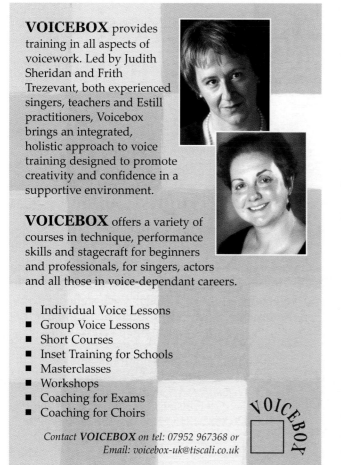

and young professional level. Residential summer school, classes and individual coaching with international artists and tutors. Public performance opportunities. Free tickets to festival concerts. See **Young String Venture** *for str players aged 6-18. Fees: £540 tbc (tuition, accommodation and festival tickets). Early booking discount available.*

Late Starters String Summer School. 1 Yewtree Close, London N22 7UY *tel:* 020 8881 5192 *email:* jenny.lloyd@btconnect.com. Jenny Lloyd, summer school admin. *18-24 Jul 2004. Open to vn, va and vc players aged 18+. All amateur levels including complete beginners. Venue: Bretton Hall, Wakefield, W Yorks. Fees: £405 full board, some concessions available.*

Latour International Festival of Music and the Arts (France). c/o Mananan Festival Office, Erin Arts Centre, Victoria Square, Port Erin, Isle of Man IM9 6LD *tel:* 01624 835858 *fax:* 01624 836658 *email:* information@erinartscentre.com. John Bethell MBE, dir. *Jul, applications by Jan. Choral study courses for amateurs. Individuals pay own travel and accommodation.*

Lauderdale House Music. 22 Gresley Rd, London N19 3JZ *tel:* 020 7272 5664 *fax:* 020 7272 5664. Murray Gordon, mus chmn. *M/classes for pno, voice, vc, gui. Concerts, gui society, Singers Guild, Suzuki, U3A, etc.*

Leeds College of Music. 3 Quarry Hill, Leeds LS2 7PD *tel:* 0113 222 3400/16 (enquiries) *fax:* 0113 243 8798 *email:* enquiries@lcm.ac.uk. *Jul and Aug. Contact for entry requirements. Summer schools include Jazz Big Band, Saxophone, Jazz/Popular Vocal, Audio Technology, DJ Technology, String Quartet, World Music and South-Asian Arts UK Community Music. Fees: from £130.*

Lets Make Music. 24b Bedford Grove, Eastbourne BN21 2DU *tel:* 01323 642116 *email:* letsmakemusic99@hotmail.com. Peter Mayes, dir. *18-20 Sep 2004. Gr 6 standard or above (ABRSM). W/end of orch mus making in Eastbourne. Fees: c £40.*

Lights, Music, Action. Fish & Bell Management, PO Box 175, Bury St Edmunds, Suffolk IP31 3TZ *tel:* 01359 271925 *fax:* 01359 271925 *email:* fishbelluk@aol.com. Phil Robson, course dir. *Aug. Student course open to those aged 9-18. Stage Band (gr 3 and above); acting, dance and mus theatre (all standards, grouped by experience); Audio-Visual course; backstagers training (make-up, scenery, costume). Adult courses opern to ages 18+. Annual residential summer school held in Suffolk. Large-scale final production. Fees: c £300 full board (tbc), discount for additional family members.*

Lionel Tertis International Viola Workshop. Erin Arts Centre, Victoria Square, Port Erin, Isle of Man IM9 6LD *tel:* 01624 835858 *fax:* 01624 836658 *email:* information@erinartscentre.com. John Bethell MBE, dir. *Triennial. Next 12-19 Aug 2006. For professional and amateur va players of all ages. Study courses and m/classes.*

Llandaff Summer Music Course *see* **Music for Fun.**

London Master Classes. 5 Lyndhurst Gardens, London N3 1TA *tel:* 020 8346 7088 *fax:* 020 8343 3669 *email:* info@londonmasterclasses.com. B Saipe, dir. *Jul, apply by mid-May. Open to those aged 18+. International master course for voice, vn, vc, pno and conducting. Daily public m/classes and concerts. Fees: £350.*

MAC (Midlands Arts Centre). Education Dept, Cannon Hill Park, Birmingham B12 9QH *tel:* 0121 440 4221 ext 266/7 *fax:* 0121 446 4372. Contact: educ dept. *Mus courses for adults and children (Western and Asian insts and styles) during term-time and holidays. Individual tuition available in pno, br, vn, vc, gui, rcdr, gr 5 theory. Jazz w/end (all insts and vocal) autumn half-term (date tbc). Fees: on application.*

Manchester University. Centre for Continuing Education (CCE), Faculty of Arts, Humanities Building, Oxford Rd, Manchester M13 9PL *tel:* 0161 275 3290 *fax:* 0161 275 3300 *email:* Veena.Seth@man.ac.uk. Glyn Davies, programme head for mus. *Apr-Aug, Sep-Mar. Open to those aged 18+. Courses for the public: 1 and 2-term courses on a wide variety of mus topics; also 1-day Sat courses. Fees: £44 per term (10 meetings), concessions available.*

Marlborough College Summer School, Marlborough, Wilts SN8 1PA *tel:* 01672 892388 *fax:* 01672 892476 *email:* admin@ mcsummerschool.org.uk. Jon Copp, dir of summer school; Tracey Burns, PA. *18 Jul-7 Aug 2004. For residents and non-residents of all ages. Weekly courses: pno for beginners and improvers, staged musical excerpts, choral w/shop, Unlock Your Voice, Lets Play Jazz I and II, Singing for Pleasure, Orchestra for Pleasure, the Organ - King of Instruments, Classical Music Through the Ages, Beginners Folk Harp, Sibelius. Plus over 200 different courses for all the family. Fees: from £97.*

Midland Festival Chorus. 130 Ainsdale Rd, Western Park, Leicester LE3 0UB *tel:* 0116 291 2242 *fax:* 0116 291 2242 *email:* dn.little@ ntlworld.com. Nicki Little, gen mgr. *2 and 9 Oct 2004. Open to those aged 16+. Frank Martin, 'In Terra Pax'. Choral event with professional artists and orch for singers, at Worcester Cathedral. Some reduced-price places for young singers aged 27 and under. Fees: on application.*

Mid-Pennine Arts. Yorke St, Burnley BB11 1HD *tel:* 01282 421986 *fax:* 01282 429513 *email:* info@midpenninearts.org.uk. Nick Hunt, dir. *Arts Development Agency for Burnley, Hyndburn, Pendle, Rossendale, Todmorden. Various mus in educ projects.*

Missenden Abbey. Great Missenden, Bucks HP16 0BN *tel:* 0845 045 4040 *fax:* 01753 651870 *email:* adultlearning@buckscc.gov.uk. Rosa Maria Welsh, programme team leader. *Aug 2004. Applications accepted until course date. Age 16+, all levels. Summer school. Also w/end courses Jan-Jun inclusive. Fees available on request.*

Morland Choristers' Camp. Garden Flat, Morland, Penrith, Cumbria CA10 3AZ *tel:* 01931 714654. Revd Canon Gervase W Markham, camp chief. *25 Jul-1 Aug 2004, apply by 30 Jun. For those aged 9-18 who are members of church or school choirs. A residential course approved by the Royal School of Church Music. Church mus, secular mus and outdoor activities. Fees: £220.*

Morley College. 61 Westminster Bridge Rd, London SE1 7HT *tel:* 020 7450 1838 *fax:* 020 7928 4074 *email:* music@morleycollege.ac.uk. Robert Hanson, dir of mus; Joan Taylor, mus access co-ord. *Aged 19+. Large range of adult educ courses, including ens, solo performance, singing, electronic mus, jazz, pop, world traditional mus, history and theory; all levels from beginners to advanced. Special theme days held regularly.*

Mostly Music. 28 Carlisle Close, Mobberley, Knutsford, Cheshire WA16 7HD *tel:* 01565 872650 *fax:* 01565 872650 *email:* mostlymusic@ btinternet.com. Roger Wilkes. *Courses and events throughout the yr, in Greater Manchester and N W England: choral, rcdr, early mus, study courses, church mus, private and correspondence tuition. For all ages. Apply by 12 days before each event.*

Music at Madingley. University of Cambridge, Institute of Continuing Education, Madingley Hall, Madingley, Cambs CB3 8AQ *tel:* 01954 280280 *fax:* 01954 280200 *email:* laf22@cam.ac.uk. Linda Fisher, programmes mgr. *Various w/end and week-long residential mus appreciation courses; also Alberni string quartet m/class for ages 18+. Fees: £142 w/end courses; £456 week-long courses.*

Music at Rendcomb. 2/228 London Rd, Cheltenham GL52 6HW *tel:* 01242 244200 *fax:* 01242 244200 *email:* MatR@228sundridge. freeserve.co.uk. Alison Mary Sutton, dir; Richard Sharpe, admin. *12-18 Apr 2004, closing date 12 Mar. Intermediate and advanced standard - no age limit. Solo singing course in opera and song. Coaching sessions, voice clinics to address specific technical problems, development of stagecraft/performance skills and staged operatic scenes. Plus daily yoga linking relaxation with breathing and sound. Fees: performers £405 (residential); £320 (non-residential); £55 (day attender).*

Music for Fun. 50 Parc-y-Coed, Creigiau, Cardiff CF15 9LY *tel:* 029 2089 2388 *fax:* 029 2089 2388. Jenny Vale, admin; Christopher Vale, course dir. *Jul/Aug. Ages 8-12. Jnr orch course.*

MusicHouse. c/o Tim Boulton, 18 Tulsemere Rd, London SE27 9EJ *tel:* 0845 456 0978; 01442 843642 *email:* tboulton@eurobell.co.uk. Tim Boulton, course organiser; James Boyd, course organiser; Catherine Manson, course organiser. *Apr and Aug 2004. Age range 14-17 (min gr 7 approx). Auditions held throughout the yr. Twice yearly residential chmbr mus courses for young str players and pianists held at the Yehudi Menuhin School, Surrey and Brockwood Park School, Hants, combining strengths of traditional teaching with creative approaches to learning and mus development. Run in association with Guildhall School of Music and Drama. Fees: vary according to course length.*

Musicale Young Artists' Programme. Homecroft, Sun Lane, Harpenden, Herts AL5 4GJ *tel:* 01582 460978 *fax:* 01582 767343 *email:* info@musicale.co.uk. David and Gillian Johnston, dirs. *Aug. Ages 12-18, gr 8. No audition necessary. National residential course held in Harpenden. A symphony orch and a wind orch play repertoire backed up with full sectional support, with a final concert appearance for each group in the Harpenden Music Festival.*

Musicfest - Aberystwyth International Summer School. Aberystwyth Arts Centre, Penglais, Aberystwyth, Ceredigion SY23 3DE *tel:* 01686 430468 *email:* musicfest@mid-wales.net. David Campbell, artistic dir. *17-25 Jul 2004 Aug, applications by Jun. Young musicians aged 16+ to mus students, adults and teachers. Runs in conjunction with Musicfest - Aberystwyth International Music Festival. Opportunity for accomplished musicians, to work with festival residents of international standing. Courses in strs, wind, pno, sax, br ens, composition. Public performance opportunities. Fees: Some bursaries, early application advised. Free tickets to all festival concerts.*

NLMS Music Summer School. c/o New London Music Society, 5 Thame Rd, Sydenham, Chinnor, Oxon OX39 4LA *tel:* 01844 354083 *fax:* 01844 354083. Philip Meaden, dir; Cynthia Gomme, admin. *31 Jul-7 Aug 2004, applications by 31 May. For ages 18+. Symphony, intermediate orch and choir courses at Queenswood School, Hatfield, Herts. Fees: £319-476.*

National Chamber Music Course. 18 Earlston Grove, Victoria Park Rd, London E9 7NE *tel:* 020 8525 1715 *email:* info@ncmc.org.uk. Simon Funnell, course dir. *1-7 Aug 2004. For str players aged 10-18. Chmbr mus course held at Temple Dinsley, Herts. 2 chmbr ens, inst classes, orch and choir. Fees: £378.*

National Children's Orchestra. 84a Elm Tree Rd, Locking, Weston-Super-Mare, N Somerset BS24 8EH *tel:* 01934 820254 *fax:* 01934 820257 *email:* mail@nco.org.uk. Vivienne Price, founder and vice-president; Roger Clarkson, dir of mus. *Easter and summer holidays. Auditions in autumn. 5 orchs divided into age groups: main orch under 14, under 13, under 12, under 11 and training orch 7-9.*

The National Children's Orchestra of Scotland. NYOS, 13 Somerset Place, Glasgow G3 7JT *tel:* 0141 332 8311 *fax:* 0141 332 3915 *email:* info@nyos.co.uk. Richard Chester, dir; Eva Flannery, admin. *Annual audition. Resident in Scotland, aged 8-14. Residential courses providing tuition from professional musicians prior to public performance.*

The National Children's Wind Orchestra of Great Britain. Homecroft, Sun Lane, Harpenden, Herts AL5 4GJ *tel:* 01582 760014 *fax:* 01582 767343 *email:* info@musicale.co.uk. Gillian and David Johnston, dirs; Caroline Marriott, admin; Melanie Ragge, associate dir. *For w/wind, br and perc players aged 12-16 and gr 6 and above. Entry by audition during the autumn term for a residential course at Easter and concerts at major venues around the country later in the yr. The 1-player-per-part National Youth Wind Sinfonia and 2 further wind orchs are formed. Study includes standard repertoire, new commissions and chmbr mus. Albert Hall Proms concert.*

National ISCis Strings Academy (NISA). Stud Farm Cottage, Stratford St Andrew, Suffolk IP17 1LW *tel:* 01728 605917 *fax:* 01728 602679 *email:* director@nisastrings.org. Viviane Ronchetti, mus dir; Sir Neville Marriner CBE, principal patron; Levon Parikian, cond. *14-15 Feb, 4-8 Apr, 18-24 Jul, 28-30 Oct 2004. For str players gr 7 and above, aged 11-21. Specialist str chmbr orch training. Residential courses. Fees: available on request.*

National Operatic and Dramatic Association (NODA). NODA House, 58-60 Lincoln Rd, Peterborough PE1 2RZ *tel:* 0870 770 2480 *fax:* 0870 770 2490 *email:* everyone@noda.org.uk. Mark Pemberton, chief exec; Jo Rowell, PA, summer school admin. *Aug, applications by 1 Jul. For ages 18+. Residential week-long theatre training course, Loughborough University.*

National Recorder School of Scotland. 18 Craigton Cres, Alva, Clackmannanshire FK12 5DS *tel:* 01259 760249 *email:* secretary@ sama.org.uk. Margaret Simpson, hon sec, mus dir. *20-22 Aug 2004. Open to those aged 10+. Gr 4 min. Held at John Burnet Hall, University of St Andrews. Fees: £160 residential, £125 non-residential.*

National Young Pianists Week. Uppingham Summer School, Uppingham, Rutland LE15 9QE *tel:* 01572 821264 *fax:* 01572 823892 *email:* summerschool@uppingham.co.uk. Brad Donelan, summer school dir. *15-21 Aug 2004 tbc. Normally for ages 9-21. Upon application and recommendation of pno teacher. Forward thinking and dynamic summer course and festival for the developing and advanced young pianist. Offers creatively stimulating programmes for pianists at advanced, intermediate and jnr levels, with each individual course designed to offer the student max choice within a challenging, innovative and comprehensive programme. Includes a series of pno m/classes, celebrity recitals, jazz concerts, lectures, one-to-one tuition, chmbr mus coaching, improvisation/jazz w/shops, composition/harmony seminars. Students will be given opportunities to perform as soloists and chmbr musicians with the resident str quartet and jazz ens. Fees: £500 residential, £400 non-residential; £300 observer, or £60 per day.*

National Youth Choir of Scotland. The Mitchell Library, 201 North St, Glasgow G3 7DN *tel:* 0141 287 2856 *fax:* 0141 287 2858 *email:* admin@nycos.co.uk. Ruth Townsend, admin; Christopher Bell, artistic dir and cond; Ian Mills, gen mgr. *12-17 Apr, Jul 2004. NYCoS open to those aged 15-24; NYCoS Boys Choir open to those aged 10-15. Entry to all choirs by audition. NYCoS and Training Choir, Jul residential course in Perthshire. Boys Choir Apr. Fees: NYCoS £385, TC £315, Boys Choir £150.*

National Youth Choirs of Great Britain. PO Box 67, Holmfirth, Huddersfield, W Yorks HD9 3YT *tel:* 01484 687023 *fax:* 01484 687023 *email:* office@nycgb.net. Mark Anyan, gen admin. *New Year, Easter and summer. Auditions held annually in spring and autumn. Must be aged 19 and under to audition for youth choir. Residential courses for members of the National Youth Choirs. Regional girls choirs (north and south) ages 11-15; boys choir age 9-until voice changes; training choir*

ages 15-19; main choir ages 17-23. Fees: £300-350 (course), £25 (audition). Substantial bursaries available.

The National Youth Jazz Orchestra of Scotland. NYOS, 13 Somerset Place, Glasgow G3 7JT *tel:* 0141 332 8311 *fax:* 0141 332 3915 *email:* info@nyos.co.uk. Richard Chester, dir; Mike Hardy, Jazz co-ord. *Resident in Scotland, aged 12-21. Residential summer course with tuition from experienced tutors followed by public performances. Additional courses throughout the yr.*

National Youth Music Camps. The Stables, Stockwell Lane, Wavendon, Milton Keynes MK17 8LU *tel:* 01908 280820 *fax:* 01908 280827 *email:* education@stables.org. Sarah Watts, dir; Deborah Ridout, campers co-ord. *4 weeks in summer. For children aged 8-17 with an interest in mus. No previous experience necessary. Mus summer camps and courses.*

The National Youth Orchestra of Scotland. NYOS, 13 Somerset Place, Glasgow G3 7JT *tel:* 0141 332 8311 *fax:* 0141 332 3915 *email:* info@nyos.co.uk. Richard Chester, dir. *Annual auditions. Resident in Scotland, aged 12-21. Winter and summer residential courses providing tuition from professional musicians and rehearsals with internationally acclaimed conds and soloists prior to concert tours. Easter residential training course. Summer residential courses in Jun-Jul followed by public performances.*

The National Youth Sinfonia. Homecroft, Sun Lane, Harpenden, Herts AL5 4GJ *tel:* 01582 760014 *fax:* 01582 767343 *email:* info@musicale.co.uk. Gillian and David Johnston, dirs; Caroline Marriott, admin; Melanie Ragge, associate dir. *For orch players aged 14-18 at gr 7 and above. Entry by audition during the autumn term for a residential course at Easter - concerts at major venues around the country later in the yr. The orch is directed from the leader's chair by Christopher Hirons. The players will play in quartets, a chmbr orch and also the National Children's Sinfonia (10-12 yrs), and the National Children's Chamber Orchestra (12-15 yrs).*

National Youth Wind Orchestra of Great Britain. 51 Highlands, Tadmarton Park, Banbury, Oxon OX15 5SR *tel:* 01295 721020 *fax:* 01295 721020 *email:* kit@nywo.org.uk. Kit Shepherd, dir. *Easter and summer. Main orch, gr 8 with distinction; Focus on Chamber course, gr 6 standard and above. Age range for all courses 15-21 yrs. Auditions*

take place every autumn for the following Easter course. Residential courses, Easter and summer; main orch; principals ens; Focus on Chamber courses include ens, fl, sax, perc; outreach days; m/classes; European tours. Fees: from £275 (Focus on Chamber course)-375 (main orch).

Nelly Ben-Or Piano Courses Incorporating the Alexander Technique. 23 Rofant Rd, Northwood, Middx HA6 3BD *tel:* 01923 822268 *fax:* 01923 822268 *email:* roger.clynes@virgin.net. Roger Clynes, course sec; Nelly Ben-Or, dir. *9-13 Jan (option of 9-11 Jan), 19-23 Jul 2004; 7-11 Jan 2005. Min gr 8 or overseas equivalent. International courses in London for pianists, teachers and advanced students. Courses include individual sessions at the keyboard and in the Alexander Technique. The principles of the Alexander Technique are applied to aspects of playing and creative study for performance, through detailed analysis of mus for interpretation and memorising. Some scholarships available from the Nelly Ben-Or Scholarship Trust (see* **Scholarships and Grants***).*

North East Early Music Forum (NEEMF). 105 Bolling Rd, Ben Rhydding, Ilkley LS29 8QH *tel:* 01943 607252; 0113 278 6886 (info) *email:* stanghan@aol.com. Margaret Kurosinski, hon sec. *For ages 16+. Day w/shops throughout yr in performance and interpretation of early mus. Some student bursary funding. Fees: £10-15 per w/shop day; w/end courses £100+.*

North London Music School. 78 Warwick Ave, Edgeware, Middx HA8 8UJ *tel:* 020 8958 5206/8368 2989 *fax:* 020 8361 2123 *email:* nlpsch@hotmail.com. M Schreider, artistic dir. *Aug 2004, applications by 26 Jun. Advanced level. Annual international mus course - pno, str and ens. Jnr and snr groups, performers' group. Intensive tuition and m/classes. Concerts, ens work, fun and sport activities.*

North London Piano School. 78 Warwick Ave, Edgeware, Middx HA8 8UJ *tel:* 020 8958 5206/8368 2989 *fax:* 020 8361 2123 *email:* nlpsch@hotmail.com. M Schreider, artistic dir/chmn; Dr Willner, exec dir/vice-chmn. *Aug 2004, closing date for applications 26 Jun. For pianists, accompanists and pno duos; also for str players and ens. Jnr and snr groups, performers' group. Summer courses in the UK and abroad. Tuition by professors from leading conservatoires, concerts and m/classes, lectures and seminars on performance technique, CD*

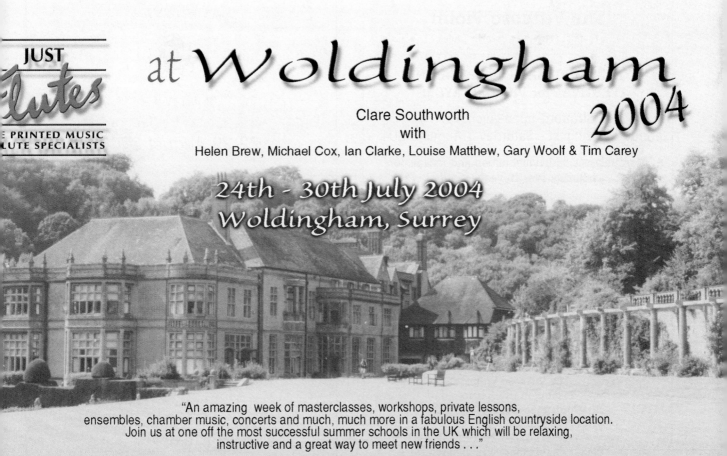

OUNDLE -
INSPIRATION FOR YOUNGE ORGANISTS

PULLING OUT THE STOPS
2-4 April at Oundle, Northants
weekend residentail course for pianists and early-stages
organists age 10-14

Saturday 29 May at Oundle
GET AHEAD!
inspiration day for organists age 10-16

July
INTERNATIONAL SUMMER SCHOOLS
NEW
courses spanning three weeks
in Oundle and Cambridge, for organists age 14-26

information@oundlefestival.org.uk
www.oundlefestival.org.uk
Tel/fax: 01832 272026

***Oundle events for young organists are promoted in
partnership with The Royal College of Organists***

OXENFOORD INTERNATIONAL
Summer School in Scotland
for singers and accompanists

Master classes, Opera course, Lieder, French song,
English song, Bel canto course, Early Music, Oratorio,
Cantata & choral course, Cabaret, Vocal technique.
 Accompanists' courses

25 July – 2 August 2004

at St Leonards School, St Andrews

Details from: Administrator
49 Dreghorn Loan, Edinburgh EH13 0DA
Tel 0131 441 2736 Fax 01875 341011
Email: r18ona@btinternet.com

www.oxenfoordinternational.co.uk

The Virtuoso Violin

Founder Patron: Dr Rosalyn Tureck
Artistic Director: Dr Rimma Sushanskaya

THE THIRD BACH and PAGANINI
FESTIVAL for VIOLIN PLAYERS

Stratford-upon-Avon, UK
Sunday 1 August - Saturday 7 August 2004

Masterclasses, individual tuition and recitals for
violinists over 16 years of age

Inspiring in-depth understanding of the violin music
of Bach and Paganini

Led by international violinists Dr Rimma Sushanskaya
(Russia/USA/UK) and Dr Savely Shalman (Russia) with
other distinguished musicians including Dr Aino
Rijkiarw (Estonia) and Catherine Leech (UK)

For further details and an application form, please contact:

Etta Mahon
The Administrator
The Virtuoso Violin
Bishopton Hill House
Stratford-upon-Avon CV37 0RG
United Kingdom
Tel/Fax: 01789 293061
Email: ettamahon@hotmail.com

The Fourth Chetham's International
Summer School and Festival for Pianists

22-29 August 2004

Daily Concerts - Masterclasses - Lectures
Jazz, Composition & Improvisation Courses
Intensive One-To-One Coaching
An Outstanding Team of Teachers and Performers

Artistic Director - Murray McLachlan
Faculty Includes
Noriko Ogawa, Joan Havill, Martin Roscoe, Yonty Solomon,
Bernard Roberts, Jeremy Seipmann and Charles Camilleri.

Further information is available from:
Murray McLachlan
Chetham's School of Music
Manchester M3 1SB
Tel: +44 (0) 161 834 9644
murraymclachlan@chethams.com

CHETHAM'S
SCHOOL OF MUSIC

recording. *Prizewinners' recital at St Martin-in-the-Fields. Individual scheduling; fun activities. Loyalty discount to former students. Fees: partial scholarships available.*

Northern Sax Course. c/o Lindsey Music, 42 St Mary's Park, Louth, Lincs LN11 0EF *tel:* 01507 605244 *email:* jeff@wwplus.freeserve.co.uk. Jeff Brown, events organiser. *15-18 Oct 2004. For adults/students. Course based on sax quartets, quintets, sextets, etc. Venue Yorkshire Dales. Tutors include J Rae, R Ingham, J Mills, Don Ashton. Fees: on application.*

Northern Woodwind/Horns Chamber-Music Weekend. c/o Lindsey Music, 42 St Mary's Park, Louth, Lincs LN11 0EF *tel:* 01507 605244 *email:* jeff@wwplus.freeserve.co.uk. Jeff Brown, events organiser. *20-23 Feb 2004. For students/adults. Course based on wind quintets, octets, etc. Tutors include Ken Smith, Richard Simpson, Kevin Banks, Stephen Reay, Bob Ashworth (provisional list). Fees: from £245.*

Northumbrian Recorder and Viol School (NORVIS). 5 Birchgrove Ave, Gilesgate Moor, Durham DH1 1DE *tel:* 0191 386 4782 *email:* enquiries@norvis.org.uk. Marlene Austin, admin. *2-9 Aug 2004. All abilities. Held at College of St Hild and St Bede, Durham. Course for any age and ability covers all aspects of early mus: rcdrs, viols, baroque strs and ob, renaissance insts, plucked insts, keyboard, singing and dancing. Fees: £493 (2003) for full board and tuition; reductions for half-board, concessions. Bursaries available for unwaged (including students).*

Nottingham University School of Continuing Education. Jubilee Campus, Nottingham NG8 1BB *tel:* 0115 951 6513 *fax:* 0115 951 6556 *email:* sharon.caine@nottingham.ac.uk; helen.frost@nottingham.ac.uk. Sharon Caine. *Holiday courses and mus courses Jun-Oct. 1-7 Jun 2004, Berlin: Music, Art and Architecture.*

Oakham International Summer School *see* **The Tallis Scholars Summer School**

The Opera School (Wales). Rhydyberi Cottages, Merthyr Cynog, Brecon, Powys LD3 9SA *tel:* 01874 690339 *fax:* 01874 690254 *email:* operaschool@pattitheatre.com. Bridgett Gill, dir. *Feb-Mar, apply by Sep. For young professional singers, aged 20-35. Intensive 3-week course based at the Adelina Patti Theatre, nr Swansea, combining stage and vocal training, make-up and stage-fighting instruction, culminating*

in several fully-staged performances with orch ens, touring theatres in Wales and London. Fees: £375, bursaries available.

Orff Society (UK). 7 Rothesay Ave, Richmond, Surrey TW10 5EB *tel:* 020 8876 1944 *fax:* 020 8876 1944 *email:* orffsocuk@talk21.com. Margaret Murray, hon sec. *Creative mus courses mainly for teachers in primary and middle schools. 'Accent on Orff' w/ends: 20-21 Mar, Glasgow and Newport; 26-27 Jun, Richmond, Surrey.*

Oundle International Summer Schools for Young Organists. The Creed Chapel, Ashton, Oundle, Peterborough PE8 5LD *tel:* 01832 272026 *fax:* 01832 272026 *email:* information@oundlefestival.org.uk. James Parsons, artistic dir; Trisha Ryan, exec dir. *Jul 2004, apply by Apr. Open to those aged 14-25. Courses for organists based in Oundle, with tuition from team of acclaimed organists. Valuable recital awards. 11-18 Jul 2004: Advanced Academy students spend 3 days resident in Cambridge. Concurrent week of festival events. Fees: (2003) £490 (bursaries available). 20-24 Jul 2004: special course for prospective org scholars, resident for the whole course in Cambridge with full access to the orgs there. Special guidance from Oxford and Cambridge Directors of Music. Fees: £490 (bursaries available).*

Oxenfoord International. 49 Dreghorn Loan, Colinton, Edinburgh EH13 0DA *tel:* 0131 441 2736 *fax:* 01875 341011 *email:* r18ona@btinternet.com. Joan Busby, dir; Rhona Bridges, admin. *Jul-Aug. Open to those aged 17+. M/classes with Della Jones, opera course, Bel Canto course, classes in Lieder, French song, early mus, American song, oratorio, cantata, courses for soloists and chorus, vocal technique, accompanists courses. St Leonard's School, St Andrews. Fees: £85-695.*

27th Oxford Baroque Chamber Music Week. c/o 13 Brackley Rd, Monton Green, Eccles, Manchester M30 9LG *tel:* 0161 281 2502 *email:* baroqueweek@ntlworld.com. Peter Collier, course dir. *2-9 Aug 2004. A secure technique and good sight-reading is required. Held at Headington School, Oxford. Course for wind, str and keyboard players of baroque or modern insts at old or modern pitch. An extensive course library enables students to explore both familiar and unfamiliar repertoire with the help of experienced tutors. Bursaries are available.*

Oxford Cello School. 67 Oxford Rd, Abingdon, Oxon OX14 2AA *tel:* 01235 530572 *email:* cello@oxfordcelloschool.freeserve.co.uk. Marianne Gottfeldt, dir; Stephen Gottfeldt, course dir. *Residential and*

non-residential summer schools for cellists. Performance course for post-gr 8, advanced course for gr 6/8, intermediate course for gr 3/6, beginners course for gr 2 and above. Also exam booster course, adult improvers course, teachers development course, course for adults in the French Alps. Technique m/classes, individual lessons, scales, video analysis, improvisation, ens, vc orch, choir and composition. Gr 6-8 aural training and theory for the younger student. AEB exam centre and Performance Diploma. Solo performance with orch for performance student.

Oxford Chamber Music Courses. 7 Turnpike Rd, Oxford OX2 9JQ tel: 01865 863236. Irene Butcher, sec. 1-4 Apr and 5-8 Aug 2004; apply by six weeks before each meeting. For any age group. 3-day meetings coached by the Maggini Quartet. Fees: approx £160 (residential); £125 (non-residential); reduction for students in f/t educ (£35).

Oxford Flute Summer School. 9 Pinehurst, Horsham, W Sussex RH12 2DL tel: 01403 259463 fax: 01403 240610. Clive Conway, dir; Janet Way, dir; Katie Bycroft, admin. mid Aug. Bursary closing date Mar. For fl players of all standards ages 14+. Annual course held at Worcester College, Oxford. Tutors include Peter Lloyd and Michel Debost. Concerts, classes, ens and individual tuition. Three options offered: general course for players of all ages and standards; intensive course, 3 individual lessons and public performance; seminar course for advanced small group tuition. Fees: £450 plus accommodation.

Oxford Philomusica 6th International Piano Festival. PO Box 150, 266 Banbury Rd, Oxford OX2 7DL tel: 0870 606 0804 fax: 020 8208 4239 email: pianofestival@oxfordphil.com. Malcolm Troup, president; Marios Papadopoulos, artistic dir. Aug 2004.

Oxford University Department for Continuing Education. 1 Wellington Square, Oxford OX1 2JA tel: 01865 270396 fax: 01865 270309 email: oussa@conted.ox.ac.uk. Anna Sandham, co-ord (summer school); Jonathan Darnborough, associate tutor in mus (day/week classes). 10 Jul-7 Aug 2004. Oxford University Summer School for Adults. For ages 18+. Wide-ranging programme of weekly courses and day schools in Oxford and surrounding area, also summer school. Fees: £395 non-residential, £595 (twin)/£695 (single) residential.

Pendrell Hall College. Codsall Wood, Wolverhampton, Staffs WV8 1QP tel: 01902 434112 fax: 01902 434113 email: pendrell.college@staffordshire.gov.uk. David Evans, principal; Linda Reeve, admin offr.

Mus study w/ends for ages 18+. Includes light mus, classical mus, rcdr playing and early mus.

Piano Duet Courses. 64 Birdwood Rd, Cambridge CB1 3TE tel: 01223 240418 fax: 01223 240418; 01279 870991 email: anne.applin@btinternet.com. Anne Applin; Geoff Pratley. Aged 18+. One, two and three-day pno duet courses, tutored by distinguished duettists Anne Applin and Geoffrey Pratley at various venues in the UK during the year. Courses planned for 2004: Mar, north of England; Jul, west of England and Scotland; Oct, Benslow Music Trust, Herts. Some courses offer a residential option. Individuals and preformed duos welcome. Courses explore a wide and exciting pno duet repertoire (including reviving works long-forgotten or from archive) and give opportunity for m/class and individual duo tuition as well as discussion, performance and participants' concert. Some courses have facility for 2-pno playing. The tutors give an evening recital. Fees: on application.

Practical Psychology for Musicians who are Teaching, Learning & Performing. Music, Mind and Movement, Flat 2, 35 Bush Lane, London EC4R 0AW tel: 020 7626 0183; 07850 912006 fax: 020 7626 0183 email: musicmindmovement@btinternet.com. Lucinda Mackworth-Young, dir. 19-22 Jul 2004. Open to all professional and student teachers and performers. Practical psychology for musicians who are teaching, learning and performing, including understanding pupils, teacher-pupil relationships, emotions and motivation, teaching styles and learning strategies, practice, problem pupils and parents, communication, anxiety and safety in performance. Plus Eurhythmics, Dance through the Ages, Improvisation and related disciplines. Fees: £220 reduced to £199 if paid early.

Pro Corda Trust (National School for Young Chamber Music Players). Leiston Abbey House, Theberton Rd, Leiston, Suffolk IP16 4TB tel: 01728 831354 fax: 01728 832500 email: mail@procorda.fsbusiness.co.uk. Sir Colin Davis, president; L Cowan, course dir; Mererid Crump, admin; M Parrington, course dir; Ioan Davies, dir of mus. School holidays. Entry by audition. Residential courses for young str players and pianists aged 8-18 attending twice yearly at preparatory, primary, jnr, intermediate and snr levels. Specialist ens tuition under the direction of distinguished musicians.

Pulling Out The Stops. The Creed Chapel, Ashton, Oundle, Peterborough PE8 5LD *tel:* 01832 272026 *fax:* 01832 272026 *email:* information@oundlefestival.org.uk. James Parsons, artistic dir; Trisha Ryan, exec dir. *2-4 Apr 2004, apply by Feb. Open to those aged 10-14. Start playing the pipe org. W/end residential course at Oundle, Northants, for beginner organists and pianists who would like to start playing the org. Fees: c £185 (2003), bursaries available.*

RSCM Courses for Organists at Sarum College. 19 The Close, Salisbury, Wilts SP1 2EE *tel:* 01722 424800 *fax:* 01722 338508 *email:* rcf@sarum.ac.uk. Robert Fielding, dir. *Wide range of courses for organists of all standards. Regular teaching and residential facilities for private study.*

Recorder Summer School. 113 Birchwood Rd, Marton, Middlesbrough TS7 8DE *tel:* 01642 310628. Miss S Foxall, sec. *31 Jul-7 Aug 2004. Open to those aged 16+ (age 15 accepted if accompanied by an adult on the course). Held at Bretton Hall, Wakefield. Classes and ens for rcdr players. All grades from beginners to advanced. Baroque chmbr mus, concert and mus w/shops. Rcdr orch, light mus and swing, multi-choir rcdrs. Fees: available on request.*

The Rehearsal Orchestra. 60-62 Clapham Rd, London SW9 0JJ *tel:* 020 7820 9994 *fax:* 01322 558912 *email:* admin@rehearsal-orchestra.org. Amanda Lockhart Knight, admin; Levon Parikian, artistic dir. *For ages 16+, gr 8 and above with good sight-reading. Advanced orch training for students and young professionals, teachers and experienced players. Wide range of orch repertoire studied, including new mus. 1 and 2-day sessions throughout the yr, plus residential week in Edinburgh during the festival. Fees: student and non-student rates.*

Reynard Music. 4 Reynard Way, Northampton NN2 8QX *tel:* 01604 845885 *email:* reynard@argonet.co.uk. Michael T Watkins, dir. *Play days and w/end residentials throughout the yr, plus summer holiday in the Pennines. Open to those of gr 6 standard and above, all ages. Mixed str and wind ens, cl ens, sax ens, jazz, cobla, Klezmer, light orch, advanced concert band. Tutors include Val Brodie, Colin Touchin, Steve Bingham, John Greaves, Alan Jeanes, Steve Ball. Fees: from £160 (residential w/end, en suite, full board).*

Royal College of Organists. 7 St Andrew Street, Holborn, London EC4A 3LQ *tel:* 020 7936 3606 ext 6 *fax:* 020 7353 8244 *email:* events@rco.org.uk. Simon Williams, educ and events offr. *Apr. Closing date Mar. For ages 16+. Residential course for organists. Apr, Cambridge, RCO Diploma preparation and general org tuition. Fees: c £320 (special rate for students), apply by Mar.*

Royal Festival Hall Gamelan Programme. Royal Festival Hall, London SE7 8XX *tel:* 020 7921 0953 *fax:* 020 7928 2049 *email:* education@rfh.org.uk. Contact: educ. *Regular evening classes in mus; course for beginners, children aged 7+, and more advanced players. Taster days and classes begin Jan, Apr, Sep; bookable in advance through the box office (tel: 020 7960 4242) before each term. Introductory w/shops for groups and special sessions by request also available. Fees: from £70 .*

Royal School of Church Music. Cleveland Lodge, Westhumble, Dorking RH5 6BW *tel:* 01306 872807 *fax:* 01306 887260 *email:* education@rscm.com. Chris Wardle, courses admin. *Offers courses on a variety of topics relating to the use of mus in Christian worship, for people of all ages. Includes singing breaks, holiday courses for children and young people, cathedral singing weeks, courses for organists, training in composing, mus directing and mus and liturgy, etc. Brochure available. Fees: vary.*

Schools Music Association of Great Britain. 71 Margaret Rd, New Barnet, Herts EN4 9NT *tel:* 020 8440 6919 *fax:* 020 8440 6919 *email:* maxwellpryce@educamus.free-online.co.uk. Maxwell Pryce, hon sec and chief exec. *Oct. Annual residential course and conference on mus in schools. Courses for mus teachers at regional centres throughout yr.*

Schreider Piano Studio. 78 Warwick Ave, Edgware, Middx HA8 8UJ *tel:* 020 8958 5206 *fax:* 020 8958 5206 *email:* MichaelSchreider@hotmail.com. M Schreider, artistic dir; Olga Malisova, sec. *Advanced level. Short courses and series of courses for advanced pianists, preparation for examinations, competitions, technical training, consultations, public concerts for eligible pianists. Limited residential places available. Fees: scholarships available.*

Scots Fiddle School. 18 Craigton Cres, Alva, Clackmannanshire FK12 5DS *tel:* 01259 760249 *email:* secretary@sama.org.uk. Margaret Simpson, hon sec; Ian M White, mus dir. *26-30 Jul 2004. Open to those aged 15+. Approx gr 4. Held at St Salvator's Hall, St Andrews University.*

Scottish Amateur Music Association. 18 Craigton Cres, Alva, Clackmannanshire FK12 5DS *tel:* 01259 760249 *email:* secretary@sama.org.uk. Margaret Simpson, hon sec. *Summer courses include String Chamber Music Weekend, 4-6 Jun; Traditional Fiddle School, 26-30 Jul; National Youth Wind Ensemble of Scotland, 26-30 Jul; National Youth Brass Band of Scotland (and Reserve Section), 2-7 Aug; National Youth*

String Orchestra of Scotland (and Training School), 9-14 Aug; National Recorder School of Scotland, 20-22 Aug 2004.

Scottish International Flute Summer School. 1 Redhills Farm Cottage, Tibbermore, Perthshire PH1 1QP *tel:* 01764 683497 *fax:* 0141 248 5756 *email:* admin@flutescotland.co.uk. Elaine McPherson, admin. *End of Jul. Open to those aged 16+. Held at Strathallen School, Perthshire. Annual course for fl players to study with Peter Lloyd, Wissam Boustany and Ruth Morley. Includes m/classes, private lessons, concerts, chmbr mus, technique w/shops, tone development and coaching with pianists Alan Hicks and Scott Mitchell. Plus related performance classes, eg, jazz improvisation, contemporary techniques, acting and performance skills, etc. May be attended by performers, participants and course members. Also includes 3-day ens course for adult amateurs. Details on application. Fees: £180-300 plus accommodation.*

Scottish Schools Orchestra Trust. 11 Melville Place, Edinburgh EH3 7PR *tel:* 0131 226 3392 *fax:* 0131 226 3392 *email:* admin@sscot.org.uk. Jean Murray, dir. *12-18 Jul 2004. Open to those aged 9-15 at gr 3 and above. Annual 1-week residential course in Perthshire. Orch and wind band playing plus sports, arts, crafts and entertainments. Occasional 'Play Away Days' in different parts of Scotland for younger, less-experienced players. Fees: £320.*

Share Music. Toynbee Studios, 28 Commercial St, London E1 6AB *tel:* 020 7247 7855 *fax:* 020 7247 7732 *email:* chris.shurety@sharemusic.org.uk. Chris Shurety, dir. *Courses held throughout the yr. Suitable for newcomers, experienced participants, students, teachers and arts practitioners. Residential and non-residential courses in all parts of UK and Ireland for young people and adults with physical disabilities to take an active and creative part in mus, theatre, dance and related arts. Courses held at centres with special facilities for disabled people. Collaborative approach leading to public performance. Fees: residential from £400 for, non-residential from £60.*

Sheffield University Division of Adult Continuing Education. 196-198 West St, Sheffield S1 4ET *tel:* 0114 222 7000 *fax:* 0114 222 7001 *email:* adultconted@sheffield.ac.uk. Adam White, mus co-ord. *Sep-May, applications by Sep. Courses in mus theory, singing, sequencing, jazz, folk mus of the British Isles, composition. Particularly suited to those aged 18+ who wish to study mus without the need to give up work. Modules are accredited and validated by the University of Sheffield. Also p/t certificate in Music Studies (120 credits), 2 yrs. Fees: £190 per 20 credit module (24 weeks); concessions available.*

Sing for Pleasure. Unit 10a, Nortonthorpe Mills, Wakefield Rd, Scissett, Huddersfield HD8 9LA *tel:* 08000 184164 *fax:* 08000 184164 *email:* admin@singforpleasure.org.uk. Michelle Eastham, office mgr. *14-22 Aug 2004. Residential and day courses throughout the country for children, teachers, singers and choral conds. International festivals through the 'A Coeur Joie' movement. Publishes repertoire suitable for schools and choral groups. Fees: £400 approx.*

Stratford-upon-Avon International Flute Festival. 10 Guild St, Stratford-upon-Avon, Warks CV37 6RE *tel:* 01789 261561 *fax:* 01789 261577 *email:* londartist@aol.com. Michael Emmerson, chief exec; Isabel Jackson, admin; Elena Durán, artistic dir. *17-31 Jul 2004, applications by 1 Jul. Annual m/classes for flautists of all ages and levels at King Edward VI School, Stratford-upon-Avon. Emphasis on performance; special sessions for young flautists.*

Summer Music International Summer School. 70 Surrenden Cres, Brighton BN1 6WF *tel:* 01273 884186 *fax:* 01273 884186 *email:* summermusic@lineone.net. Jacqueline Froom, organiser. *21-29 Aug 2004, closing date for solo singers May. Open to those aged 16+. Renowned internationally for solo singing courses. Also offers courses for choral singers and accompanists. Fees: £370.*

Sussex University. Centre for Continuing Education, Education Development Building, Falmer, Brighton BN1 9RG *tel:* 01273 678040 *fax:* 01273 678848 *email:* j.broughton@sussex.ac.uk. Julian Broughton, mus convener. *Oct 2004-Jun 2006 priority given to applications received before Jul 2004. Open entry (subject to convenor's discretion). P/t certificate in opera, plus open courses and a summer programme for adults. Fees: please consult brochure.*

The Tallis Scholars Summer School (formerly Oakham International Summer School). PO Box 992, Waterbeach, Cambridge CB5 9SQ *tel:* 01223 693281 *fax:* 08700 516828 *email:* juliet.allan@oiss.org.uk. Juliet Allan, gen mgr; David Woodcock, associate dir; Peter Phillips, artistic dir. *10-17 Jul 2004, applications by Mar. Open to those aged 16+. Choral course directed by Peter Phillips (dir of The Tallis Scholars) at Oakham School in Rutland.*

Temple Dinsley Summer School. 86 Cromwell Ave, London N6 5HQ *tel:* 020 8340 8362 *fax:* 020 8341 7616 *email:* e.waterhouse@btinternet.com. Elisabeth Waterhouse, dir. *9-12 Aug 2004, applications*

by Jun. For children aged 3-11 playing vn, vc or pno. Suzuki camp in Herts. Inst lessons, group lessons and related activities.

Tobin Music System of Musical Education. The Old Malt House, Herts CM21 9AX *tel:* 01279 726625 *email:* candida@tobinmusic.co.uk. Candida Tobin, course tutor. *W/end courses all yr round including infant/primary mus teaching, classical gui, pno/keyboard, rcdr and simple composition. Fees: £80.*

Tonalis Music Centre. 4 Castle Farm Close, Leighterton, Glos GL8 8UY *tel:* 01666 890460 *fax:* 01666 890460 *email:* tonalis@aol.com. Michael Deason-Barrow, dir. *Offers short courses (w/end and week long) on: Mus Educ - the singing child, teaching mus through movement, sharing mus, creating mus with children, world mus in educ; Community Musicing - renewing mus as a community art, soundscapes of the world, giving voice to community; Voice Work - singing with the whole voice, singing the world, sing freedom; Mus in Spiritual Practice - singing the sacred song of the spirit, mus pilgrimages; Mus Therapy - mus as a healing art, the healing voice, mus in remedial educ.*

Urchfont Manor. Devizes, Wilts SN10 4RG *tel:* 01380 840495 *fax:* 01380 840005 *email:* urchfont@wcc.youth.org.uk. Susan Delaney, dir. *Short courses including mus appreciation: classical/jazz; piping and drumming, classical gui w/shops and choral w/shops.*

Vacation Chamber Choirs. Ashley House, Ure Bank, Ripon, N Yorks HG4 1JG *tel:* 01765 602856 *email:* mail@vaco.net. Xenophon Kelsey, mus dir; Jane Lomax, admin. *Open to students aged 16-24 (gr 8 and above standard or equivalent). Residential courses each vacation for advanced singers. Expert coaching. Frequent concerts. Fees: vary £90-120.*

Vacation Chamber Orchestras. Ashley House, Ure Bank, Ripon, N Yorks HG4 1JG *tel:* 01765 602856 *email:* mail@vaco.net. Xenophon Kelsey, mus dir; Jane Lomax, admin. *Easter, summer, Christmas. Open to those aged 16-22 with gr 8 and above. Residential courses each vacation for advanced players. Expert professional coaching. Frequent concerts in Yorkshire Dales, North York Moors, Northern Pennines, etc. Fees: vary £95-£150.*

Wansfell College. Theydon Bois, Epping, Essex CM16 7LF *tel:* 01992 813027 *fax:* 01992 814761 *email:* education@wansfellcollege.net. Marilyn Taylor, principal. *W/end and midweek courses throughout yr in all subjects including mus, mus appreciation, history and performance. Fees: from £120.*

Wessex Band Summer School. 14 Lockwood Gardens, Hoylandswaine, Sheffield S36 7LN *tel:* 01226 765579 *email:* john@ wessexband.fsnet.co.uk. John and Margaret Grinnell, organisers. *Jul-Aug. Snr (gr 4 and above) and jnr (pre gr 4 standard). All ages - families encouraged. Courses held in Dorset, for br and wind band players. Fees: c £65.*

West Dean College. West Dean, Chichester, W Sussex PO18 0QZ *tel:* 01243 811301 *fax:* 01243 811343 *email:* short. courses@westdean.org.uk. Marcus Martin, mus course organiser. *Open to those aged 18+, occasional bursaries available. 9-14 Jul, The Chilingirian String Quartet Course with Levon Chilingirian, Charles Sewart, Susie Mészáros and Philip de Groote. Intensive coaching and concerts for str quartets who already play together. 22-27 Aug, Voices and Viols - an early mus w/shop with Andrew King, Susanna Pell and Steven Devine. Individual playing and ens coaching, for singers and viol players. 14-20 Aug, International Classical Guitar Festival and Summer School, directed by John Mills. Ens and individual tuition and mus-making for gui players of all levels. Evening recitals by international soloists. 17-20 Oct 2004, Celebration of English song, directed by Lena Phillips.*

William Bennett International Flute Summer School. 50 Lansdowne Gardens, London SW8 2EF *tel:* 020 7498 9807 *fax:* 020 7498 1155 *email:* Mmichie@msn.com. Michie Bennett, sec. *Jul-Aug. Courses take place at Frensham Heights, Farnham, Surrey. Tutor: William Bennett. Fees: £335 (performer); £295 (participant).*

Winchester Summer Music Course. 37 St David's Rd, Clifton Campville, nr Tamworth, Staffs B79 0BA *tel:* 01827 373586 *email:* maddocks@ concordiamusic.fsnet.co.uk. James Maddocks, dir; Joan Maddocks, sec. *24-31 Jul, apply by 17 Jun. Aged 16+. Chmbr mus, strs, wind and pno, str orch, chmbr orch.*

Wind Band Courses. 52 Blackhorse Rd, Mangotsfield, Bristol BS16 9BE *tel:* 0117 956 1950 *email:* harriscg@waitrose.com. Chris Harris, festival dir. *Applications by Jul. Adults gr 3 and above and gr 6 and above. Wind Band Festival for all able wind band players, at Queens Hotel, Southsea. Fees: £125 including full board.*

Wingfield Arts. College Yard, Church Rd, Wingfield, nr Stradbroke, Suffolk IP21 5RA *tel:* 01379 384505 *fax:* 01379 384034 *email:* sharon.lewis@wingfield-arts.co.uk. Emma Lister, gen mgr; Sharon Lewis, educ mgr; Carl Bayliss, communication and research; Clare Lovell, projects admin. *Wingfield Arts and Music offers an on-going programme of arts events and educ activities in Suffolk and Norfolk. Broad selection of one-off events: world mus, classical mus, folk, early mus, opera, visual arts, digital media, written and spoken word and heritage. Including opportunities for artists: training, commissions, residencies, etc. Fees: on application.*

Workers' Music Association Summer School. Thornton Croft, 7 Huby Rd, Sutton on Forest, York YO61 1DY *tel:* 01347 811707 *email:* wmaschool@aol.com. Jill Snowdon, organiser. *7-14 Aug 2004, apply by Feb. Open access. 18-20 participatory courses held at Wortley Hall, Yorks, for amateur musicians, all ages. Br band, orch, chmbr mus, folk, jazz, wind band, choral, solo and ens singing, composition, rudiments, etc. Fees: £395.*

World Music Summer School at SOAS. University of London, Thornhaugh St, Russell Square, London WC1H 0XG *tel:* 020 7898 4010 *email:* worldmusic@soas.ac.uk. *Jun-Aug 2004. Beginners to professional. 8 distinctive cultures and a wide range of mus and dance traditions in weekly modules. Including mus from Zimbabwe, Japan, Indonesia, Greece and China. Intensive tuition, w/shops, m/classes, concerts, etc.*

Wycombe Music Summer School *see* **NLMS Music Summer School.**

Young Musicians Week. Uppingham Summer School, Uppingham, Rutland LE15 9QE *tel:* 01572 821264 *fax:* 01527 823892 *email:* summerschool@uppingham.co.uk. Brad Donelan, dir. *19-23 Jun 2004. A fun week of mus making tailor made for all levels of young musicians between 6-16 years. Coached by professional musicians, students will work at appropriate levels in groups and ens from quartet to bands and trios to orchs. All of the groups will have the opportunity to perform in public concerts throughout the week. Well balanced programme of mus and recreation. Fees: £180 (non-residential); £285 (residential).*

Young String Venture (Lake District Summer Music). Stricklandgate House, 92 Stricklandgate, Kendal, Cumbria LA9 4PU *tel:* 0845 644 2505 *fax:* 0845 644 2506 *email:* info@ldsm.org.uk. Christopher Rowland, summer schools dir; Penny Stirling, course dir; Rachel Moore, course dir; Andrew Lucas, admin. *2-7 Aug 2004. For str players aged 6-18. Summer chmbr mus course. Coaching with specialist tutors includes Dalcroze eurythmics and orch training: children's w/shop, intermediate and advanced levels. Solo Performers and Residential options. End of course concerts. Application form from the administrator. Fees: £140-420 tbc. Early booking discount available.*

International Summer Schools and Short Courses

The music courses listed below are held at various times of the year and the course content may vary from year to year. The addresses given here are those of the organising bodies, and are not necessarily the same as the address of the course itself. Financial grants may be offered on scholarship terms. For foreign government grants, enquiries should be made to the appropriate embassy.

Australia

National Music Camp. c/o Australian Youth Orchestra, Level 1, The Arts Exchange, 18 Hickson Rd, Millers Point, Sydney NSW 2000, Australia *tel:* +61 2 9252 3855 *fax:* +61 2 9252 8033 *email:* info@ayo.com.au. Simon Rogers, artistic admin. *January; applications by July; fees: $700; age range: 14-25. Provides young Australians with comprehensive approach to excellence in music training and performance (positions may be available to international students on written request). Programmes include orchestra, advanced chamber music, keyboard, composition, arts admin about words and music (music journalism).*

Ronald Dowd National Summer School for Singers. 171 Albion St, Surry Hills NSW 2010, Australia *tel:* +61 2 9360 4049 *fax:* +61 2 9332 1585 *email:* victormorris@madridroad.freeserve.co.uk. Maggie Niven, executive director; Victor Morris, artistic director. *January, applications by November. Opera mastercourses in Sydney for singers and repetiteurs.*

Austria

Berwang Holiday Music Course (Austria). Willowdown, Megg Lane, Chipperfield, Herts WD4 9JN, UK *tel:* +44 1923 263715 *fax:* +44 1923 268412 *email:* bhmc@musicholiday.com. *August-September. All ages. Strings, woodwind, singers.*

Eichendorff's Ruh Walter Hermann Sallagar, Furth A-2564, Austria *tel:* +43 267 488265 *fax:* +43 1 714 1710. *3-11 July 2004, applications by 6 June. Courses in bassoon ensemble and repair, Fagottissimo. Age 16+. Fees: 800 euros (including board and accommodation).*

International Summer Course 'Music & Dance Education: Orff-Schulwerk'. Orff Institute, Frohnburgweg 55, Salzburg A-5020, Austria *tel:* +43 662 6198 6100 *fax:* +43 662 6198 6109 *email:* sonja.czuk@moz.ac.at. *Annual. July.*

International Workshops. 187 Aqua View Rd, Cedarburg WI 53012, USA *tel:* +1 262 377 7062 *fax:* +1 262 377 7096 *email:* thintz@execpc.com. Tori Hintz, manager. *18-31 July 2004, applications by 1 June. In Gratz, Austria. String and piano pedagogy, performance, jazz, and conducting. Ages 16-90. Fees: US$1795.*

Salzburg International Summer Academy Mozarteum. Mirabellplatz 1, Salzburg A-5020, Austria *tel:* +43 662 6198 4500 *fax:* +43 662 6198 4509 *email:* summer.academy@moz.ac.at. Michaela Bartsch, students' officer. *Annual. August, applications by 1 June. No age limit, although most participants aged 20-30. Masterclasses for voice and instruments. Fees: 570 euros.*

Wiener Meisterkurse. Reisnerstrasse 3, Wien A-1030, Austria *tel:* +43 1 714 8822 *fax:* +43 1 714 8821 *email:* wiener-meisterkurse@music.at. Elisabeth Keschmann; Monika Wildauer. *5 July-20 September 2004, applications by 1 June. 2-week mastercourses with leading professional musicians in flute, guitar, piano, cello; also choral, chamber, opera, conducting and singing. Final concert, diploma. Fees: 400 euros (participant), 190 euros (audience member).*

Belgium

Musica. Toekomstlaan 5B, Neerpelt B-3910, Belgium *tel:* +32 11 610 510 *fax:* +32 11 610 511 *email:* info@musica.be. *Courses and festivals for children, youths and adults.*

Canada

Acadia Summer Music Institute. Division of Continuing & Distance Education, Acadia University, Wolfville NS B4P 2R6, Canada *tel:* +1 902 585 1434 *fax:* +1 902 585 1068 *email:* continuing.education@acadiau.ca. *2 July-9 August 2004. Summer music camps in jazz, concert band, strings, classical guitar, music theatre and piano. For those aged 8-18. Fees: $200-300 for tuition.*

Adventures in Summer Music. PO Box 5005, Red Deer AB T4N 5H5, Canada *tel:* +1 403 342 3526 *fax:* +1 403 347 4041 *email:* jhowdle@rdc.ab.ca. Joyce Howdle, performing arts co-ordinator. *16-20 August*

2004, applications by 1 August. Introductory, junior, intermediate band workshop, including full band rehearsals, sectionals, options and theory for ages 9-15. For junior and intermediate must have 2-4 years playing experience. Fees: $150 (not including instrument rental).

Camp Musical de Lanaudiere. PO Box 44, Joliette PQ J6E 3Z3, Canada *tel:* +1 450 755 2496 *fax:* +1 450 755 4385. Nicole Bourassa, executive secretary. *Four sessions: 27 June-10 July; 11-24 July; 25 July-7 August; 8-21 August 2004. Applications by mid-June. Chamber music, choral and orchestral programmes for ages 9-17 who have studied for a minimum of 2 years. Fees: $783.*

Courtenay Youth Music Centre (CYMC). PO Box 3056, Courtenay BC V9N 5N3, Canada *tel:* +1 250 338 7463 *fax:* +1 250 703 2251 *email:* cymc@island.net. Bettyanne Hampton, general manager. *July-August. Ages 12-adult. Programmes of orchestra, chamber music, concert band, harp, percussion, jazz, musical theatre, choral for intermediate to advanced students. Concerto competition.*

Lake McDonald Music Centre. Cammac National Office, 85 Chemin Cammac, Harrington, Quebec J8G 2T2, Canada *tel:* +1 819 687 3938 *fax:* +1 819 687 3323 *email:* national@cammac.ca. Raymond Sealey, executive director. *June-August. All ages, children's programme available. One-week sessions for amateur musicians - orchestral, early music, jazz, opera and many other courses. Fees: $300-900.*

Czech Republic

International Workshop for Conductors. c/o Symphonic Workshops Ltd, 281 Pacific Ave, Toronto ON M6P 2P8, Canada *tel:* +1 416 760 9319 *fax:* +1 416 762 6258 *email:* info@symphonicworkshops.com. Harry Hurwitz, director. *July/August 2-week workshop for experienced conductors with the Bohuslav Martinu Philharmonic Orchestra in Kromeriz and Zlin, Czech Republic. Daily podium time, option to record.*

Karlsbad Technique Workshop. c/o Symphonic Workshops, 281 Pacific Ave, Toronto ON M6P 2P8, Canada *tel:* +1 416 760 9319 *fax:* +1 416 762 6258 *email:* info@symphonicworkshops.com. Harry Hurwitz, director. *March, December, 10-day programme. Technique and repertoire workshop for conductors with the Karlsbad Symphony Orchestra, Karlovy Vary (Karlsbad) Czech Republic.*

Kromeriz Piano Workshops. c/o Symphonic Workshops, 281 Pacific Ave, Toronto ON M6P 2P8, Canada *tel:* +1 416 760 9319 *fax:* +1 416 762 6258 *email:* info@ symphonicworkshops.com. Harry Hurwitz, director. *2 weeks in July. Private lessons, masterclasses and seminars from an international faculty in Kromeriz. Recitals in baroque churches and medieval castles. Practice facilities available. Concerts to be awarded. Fees: 610 (inclusive of private accommodation with breakfast, some dinners, all tuition and practice facilities plus local transportation to recitals). New Concerto with Chamber Orchestra Competition, winners play in concert with orchestra as part of the Kromeriz International Music Festival.*

La Pellegrina Early Music Summer School in the Czech Republic. La Pellegrina, Twijnstraat 42 bis, Utrecht NL-3511 ZL, Netherlands *tel:* +31 30 238 2535 *email:* info@pellegrina.net. Dirkjan Horringa, director. *August, closing date for applications 1 May. For experienced singers (soloists and choral) of all ages with good sight-reading ability, and instrumentalists (baroque violin, viola, cello, gamba, lute, theorbo, harpsichord, recorder, curtal). Culminates in 3 public performances in Czech Republic. Fee: c 550 euros.*

MusicEnterprise. 24 rue des Cerisiers L-1322, Luxembourg *tel:* +352 474269 *fax:* +352 223585 *email:* pipergeo@pt.lu. *Several chamber music, piano or orchestral courses throughout the year for amateur adults of good ability.*

Opera Workshop for Conductors and Singers. c/o Symphonic Workshops, 281 Pacific Ave, Toronto ON M6P 2P8, Canada *tel:* +1 416 760 9319 *fax:* +1 416 762 6258 *email:* info@symphonicworkshops.com. Harry Hurwitz, director. *1-month workshop July/August. Singers and conductors perform in a fully staged production.*

Repertoire Workshop. c/o Symphonic Workshops, 281 Pacific Ave, Toronto ON M6P 2P8, Canada *tel:* +1 416 760 9319 *fax:* +1 416 762 6258 *email:* info@symphonicworkshops.com. Harry Hurwitz, director. *Experienced conductors can expand their repertoire with the Hradec Kralove Philharmonic Orchestra in Czech Republic.*

Finland

Kuhmo Chamber Music Course. Fredrikinkatu 77 a 2-4, Helsinki FIN-00100, Finland *tel:* +358 9 493867 *fax:* +358 9 493956 *email:* seija.kahkonen@kuhmofestival.fi. Seija Kähkönen, secretary. *July 2004, applications by 1 April. Workshops, masterclasses, individual and ensemble tuition. Ages 12-25. Fees: 490 euros.*

France

Académie International d'Eté de Nice. 24 Blvd de Cimiez, Nice F-06000, France *tel:* +33 04 93 81 01 23 *fax:* +33 04 93 53 33 91 *email:* academies@expomed.org. Jacques Taddei, president; Hubert Tassy, admin. *July-August. Applications by June. Instrumental, vocal, chamber, composition masterclasses. Fees: from 400 euros for 1 week to 1400 euros for 4 weeks.*

Beauville Arts. L'ancien Presbytère, Beauville F-47470, France *tel:* +33 5 53 87 72 18 *email:* claire.mallalieu@wanadoo.fr. Claire Mallalieu, admin director. *July 2004. Residential performing arts summer camps in S W France for those aged 8-18. Music, dance, drama and set design culminating in weekly performances. Fees: 400 euros per week, reductions for siblings.*

Bruges Early Music Week. Cantax House, Lacock, Chippenham, Wiltshire SN15 2JZ, UK *tel:* +44 1249 730468 *fax:* +44 1249 730468 *email:* avdb@cantax.freeserve.co.uk. Andrew van der Beek, admin. *5-11 June 2004. Week fo singers and instrumentalists in the Abbey of Male with Deborah Roberts.*

Centre Acanthes. 3 Rue des Couronnes, Paris F-75020, France *tel:* +33 1 40 33 45 35 *fax:* +33 1 40 33 45 38 *email:* acanthes@acanthes.com. Claude Samuel, director of Centre Acanthes. *July, in Chartreuse de Villeneuve-lez-Avignon, applications by beginning of January. For composers, instrumentalists, teachers and students interested in contemporary music. Lecture series, composition and instrumental music workshops, musical computing, public performances. Scholarships available.*

Chant Sans Frontieres. Hurel, Buais, Manche, Normandie F-50640, France *tel:* +33 2 33 59 86 75. Isobel Tedstill, general manager. *Early August (tbc), applications by 31 May. 1-week intensive tuition, all aspects of singing; technique, interpretation, presentation by highly experienced tutors, performance opportunity. Age 18+. Fees: £200-325 (including full board). Spectators welcome if room available.*

International Summer Academy for Choral Singing and Painting. Rintheimer Str 50, Karlsruhe D-76131, Germany *tel:* +49 721 616450 *fax:* +49 721 623 89530 *email:* MicProc@aol.com. Michael Procter, musical director. *Many courses, mainly for singers in Renaissance sacred music. Summer Academy: 1000 years of sacred music 17-25 July 2004, Abbaye St Martin de Mondaye, near Bayeux, Normandy. Intensive course for experienced singers only, preparing music for daily monastic Vespers, a concert, and the High Mass on the final Sunday. Summer Academy also includes course for painters, and optional French language classes.*

Latour de France International Festival of Music and the Arts (France). c/o Mananan Festival Office, Erin Arts Centre, Victoria Square, Port Erin, Isle of Man IM9 6LD, UK *tel:* +44 1624 835858 *fax:* +44 1624 836658 *email:* information@erinartscentre.com. John Bethell MBE, director; Richard Pattison, admin. *24-30 July 2004, applications by 28 February, open to any age. Choral study course for amateurs. Individuals pay travel and accommodation.*

Medecine & Musique. 1133, Rue des Bouisses, Montpellier F-34070, France *tel:* +33 4 67 10 09 36 *fax:* +33 4 67 10 09 36 *email:* Yves.Allieu@wanadoo.fr. Yves Allieu, president.

Michael Procter Courses. Rintheimer Str 50, Karlsruhe D-76131, Germany *tel:* +49 721 616450 *fax:* +49 721 623 89530 *email:* MicProc@aol.com. Michael Procter, director. *December-January, Christmas Octave in Alsace. Sacred music for the Feast Days in the week of Christmas. Daily Mass in the pilgrim church of St Odile, near Strasbourg.*

Normandy Piano Week. La Maison Rouge, Ste Marguerite des Loges, Livarot F-14140, France *tel:* +33 2 31 63 12 63 *email:* oleary@club-internet.fr. Michael Stembridge-Montavont. *September, open to those aged 18+. A residential course, for amateur pianists, in a 17th century Chateau close to Cherbourg. All levels of playing; practice facilities; opportunities to perform; introduction to the piano method of Alfred Cortot.*

Germany

Cello Masterclasses. Kronberg Academy, Friedrich-Ebert Str 6, Kronberg D-61476, Germany *tel:* +49 6173 783378 *fax:* +49 6173 783379 *email:* administration@kronbergacademy.de. Oda Cramer von Laue, responsable; Raimund Trenkler, director. *15-22 October 2004. Open to those aged 28 and under. Active participants selected by audition.*

Chamber Music Connects the World. Kronberg Academy, Friedrich-Ebert Str 6, Kronberg D-61476, Germany *tel:* +49 6173 783378 *fax:* +49 6173 783379 *email:* administration@kronbergacademy.de. Oda Cramer von Laue, responsable; Raimund Trenkler, director. *11-22 June 2004. Exceptionally talented violinists, viola players and cellists are invited to take part in this project as juniors, studying and performing together in Kronberg. Age limit 29 years.*

Course in Bayreuth. Bela Bartók Centre for Musicianship, 6 Frognal Court, 158 Finchley Rd, London NW3 5HL, UK *tel:* +44 20 7435 3685 *email:* Agnes.Kory@kcl.ac.uk. Agnes Kory, director. *July/August. 5-7 days intensive course for musicians, music teachers, music students. Covers general musicianship, history and analysis, and chamber music. Contact for details of dates and fees.*

Europa Cantat - European Federation of Young Choirs (EFYC). Weber Str 59a, Bonn D-53113, Germany *tel:* +49 228 9125663 *fax:* +49 228 9125658 *email:* info@europacantat.org. Sonja Greiner, secretary general. *Summer. International singing weeks and workshops with well-known conductors throughout Europe. Including World Youth Choir European Session and International Competition for Young Choral Conductors (ages 27 and under); European Academy for Young Choral Conductors (ages 30 and under); International Study Tour.*

European Youth Music Week (formerly Anglo-German Youth Music Week). 11 Seven Acres, Abbeymead, Glos GL4 4QU, England *tel:* +44 7967 604463/1452 627860 *fax:* +44 1452 627860 *email:* jane@thornton57.fsnet.co.uk. Jane Thornton, course admin. *Annual residential week. 23 July-8 August 2004. Held in Trossingen. Open to those aged 16-25 of gr 7-8 and above on first instrument. Full symphony orchestra forming 2 chamber orchestras, wind and string orchestra. Fees: approx £270.*

International Association for Music & Education. Am Kloster 1a, Bramsche-Malgarten D-49565, Germany *email:* iamev@t-online.de. Peter Koch, executive director. *Choral/orchestral weeks, jazz workshops and renaissance/specialist instrumental sessions throughout Germany and neighbouring countries, open to all aged 8+.*

Internationale Bachakademie. Johann-Sebastian-Bach-Platz, Stuttgart D-70178, Germany *tel:* +49 7116 192133 *fax:* +49 7116 192130 *email:* christa.richter@bachakademie.de. Christa Richter, course officer. *22 August-5 September 2004, in Stuttgart. Open to any age. Conducting and vocal masterclasses and seminars in musicology. Fees: 450 euros.*

Karl-Klinger Masterclass. c/o ARD Wettbewerb, Bayerischer Rundfunk, München D-80300, Germany *tel:* +49 89 5900 2091 *fax:* +49 89 5900 3573 *email:* karl-klinger-stiftung@gmx.de. Karl Klinger. *27 August-4 September 2004, applications by 15 June. String quartets. Entry fee 800 euros.*

Michael Procter Courses. Rintheimer Str 50, Karlsruhe D-76131, Germany *tel:* +49 721 616450 *fax:* +49 721 623 89530 *email:* MicProc@aol.com. Michael Procter, director. *Courses for singers in Renaissance sacred music. 16-18 January, Early Music in Berlin, Berlin; 6-8 February, Early Music in Baden, Karlsruhe; 23-25 April 2004, English Music for Easter and St George, Munich.*

Musicosophia International. Finkenherd 6, Sankt Peter D-79271, Germany *tel:* +49 776 0581 *fax:* +49 766 01536. Pausinger Hubert, manager; George Balan, founder. *Variety of courses including The Art of Conscious Music Listening in France, Germany, Italy, Spain, USA and South America. Applications by 2 weeks before course. Ages 6+. No musical knowledge required. Fees: 70 euros (1-day), 130 euros (weekend), 245 euros (5-day). Courses weekly in Sankt Peter; monthly in Italy, Spain and France. Also annual international congress, August in Sankt Peter.*

String Chamber Music Course. Landesmusikrat Hessen EV, Eschersheimer Landstr 419, Frankfurt Am Main D-60431, Germany *tel:* +49 695 67155; +49 696 37111 (evenings) *fax:* +49 695 308 8625; +49 699 567045 *email:* info@landesmusikrat-hessen.de. Juan von Haselberg, co-ordinator and organiser. *15-19 October 2004, applications by 2 September. Intensive string chamber music course for serious-minded amateurs and music teachers aged 21-65. Fees: 300 euros (tuition and board).*

Hungary

Course in Budapest. Bela Bartók Centre for Musicianship, 6 Frognal Court, 158 Finchley Rd, London NW3 5HL, UK *tel:* +44 20 7435 3685 *email:* Agnes.Kory@kcl.ac.uk. Agnes Kory, director. *July/August.*

5-day intensive course for musicians, music teachers, music students. Covers general musicianship, history and analysis, and chamber music. Contact for details of dates. Fees: £250.

Early Music Days, Sopron. Hungaro Fest, Rakoczi ut 20, Budapest H-1072, Hungary *tel:* +36 1 226 1459 *fax:* +36 1 266 5972 *email:* liszkay.maria@hungarofest.hu. *Mária Liszkay, manager. 26 June-3 July 2004 in Sopron, applications by 1 May. Fortepiano, violin, flute, dance. Fees: 250-400 DEM.*

International Bartok Seminar and Festival. c/o Hungarofest Kht, Rakoczi ut 20, Budapest H-1072, Hungary *tel:* +36 1 266 1459 *fax:* +36 1 266 5972 *email:* kadar.csilla@hungarofest.hu. *Kádár Csilla, manager. July-August, in Szombathely, applications by 15 May. Course for piano, singing, cello, conducting, string quartet, composition and computer music. Fees: 200-600 euros. Open to music college students/young professionals.*

International Kodály Seminar. Kodály Institute, Kecskemét H-6001, Hungary *tel:* +36 76 48 1518 *fax:* +36 76 32 0160 *email:* lkeri@kodaly-inst.hu; office@kodaly-inst.hu. *Laura Kéri, registrar. Next 18 July-5 August 2005, applications by 31 March 2005. In-depth course for music pedagogues and choral conductors to enhance their knowledge in Kodály's educational concept; masterclasses. Also International Kodály Festival.*

Music without Borders. POB 10, Balassagyarmat H-2661, Hungary *tel:* +36 35 301841 *fax:* +36 35 301841 *email:* music@is.hu. *Csaba Ember, artistic director; Gyorgyi Ember, English language contact (tel: +36 70 5181866). 20-31 July, closing date for applications June. Individual classes, orchestra, choir, chamber music, opportunity to perform, free-time activities. Open to those aged 12-26. Fees: 350 euros.*

'Pro Musica' International Summer Academy. Botfalu u.43, Budapest H-1112, Hungary *tel:* +36 1 317 6517 *fax:* +36 1 319 6517 *email:* pro_musica@nexus.hu. *Gyula Csetenyi, artistic director. August, applications by June. Flute, oboe, clarinet, bassoon, violin, cello, piano and chamber music. Ages 14-30. Fees: US$400 (inclusive of tuition and board).*

Republic Ireland

Association of Irish Choirs. 4 Drinan St, Cork, Republic of Ireland *tel:* +353 21 431 2296 *fax:* +353 21 496 2457 *email:* info@cnc.ie. *Margaret O'Sullivan, executive director. July. Basic transition, intermediate and advanced choral conducting, vocal training, masterclasses and lectures during an annual summer school for choral conductors and teachers. Other regional courses and choral days. Ages 17+. Fees: 200 euros (non-members), 150 euros (members), 125 euros (students).*

International String, Keyboard and Chamber Music Masterclasses. Young European Strings, The Close, Cypress Downs, Templeogue, Dublin 6W, Republic of Ireland *tel:* +353 1 490 5263 *fax:* +353 1 492 0355 *email:* yes@iol.ie. *Maria Kelemen, director. October. Closing date for applications previous December. Ages 12-18. Fees: 400 euros (not including accommodation). Individual lessons, ensemble practice.*

Irish Composition Summer School. 11 Belgrave Road, Rathmines, Dublin 6, Republic of Ireland *tel:* +353 1 496 1484 *fax:* +353 1 496 1484 *email:* helenhaughey@eircom.net. *Helen Haughey, admin; John McLachlan, admin; Martin O'Leary, tutor; Nicola Le Fanu, tutor; Ian Brabazon, tutor. July 2004, course to focus on composition for i) keyboard (organ, piano and harpsichord) and ii) electroacoustic forces. Lectures and tuition by course directors and international guest composer. Performance and recording of students' work by professional musicians. Fees: 400 euros. On-campus accommodation.*

Irish Vocal Masterclasses. 32 Miller's Lane, Skerries, Co Dublin, Republic of Ireland *email:* ivm@oceanfree.net. *Brian MacKay, director. Annual summer course and short courses for advanced singers with internationally experienced tutors.*

Israel

The Israel Jeunesses Musicales International Summer Camp. c/o Jeunesses Musicales, 2 Rothschild Blvd, Tel Aviv 66881, Israel *tel:* +972 3 516 5077 *fax:* +972 3 516 5016 *email:* wijmisr@internet-zahav.net. *Meir Wiesel, director. Annual. July-August, entries by 15 May. Strings, woodwind, piano. Ages 13-18 (camp) and 16-26 (advanced seminar). Fees: $800.*

Keshet Eilon Violin Mastercourse. Kibbutz Eilon, Western Galilee 22845, Israel *tel:* +972 4 985 8191 *fax:* +972 4 980 6766 *email:* keshet@eilon.org.il. *Gilad Sheba, managing director. 24 July-12 August 2004, applications by 5 April. Ages 25 and under. Course for gifted young violinists of all nationalities. Special project: Archery and the Violin. Private lessons, masterclasses and solo concert experience. Fees: $2000.*

Italy

Accademia Musicale Chigiana - Corsi di Perfezionamento Estivi. 89 Via di Citta, Siena I-53100, Italy *tel:* +39 057 722091 *fax:* +39 057 728 8124/723 7413 *email:* stampa@chigiana.it. *Annual summer schools for young musicians, including masterclasses, seminars, concerts and a festival. Age limits vary between courses from 30-35. Registration by 15 May for Orchestral Conducting, 31 May for Composition, and 10 June for all other instrumental courses. Fees vary. Entrance exam on first day of each course.*

Egida Sartori Early Music Seminars and Courses. Fondacione Giorgi Cini, Isola di San Giorgio Maggiore, Venezia VE I-30124, Italy *tel:* +39 041 271 0228 *fax:* +39 041 522 3563 *email:* fondacini@cini.it. *Annual. July in Venice.*

The Inner Voice in Italy. The White House, Aston Hill, Aston Rowant, Watlington, Oxon OX49 5SG, UK *tel:* +44 1844 351561 *fax:* +44 1844 354891 *email:* elisabeth@innervoice.demon.co.uk. Elisabeth Wingfield; Aliya Gordon-Creed. *Residential courses designed to help performers free themselves from problems associated with nerves, lack of self-confidence and the inner critic. Also courses on the psychology of musical performance, held in England and Italy.*

International Academy of Sacred Music. Riutheimer Str 50, Karlsruhe D-76131, Germany *tel:* +49 721 616450 *fax:* +49 721 6238 9530 *email:* veniceacademy@aol.com. Michael Procter, director. *29 May- 6 June 2004. Annual course for experienced singers. Housed at the Palazzo Giustinian, on the Grand Canal. Concert in St Stefano, High Mass in San Marco. Fees: 1200 euros.*

Michael Procter Early Music Courses. Rintheimer Str 50, Karlsruhe D-76131, Germany *tel:* +49 721 616450 *fax:* +49 721 6238 9530 *email:* MicProc@aol.com. Michael Procter, director. *Many courses, mainly for singers in Renaissance sacred music. Weekend courses in Germany and England.*

Music, Dance and Didactics Symposium. Coop Co Gi Tur, via Pisacane 6, Selargius, Cagliari I-09047, Italy *tel:* +39 070 841297 *fax:* +39 070 841297 *email:* cogitur@tiscalinet.it. *Residential courses for renaissance and baroque music, singing, organ, renaissance and baroque dance, international and Sardinian folk dance, music teaching methods (Orff, Kodály). Held in Selargius, Sardinia.*

Sillico Masterclass Series for Singers. 34 Hill Hay Cottage, Fowey, Cornwall PL23 1EN, UK *tel:* +44 1726 833553 *fax:* +44 1726 833553 *email:* m.elliott@ucc.ac.uk. Paul Thomas, admin; Martin Elliott, tutor; Alison Pearce, tutor. *2004 dates tbc. Daily masterclasses, concluding concert, for the development of vocal repertoire with internationally renowned teachers. Maximum 12 singers. Fees: £440 including tution, accommodation and meals, 10% reduction if paid by 31 March.*

Singing in Venice. Cantax House, Lacock, Chippenham, Wiltshire SN15 2JZ, UK *tel:* +44 1249 730468 *fax:* +44 1249 730468 *email:* avdb@cantax.freeserve.co.uk. Andrew van der Beek, admin. *29 February-6 March 2004. Monteverdi and Gabrieli in a palazzo on the Grand Canal, Venice with Robert Hollingworth.*

Zoagli Singing Week. Cantax House, Lacock, Chippenham, Wiltshire SN15 2JZ, UK *tel:* +44 1249 730468 *fax:* +44 1249 730468 *email:* avdb@cantax.freeserve.co.uk. Andrew van der Beek, admin. *15-21 and 24-30 August 2004. Two separate weeks of choral singing in a castle on the Ligurian Riviera of northern Italy.*

Monte Carlo

Reding-Piette Seminar For Duo Piano Teams. Reding-Piette School, Chateau Perigord, Monte Carlo MC-98000, Monaco *tel:* +377 93 300721 *fax:* +377 93 300721 *email:* secretary@reding-piette.ch. Janine Reding Piette, creative director. *Masterclasses throughout the year.*

Netherlands

Belcanto Summer School, Holland. c/o Belcanto Festival Dordrecht, Groenmarkt 76, Dordrecht NL-3311 BE Dordrecht, Netherlands *tel:* +31 78 631 4029/39 *fax:* +31 78 639 0847 *email:* belcanto@dordt.nl. Luca Gorla, artistic director, vocal coach; Nicolai Cok, creative director, vocal coach. *August-September. Closing date for applications April. For young singers with an interest in the Belcanto period. Initial audition by tape: two arias performed in Italian. Selection means performance at the Belcanto Festival after five weeks of intensive training (accommodation free). Open to those aged under 32 years. 3 catagories: free, 500 euros, 1000 euros.*

Brielle - English Weekend. Cantax House, Lacock, Chippenham, Wiltshire SN15 2JZ, UK *tel:* +44 1249 730468 *fax:* +44 1249 730468 *email:* avdb@cantax.freeserve.co.uk. Andrew van der Beek, admin. *13-14 March 2004. Choral evensong in South Holland with Nigel Perrin.*

Dordrecht - English Weekend. Cantax House, Lacock, Chippenham, Wiltshire SN15 2JZ, UK *tel:* +44 1249 730468 *fax:* +44 1249 730468

email: avdb@cantax.freeserve.co.uk. Andrew van der Beek, admin. *19-20 June 2004. Choral evensong with Jeremy Jackman.*

13th International Flute Summer Course 2004 by Wil Offermans. Studio E, Vrolikstraat 195 D, Amsterdam NL1091 TX, Netherlands *tel:* +31 20 668 2478 *fax:* +31 20 665 1425 *email:* course@studio-e.nl. Wil Offermans, creative director. *23-28 August 2004. Flute course on contemporary techniques given by Wil Offermans. Open to flute students, flautists and teachers. Technical information as well as cultural and historical references. Group sessions and private lessons. Fees: 325 euros (including board, tuition).*

The International Holland Music Sessions. PO Box 250, Bergen NL-1860 AG, Netherlands *tel:* +31 72 582 1300 *fax:* +31 72 582 1309 *email:* info@hollandmusicsessions.com. Jan Marisse Huizing, artistic director; Perry Reitsma, managing director. *August, apply by internet 1 April. Ages 15-27. Classes in piano, cello, violin. Also possibilities for auditors. Daily concerts by active participants in several venues, including the Concertgebouw, Amsterdam. Application fee: 50 euros. Fees: 400 euros per week (excluding full board and accommodation).*

Summer Course Woudschoten. Hageheldlaan 70, Eindhoven NL-5641 GP, Netherlands *tel:* +31 40 281 6572 *fax:* +31 40 281 0033 *email:* info@zomercursuswoudschoten.com. Bekkie Bredschneyder, secretary. *11-20 August 2004. Chamber music camps for ages 12-22, all instruments from early to contemporary. Fees: 550 euros.*

Summer School around Mozart and Dvorak. La Pellegrina, Twijnstraat 42 bis, Utrecht NL-3511 ZL, Netherlands *tel:* +31 30 238 2535 *fax:* +31 30 238 2536 *email:* info@pellegrina.net. Dirkjan Horringa, director. *18-28 July 2004, applications by 1 May. Orchestral and chamber music coaching for strings, wind and piano. All ages. Fees: 550 euros.*

Norway

Ringve Museum International Summer Course in Early Music. PO Box 2045, Trondheim N-7001, Norway *tel:* +47 73 84 1450 *fax:* +47 73 84 1551. *July/August in Trondheim, applications by 1 May. Early music performance practice, chamber music and dance. Ages 18-65. Fees: 800-1200 NKR.*

Portugal

International Courses for Early Music. Academia de Musica Antiga de Lisboa, Rua Abilio Lopes do Rego, 8, Lisboa P-1200-601, Portugal *tel:* +351 21 390 7734 *fax:* +351 21 390 7734 *email:* musicantiga@mail.telepac.pt. Sofia de Mendia, director. *International course for early music, August 2004. Masterclasses in singing, recorder, traverso, violin and viola, cello and gamba, harpsichord, chamber music, choir. Fees: 270 euros. Also 2/3 day workshops throughout the year.*

Romania

Constantin Silvestri Summer Academy. 72 Warwick Gardens, London W14 8PP, UK *tel:* +44 20 7603 1396 *fax:* +44 20 7603 1396 *email:* foundation@constantinsilvestri.com. *July. Masterclasses in piano, violin, cello and chamber music. Aged 16+. Fees: £300.*

Russia

Course in St Petersburg. Bela Bartók Centre for Musicianship, 6 Frognal Court, 158 Finchley Rd, London NW3 5HL, UK *tel:* +44 20 7435 3685 *email:* Agnes.Kory@kcl.ac.uk. Agnes Kory, director. *Spring. Intensive course for musicians, music teachers, music students. Covers general musicianship, history and analysis and chamber music. Contact for details of dates and fees.*

Lets Make Music. 24b Bedford Grove, Eastbourne BN21 2DU, UK *tel:* +44 1323 642116 *email:* letsmakemusic99@hotmail.com. Peter Mayes, director. *18-25 August, Orchestra closing date 2 April 2004; 19-26 August, Choir, St Petersburg. September, Orchfest, weekend of music making in Eastbourne, UK. Fees: £40.*

Spain

Escuela de Musica Segovia. Avda Vicente Aleixandre 17, Segovia E-40006, Spain *tel:* +34 92 143 4423 *fax:* +34 92 143 4423 *email:* kent-id@teleline.es. Jose Miguel Arranz, manager. *Piano, guitar and singing summer courses in July and August for national and international students. Applications by 1 June. Ages 16-30.*

Francisco Vinas International Musical Interpretation Course. Bruc 125, Barcelona E-08037, Spain *tel:* +34 93 215 4227/457 8646 *fax:* +34 93 457 4364 *email:* info@francisco-vinas.com. Maria Vilardell, president; Bonaldo Giaiotti, tutor; Dalton Baldwin, tutor. *3 January-4 February 2004, in Barcelona. Applications by previous December. Italian Opera and Operatic Performance and acting course; German*

Classical Lied, French melodies and Lied piano accompaniment. Open to all voices and nationalities. Fees: 192 euros; auditors 45 euros.

Jimena Early Music Week. Cantax House, Lacock, Chippenham, Wiltshire SN15 2JZ, UK *tel:* +44 1249 730468 *fax:* +44 1249 730468 *email:* avdb@cantax.freeserve.co.uk. Andrew van der Beek, admin. *4-10, 11-17 April 2004. Two separate weeks for amateur choral singers, with David Allinson and JanJoost van Elburg.*

Switzerland

Académie de Musique de Sion. Sion Summer Music Academy, CP 107, Sion CH-1951, Switzerland *tel:* +41 027 322 6652 *fax:* +41 027 322 6652 *email:* info@amsion.ch. Liliane Martin, admin. *July-August 2004, applications by 1 June. No age limit. 16 different disciplines, masterclasses. Fees: 300-400 SFR per week.*

HKB Hochschule der Kuenste Bern. Music Department, Papiermuehlestrasse 13a, Bern 22 CH-3000, Switzerland *tel:* +41 31 634 9361 *fax:* +41 31 634 9390 *email:* rita.weber@hkb.bfh.ch. Rita Weber. *October. Festival, masterclasses, seminars on aspects of Jewish music and culture.*

Jeunesses Musicales. Rue Merle d'Aubigné 25, Genève CH-1207, Switzerland *tel:* +41 22 786 3273 *fax:* +41 22 786 3273 *email:* jmusicales@bluewin.ch. Magdalena Burdet, secretary; Laura Ponti, secretary. *Wide range of summer courses.*

Scuola Teatro Dimitri. Verscio CH-6653, Switzerland *tel:* +41 91 796 2414 *fax:* +41 91 796 2982 *email:* schola@teatrodimitri.ch. *Theatrical school where teaching is based primarily on study of movement of the body and theatrical expression. Complete full-time training course lasts three years, for ages 18-26. Also workshops 8-12 April and 19 July-20 August 2004 for ages 8-adult covering storytelling, pantomime, acrobatics, clowning, tightrope walking, theatrical improvisation, dance, voice. Closing date for applications 24 April 2004. Examintation 17-19 May 2004.*

Verbier Festival and Academy. 4 JJ Rousseau, Vevey CH-1800, Switzerland *tel:* +41 21 925 9060 *fax:* +41 21 925 9068 *email:* academy@verbierfestival.com. Minh-Tâm Trân, academy director. *16 July-1 August 2004, applications by 1 February. Aged under 30. Workshops for violin, viola, cello, piano, voice and dance. Fees: 2000 SFR (tuition and accommodation) plus 100 SFR registration.*

The White Prince Studio. PO Box 84, Vacallo CH-6833, Switzerland *fax:* +41 91 682 7185 *email:* thewhiteprincestudio@hotmail.com. *String academy, summer masterclasses and workshops.*

USA

Aspen Music School. Office of Student Services, 2 Music School Rd, Aspen CO 81611, USA *tel:* +1 970 925 3254 *fax:* +1 970 925 5708 *email:* school@aspenmusic.org. Joan O Gordon, student services. *21 June-22 August 2004, applications by February. Full range of courses and private lessons; orchestral, opera, vocal concert studies, composition, conducting, chamber music, classical guitar. No age restriction (most aged 18-22). Fees: $2500, tuition; $2800, room and board.*

Indiana University School of Music. Special Programs, Merrill Hall, 003 Indiana University, School of Music, Bloomington, Indiana 47405, USA *tel:* +1 812 855 6025 *fax:* +1 812 855 4936 *email:* musicsp@indiana.edu.

Helena Walsh, director. *June-end July 2004. Aged 12+. Variety of programmes from pre-college to adult music masterclasses. Contact for brochure.*

The International Festival-Institute at Round Top. PO Box 89, Round Top TX 78954-0089, USA *tel:* +1 979 249 3129 *fax:* +1 979 249 3100 *email:* jamesd@festivalhill.org. James Dick, founder/artistic director; Alain G Declert, programme director. *30 May-11 July 2004, applications by 20 February. A professional summer institute for advanced study and performance. Orchestral and chamber music. Fees: $600. Scholarships available. Open to those aged 18+.*

Ithaca College Chamber Music Institute. Ithaca Talent Education, PO Box 669, Ithaca NY 14851, USA *tel:* +1 607 272 6006 *fax:* +1 607 275 0239 *email:* ite@lakenet.org. Sanford Reuning, director. *July, applications by March. Ages 12-18. Fees: $1900.*

Ithaca Violoncello Institute. 125 Ridgecrest Rd, Ithaca NY 14850, USA *tel:* +1 607 273 8896 *email:* einar_jeff_holm@hotmail.com. Einar Holm, director/founder. *Late June-August for 7 weeks. About 12 serious amateur or professionally-minded cellists, aged (mature) 16+. All perform solo and ensemble weekly in concert. 2-6 lessons weekly. Practice habits analysed. Fees: c $3300 including tuition, room and board.*

The Kodály Institute at Capital University. Conservatory of Music, Capital University, 2199 E Main Street, Columbus OH 43209-2394, USA *tel:* +1 614 236 6267 *fax:* +1 614 236 6935 (FAO Dr Mathias) *email:* smathias@capital.edu. Sandra Mathias, director. *19 July-6 August 2004, applications by 1 June. Teacher-training course utilising the Kodály philosophy of music education, levels 1, 2 and 3. Adults only. OAKE endorsed certification course. Also Master of Music in Music Education with a Kodály emphasis available, and a 1-week boy-choir day camp for young male singers.*

Magic Mountain Music Farm, Practice Marathon Retreats. 817 West End Ave, New York NY 10025, USA *tel:* +1 212 662 6634; +1 607 263 2304 *fax:* +1 212 662 2916; 607 263 9647 *email:* musicfarm@mindspring.com. Burton Kaplan, director. *2-17 January, 9-16 February, 8-15 March, 22 May-6 June, 3-18 July, 31 July-10 August (performance power session), 21 August-5 September (orchestral excerpts session), 18-25 October 2004. For professional string performers and teachers and advanced college and conservatory students. Daily workshops to improve concentration, practising effectiveness, etc. Fees: $40 registration; $1525 tuition and board for 16 days; $800 tuition and board for 8 days.*

Steans Institute for Young Artists. Ravinia Festival, 418 Sheridan Rd, Highland Park IL 60035, USA *tel:* +1 847 266 5106 *fax:* +1 847 266 5063. Diane P Dorn, director. *June-August. Open to those aged 15-30. Four programmes: singers, piano and strings, jazz, vocal chamber music. Entry by audition. Private coaching and masterclasses with internationally renowned tutors. Preview concerts presented as part of the Ravinia Festival. Everyone accepted receives full scholarship.*

Western Wind Summer Workshops in Ensemble Singing. Western Wind Vocal Ensemble, 263 West 86th St, New York NY 10024, USA *tel:* +1 800 788 2187 *fax:* +1 212 873 2849 *email:* workshops@westernwind.org. William Zukof, executive producer. *Late June/July, apply by early June. Workshops in ensemble singing from medieval and renaissance to contemporary including jazz and pop for all ages. Fees: $149-399 (tuition), $150-600 (room and board).*

Services

Marketing

Suppliers and Services

Recording

Marketing, Fundraising and Related Services

This section provides information on the resources necessary for the successful marketing of music and musicians, and on fundraising, whether in the form of patronage or sponsorship.

Marketing and Organisational Management

Entrants listed here usually offer a comprehensive service which may include guidance on market research, marketing planning, advertising, public and media relations, design and print, sales and sales promotion, pricing, personnel selection and training; some offer an event management service and some will provide an interim management service for organisations. There are also some organisations, closely allied in terms of their function, who specialise in arranging and promoting concerts; these are Concert Managements and are listed in the next sub-section. Readers seeking a service should first look here and then move on to the specialist sub-sections which follow. If uncertain as to which service is required, do not hesitate to make preliminary enquiries by telephone. There now exists a membership organisation for practitioners in arts marketing, the **Arts Marketing Association,** 7a Clifton Court, Cambridge CB1 7BN *tel:* 01223 578078 *fax:* 01223 245862 *email:* info@a-m-a.co.uk.

ABL Cultural Consulting. 31 St Martin's Lane, London WC2N 4ER *tel:* 020 7420 9700 *fax:* 020 7420 9701 *email:* info@ablconsulting.com. Sheila Benjamin, head of business and admin.

AEA Consulting. Studio 2.3, 11-29 Fashion St, London E1 6PX *tel:* 020 7377 6559 *fax:* 020 7377 5992 *email:* office@aeaconsulting.com. Kelly Gerrard, snr consultant; Magnus von Wistinghausen, snr consultant; Sue Daniels, snr consultant. *Works with clients to provide innovative and well-grounded solutions to strategic, operational and financial problems. Areas of expertise include business planning and financial modelling, cultural planning, organisational development, feasibility studies for capital projects and policy development and review.*

Anderton, Robin. 61 Brassey Rd, Winchester SO22 6SB *tel:* 01962 856326 *fax:* 01962 852851 *email:* robin.anderton@lineone.net. *Admin for w/shops, courses and auditions. Concert mgt.*

Anna Hassan Arts Marketing. 54 Elm Rd, Hale, Altrincham, Cheshire WA15 9QP *tel:* 0161 928 3085 *fax:* 0161 929 9648 *email:* ahassan@easynet.co.uk. *Freelance arts mkt and admin consultant.*

Blue Frog Music Management. 3 Ivy Mews, 153 Burton Rd, West Didsbury, Manchester M20 1LD *tel:* 0161 448 7598 *fax:* 0161 445 0587 *email:* info@bluefroguk.com. Bob Riley; Fiona Sinclair. *Specialist mus events designers, corporate entertainment, concert and festival mgt, artists' promotional services.*

Carboni Classical Media. PO Box 308, Sevenoaks, Kent TN15 0ZW *tel:* 01732 811036 *fax:* 01732 811105 *email:* carbonimedia@aol.com. *PR and mkt for mus, arts and educ. Projects for UK, Europe and USA.*

Cardiff Arts Marketing Ltd. 2 Market House, Market Rd, Canton, Cardiff CF5 1QE *tel:* 029 2037 3736 *fax:* 029 2038 4141 *email:* mail@

cardiff-arts-marketing.co.uk. Joanna Sargeant, dir; Rebecca Shepperd, mkt development mgr; Roisin O'Brien, mkt information mgr; Julia Griffiths, admin mgr. *Marketing and mkt research, audience development and consultancy. Tactical services include print distribution, database mgt, direct mail and campaign co-ordination.*

Chadwick Jones Associates. 2 Kelvedon Rd, London SW6 5BW *tel:* 020 7731 6012 *fax:* 020 7736 7271 *email:* projects@cja-arts.com. Anna Gaio, partner; Ian Jones, partner; Siarlys Evans. *Feasibility studies, planning, mkt, mgt, mkt research, fundraising, building projects.*

Cultural Intelligence Ltd. 50 The Street, Melton, Woodbridge, Suffolk IP12 1PW *tel:* 01394 388029 *fax:* 01394 382672 *email:* info@ audience.co.uk. Eric Orme, dir; Tina Neill, research mgr. *Research methodology, project design, data collection, analysis and reporting. Audience surveys, data mapping, focus groups, data analysis providing full report of findings and recommendations for local authorities, theatres, ACE offices, etc.*

David Jackson and Associates. Crowlin Cottage, Little London Rd, Cross in Hand, nr Heathfield, E Sussex TN21 0LT *tel:* 01435 868808 *fax:* 01435 868808 *email:* davidjaay@aol.com. David Jackson, dir. *Arts mgt consultancy, audience development, box office organisation, mkt schemes, customer care, events planning and mgt, gala concerts.*

Gillian Perkins, Arts Consultant. 10 Gurney Way, Cambridge CB4 2ED *tel:* 01223 350544 *email:* gillian.perkins@dsl.pipex. *Concert and educ project mgt, mkt and profile raising for mus events. Sensible evaluation throughout.*

Helen Fraser Arts Management. Gordon Lodge, Snitterton Rd, Matlock, Derbys DE4 3LZ *tel:* 01629 760791 *fax:* 01629 760791 *email:* hf@artsland.demon.co.uk. *Business planning, funding, organising events, concert mgt.*

Impulse Music Consultants. 18 Hillfield Park, Muswell Hill, London N10 3QS *tel:* 020 8444 8587 *fax:* 020 8245 0358 *email:* impulse@ impulse-music.co.uk. Geraldine Allen; Sarah Rodgers. *Mus consultants for professional mus-making in every context. Specialists in project co-ordination, copyright advice and internet services.*

Jackson Quigg Associates Ltd. 26 Artral Ave, Hipperholme, Halifax HX3 8NN *tel:* 01422 204405 *fax:* 01422 200183 *email:* JacksonQuigg@aol.com. Piers Jackson, dir; Anne-Marie Quigg,

dir. *Development consultants: arts, community, media. Business planning, fundraising, feasibility studies, profile raising, strategic planning, training, mgt development.*

Kallaway Ltd. 2 Portland Rd, Holland Park, London W11 4LA *tel:* 020 7221 7883 *fax:* 020 7229 4595. William Kallaway, mgr dir. *Communications and mkt through sponsored arts, educ and community events and programmes. Services include consultancy, event production and mgt, promotion and media planning.*

Kivity, Sharon. 19b Albert Rd, Teddington, Middx TW11 0BD *tel:* 020 8977 2961 *fax:* 020 8977 6281 *email:* sharonarts@btinternet.com. Sharon Kivity, snr consultant. *Training, promotion, publicity and PR services. Event mgt. Festival programming and organisation.*

The Management Centre. Blue Jay Works, 117 Gauden Rd, London SW4 6LE *tel:* 020 7978 1516 *fax:* 020 7978 2125. Bernard Ross, dir; Clare Segal, dir. *Provides mgt and fundraising training through open and in-house programmes for non-profit organisations. Also carries out consultancy.*

Manygate Management. Trees, Ockham Rd South, East Horsley, Surrey KT24 6QE *tel:* 01483 281300 *fax:* 01483 281811 *email:* manygate@easynet.co.uk. John Boyden, dir. *Sponsorship and fundraising for orchs, recordings, festivals and concerts. Concert mgt, mkt strategies, concepts, research.*

Matthews Millman Ltd. Marine House, 23 Mount Stuart Square, Cardiff Bay, Cardiff CF10 5DP *tel:* 029 2046 2121 *fax:* 029 2046 2122 *email:* maimie@matthewsmillman.co.uk. John Matthews, dir; Rhoslyn Davies, project mgr; Maimie Davis, admin. *London office: Unit 6, Burghley Yard, 106 Burghley Rd, London NW5 1AL tel: 020 7284 4286 fax: 020 7284 4287. Anne Millman, dir. Specialist consultants in strategic planning, feasibility studies, research and training for the arts.*

Millward Brown Market Research Ltd. Olympus Ave, Tachbrook Park, Warwick CV34 6RJ *tel:* 01926 452233 *fax:* 01926 833600 *email:* bob.barnes@uk.millwardbrown.com. Bob Barnes, charts dir. *Specialist in mkt research for arts, sponsorship, audience development. Compilers of the official record industry charts.*

Music Company (London) Ltd. 103 Churston Drive, Morden, Surrey SM4 4JE *tel:* 020 8540 7357 *fax:* 020 8542 4854 *email:* musicco@ musicco.force9.co.uk. Melanne Mueller, mgr dir; Simon Foster, exec dir.

Natalie Steed Productions. BAC, Lavender Hill, London SW11 5TN *tel:* 020 7228 6001/6010 *email:* ns@nataliesteedproductions.co.uk. Natalie Steed; Kate Wyatt, project asst. *Arts mgt company managing and producing new mus theatre and opera projects for the UK and internationally. Deals in all aspects of mgt, fundraising and promotion.*

Nicky Webb Associates. 77 Thrale Road, London SW16 1NU *tel:* 020 8769 7002 *fax:* 020 8696 7293 *email:* nickywebb@tiscali.co.uk. Nicky Webb. *Specialist mkt and PR for the arts.*

Open Play Ltd. Suite 106, Hittongrove Business Centre, Hatherley Mews, London E17 4QP *tel:* 020 8520 6644 *fax:* 020 8520 7755 *email:* info@openplay.co.uk. David Hoskins, dir. *CD and multimedia promotion company; specialist project mgt service to produce compilation CDs, CD-ROM, enhanced CD and DVD for event promotion; on site audio mastering, CD manufacturing, design and mgt of bespoke multimedia information systems.*

Positive Solutions. 6 Bluecoat Chambers, School Lane, Liverpool L1 3BX *tel:* 0151 709 6511 *fax:* 0151 707 2577 *email:* solutions@ positive.demon.co.uk. Peter Booth, snr consultant. *Specialises in research and consultancy in the arts and cultural industries.*

STR Music Marketing and Management. 296 Hughenden Rd, High Wycombe, Bucks HP13 5PE *tel:* 01494 462048 *fax:* 01494 462048 *email:* admin@strmmm.demon.co.uk. Sean Rourke, mgr dir; Deborah Keyser, gen mgr. *Strategic planning, comprehensive mkt campaigns and sponsorship consultant, lottery assessments and feasibility studies. Exhibition concepts.*

Spero Communications Ltd. Grampian House, Meridian Gate, Marsh Wall, London E14 9YT *tel:* 020 7538 9946 *fax:* 020 7538 4747 *email:* spero@sperocom.co.uk. Ian Spero, mgr dir; Caroline Teunissen, business development mgr. *Interactive mkt programmes which combine innovation with sound business objectives.*

TEAM - The Entertainment and Arts Marketers (Merseyside) Ltd. 4th Floor, Gostin Building, 32-36 Hanover St, Liverpool L1 4LN *tel:* 0151 709 6881 *fax:* 0151 707 2555 *email:* info@team-uk.org. Bernard Martin, dir; Rachael Hazzard, audience development mgr; Garnet Marshall, operations mgr. *Primary and secondary research, project mgt, mkt audits and planning, skills audits; other audience development work. Print distribution via subsidiary.*

Theatre Projects Consultants Ltd. 4 Apollo Studios, Charlton Kings Rd, London NW5 2SW *tel:* 020 7482 4224 *fax:* 020 7284 0636 *email:* post@tpc-lon.com. D Staples, A Russell, J Godden, A Field, L Fleming, I Mackintosh, Marion Daehms, Andy Hayles, Mark Stroomer, dirs. *Theatre design consultancy (not a leisure consultancy) including feasibility, planning, design, project development and implementation. Also offices in the USA.*

Tom Petzal and Associates. Pantiles Chambers, 85 High St, Tunbridge Wells, Kent TN1 1YG *tel:* 01892 506968 *fax:* 01892 547120 *email:* tompetzal@aol.com. Tom Petzal, mgr dir. *PR, artists mgt, mkt, sponsorship consultancy, fundraising. 25 years' experience in the arts worldwide.*

Concert and Personal Management

This sub-section includes organisations specialising in the marketing and overall management of concerts, tours, festivals and music for special occasions; the service offered will frequently include booking of venues, concert programme production, organisation of press and other receptions. The sub-section also includes organisations providing a personal PR service and/or a representation/agency service for musicians. Concert Managements do not act as principals, ie, they are not risk-takers. *See also* **Marketing and Organisational Management.**

All Music Management. 11 Robin Close, Sandy, Beds SG19 2TB *tel:* 01767 692521; 07876 337599 *email:* karen@allmusicmgmt.co.uk. Karen Foster, mgr. *Efficient and creative specialists in orch, tour and concert mgt. Also provides ens for corporate and private functions.*

Anglo-European Arts. 25 Fournier St, Spitalfields, London E1 6QE *tel:* 020 7247 7219. Carolyn Humphreys, dir. *Concert, event and festival mgt; PR consultant.*

Antony Pristavec. 3 Plough Way, Surrey Quays, London SE16 2LS *tel:* 020 7231 5235 *fax:* 020 7231 0535 *email:* Pristavec@aol.com. Antony Pristavec. *Personal, concert, festival and tour mgt.*

Arts Bazaar. 99b Osbaldeston Rd, London N16 6NP *tel:* 020 8806 6875 *fax:* 020 8806 9943 *email:* info@artsbazaar.com. Huw Davies, mgr dir, Ian Pressland, gen mgr. *Mus mgt, promotion and consultancy.*

Blue Frog Music Management. 3 Ivy Mews, 153 Burton Rd, West Didsbury, Manchester M20 1LD *tel:* 0161 448 7598 *fax:* 0161 445 0587 *email:* info@bluefroguk.com. Fiona Sinclair; Robert Riley. *Events mgt, festival mgt, concert promotion.*

Brougham Associates. 48 Woolstone Rd, London SE23 2SG *tel:* 020 8291 6694 *fax:* 020 8291 6694 *email:* brougham.associates@virgin.net. Henrietta Brougham. *Festival admin (Paxos festival); contemporary mus promotion (Metier records, UYMP); website design and multimedia projects for individuals and organisations.*

Cabaret International Ltd. PO Box 208, Walsall WS3 3YP *tel:* 01922 476201 *fax:* 01922 476201 *email:* ent@cabaretinternational.com. M A Ray, dir. *Concert and personal mgt, tour and event mgt, organisers.*

Fox Jones & Associates. 54 Crofton Rd, London SE5 8NB *tel:* 020 7701 3107 *fax:* 020 7701 6918 *email:* foxjones@compuserve.com. Jeremy Fox, president; Margaret Barkman, mgr. *Mgt consulting; personal mgt for violist Rivka Golani, pianist Daniel Hoexter and cond Eduard Serov.*

GBZ Management. PO Box 11845, London SE21 8ZS *tel:* 020 8761 6565 *fax:* 020 8670 3195 *email:* music@gbz.demon.co.uk. Gwenneth Bransby-Zachary, dir. *PR, concert and event mgt.*

Hazard Chase Ltd. Norman House, Cambridge Place, Cambridge CB2 1NS *tel:* 01223 312400 *fax:* 01223 460827 *email:* helen.poole@hazardchase.co.uk. Helen Poole, dir, events and mkt. *Concert and event mgt and mkt for solo artists and ens. Mkt and PR consultancy.*

Helen Fraser Arts Management. Gordon Lodge, Snitterton Rd, Matlock, Derbyshire DE4 3LZ *tel:* 01629 760791 *fax:* 01629 760791 *email:* hf@artsland.demon.co.uk. *Organises events, tour co-ordination, concert mgt.*

Influence. Gazeley Gate, Bures, Suffolk CO8 5BW *tel:* 01787 227361 *fax:* 01787 227361 *email:* michaelheyland@btinternet.com. Michael Heyland, events consultant. *Events consultant, specialising in charity and corporate events in the UK and abroad, from concerts and conferences to rallies and wine tastings.*

JBBS. Flat 5, 125 Hornsey Lane, London N6 5NH *tel:* 020 7263 0705 *email:* jbbs@easynet.co.uk. John Batten. *Personal mgr to Ana-Maria Vera, Charles Owen, Sara Trickey and the Bronte String Quartet.*

JLM Artists. 1 Venice House, 272 Willesden Lane, London NW2 5RB *tel:* 020 8451 2004 *fax:* 020 8208 5004 *email:* jlm.artists@virgin.net. John Nicholas, dir. *Concert mgt, career consultation and promotion. Profile enhancement.*

Kantor Concert Management and Public Relations. 67 Teignmouth Rd, London NW2 4EA *tel:* 020 8208 2480 *fax:* 020 8208 2490 *email:* dkantor.kcm@btinternet.com. Denise Kantor, proprietor. *Concert mgt; publicity and PR for one-off and long-term contracts; personal and financial mgt; PA and secretariat services; brochure, leaflet and website design.*

Kathy Avdiev. 28 Rivermount, Walton-on-Thames, Surrey KT12 2PR *tel:* 01932 246796 *fax:* 01932 267188 *email:* pitcairn@globalnet.co.uk. *Artist, concert and personal mgt, project mgt; programme advertising sales. General mgt for Divertimenti.*

Ken Chaproniere Arts and Events Management. 3 The Clock House, Little Brickhill, Milton Keynes MK17 9NR *tel:* 01525 261670 *fax:* 01525 261291 *email:* kchaproniere@aol.com. Ken Chaproniere. *Mkt, fundraising, event mgt and strategic planning within the arts and entertainment industry, specialising in mus.*

Ken Spencer Personal Management/PAG Concert Promotions. 138 Sandy Hill Rd, London SE18 7BA *tel:* 020 8854 2558 *fax:* 020 8854 2258 *email:* pagandferret@hotmail.com. Michael Green, promotion/media. *Artist personal mgt (classical singers, pianists, accompanists). Concert booking and promotion.*

Keown Artists' Management. 62 Chestnut Rd, London SE27 9LE *tel:* 020 8761 4221 *email:* julianshaw@ntlworld.com. Sarah Keown. *Concert and personal mgt.*

Lana Bezanov (LB) Promotions. 70 Gowan Ave, London SW6 6RF *tel:* 020 7736 4717; 020 7731 5410 (ISDN) *fax:* 020 7731 8009 *email:* info@lbproms.co.uk. Lana Bezanov, dir; Margarita Kazala,

admin; G Bezanov, IT dir. *Concert, project and festival mgt; educ tours and charity event mgt; public and media relations consultancy; all forms of media advertising (buying and sales); brochure, programme, leaflet, poster and advertising design and production. Member of IAMA.*

Lisa Peacock Concert Management. 23a Holland Rd, London W14 8HJ *tel:* 020 7602 1416 *fax:* 020 7371 2726 *email:* lisapeacok@aol.com. Lisa Peacock. *Concert mgt.*

Maureen Lunn Management. Top Farm, Parish Lane, Hedgerley, Bucks SL2 3JH *tel:* 01753 645008 *fax:* 01753 647431 *email:* m.m.lunn@amserve.net. *Concert mgt.*

Michael Etherton Concert Management. 57 Golders Green Rd, London NW11 8EL *tel:* 020 8381 4707 *fax:* 020 8381 4606 *email:* michael.etherton@metherton.co.uk. Michael Etherton. *Concert mgt for solo artists, ens and orchs.*

Music Inter Alia. 80 Hackford Rd, London SW9 0RG *tel:* 020 7642 9415 *fax:* 020 7642 9412 *email:* info@musicinteralia.com. Lorna Neill, dir. *UK and international media, promotion and mus mgt.*

Music Management (UK) Ltd. PO Box 1105, London SW1X 7DX *tel:* 020 7823 1111 *fax:* 020 7823 1001 *email:* mm@musicmanagement.demon.co.uk. *Corporate entertainment specialists and concert promotion.*

NB Management. PO Box 100, East Horsley KT24 6WN *tel:* 01483 282666 *fax:* 01483 284777 *email:* nick@bomford.com. Nick Bomford. *Concert mgt and admin for orchs, ens and mus-theatre companies.*

Pascall Promotions. 31 Lanchester Rd, London N6 4SX *tel:* 020 8883 8740 *fax:* 020 8883 5961 *email:* cdpascall@aol.com. Carolyn Pascall, dir. *Concert mgt and promotion for inst and vocal ens and event mgt for corporate sponsors. Brochure and leaflet design and PR. Admin and promotion for conds and composers.*

Performing Arts Management Ltd. 7 Canalside, Clarence Mill, Bollington, Macclesfield, Cheshire SK10 5JZ *tel:* 01625 575681 *fax:* 01625 572839 *email:* office@performingarts.co.uk. Clare Scott. *Specialists in promotion and mgt of large-scale, open-air orch concerts.*

Peter Zander Artist and Concert Management. 22 Romilly St, London W1D 5AG *tel:* 020 7437 4767 *email:* peterzan.berlin@virgin.net. Peter Zander, dir. *Artist mgt. Promotion, PR and sponsorship for festivals, concerts and recitals. Supervision of leaflet, brochure, poster and advertising design and distribution.*

Prelude. The Old Stables, 10 Timber Lane, Caterham, Surrey CR3 6LZ *tel:* 01883 344300 *fax:* 01883 347712 *email:* sales@preludeentertainment.co.uk. Philippa Lunn, dir. *Wide range of entertainment from background mus to major concerts for business and social events.*

Robert Masters Artistes' Personal Management. Lower Marshay, Pennymoor, Tiverton EX16 8LZ *tel:* 01363 866665 *fax:* 01363 866667 *email:* statementrecords@yahoo.co.uk. *Concert promotion and personal mgt.*

Roy Baker Concert Management. 25 Lynors Ave, Rochester, Kent ME2 3NQ *tel:* 01634 714434 *fax:* 01634 714434. *Arranges and promotes concerts, special events, educ projects and tours on behalf of charity organisations and foreign embassies; also fundraising and sponsorship.*

STR Music Marketing and Management. 296 Hughenden Rd, High Wycombe, Bucks HP13 5PE *tel:* 01494 462048 *fax:* 01494 462048 *email:* admin@strmmm.demon.co.uk. Sean T Rourke, mgr dir; Deborah Keyser, gen mgr. *Mkt, publicity, PR consultant, personal and concert mgt, media focus and mailing service. Lottery assessments.*

Sarah Gordon Concert Management. 110 Gloucester Ave, London NW1 8HX *tel:* 020 7483 2681 *fax:* 020 7586 5343 *email:* sarah.gordon@easynet.co.uk. *Concert mgt and mus festival admin. Some artist mgt.*

Smith, Amanda. 25 Prospect Park, Southborough, Tunbridge Wells, Kent TN4 0EQ *tel:* 01892 534525 *fax:* 01892 534525 *email:* amandasmith@toadinthehole.org.uk. *Orch, tour and concert mgt.*

Valerie Barber PR. Suite 2, 9a St John's Wood High St, London NW8 7NG *tel:* 020 7586 8560 *fax:* 020 7586 9246 *email:* vbpr@btclick.com. *General mgt of Melvyn Tan; UK, Australia and New Zealand mgt of Skampa quartet.*

Public and Media Relations

These organisations help musicians and music organisations create public awareness of themselves via newspapers, magazines, radio and TV; their work often inter-relates with that of organisations listed in other sub-sections. *See also* **Marketing and Organisational Management.**

A P Associates. 25e Frognal, London NW3 6AR *tel:* 020 7794 7633 *fax:* 020 7431 7320 *email:* alexandra@mercer.uk.com. *PR and mgt for the classical mus industry.*

Allegro Arts Marketing. 25 The Chine, London N10 3PX *tel:* 020 8883 1724 *fax:* 020 8883 1724 *email:* euroartsco@aol.com. Bob Moffat. *Full service mkt and PR agency. Considerable experience in opera and choral mus.*

Annon Music Services. 44 Cromwell Rd, Canterbury, Kent CT1 3LE *tel:* 01227 463867 *fax:* 01227 463867 *email:* annonmusic@aol.com. Anne Hancox, dir. *Agency working on behalf of musicians and singers.*

Brown, Peter J. 25 Fair Acres, Roehampton Lane, London SW15 5LX *tel:* 020 8876 9011 *fax:* 020 8876 9011. Peter Brown, chief exec; Christopher Brown, account supervisor. *PR and mkt consultant for mus organisations and artists.*

Carboni Classical Media. PO Box 308, Sevenoaks, Kent TN15 0ZW *tel:* 01732 811036 *fax:* 01732 811105 *email:* carbonimedia@aol.com. Marius Carboni, mgr; Gill French. *PR and mkt for mus, arts and educ. Projects for UK, Europe and USA.*

Carlson, Mary De Camp. 9 Campden Hill Square, London W8 7LB *tel:* 020 7221 8296 *fax:* 020 7792 8847 *email:* marycarlson@easynet.co.uk. *Specialist in PR and exec recruitment for the classical mus industry.*

Clare Adams Associates. Clattercote House, Claydon, Banbury, Oxon OX17 1ES *tel:* 01295 690344 *fax:* 01295 690413 *email:* adamsarts@aol.com. *Press and PR consultant.*

Clarke Agency. 39 Birnam Rd, Islington, London N4 3LJ *tel:* 020 7281 0672 *fax:* 020 7281 0672 *email:* herbie@birnam39.freeserve.co.uk. Herbie Clarke, mgr dir. *Freelance public and media relations for musicians and performing artists.*

David Fraser PR. 22 Dairsie Rd, London SE9 1XH *tel:* 020 8859 2112 *fax:* 020 8859 2112 *email:* davidfraser@fraserpr.freeserve.co.uk. David Fraser, dir. *Publicity and editorial services for mus and the arts; PR consultant specialising in classical mus, jazz and broadcasting.*

Diana Hirst Public Relations. 55 Marmora Rd, Honor Oak, London SE22 0RY *tel:* 020 8299 1914 *fax:* 020 8299 1914 *email:* HirstPR@aol.com. Diana Hirst; Joanne Whalley. *PR and promotion for soloists, composers, performing groups; advice surgeries on PR and self-promotion.*

Elizabeth Day Public Relations. 15 Grove Court, Circus Rd, London NW8 9EN *tel:* 020 7286 5390 *fax:* 020 7286 4218 *email:* elizabeth@daylight.clara.co.uk. Elizabeth Day, dir. *Press, media and PR advisers for all arts, festivals and artists.*

Graham-Dixon, Suzanne. Masketts Manor, Nutley, E Sussex TN22 3HD *tel:* 01825 712719 *email:* sue@graham-dixon.com. Suzanne Graham-Dixon. *UK press offr for Drottningholm, Pesaro and Wexford festivals.*

Hazard Chase Promotions. Norman House, Cambridge Place, Cambridge CB2 1NS *tel:* 01223 312400 *fax:* 01223 460827 *email:* promotions@hazardchase.co.uk. Helen Poole, dir. *PR and mkt for the arts.*

Helen Anderson Press and Public Relations. 58 Claylands Rd, London SW8 1NZ *tel:* 020 7735 1860 *fax:* 020 7735 1860 *email:* helen@helenandersonpr.co.uk. Helen Anderson, consultant. *Press and PR consultant.*

Ian Martin Public Relations. 27 Great Pulteney Street, Bath BA2 4BU *tel:* 01225 464898; 07970 895194 *fax:* 01225 464898 *email:* ianmartinpr@phonecoop.coop. Ian Martin, PR consultant. *Press and media relations, writing and design of brochures, programmes, newsletters and internet sites, and event mgt for artists, concerts and festivals.*

Kantor Concert Management and Public Relations. 67 Teignmouth Rd, London NW2 4EA *tel:* 020 8208 2480 *fax:* 020 8208 2490 *email:* dkantor.kcm@btinternet.com. Denise Kantor, proprietor. *Publicity and PR for one-off and long-term contracts; concert mgt; personal and financial mgt; PA and secretarial services; brochure, leaflet and website design.*

Katherine Howard Public Relations. Hope House, Pettaugh Lane, Gosbeck, Suffolk IP6 9SD *tel:* 01473 892007 *fax:* 08700 511772 *email:* info@katherinehoward.co.uk. *Specialising in all areas of UK*

media - classical, jazz, contemporary,world mus and mainstream projects. Clients include record companies, artists, arts events, book publishing and personalities.

LAP International Public Relations and Marketing. Strategy House, 51a Westgate, Almondbury, Huddersfield, W Yorks HD5 8XF *tel:* 01484 426000 *fax:* 01484 421209 *email:* roz@redwards45.fsnet.co.uk. Rosamund Edwards, principal.

Lana Bezanov (LB) Promotions. 70 Gowan Ave, London SW6 6RF *tel:* 020 7736 4717; 020 7731 5410 (ISDN) *fax:* 020 7731 8009 *email:* info@lbproms.co.uk. Lana Bezanov, dir; Margarita Kazala, admin; G Bezanov, IT dir. *Concert, project and festival mgt; educ tours and charity event mgt; public and media relations consultancy; all forms of media advertising (buying and sales); brochure, programme, leaflet, poster and advertising design and production. Member of IAMA.*

Lewis, Dvora. 12 Pilgrim's Lane, London NW3 1SN *tel:* 020 7435 9257 *fax:* 020 7435 1417 *email:* dl@dvoralewis.com. *Freelance PR consultant.*

Liaisons Abroad. Chenil House, 181-183 King's Rd, Chelsea, London SW3 5EB *tel:* 020 7376 4020 *fax:* 020 7376 4442 *email:* info@liaisonsabroad.com. Massimina Caneva, mgr dir. *A mkt leader in promotion of international mus events and ticket reservations. Well established links with the travel industry.*

Macbeth Media Relations. Suite 3 Mountfort House, 15-16 Barnsbury Square, London N1 1JL *tel:* 020 7700 5959 *fax:* 020 7700 1329 *email:* macbethg@btinternet.com. Ginny Macbeth; Anne White; Miriam McCarthy. *UK and international press for soloists, orchs, festivals and record companies.*

Margaret Skeet PR. 12 Silverdale Rd, London E4 9PN *tel:* 020 8527 4512 *fax:* 020 8527 4512 *email:* margaretskeet@aol.com. Margaret Skeet. *PR consultant for performing arts and recording industries, particularly DVD/video.*

Music Company (London) Ltd. 103 Churston Drive, Morden, Surrey SM4 4JE *tel:* 020 8540 7357 *fax:* 020 8542 4854 *email:* musicco@ musicco.force9.co.uk. Melanne Mueller, mgr dir; Simon Foster, exec dir.

Music Inter Alia. 80 Hackford Rd, London SW9 0RG *tel:* 020 7642 9415 *fax:* 020 7642 9412 *email:* info@musicinteralia.com. Lorna Neill, dir. *PR, promotion and international mgt of artists and the arts.*

Music Management (UK) Ltd. PO Box 1105, London SW1X 7DX *tel:* 020 7823 1111 *fax:* 020 7823 1001. *Corporate entertainment specialists and concert promotion.*

Nicky Webb Associates. 77 Thrale Rd, London SW16 1NU *tel:* 020 8769 7002 *fax:* 020 8696 7293 *email:* nickywebb@tiscali.co.uk. Nicky Webb. *Specialist mkt and PR for the arts.*

Phillips, Richard. Northgate Music, Northgate, Warwick CV34 4JL *tel:* 01926 492468 *fax:* 01926 407606 *email:* richardp@ warwickarts.org.uk. *Freelance publicist and sponsorship expert.*

STR Music Marketing and Management. 296 Hughenden Rd, High Wycombe, Bucks HP13 5PE *tel:* 01494 462048 *fax:* 01494 462048 *email:* admin@strmmm.demon.co.uk. Sean T Rourke, mgr dir; Deborah Keyser, gen mgr. *PR consultant for festivals, orchs and local authorities. Sponsor liaison services. Lottery feasibility studies. Media campaigns.*

Tom Petzal and Associates. Pantiles Chambers, 85 High St, Tunbridge Wells, Kent TN1 1YG *tel:* 01892 506968 *fax:* 01892 547120 *email:* tompetzal@aol.com. Tom Petzal, mgr dir. *Mgt, fundraising, promotion, artist mgt, PR.*

Tony Barlow Associates. 3 Choumert Square, London SE15 4RE *tel:* 020 7358 9291; 07774 407385 *fax:* 020 7358 9291 *email:* artspublicity@hotmail.com. *Concert mgt; mkt and press for mus, dance and theatre; fundraising.*

Town House Publicity Ltd. 45 Islington Park St, London N1 1QB *tel:* 020 7226 7450 *fax:* 020 7359 6026 *email:* thp@townhousepublicity.co.uk. Mary Fulton, mgr dir; Krista Goodman, account mgr. *Specialist in arts and media PR, and campaigns throughout the UK and Europe.*

Valerie Barber PR. Suite 2, 9a St John's Wood High St, London NW8 7NG *tel:* 020 7586 8560 *fax:* 020 7586 9246 *email:* vbpr@btclick.com. *PR consultancy specialising in UK and European media coverage, including jazz and world mus.*

WebProjects. Suites 5-7 Meridian House, 28 Station Rd, Redhill, Surrey RH1 1PD *tel:* 01737 768127 *email:* mark@webprojects.co.uk. Mark Walmsley, mgr dir; Ben Sauer, technical dir; Matthew Lindop, project dir; Andy Walker, creative dir. *Efficient creation, sharing and distribution of information.*

Advertising

Organisations listed here will advise on the advertising content of a marketing campaign and will buy advertising space for clients; some specialise in selling advertising on behalf of clients in concert programmes. *See also* **Marketing and Organisational Management.**

Cabbell Publishing Limited. Woodman Works, 204 Durnsford Rd, London SW19 8DR *tel:* 020 8971 8450 *fax:* 020 8971 8480 *email:* andrew@cabbell.co.uk. Andrew Todd, mgr dir; Jane Stoggles, ad mgr; Zoya Berkeley, ad mgr. *Specialist in opera, classical mus, festival and theatre advertising. Souvenir brochures, booking brochures and performance programmes.*

Lana Bezanov (LB) Promotions. 70 Gowan Ave, London SW6 6RF *tel:* 020 7736 4717; 020 7731 5410 (ISDN) *fax:* 020 7731 8009 *email:* info@lbproms.co.uk. Lana Bezanov, dir; Margarita Kazala, admin; G Bezanov, IT dir. *Concert, project and festival mgt; educ tours and charity event mgt; public and media relations consultancy; all forms of media advertising (buying and sales); brochure, programme, leaflet, poster and advertising design and production. Member of IAMA.*

Radford Advertising Marketing Ltd. Blackfriars House, Parsonage, Manchester M3 2JA *tel:* 0161 832 8807 *fax:* 0161 832 2460 *email:* r@dford.com. Catherine Warrington, account dir. *Mkt-led approach. Services include all forms of media advertising, direct mail, promotions, video, broadcast.*

Space Marketing. 10 Clayfield Mews, Newcomen Rd, Tunbridge Wells, Kent TN4 9PA *tel:* 01892 677740 *fax:* 01892 677743 *email:* sales@spacemarketing.co.uk. Brian Shilling. *Advertising sales contractor for Making Music News.*

Unit Communications Group. 1 Canal St, Manchester M1 3HE *tel:* 0161 236 8002 *fax:* 0161 228 6258 *email:* traceyh@unitcomms.co.uk. Tracey Hughes, dir. *Arts specialist offering expertise in all areas of media communications including media strategy, planning, buying, creative, mkt and production.*

Design and Print

See also **Marketing and Organisational Management.**

Colophon. 9a New Road, Watlington, Oxon OX49 5QS *tel:* 01491 614499 *fax:* 01491 614488. Ross Speirs. *Information design for business and the arts: brochures, catalogues, books.*

The Design Stage. 21 West Bute St, Cardiff CF10 5EP *tel:* 029 2046 5366 *fax:* 029 2049 0104 *email:* steve@design-stage.co.uk. Steve Allison, mgr dir. *Graphic design consultants specialising in the arts and leisure industries.*

GWA. 79 Long Acre, London WC2E 9NG *tel:* 020 7836 0414 *fax:* 020 7240 7793 *email:* gwa@gwadesign.co.uk. Graeme Wilson.

John Good Holbrook Ltd. Elm Place, Old Witney Rd, Eynsham, Oxford OX29 4BD *tel:* 01865 885400 *fax:* 01865 885401 *email:* [name]@johngood-ox.co.uk. Caroline Good, mgr dir; Joanna Atherden, sales and mkt dir. *Publisher of programmes, posters and leaflets for concerts, festivals, theatres and lyric companies throughout the UK. Extensive in-house design and print capability.*

Lana Bezanov (LB) Promotions. 70 Gowan Ave, London SW6 6RF *tel:* 020 7736 4717; 020 7731 5410 (ISDN) *fax:* 020 7731 8009 *email:* info@lbproms.co.uk. Lana Bezanov, dir; Margarita Kazala,

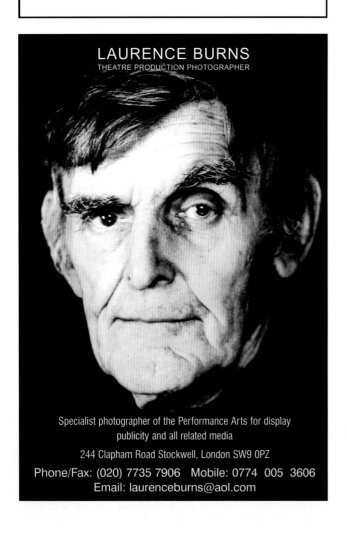

admin; G Bezanov, IT dir. *Concert, project and festival mgt; educ tours and charity event mgt; public and media relations consultancy; all forms of media advertising (buying and sales); brochure, programme, leaflet, poster and advertising design and production. Member of IAMA.*

Nickol, Peter. 50 St Leonards Rd, Exeter EX2 4LS *tel:* 01392 255512 *fax:* 01392 255512 *email:* PNickol@ninoakes.freeserve.co.uk. Peter Nickol. *Editing, writing, design and typesetting. Copyright clearance. Mus educ specialist.*

Ricardo Insua-Cao. 240 Brighton Road, S Croydon, Surrey CR2 6AH *tel:* 020 8686 2026; 07986 605774 *email:* ricardo@rinsua.co.uk. Ricardo Insua-Cao, artist and designer. *Graphic design, website design and artwork for musicians.*

Zincpark Screen Printers. Kaymar Industrial Estate, Trout St, Preston, Lancs PR1 4AL *tel:* 01772 562211 *fax:* 01772 257813 *email:* sales@bernard-kaymar.co.uk. Lucille Baines. *Posters and leaflets for the entertainment industry. 4 colour screen printing up to 60X40.*

Photographers and Photograph Libraries

Alan Wood Photography. 36a Park Field Rd, Oldbury, W Midlands B68 8PS *tel:* 07733 241100 *fax:* 0121 552 9977. *Specialist in mus, theatre and arts photography including press and PR.*

Alan Wylie Photography. 7 Lothian Gardens, North Kelvinside, Glasgow G20 6BN *tel:* 0141 946 4427; 07932 080071 *fax:* 0141 946 4427 *email:* mail@alanwylie.com.

ArenaPAL. Lambert House, 55 Southwark St, London SE1 1RU *tel:* 020 7403 8542 *fax:* 020 7403 8561 *email:* enquiries@arenapal.com. Primrose Metcalf, researcher; Christina Fallara, researcher. *Over 2 million images specialising in performing arts. Opera, ballet, theatre, mus, composers, venues, performances, festivals, etc. Archive and contemporary collections.*

Ashmore, Catherine. 4b Moore Park Rd, London SW6 2JT *tel:* 020 7381 0007 *fax:* 020 7381 0008. *Photographer of the entertainment world. Library containing 250,000 colour and b/w.*

Bache, David. 433 Upper Richmond Rd, London SW15 5QY *tel:* 07790 018315 *fax:* 020 8876 0115 *email:* bache.photography@virgin.net. *Portraits for press and publicity uses.*

Barda, Clive. 50 Agate Rd, London W6 0AH *tel:* 020 8741 0805 *fax:* 020 8563 0538 *email:* clivebarda@pobox.com. *Publicity, portrait and stage photography; comprehensive mus, opera, drama and ballet photo library.*

Burn, Sisi. Hermitage House, Church Terrace, Richmond, Surrey TW10 6SE *tel:* 020 8332 7958 *fax:* 020 8287 8448 *email:* sisiburn@ukonline.co.uk. *Mus images for musicians, contemporary, classical, jazz. Documentary, performance and portraits.*

Burns, Laurence. 244 Clapham Rd, Stockwell, London SW9 0PZ *tel:* 020 7735 7906; 07740 053606 *fax:* 020 7735 7906 *email:* laurenceburns@aol.com. *Also at:* 105 Beach St, Deal, Kent CT14 6JQ *tel:* 01304 389750. *Specialist photographer of the performance arts for display publicity and all related media.*

Carpenter Turner, Robert. The Studio, 63 Hemstal Rd, W Hampstead, London NW6 2AD *tel:* 020 7624 2225 *fax:* 020 7624 7731 *email:* robert@carpenterturner.co.uk. *Photo studio specialising in the needs of professional musicians. Grand pno. Price list and details available on website.*

Chlala, Hanya. c/o Arena Agency, Lambert House, 55 Southwark St, London SE1 1RU *tel:* c/o 020 7403 8542 *fax:* c/o 020 7403 8561 *email:* enquiries@arenaimages.com. *Studio shots, publicity, individual and large groups. Extensive picture library available.*

Crowthers, Malcolm. 40 Buckingham Palace Rd, London SW1W 0RE *tel:* 020 7828 4894 *fax:* 020 7233 8971 *email:* malcolmcrowthers@hotmail.com. *Specialist mus and creative photography. Archive of photographs of composers and musicians since 1980.*

Dominic Photography. 4b Moore Park Rd, London SW6 2JT *tel:* 020 7381 0007 *fax:* 020 7381 0008. Zoe Dominic; Catherine Ashmore. *Photographer of the entertainment world. Library containing 250,000 colour and b/w. 1956-present day.*

Donnier-Valentin, Christine. No.1 The Yard, Pegasus Place, Kennington, London SE11 5SD *tel:* 020 7735 5454; 07850 025254 *fax:* 020 7735 9344 *email:* cdv@lineone.net. *Single and group portraits.*

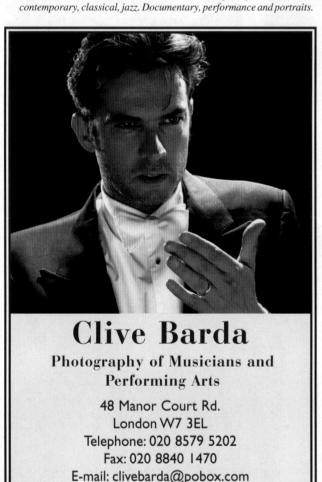

Sara Trickey
www.saratrickey.com

Charles Owen
www.charlesowen.net

Ana-Maria Vera
www.ana-mariavera.com

Richard Burkhard, baritone
www.richardburkhard.com

Sir Peter Maxwell Davies
www.maxopus.com

Wolfgang Holzmair and Imogen Cooper

The Micallef-Inanga Piano Duo
www.site-read.com

The Bronte String Quartet
www.brontequartet.com

Elliott, Nick *tel:* 07881 650883 *fax:* 01572 771767 *email:* nick@nicksgreatestflix.co.uk. *Creative photographer specialising in the mus industry.*

Four, Jim. 28 Woolwich Rd, Greenwich, London SE10 0JU *tel:* 020 8853 2291; 07973 669370 *fax:* 020 8858 5388. *Photo documentary specialist, covering all aspects, formal and informal, of classical mus.*

Haddon Davies Contemporary Photography. Barnside Studios, Spelsbury Rd, Charlbury OX7 3LR *tel:* 01608 811595 *email:* haddon@haddondavies.co.uk. *Contemporary studio and location photography, using the latest digital equipment. Specialist in relaxed, effective portraiture for mkt/promotional purposes.*

Ivory Images. 45 Garibaldi Rd, Redhill, Surrey RH1 6PB *tel:* 01737 763708; 07976 402178 *fax:* 01737 763708 *email:* ivorimages@aol.com. Graham Ivory, photographer. *Publicity and portrait photography on location and in studio.*

John Batten Photography. Flat 5, 125 Hornsey Lane, London N6 5NH *tel:* 07730 824524 *email:* johnbatten@easynet.co.uk. *Publicity, portrait, corporate brochures, TV and film stills.*

Jonathan Keenan Photography. 5 Oak St, Northern Quarter, Manchester M4 5JD *tel:* 0161 834 8585; 07968 488551 *email:* studio@ jkphotography.com. *Nationwide creative photographic services with particular understanding of musicians' needs. Location or studio.*

Keith Saunders Photography. c/o Arena Agency, Lambert House, 55 Southwark St, London SE1 1RU *tel:* 020 7403 8542 *fax:* 020 7403 8561 *email:* enquiries@arenapal.com. Primrose Metcalf, agent. *Studio and location publicity, promotion and press photography. Signature portraiture and action shots for performers. Works extensively with individual musicians and groups.*

Lebrecht Music Collection. 58b Carlton Hill, London NW8 0RJ *tel:* 020 7625 5341; 020 7372 8233 *fax:* 020 7625 5341 *email:* pictures@lebrecht.co.uk. *Mus picture library - musicians, composers, scores, insts, opera divas, jazz, librettists, concert halls, rock. Plus historical and social context.*

Linda Chapman Photography. 69 Rectory Grove, London SW4 0DS *tel:* 020 7627 1208; 07931 592560 *email:* lindachapman@ lcphotography.demon.co.uk. *Specialist in the performing arts. Studio,* location, rehearsal or performance pictures for promotion, publicity, portfolios and brochures; colour or b/w.

Luckhurst, Nigel. 40 Orchard Estate, Cherry Hinton, Cambridge CB1 3JP *tel:* 01223 246990 *fax:* 01223 246990 *email:* nigelluckhurst@ ntlworld.com. *Specialist in portrait session photography.*

Maeder, Suzie. 26 Batoum Gardens, London W6 7QD *tel:* 020 7602 5966 *fax:* 020 7602 5966 *email:* szmaeder@btinternet.com. *Specialist portrait and innovative photography.*

Mary Robert Photoworks. 47 Creffield Rd, London W5 3RR *tel:* 020 8993 4378 *fax:* 020 8993 3984 *email:* robertm@richmond.ac.uk. *Photographic portraits of individuals and groups for all publicity purposes. Studio and location including action shots.*

Medley, Paul. 28 Fairacres Rd, Oxford OX4 1TF *tel:* 01865 723316 *email:* p.medley@ntlworld.com. *Photography on-site or in studio. Also graphic design for publicity, brochures, programmes, etc.*

The Neil Williams Classical Collection. 22 Avon, Hockley, Tamworth, Staffs B77 5QA *tel:* 01827 286086 *fax:* 01827 286086 *email:* neil@classicalcollection.co.uk. Neil Williams, owner/proprietor. *Picture archive specialising in classical mus ephemera, particularly portraits and scenes of composers, musicians, conds and opera singers and any references to them, including graves, monuments, museums, opera scenes, etc. Rare photographs, postcards, prints, stamps, concert programmes. Subjects include mus insts, concert halls, opera houses, manuscripts and 'music in art'. Also writes programme notes.*

PR Pictures. Cherry Trees, Loudwater Heights, Loudwater, Herts WD3 4AX *tel:* 01923 718555 *email:* john@prpictures.co.uk. John Willan. *Digital Photo Lab.*

PhotoWork. 71 Jersey Rd, Wolverton, Milton Keynes MK12 5BQ *tel:* 01908 311142; 07885 213449 *email:* stuart@photowork.co.uk. Stuart Isaac, photographer. *Mus specialist. Soloists to orchs, PR and mkt portfolios, opera, insts, competitions, corporate events and educ. Layout and design.*

Place, Gerald. Studio Venosa, 112 Wordsworth Rd, Hampton, Middx TW12 1ET *tel:* 020 8941 2684 *fax:* 020 8941 2684 *email:* venosa@ndirect.co.uk. *Promotional photography for the arts; studio or location. Digital manipulation.*

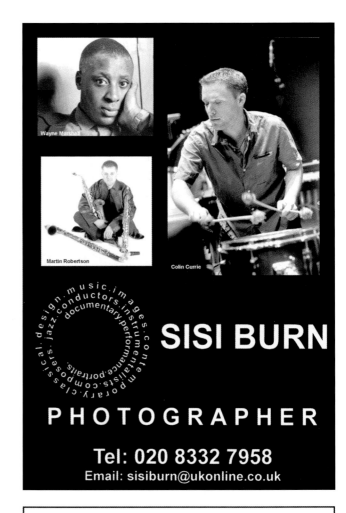

Rebecca Valentine - Illustration and Photography Representation. The Rebecca Valentine Avency, The Basement, 11c Stoke Newington Common, London N16 7ES *tel:* 07968 190411 *fax:* 020 7502 1636 *email:* rebecca@rebeccavalentine.com. Rebecca Valentine, agent; Paul Spencer, photographer; Martyn Rose, photographer; Subsurface Illustration, illustrators; Catherine Land, illustration. *Artist representation (portraiture, mus, landscape, reportage, film work, art installation, interiors, animation, murals, graffiti, 3D art installations) for the mus and advertising industries.*

Redferns Music Picture Library. 7 Bramley Rd, London W10 6SZ *tel:* 020 7792 9914 *fax:* 020 7792 0921 *email:* info@redferns.com. Dede Millar, dir; David Redfern, dir; Jon Wilton, dir. *Extensive range of mus artists from late 18th C classical to current Top Ten. Plus insts, crowds, festivals, generics. Brochure available.*

Richmond, Eric. c/o Arena Agency, Lambert House, 55 Southwark St, London SE1 1RU *tel:* 020 7403 8542 *fax:* 020 7403 8561 *email:* enquiries@arenapal.com. Primrose Metcalf, agent. *Characteristic portraiture and action shots for performers. Works extensively both in studio and on location.*

S L Chai *tel:* 020 8771 3970 *fax:* 020 8771 3694 *email:* info@colourblind.com. *Photography, broadcast quality video, graphic and web design, showreel production on DVD.*

Sharples, Steve. Fotobrew Picture Library, 54 Platts Cres, Amblecote, Stourbridge, W Midlands DY8 4YZ *tel:* 01384 376557; 01856 721413 *fax:* 0870 056 1113 *email:* steve.sharples@fotobrew.com. *Classic photography for musicians, singers and dancers for PR and mkt portfolios, taken in studio, rehearsal, performance or chosen venue.*

Vandyck, Katie. 33 Lansdown Place, Lewes, E Sussex BN7 2JU *tel:* 01273 473218. *Specialises in photographing musicians. Studio, location, during sessions.*

Visualeyes Imaging Services. 11 West St, Covent Garden, London WC2H 9NE *tel:* 020 7836 3004 *fax:* 020 7240 0050 *email:* imaging@visphoto.co.uk. *Premier photographic and duping services provider to the entertainment industry. Full range of digital services, image database system.*

Window on the World Ltd. 124 Cornwall Rd, London SE1 8TQ *tel:* 020 7928 3448; 07831 289190 *fax:* 020 7620 0350 *email:* usill@winworld.co.uk. David Usill, photographer; Judith Stewart, stylist. *Photography and graphic design studio. Portraits (studio or location), publicity material (brochures, programmes, posters, etc).*

Workman, Robert. Studio 103b, The Business Village, 3-9 Broomhill Rd, Wandsworth, London SW18 4JQ *tel:* 020 7385 5442 *email:* bob@robertworkman.demon.co.uk. *Publicity, portrait and stage photography; actors and singers photo library.*

Zuboff, Tatjana. Hill Cottage, Chapel Lane, Forest Row, E Sussex RH18 5BU *tel:* 0870 787 5426 *fax:* 01342 825939 *email:* TZuboff@aol.com. *Portrait and stage photography, portfolios, creative b/w.*

Leaflet Distributors

EAE Distribution Ltd. 11 Pirrie St, Edinburgh EH6 5HY *tel:* 0131 555 1897 *fax:* 0131 555 2905 *email:* iain@eae.co.uk. Glen Bennett, mgr dir; Iain Armit, sales and customer care mgr. *Posters, leaflets, brochures, programmes, distributed nationwide. 5800 display sites. Precision targeting to reach any audience. New services include guaranteed display in supermarkets and shopping centres.*

Parade Marketing Ltd. 199 Tyburn Rd, Birmingham B24 8NB *tel:* 0870 066 4266 *fax:* 0870 066 4267 *email:* sales@paradedirect.co.uk. John Dyson, dir; Clive Urwin, dir; Francesca Thomkins, account dir. *Printer, packer and distributor of promotional literature for the mus industry.*

Precision Media Group Ltd. Century Point, Halifax Rd, Cressex, High Wycombe, Bucks HP12 3SL *tel:* 01494 888500 *fax:* 01494 436914 *email:* info@brochuredisplay.co.uk. Martin Jones, mgr dir. *Display and distribution service for promotional brochures throughout London, the home counties and the Midlands, and at all UK airports.*

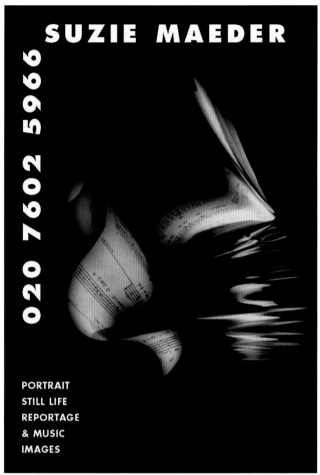
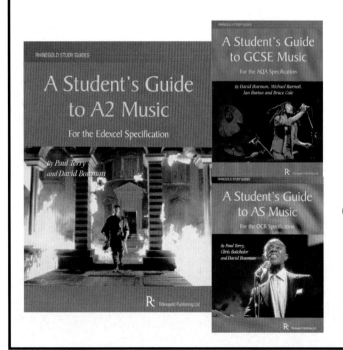

MARKETING, FUNDRAISING AND RELATED SERVICES

spnm - promoting new music. 4th Floor, 18-20 Southwark St, London SE1 1TJ *tel:* 020 7407 1640 *fax:* 020 7403 7652 *email:* spnm@spnm.org.uk. Shoël Stadlen, publications offr. *New mus leaflet distribution with 'new notes' magazine.*

Box Office Services

Galathea STS Ltd. Seatem House, 39 Moreland St, London EC1V 8BB *tel:* 020 7014 8686 *fax:* 020 7490 3530 *email:* sales@galatheasts.com. Richard Leggatt, gen mgr; Christian Terrill, head of sales and mkt. *Event mgt system software for ticketing and mkt operations.*

Just Tickets. Unit 2, Empstead Works, Greys Rd, Henley-on-Thames, Oxon RG9 2EF *tel:* 0845 126 0631 *fax:* 01491 413152 *email:* sales@just-tkts.com. J Birney, mgr dir. *Theatrical and leisure ticket printers, major supplier to the amateur and professional theatre and leisure industries.*

Number-Tec Ltd. Unit 8, Acorn Industrial Estate, Bontoft Ave, Kingston upon Hull HU5 4HF *tel:* 01482 492022 *fax:* 01482 492023. Beryl Hutchinson, sales exec. *Printer of tickets of all types, plus self-adhesive labels.*

Performance Ticket Printers. Freepost, The Smithy, Brownlow Heath, Congleton, Cheshire CW12 4AT *tel:* 01260 276164 *fax:* 01260 270984 *email:* mailbox@ticketprinters.co.uk. Keith Arnold, managing partner. *Low-cost, computer-printed, perforated tickets.*

Ticketmaster UK Ltd. 48 Leicester Square, London WC2H 7LR *tel:* 020 7344 4000 *fax:* 020 7915 0411 *email:* jeanette.larkin@ ticketmaster.co.uk. Simon Marples, mgr dir; Tim Chambers, national sales mgr; Dominic Hazlehurst, group mkt dir. *Entertainment ticket retailer providing computerisation, retail and mkt services. 24-hr credit card booking, group booking service, nationwide outlet network. Fully transactional and secure website.*

Tickets.com Ltd. Midsummer House, 405 Midsummer Boulevard, Milton Keynes, Bucks MK9 3BN *tel:* 0845 330 2343; 01908 232404 *fax:* 01908 232414 *email:* uksales@tickets.com. Natalie Peacock, sales and mkt admin; Stephen Beadle, sales and mkt co-ord. *Develop and support computerised admission systems for all types of visitor attractions. The systems can offer on-line bookings direct from a venue's website and come with an extensive range of customer relationship mgt tools as standard.*

TicketWeb UK. 48 Leicester Square, London WC2H 7LR *tel:* 020 7344 4000 *fax:* 020 7915 0411. Simon Marples, mgr dir; Tim Chambers, national sales mgr; Dominic Hazlehurst, group mkt dir. *Internet-based box office solution offering live and interactive remote access for ticket sales and database interrogation.*

Fundraising and Sponsorship

Many, if not most, music organisations need money from sources other than ticket sales and hope to raise it in the form of grants from official funding bodies, gifts from charities, commercial companies and private individuals and sponsorship (which has been defined as a *quid pro quo* relationship between a sponsoring company and a music organisation under which both parties benefit). Organisations listed here may be involved in raising money for music in a variety of ways; some work directly on behalf of the music organisation by actively seeking money on its behalf; some offer advice; some prefer to work exclusively with commercial companies that choose to sponsor musical events. A preliminary telephone call is recommended to determine precisely what service is offered.

Andrew de Mille Fundraising Consultants. Hedsordene, Cookham, Berks SL6 9HW *tel:* 01628 527753 *fax:* 01628 529938 *email:* andrew@demille.co.uk. Andrew de Mille, partner. *Fundraising and organisational development consultants, particularly capital fundraising campaigns. Also fundraising reviews, mgt studies, feasibility studies and training. Not sponsorship.*

Brakeley Ltd. Paramount House, 162-170 Wardour St, London W1V 4AB *tel:* 020 7287 3361 *fax:* 020 7287 8705 *email:* info@brakeley.com. John G Kelly, president and mgr dir; William J Connor, exec vice president and mgr dir. *Specialist in major-gift fundraising, offering strategic advice on all aspects of fundraising and external relations to not-for-profit clients worldwide.*

The Factary Ltd. The Coach House, 2 Upper York St, Bristol BS2 8QN *tel:* 0117 924 0663 *fax:* 0117 944 6262 *email:* info@factary.com. Vannesa Hillman, sales mgr. *Specialist donor research for fundraisers and development mgrs in the arts, charity and educ.*

Friedland Consulting. 18a St James's Place, London SW1A 1NH *tel:* 07815 123337 *fax:* 07971 211824 *email:* friedlandgroup@aol.com. Freda G Wooldridge, mgr dir. *Fundraising and sponsorship as part of strategic development and financial planning. Feasibility studies and fundraising mgt services available.*

Kallaway Ltd. 2 Portland Rd, Holland Park, London W11 4LA *tel:* 020 7221 7883 *fax:* 020 7229 4595 *email:* info@kallaway.co.uk. Bill Kallaway, mgr dir. *Communications and mkt through sponsored arts, educ and community programmes. Services include consultancy, event production and mgt, promotion and media planning.*

The Management Centre. Blue Jay Works, 117 Gauden Rd, London SW4 6LE *tel:* 020 7978 1516 *fax:* 020 7978 2125. Yuen lin Ip, mkt exec. *Fundraising and sponsorship consultancy, open and in-house mgt development programmes for not-for-profit organisations.*

Manygate Management. Trees, Ockham Rd South, East Horsley, Surrey KT24 6QE *tel:* 01483 281300 *fax:* 01483 281811. John Boyden, dir.

PB Communications International. 25 Fair Acres, Roehampton Lane, London SW15 5LX *tel:* 020 8876 9011 *fax:* 020 8876 9011. Peter Brown, chief exec; Christopher Brown, account supervisor. *Mgt and sponsorship consultants, public and media relations.*

Tom Petzal and Associates. Pantiles Chambers, 85 High St, Tunbridge Wells, Kent TN1 1YG *tel:* 01892 506968 *fax:* 01892 547120 *email:* tompetzal@aol.com. *Arts sponsorship and fundraising advice, appeals, events, strategic planning, promotion and PR, feasibility studies.*

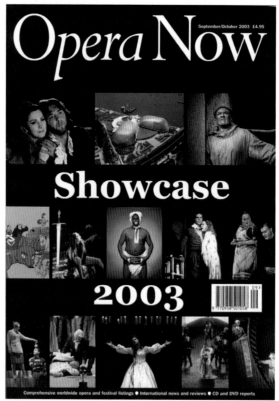

Orchestral Contractors

The list below includes the orchestral managers/contractors of professional orchestras and freelance contractors. The address given is either a personal address or that of the orchestra if contracting is done only from the orchestra's offices. The orchestras (or types of freelance booking) for which the person named is responsible are listed at the end of the entry.

Bebb, Mansel. Flat 2, 42 Gipsy Hill, Upper Norwood, London SE19 1NL *tel:* 020 8655 7255 *fax:* 020 8655 7255. *The Philharmonia Orchestra.*

Bentley, Andrew. Royal Ballet Sinfonia, c/o Birmingham Royal Ballet, Thorp St, Birmingham B5 4AU *tel:* 0121 245 3503 *fax:* 0121 245 3572 *email:* andrewbentley@brb.org.uk. *Royal Ballet Sinfonia, The Orchestra of Birmingham Royal Ballet.*

Blue Frog Music Management. 3 Ivy Mews, 153 Burton Rd, West Didsbury, Manchester M20 1LD *tel:* 0161 448 7598 *fax:* 0161 445 0587 *email:* info@bluefroguk.com. Bob Riley, Fiona Sinclair. *The Lancashire Sinfonietta, freelance orch and chmbr mus bookings.*

Brignall, Ian. English National Opera, London Coliseum, St Martin's Lane, London WC2N 4ES *tel:* 020 7845 9424; 07887 715104 *fax:* 020 7845 9277 *email:* ibrignall@eno.org. *Orchestra of English National Opera.*

Chameleon Arts Management. 32 St Michael's Rd, Sandhurst, Berks GU47 8HE *tel:* 0845 644 5530 *fax:* 01252 871517 *email:* orchestra@chameleon-arts.co.uk. *Chameleon Arts Orchestra. Films, recordings, choral society accompaniment.*

COOL Music Productions. 20 Spruce Hills Rd, Walthamstow, London E17 4LD *tel:* 07768 570383 *fax:* 0870 125 4057 *email:* coolmp@iname.com. *Concert Orchestra of London. Bookings of all types of groups or individuals from harpists to rock bands.*

Evans, Vicky. Divertimento, Ashbrook, Newton Rd, Totnes, Devon TQ9 5BB *tel:* 01803 863677 *fax:* 01803 863677 *email:* vicky.evans@divertimento.uk.com. *Ten Tors Orchestra and ad hoc orch fixing for any occasion in the South West.*

Fixers of Note. 15 Green St, Milton Malsor, Northampton NN7 3AT *tel:* 01604 858243 *fax:* 01604 859269 *email:* nick.turner@nsv.uk.com. *The National Sinfonia, London Orchestra da Camera, Midland Sinfonia, New English Baroque Ensemble. Freelance orch and session booking, concert tours and festivals.*

Ford, Trevor. 151 Mount View Rd, London N4 4JT *tel:* 020 8341 6408 *fax:* 020 8340 0021 *email:* tfordandco@aol.com. *English Festival Orchestra, English Concert Orchestra. TV, film, library, pop sessions.*

Goddard, Wilfred. 14 Lytton Rd, London E11 *tel:* 020 8556 8294 *fax:* 020 8556 8658 *email:* wilf.goddard@freeuk.com. *Brighton Philharmonic Orchestra, London Gala Orchestra.*

Goold, Nicola. Millmead House, Millmead, Guildford, Surrey GU2 4BB *tel:* 01483 444666 *fax:* 01483 444732 *email:* guildfordphil@guildford.gov.uk. *Guildford Philharmonic Orchestra.*

Hawley, Richard. CBSO, Berkley St, Birmingham B1 2LF *tel:* 07976 945034 *fax:* 0121 616 6518 *email:* rhawley@cbso.co.uk. *City of Birmingham Symphony Orchestra.*

Jenkins, Byron. Room G008, BBC National Orchestra of Wales, Broadcasting House, Llandaff, Cardiff CF5 2YQ *tel:* 029 2032 2524 *fax:* 029 2032 2575 *email:* byron.jenkins@bbc.co.uk. *BBC National Orchestra of Wales.*

Johnny Douglas Enterprises Ltd. 39 Tadorne Rd, Tadworth, Surrey KT20 5TF *tel:* 01737 812922 *fax:* 01737 812922. Norma Camby, dir. *Session orchs, concert orchs, dance bands.*

The King's Consort. 34 St Mary's Grove, London W4 3LN *tel:* 020 8995 9994 *fax:* 020 8995 2115 *email:* info@tkcworld.com. *Nigel Boon, artistic consultant; Simon Funnell, admin; Robert King, artistic dir; Karen Morris, head of development. Freelance booking for baroque and classical performers.*

Knifedge Ltd. 147 Drummond St, London NW1 2PB *tel:* 020 7383 5003 *fax:* 020 7383 5004 *email:* info@knifedge.net. Jonathan Brigden, dir; Theresa Bampton-Clare, dir. *Freelance orch bookings. The Orchestra, Millennia Strings, Hornography.*

Knowles, Richard. BBC Maida Vale Studios, Delaware Rd, London W9 2LG *tel:* 020 7765 5401 *fax:* 020 7286 3251 *email:* bbcso@bbc.co.uk. *BBC Symphony Orchestra.*

Larpent, Ben. 4 Royal Terrace, Edinburgh EH7 5AB *tel:* 0131 478 8336 *fax:* 0131 557 6933. *Scottish Chamber Orchestra.*

Logie, Nicholas. Lott's End, Highgate, Forest Row, E Sussex RH18 5BE *tel:* 01342 824536 *fax:* 01342 824536 *email:* nlogie@onetel.net.uk. *Glyndebourne Touring Opera Orchestra.*

London Musicians Ltd. Cedar House, Vine Lane, Hillingdon, Middx UB10 0BX *tel:* 01895 252555 *fax:* 01895 252556 *email:* mail@londonmusicians.co.uk. *Freelance orch booking, sessions, concerts, West End shows.*

Manly, Ann. 8 Alma Square, London NW8 9QD *tel:* 020 7286 3944 *fax:* 020 7289 9081 *email:* annmanly.protheroe@btinternet.com. *English Chamber Choir, English Players. Freelance orch and choral booking, sessions.*

Moss, Jane. RPO, 16 Clerkenwell Green, London EC1R 0QT *tel:* 01948 780180; 07850 841385 *fax:* 01948 780187 *email:* info@rpo.co.uk. *Royal Philharmonic Orchestra and Royal Philharmonic Concert Orchestra; concerts, TV, film, library sessions.*

Munro, Julian. RSNO Centre, 73 Claremont St, Glasgow G3 7JB *tel:* 0141 225 3563 *fax:* 0141 221 4317 *email:* admin@rsno.org.uk. *Royal Scottish National Orchestra.*

National Symphony Orchestra. 177 John Ruskin St, London SE5 0PQ *tel:* 020 7703 3148 *fax:* 020 7703 5334 *email:* enquiries@NSO.co.uk. *National Symphony Orchestra, also Leading Lights, NSO leading players.*

Neiman, Stephen. The Old Market, Upper Market St, Hove, E Sussex BN3 1AS *tel:* 01273 206978 *fax:* 01273 329636 *email:* mailbox@hanoverband.com. *The Hanover Band.*

Province, Hazel. Royal Opera House, Covent Garden, London WC2E 9DD *tel:* 020 7212 9381 *fax:* 020 7212 9728 *email:* hazel.province@roh.org.uk. *Orchestra of the Royal Opera House.*

Pye, Delia. 200 Broomwood Rd, London SW11 6JY *tel:* 020 7228 6388 *fax:* 020 7738 1706 *email:* delia.pye@virgin.net. *St James's Baroque Players. Freelance booking for period inst performers.*

Raymond Gubbay Ltd. Knight House, 29-31 East Barnet Rd, New Barnet, Herts EN4 8RN *tel:* 020 8216 3000 *fax:* 020 8216 3001 *email:* info@raymondgubbay.co.uk. *London Concert Orchestra, Johann Strauss Orchestra, Mozart Festival Orchestra, Manchester Concert Orchestra.*

Scott, Paul. 1 Springfield Close, Eckington, Sheffield S21 4GS *tel:* 01246 431562 *email:* paul@syso.co.uk. *South Yorkshire Symphony Orchestra, Sheffield Bach Players.*

Secret, Robert. 1 Poplars Close, Preston Bissett, Bucks MK18 4LR *tel:* 01280 848275 *fax:* 01280 848933 *email:* robert_secret@hotmail.com.

Studt, Richard. 11 Boileau Rd, Ealing, London W5 3AL *tel:* 020 8991 5214 *fax:* 020 8991 5214 *email:* rstudt@ntlworld.com. *Tate Music Group of London.*

Williams, Carys. Philharmonic Hall, Hope St, Liverpool L1 9BP *tel:* 0151 210 3805 *fax:* 0151 210 2902 *email:* carys.williams@liverpoolphil.com. *Royal Liverpool Philharmonic Orchestra.*

Willison, Peter. Pigeon House Meadow, 27 Grove Rd, Beaconsfield, Bucks HP9 1UR *tel:* 01494 677934 *fax:* 01494 670443 *email:* gbmuswill@aol.com. *Sinfonia of London. Recording and film-scoring.*

Wilson, David. 92 Chatsworth Rd, Croydon CR0 1HB *tel:* 020 8686 1996 *fax:* 020 8686 2187 *email:* info@lmp.org. *London Mozart Players.*

Wing, Paul. Selbourne, 3 Deermead, Little Kingshill, Great Missenden, Bucks HP16 0EY *tel:* 01494 890511 *fax:* 01494 890522 *email:* admin@winformd.co.uk. *Freelance session, orch, film, TV booking.*

Wordsworth, Judith S. Judith Webber Associates, 4a Harewood Rd, S Croydon, Surrey CR2 7AL *tel:* 020 8688 2430 *fax:* 020 8688 2430 *email:* jswordsworth@hotmail.com. *London Lyric Orchestra. Film and stage sessions, functions, promotions, freelance jazz and classical booking from soloists to full-size orch.*

UK Music Publishers

This list contains British publishers of mainly classical music and is divided into two parts. Major and independent publishers are listed first, and the second part (**Subsidiary Publishers**) lists major foreign and some UK companies whose interests are represented by another firm in the UK. Many publishers are members (indicated by an asterisk) of the **Music Publishers Association Ltd**, 3rd Floor, Strandgate, 20 York Buildings, London WC2N 6JU *tel:* 020 7839 7779 *email*: info@mpaonline.org.uk.

A & C Black Publishers Ltd. Music Dept, 37 Soho Square, London W1D 3QZ *tel:* 020 7758 0200 *fax:* 020 7758 0222/0333 *email:* enquiries@acblack.com. Sheena Roberts, head of mus; Marie Penny, asst ed. *Children's, educ mus, song books, classroom resources, inst tutors and repertoire.*

ADN Creation Music Library *see* **Panama Music (Library)**.

Acuta Music. Hambrook, Ledbury HR8 2PX *tel:* 01531 670634 *fax:* 01531 670634. *Late Elgar works, w/wind ens.*

Ad-Chorel Music Ltd. 86 Causewayside, Edinburgh EH9 1PY *tel:* 0131 668 3366 *fax:* 0131 662 4463 *email:* info@ad-choralmusic.com. *All types of mus projects.*

Alan Hawkshaw Music Ltd. PO Box 46, Radlett, Herts WD7 7DX *email:* bigal@globalnet.co.uk.

Alchemy Records. PO Box 393, Maidstone, Kent ME14 5XU *tel:* 01622 729593 *email:* alchemy@crescentmoon.org.uk.

Alfred Lengnick & Co (division of Complete Music Ltd). 27 Grove Rd, Beaconsfield, Bucks HP9 1UR *tel:* 01494 681216 *fax:* 01494 670443 *email:* gbmuswill@aol.com. *Classical symphonies, chmbr, choral, vocal, inst, educ books, World Renowned series. Distributor: Faber Music, hire library Chester Music.*

* **Alfred Publishing Co (UK) Ltd.** Burnt Mill, Elizabeth Way, Harlow, Essex CM20 2HX *tel:* 01279 828960 *fax:* 01279 828961 *email:* music@alfredpublishing.demon.co.uk. *All insts, especially pno and gui; band, orch, choral and vocal mus. Exclusive distributors: FM Distribution.*

Alison Hedger Children's Music. Hinton House, Hinton, Christchurch, Dorset BH23 7EA *tel:* 01425 274993 *email:* alison_hedger@lineone.net. *Children's educ mus, school and Sunday school mus.*

Amber Rose Guitar Music. Nockalls, Charnwood House, High St, Wroot, Doncaster DN9 2BT *tel:* 01302 772677 *fax:* 01302 772677 *email:* ambrosmus@aol.com. *Gui mus.*

* **Amphonic Music Ltd.** Kerchesters, Waterhouse Lane, Kingswood, Tadworth, Surrey KT20 6HT *tel:* 01737 832837 *fax:* 01737 833812 *email:* music@amphonic.co.uk.

Anderson Guitar Publications. 4 The Close, Upton, Southwell, Notts NG23 5SS *tel:* 01636 813405 *email:* anderson.j.m@talk21.com.

Andresier Editions. 63 Marlborough Mansions, Cannon Hill, West Hampstead, London NW6 1JS *tel:* 020 7794 9108 *fax:* 020 7794 9108; 01296 428609 *email:* mikedaniels@onetel.net.uk. *Solo, ens (gui only).*

Andrews of Harrogate (Music Typography). 100 Duchy Rd, Harrogate HG1 2HA *tel:* 01423 504373 *fax:* 01423 504373 *email:* info@andrews-music.co.uk. *Mus processing from ms to print.*

Anglian Edition. The Old White Horse, 34 Parsonage St, Halstead, Essex CO9 2JZ *tel:* 01787 475845. *S/publishing company for Eric Hudes (see Composers) and Alan Parsons.*

Animus. 4 Rawlinson St, Dalton-in-Furness, Cumbria LA15 8AL *tel:* 01229 467432 *email:* selfmus@aol.com. *Choral, org, inst, vocal.*

Antico Edition. PO Box 1, Moretonhampstead, Newton Abbot, Devon TQ13 8UA *fax:* 0870 787 7421 *email:* earlymusic@anticoedition.co.uk. *Medieval, renaissance, sacred and secular mus, including Hildegard of Bingen and the Use of Salisbury.*

Ararat Music. 93 Wellmeadow Rd, London SE6 1HL *tel:* 020 8697 6351 *fax:* 020 8697 0038 *email:* ararat@gibmusic.freeserve.co.uk. *S/publishing company of Stephen Gibson (see Composers).*

* **Ariel Music.** Malvern House, Sibford Ferris, Banbury, Oxon OX15 5RG *tel:* 01295 780679 *fax:* 01295 788630 *email:* jane@arielmusic.co.uk. *Concert and chmbr mus, ballets, operas, musicals, incidental mus for theatre.*

Aristocrat Music Ltd. Bournemouth Business Centre, 1052-1054 Christchurch Rd, Bournemouth, Dorset BH6 1RD *tel:* 01202 436184 *fax:* 01202 423297 *email:* music@kingdomrecords.co.uk.

Asclepius Editions. The Coach House, Blackheath Way, Malvern, Worcs WR14 4DR *tel:* 01684 891156 *email:* asclepius@viols.co.uk. *Academic performing editions of lesser-known renaissance, baroque and contemporary mus, especially for viols, rcdr and small ens.*

* **Ashley Mark Publishing Co.** Trans-Britannia Enterprise, 1-2 Vance Court, Bladon on Tyne NE21 5NH *tel:* 0191 414 9000 *fax:* 0191 414 9001. Simon Turnbull, mkt. *Gui mus.*

* **The Associated Board of the Royal Schools of Music (Publishing) Ltd.** 24 Portland Place, London W1B 1LU *tel:* 020 7636 5400 *fax:* 020 7467 8833 *email:* publishing@abrsm.ac.uk. *Keyboard, classical inst, theory of mus textbooks and exam material; books on mus; educ inst; jazz pno, jazz inst and ens.*

Aureus Publishing Limited. Castle Court, Castle-upon-Alun, St Bride's Major, Vale of Glamorgan CF32 0TN *tel:* 01656 880033 *fax:* 01656 880033 *email:* info@aureus.co.uk. *Concert and chmbr mus, operas, musicals, vocal, inst, children's mus, educ, choral, ens. Mus for hire.*

BGS Music Publications. Bath Spa University College, Newton Park, Newton St Loe, Bath BA2 9BN *tel:* 01225 875609 *fax:* 01225 875495 *email:* igf@bathspa.ac.uk. Philip Castang. *Bath Guitar Series publishing arm of the International Guitar Festival. Dedicated to publication of new work for gui.*

* **Banks Music Publications.** The Old Forge, Sand Hutton, York YO41 1LB *tel:* 01904 468472 *fax:* 01904 468679 *email:* banksramsay@cwcom.net. *Choral and inst mus.*

* **Bardic Edition.** 6 Fairfax Cres, Aylesbury, Bucks HP20 2ES *tel:* 01296 428609 *fax:* 01296 581185 *email:* info@bardic-music.com. *Choral, educ, inst, pno, vocal, band and orch mus.*

* **Bärenreiter Ltd.** Burnt Mill, Elizabeth Way, Harlow, Essex CM20 2HX *tel:* 01279 828930 *fax:* 01279 828931 *email:* baerenreiter@ dial.pipex.com. *Solo, ens, str, wind, pno, org, choir, opera. Complete editions, facsimilies, mus books. Choral and orch performance material. Vocal and study scores.*

Baroque Publications. Treadam Farm, Llantilio Crossenny, Abergavenny, Monmouthshire NP7 8TA *tel:* 01600 780233 *fax:* 01600 780233. *Orch parts and vocal scores for baroque operas, mainly Handel, (with libretto in English) edited for the Handel Opera Society; 18th and 19th C ballet mus with pno scores and orch parts; reduced scores for some Mozart and Rossini operas, 'Hansel and Gretel' (Humperdinck) and 'Falstaff' (Verdi).*

Barry Brunton Music Publisher. 52a Broad St, Ely, Cambs CB7 4AH *tel:* 01353 663252 *fax:* 01353 663371. *Choral, keyboard, solo song, ens.*

Bartholomew Music Publications. 105 Bartholomew Rd, Kentish Town, London NW5 2AR *tel:* 020 7267 0437 *fax:* 020 7267 0437 *email:* bmp@dial.pipex.com. *Specialising in mus for teachers and students of db.*

Basil Ramsey Publisher of Music Ltd. 604 Rayleigh Rd, Eastwood, Leigh-on-Sea, Essex SS9 5HU *tel:* 01702 524305 *fax:* 01702 526142 *email:* basilmusic@freeserve.co.uk. *Choral, inst, church mus.*

Bearsongs. PO Box 944, Edgbaston, Birmingham B16 8UT *tel:* 0121 454 7020 *fax:* 0121 454 9996 *email:* bearsongs@bigbearmusic.com. *Jazz, blues, swing, R&B.*

Belgarum Music Publishing. c/o The Winchester Music School, King Alfred's College, Sparkford Rd, Winchester, Hants SO22 4NR *tel:* 01962 885483; 07803 108265 *email:* Tim.Norris@wkac.ac.uk. *Br, w/wind, duet, trio, quartet, quintet, orchestral, symphonic wind bands, br bands, br chmbr ens and rcdr ens. Cat available. Distributer: Mostyn Music, 8 Milvil Court, Milvil Rd, Lee-on-Solent, Portsmouth PO13 9LY.*

* **Bocu Music Ltd.** 1 Wyndham Yard, Wyndham Place, London W1H 2QF *tel:* 020 7402 7433 *fax:* 020 7402 2866. *All types.*

Bonsormusic. Grove House, 37 Weensland Rd, Hawick, Roxburghshire TD9 9NW *tel:* 01450 372643 *email:* bonsormusic@aol.com. *Educ mus and concert items for rcdr groups.*

* **Boosey & Hawkes Music Publishers Ltd.** 295 Regent St, London W1B 2JH *tel:* 020 7580 2060 *fax:* 020 7291 7109/7637 3490 (promotion)/7291 7199 (sales) *email:* marketing.uk@boosey.com. *Classical, leisure, educ and media mus. Cats available: mus for schools, keyboard, str, w/wind, br, perc, ens, symphonic band, vocal, choral. Also Bote & Bock, Editio Musica Budapest, Fazer, Guildhall School, Itchy Fingers and Richard Schauer (Simrock, Benjamin and Rahter) and Ricordi/BMG.*

* **Bosworth & Co Ltd** *see* **Music Sales Ltd.**

* **Brass Wind Publications.** 4 St Mary's Rd, Manton, Oakham, Rutland LE15 8SU *tel:* 01572 737210/409 *fax:* 01572 737210/409 *email:* brasswnd@globalnet.co.uk. *Solo, br ens, br band, w/wind ens, mixed ens (cat).*

* **Breitkopf & Härtel.** Broome Cottage, The Street, Suffield, Norwich NR11 7EQ *tel:* 01263 768732 *fax:* 01263 768733 *email:* sales@breitkopf.com. *Renaissance, baroque, classical, romantic, contemporary, collected editions, inst, orch, vocal, choral.*

* **Broadbent & Dunn Ltd.** 66 Nursery Lane, Dover, Kent CT16 3EX *tel:* 01304 825604 *fax:* 0870 135 3567 *email:* bd.music@ broadbent-dunn.com. *Solo and ens mus for br, w/wind, strs and pno.*

* **CMA Publications.** Strawberry Holt, Westfield Lane, Draycott, Somerset BS27 3TN *tel:* 01934 740270 *email:* grp@cma-publications.co.uk. *Inst, orch, ens, choral, wind band and br band.*

Cabot Music Publications. 29 Long Mead, Brimsham Park, Yate, Bristol BS37 7YT *tel:* 01454 326509 *email:* sheetmusic@compuserve.com. David Kear, proprietor. *Off-the-record transcriptions of pop/rock/jazz mus for small group, big band and pno/vocal.*

Caddy Publishing. Convent Lodge, Andover Down, Hants SP11 6LR *tel:* 01264 337205 *fax:* 01264 350823 *email:* caddy@tiscali.co.uk. *Choral, orch, orch solo cantatas, str quartet, songs, books.*

Cadenza Music. 48 Ridgeway Ave, Newport NP20 5AH *fax:* 01633 674934 *email:* info@candenza-music.com. *Special emphasis on the mus of Stephen Dodgson and chmbr mus with gui.*

Camden Music. 85 Waldegrave Park, Twickenham, Middx TW1 4TJ *tel:* 020 8744 9005 *fax:* 020 8607 9536 *email:* info@camdenmusic.com. *Orch, wind, br, vocal, urtext editions, educ.*

Campion Press. Sandon, Buntingford, Herts SG9 0QW *tel:* 01763 247287 *fax:* 01763 249984 *email:* CampionPress@hotmail.com. Simon Campion. *Mus by Malcolm Williamson and Elizabeth Poston. Orch, choral, opera, songs, ballet, chmbr and inst mus.*

Canterbury Press Norwich. St Mary's Works, St Mary's Plain, Norwich NR3 3BH *tel:* 01603 612914 *fax:* 01603 624483 *email:* admin@ scm-canterburypress.co.uk. *Hymn and worship song books, associated titles including reference, commentaries and biographies.*

Cantiones Press. 10 Kensington Hall Gardens, Beaumont Ave, London W14 9LS *tel:* 0870 710 6102 *fax:* 0870 710 6102 *email:* cantiones@newrenaissance.co.uk. *Sacred renaissance and contemporary mus.*

Caribbean Music Library (GB) *see* **Panama Music (Library).**

Caritas Music Publishing. 28 Dalrymple Cres, Edinburgh EH9 2NX *tel:* 0131 667 3633 *fax:* 0131 667 3633 *email:* caritas@ caritas-music.co.uk. *All genres.*

Cascade Music Publishing. 30 College Green, Bristol BS1 5TB *tel:* 01454 323608 *fax:* 01454 323608. *Classical and jazz-based pieces for pno, w/wind and br solos and ens.*

* **Cathedral Music Ltd.** King Charles Cottage, Racton, Chichester, W Sussex PO18 9DT *tel:* 01243 379968 *fax:* 01243 379859 *email:* enquiries@cathedral_music.co.uk. *Classical, particularly choral.*

Chamberlain Music. Weyhill, Haslemere, Surrey GU27 1HN *tel:* 01428 658806 *fax:* 01428 658807 *email:* info@chamberlainmusic.com.

* **Chandos Music Ltd.** Chandos House, Commerce Way, Colchester, Essex CO2 8HQ *tel:* 01206 225200 *fax:* 01206 225201 *email:* shogger@ chandos.net. *Br band, vocal, hp mus. Orch hire library.*

* **Chelsea Music Publishing Co Ltd.** 124 Great Portland St, London W1W 6PP *tel:* 020 7580 0044 *fax:* 020 7580 0045 *email:* eddie@ chelseamusicpublishing.com.

* **Chester Music** *see* **Music Sales Ltd.**

Chilmark Publications. 1000 Westbury Rd, Little Cheverell, Devizes SN10 4JW *tel:* 01380 816338 *fax:* 01380 816467 *email:* chilmark@wessexmusic.co.uk. John Bickerton, proprietor. *Solo and ens mus for br.*

Chiltern Music. King Charles Cottage, Racton, Chichester, W Sussex PO18 9DT *tel:* 01243 379968 *fax:* 01243 379859 *email:* enquiries@cathedral_music.co.uk. *Orch, inst, pno and secular choral.*

Chiswick Music. Malting Cottage, Church Rd, Peldon, Colchester CO5 7PU *tel:* 01206 735770 *fax:* 01206 735770 *email:* bill.tamblyn@ aspects.net. *Recordings of liturgical mus. S/publishing company for Bill Tamblyn (see Composers).*

* **Chrysalis Music Ltd.** 13 Bramley Rd, London W10 6SP *tel:* 020 7221 2213 *fax:* 020 7465 6178.

Clairmont Press. Clairmont, The Square, Clun, Shropshire SY7 8JA *tel:* 01588 640398 *fax:* 01588 640057 *email:* talent@ clairmontpress.co.uk. *Early stages, vc and pno course books and ens packs and mus theory for beginners.*

Clive Morley Harps. Goodfellows, Filkins, nr Lechlade, Glos GL7 3JG *tel:* 01367 860493 *fax:* 01367 860659 *email:* harps@morleyharps.com.

Clyde, R. 6 Whitelands Ave, Chorleywood, Rickmansworth, Herts WD3 5RD *tel:* 01923 283600 *fax:* 01923 283600 *email:* r.clyde@ dial.pipex.com. Roger Harris, proprietor. *Mus by Arthur Sullivan.*

Colne Edition. 11 Christ Church Court, Ireton Rd, Colchester, Essex CO3 3AU *tel:* 01206 562607/513523 *email:* alan.bullard@ntlworld.com. Alan Bullard, dir. *Solo, ens, br band, wind band, orch, choral mus for adults and children. S/publishing company for Alan Bullard.*

Composers Library. 106 High St, Bildeston, Suffolk IP7 7EB *tel:* 01449 741707. *Orch, str orch and cantata from professional contemporary composers.*

* **Comus Edition.** Leach Cottage, Heirs House Lane, Colne, Lancs BB8 9TA *tel:* 01282 864985 *fax:* 01282 860770 *email:* wmd@ comusic.demon.co.uk. *Inst, solo, ens, va mus, br band. Mus of Arthur Butterworth.*

Con Moto Publications UK. 8 Milvil Court, Milvil Rd, Lee-on-the-Solent, Hants PO13 9LY *tel:* 023 9255 0700 *fax:* 023 9255 0566 *email:* tony@mostynmusic.com. *Br, w/wind mus, school classroom ens.*

Concord Partnership. 5 Bushey Close, Old Barn Lane, Kenley, Surrey CR8 5AU *tel:* 020 8660 4766 *fax:* 020 8668 5273 *email:* concordptnrship@aol.com. *Concord Music Hire Library, Maecenas Music Ltd, Maecenas Contemporary Composers, EF Kalmus Wind Band (cat), Masters Music Wind Band (cat), Warner Chappell Music Hire Library, GIA Publications Inc, LSO Explorer, Music Unlimited Limited, Warner Bros Publications, Belwin Kalmus Library, Masters Music Publications, Klavier and Citadel (CD cat), Carl Fischer Publications.*

Consonanza. 12 Beverley Gardens, Barnes SW13 0LZ *email:* David@davidhoyland.co.uk. *Chmbr and orch mus.*

Cool Wind Music. 22 Ivybridge Close, Twickenham, Middx TW1 1EA *tel:* 020 8892 1833 *fax:* 0870 126 8552 *email:* coolwind.music@ virgin.net. *W/wind (including solo fl, ob, cl, sax with pno), rcdr; w/wind duos, trios and quartets; developing series of mus for fl and cl.*

Corda Music Publications. 183 Beech Rd, St Albans, Herts AL3 5AN *tel:* 01727 852752 *fax:* 01727 852752 *email:* orders@ cordamus.demon.co.uk. *Mus for schools and private tuition, str ens, guis, specialist early mus.*

Cornish Music Guild. 28 Disraeli Rd, Forest Gate E7 9JP *tel:* 020 8534 2503. Jane Lofthouse. *Mus relating to Cornwall.*

Cottage Harmony Productions. Keens Barn Cottage, Keens Lane, Othery, nr Bridgwater, Somerset TA7 0PU *tel:* 01823 698162; 01296 424455 *email:* ce.cowles@btopenworld.com. Evelyn Stephens. *Ens mus, pno, solo instrumentation.*

* **Cramer Music.** 23 Garrick St, London WC2E 9RY *tel:* 020 7240 1612 *fax:* 020 7240 2639. *Solo, ens, classroom ens, mus courses, school orch, vocal mus (cat). Cat includes Middle Eight Music and Portland Publications. Also hire cat.*

* **Curiad.** The Old Library, County Rd, Pen-y-Groes, Caernarfon, Gwynedd LL54 6EY *tel:* 01286 882166 *fax:* 01286 882692 *email:* curiad@ curiad.co.uk. *Vocal, choral, orch and inst mus.*

Cwmni Cyhoeddi Gwynn Cyf. Y Gerlan, Heol y Dwr, Penygroes, Caernarfon, Gwynedd LL54 6LR *tel:* 01286 881797 *fax:* 01286 882634 *email:* info@gwynn.co.uk. *Vocal and choral mus (cat).*

Da Capo Music Ltd. 26 Stanway Rd, Whitefield, Manchester M45 8EG *tel:* 0161 766 5950 *email:* colin@dacapomusic.co.uk. *British contemporary classical mus. Cat of over 600 titles. Also M Karkoff (Sweden).*

David Johnson Music Editions. 8 Shandon Close, Edinburgh EH11 1QE *tel:* 0131 337 4621 *email:* david@djmusiceditions.freeserve.co.uk. *Scottish mus editions, educ str books, consultancy on historical Scottish mus.*

* **De Haske Music (UK) Ltd.** Fleming Rd, Earlstreets, Corby, Northants NN17 4SN *tel:* 01536 260981 *fax:* 01536 401075 *email:* sales@ dehaske.co.uk. Mark Coull. *Educ, solo, pno, vocal, w/wind, br, gui, strs (especially quartet), concert band, br band, orch. Cat available.*

Denis Wick Publishing. Clive House, The Chase, Oxshott KT22 0HR *tel:* 01372 849829 *fax:* 01372 849707 *email:* denis@deniswick.co.uk. *Wind band and br ens.*

* **Depotsound Ltd.** 12 Raddington Rd, London W10 5TG *tel:* 020 8968 0968 *fax:* 020 8968 0177 *email:* info@carnival-films.co.uk. *Incidental mus used in film and TV productions.*

Disc Imports Ltd. 1st & 2nd Floors, 7 High St, Cheadle, Cheshire SK8 1AX *tel:* 0161 491 6655 *fax:* 0161 491 6688 *email:* dimus@aol.com. *Classical.*

Dolce Edition. PO Box 1088, Bradford BD1 3XT *tel:* 01274 728884 *fax:* 01274 728882 *email:* orders@londonpromusica.com. *Rcdr mus only.*

Duettino Publications. Ardencaple, 16 Batchworth Heath, Rickmansworth, Herts WD3 1QB *tel:* 01923 825625 *email:* george@batchworthheath.ndo.co.uk. *Arrangements for pno duet.*

* **EG Music Ltd.** PO Box 4397, London W1A 7RZ *tel:* 020 8540 9935. *Popular, rock, world mus.*

EMU Publishing. The Paddocks, West Melbury, Shaftesbury, Dorset SP7 0DA *tel:* 01747 854108; 01980 603627 *fax:* 01747 854108 *email:* music@emupublishing.freeserve.co.uk. *Specialist publisher of mus for br and wind ens.*

ESG Music. 54 St David's Hill, Exeter EX4 4DT *tel:* 01392 254097 *fax:* 01392 254097 *email:* esgmusic@eclipse.co.uk. *Classical gui mus, tutors and ens mus.*

* **Eaton Music Ltd.** 39 Lower Richmond Rd, Putney, London SW15 1ET *tel:* 020 8788 4557 *fax:* 020 8780 9711 *email:* info@eatonmusic.com.

Eden Music Publishing/SMIC. 42 Killermont Rd, Bearsden, Glasgow G61 2JA *tel:* 0141 942 3089 *fax:* 0141 337 1161 *email:* info@ smic.dircon.co.uk. *S/publishing company for John Rose (see Composers). Choral, str quartet, pno, org songs.*

* **Edition HH Ltd.** 68 West End, Launton, Oxon OX26 5DG *tel:* 01869 241672 *fax:* 01869 323509 *email:* ph@editionhh.co.uk. Per Hartmann, dir. *Focus on scholarly critical editions, particularly Italian baroque and contemporary mus.*

Electrophonic Music Company. Lancaster Farm, Chipping Lane, Longridge, Preston PR3 2NB *tel:* 01772 783646 *fax:* 01772 786026. *S/publishing company for Ernest Tomlinson (see Composers). Orch, ens, solo instrumental, band, songs and choral mus.*

* **Emerson Edition Ltd.** Windmill Farm, Ampleforth, York YO62 4HF *tel:* 01439 788324 *fax:* 01439 788715 *email:* JuneEmerson@compuserve.com.

Emeryson Music Press. Melindwr, Ponterwyd, Aberystwyth, Dyfed SY23 3JY *tel:* 01970 890603 *fax:* 020 7580 4754 *email:* tecartpro@aol.com. *S/publishing company for Albert Alan Owen (see Composers). Also mus production company, Techno Arts Productions (TAP Records).*

Encore Publications. Juglans House, Brenchley Rd, Matfield, Kent TN12 7DT *tel:* 01892 725548 *fax:* 01892 725568 *email:* info@ encorepublications.com. *Choral and org.*

English Folk Dance & Song Society. Cecil Sharp House, 2 Regents Park Rd, London NW1 7AY *tel:* 020 7485 2206 *fax:* 020 7284 0534 *email:* info@efdss.org. *Folk song and dance mus; National Curriculum teaching manuals.*

Environ Music. 5 Church Green, Boreham Village, Essex CM3 3EH *tel:* 01245 450192 *email:* environmusic@hotmail.com. *S/publishing company for Jeffery J Wilson (see Composers). Educ, wind band, orch and jazz, choral mus.*

* **Eschenbach Editions.** 28 Dalrymple Cres, Edinburgh EH9 2NX *tel:* 0131 667 3633 *fax:* 0131 667 3633 *email:* eschenbach@caritas-music.co.uk. *Solo, ens, str orch, orch, choir, org, songs, choral, opera, ballet, chmbr mus.*

Escorial Edition. c/o 17-19 St George's Street, Norwich, Norfolk NR3 1AB *tel:* 01603 626414 *fax:* 01603 618811 *email:* escorial@ stgeorgesmusic.co.uk. *Publishers of choral and inst mus by Carl Rtti, Alan Gibbs, Ian Kellam, Sasha Johnson Manning, Ronald Watson and other contemporary musicians.*

Evening Star Music UK. 223 Windsor Rd, Carlton-in-Lindrick, Notts S81 9DH *tel:* 01909 733690 *email:* eveningstarmusic@planetpulman.com. *Popular/MOR, popular educ mus.*

Eventide Music (GB) *see* **Panama Music (Library).**

* **Faber Music Ltd.** 3 Queen Square, London WC1N 3AU *tel:* 020 7833 7900 *fax:* 020 7833 7939 *email:* information@fabermusic.com. *Distribution and Sales: FM Distribution, Burnt Mill, Elizabeth Way, Harlow, Essex CM20 2HX tel: 01279 828989 fax: 01279 828990. Contemporary concert and media composers, choral, educ, jazz, tutors/repertoire for pno, keyboard, strs, w/wind, br, etc.*

Fand Music Press. The Barony, 16 Sandringham Rd, Petersfield, Hants GU32 2AA *tel:* 01730 267341 *fax:* 01730 267341 *email:* sales@ fandmusic.com. *Pno, vocal, chmbr, choral and orch mus.*

Fentone Music Ltd *see* **De Haske Music (UK) Ltd.**

* **Fireworks Music Ltd.** 8 Berwick St, London W1F 0PH *tel:* 020 7292 0011 *fax:* 020 7292 0016 *email:* fwx@fireworksmusic.co.uk. *Film, TV, library, classical.*

First Time Music (Publishing) UK *see* **Panama Music (Library).** *All contemporary styles.*

Fitzjohn Music Publications. 45 Fitzjohn Ave, Barnet, Herts EN5 2HN *tel:* 020 8449 4873 *email:* deekaypea@argonet.co.uk. *A unique cat of new editions of pno, org and vocal mus, much of which is otherwise unobtainable. Cat includes the London Piano Quartet Series of mus for 8 hands on 2 pnos and pno trios.*

Folktrax and Soundpost Publications. 16 Brunswick Square, Gloucester GL1 1UG *tel:* 01452 415110 *email:* peter@folktrax.demon.co.uk. *Traditional mus.*

Formedia Music. Holly Hall, The Orchards, Meare BA6 9PU *tel:* 01458 860006 *email:* mail@vallis-davies.com. Nicholas and Sien Vallis-Davies. *Mus for TV and film. Mus books with CDs.*

Forsyth Brothers Ltd. 126 Deansgate, Manchester M3 2GR *tel:* 0161 834 3281 *fax:* 0161 834 0630 *email:* publishing@forsyths.co.uk. *Educ, classical, rcdr, theory, pno.*

Forward Music. 449 Loose Rd, Loose, Maidstone, Kent ME15 9VJ *tel:* 01622 743834 *email:* michael@forwardmusic.fsnet.co.uk. *Contemporary mus.*

Fraser-Enoch Publications. 64 Tremaine Rd, London SE20 7TZ *tel:* 020 8778 4670 *fax:* 020 8659 7716 *email:* info@fraser-enoch.com. Steve Kennett. *Educ pno mus: solo, duets and trios (grs 1-8). Mss to the above address.*

Fretwork. 16 Teddington Park Rd, Teddington, Middx TW11 8ND *tel:* 020 8977 0924 *fax:* 020 8404 2414 *email:* info@fretwork.co.uk. *Mus for viols; renaissance, baroque and contemporary.*

Friendly Music. 2 Greenway, Cranbrook, Kent TN17 3LL *tel:* 01580 713281 *email:* j.rutland@lineone.net. *Coll of solos and duets for w/wind insts; also cl quartets, wind quintets and mus for other wind groups.*

Frontier Press. 36 Riverdale Rd, Plumstead, London SE18 1NZ *tel:* 020 8473 2213. *Contemporary mus, British Contemporary Music Anthology.*

Fulcrum Music Publications. 10 Trafalgar St, Cheltenham, Glos GL50 1UH *tel:* 01242 226101 *fax:* 01242 226101 *email:* philiptlane@aol.com. *Orch, br band, chmbr and educ mus.*

The Full Pitcher Music Resources. 9 Mallard Close, Haslemere, Surrey GU27 1QU *tel:* 01428 648854 *fax:* 0870 429 2123 *email:* mail@ fullpitcher.co.uk. *Resources for teachers, parents and amateur musicians of all ages, with particular emphasis on creative and inclusive mus-making (cat).*

G & M Brand Publications Ltd. PO Box 367, Aylesbury, Bucks HP22 4LJ *tel:* 01296 682220 *fax:* 01296 681989 *email:* info@rsmith.co.uk.

Gee Music Group. 7 Fleetsbridge Business Centre, Upton Rd, Poole, Dorset BH17 7AF *tel:* 01202 686368 *fax:* 01202 686363 *email:* sheetmusic@musicgifts.co.uk. *Including Edwin F Kalmus Orchestral, Music Forte, Music Gifts Co and Musigraphic Publishers.*

Glentworth Music Limited. The Manor House, Langaller, Taunton TA2 8DA *tel:* 07885 848188 *email:* info@glentworthmusic.co.uk. Rachel Covey. *Specialist in perc mus.*

* **Golden Apple Productions** *see* **Music Sales Ltd.**

Gonzaga Music Ltd. 43 Victor Rd, London NW10 5XB *tel:* 020 8964 3384 *fax:* 020 8964 3384 *email:* sales@gonzagamusic.co.uk. Contemporary, classical, choral, orch, pno, educ, str quartet arrangements.

* **Goodmusic Publishing.** PO Box 100, Tewkesbury, Glos GL20 7YQ *tel:* 01684 773883 *fax:* 01684 773884 *email:* sales@goodmusic-uk.com. *Educ, inst, orch, choral.*

Grail Publications. Grail Centre, 125 Waxwell Lane, Pinner, Middx HA5 3ER *tel:* 020 8866 2195/0505 *fax:* 020 8866 1408 *email:* grailpublications@compuserve.com.

Grainger Society Edition. 6 Fairfax Cres, Aylesbury, Bucks HP20 2ES *tel:* 01296 428609 *fax:* 01296 581185 *email:* info@bardic-music.com. *Mus by Percy Grainger, original compositions and arrangements by others.*

Griffin Music. Hill House, 9 Redford Cres, Edinburgh EH13 0BS *tel:* 0131 441 3035 *fax:* 0131 441 5218 *email:* griffin.music@btinternet.com. *Works by John McLeod.*

Guitarnotes. Spanish Guitar Centre, 44 Nottingham Rd, New Basford, Nottingham NG7 7AE *tel:* 0115 962 2709 *fax:* 0115 962 5368 *email:* sales@spanishguitar.com. *Specialist classical gui mus.*

Hallamshire Music. Bank End, N Somercotes, Louth, Lincs LN11 7LN *tel:* 01507 358141 *fax:* 01507 358034 *email:* sales@ hallamshiremusic.co.uk. *Solo, ens, br band, br ens, wind band and school band.*

The Hardie Press. 17 Harrison Gardens, 17 Harrison Gardens, Edinburgh EH11 1SE *tel:* 0131 313 1383 *fax:* 0131 313 1388 *email:* admin@ hardiepress.co.uk. *Scottish mus: solo inst, vocal and baroque. Publishers for The Liszt Society.*

Harper Collins Publishers. 77-85 Fulham Palace Rd, Hammersmith, London W6 8JB *tel:* 020 8741 7070 *fax:* 020 8307 4440 *email:* ian.metcalfe@harpercollins.co.uk. *Christian mus, hymn books.*

* **Hatton & Rose Publishers.** 46 Northcourt Ave, Reading, Berks RG2 7HQ *tel:* 0118 987 4938 *fax:* 0118 987 4938. *Orch, chmbr, pno, vocal, choral.*

Hawthorns Music. The Hawthorns, Hawthorn Drive, Wheaton Aston, Staffs ST19 9NQ *tel:* 01785 840186 *fax:* 01785 840476 *email:* hawthorn@hawthornsmusic.co.uk. *Specialising in editions of early mus, particularly medieval mus and rcdr ens. 18th C English org mus editions.*

Helemuse Publications. St Edwards House, 700 Finchley Rd, London NW11 7NE *tel:* 020 8209 0015 *email:* helemuse@aol.com. *Mainly org and choral mus.*

Heraldic Music Publishing Library *see* **Panama Music (Library).**

Hughes a'i Fab. S4C Parc Ty Glas, Llanisien, Cardiff CF14 5DU *tel:* 029 2074 1484 *fax:* 029 2074 1371 *email:* luned.whelan@s4c.co.uk. *Traditional and hymn mus, Welsh language.*

Hunt Edition. 40 Portland Rd, London W11 4LG *tel:* 020 7727 5965 *fax:* 020 7727 7854 *email:* simonhunt@spartanpress.co.uk. *Wind mus for recreation and educ.*

Hymns Ancient & Modern Ltd. St Mary's Works, St Mary's Plain, Norwich NR3 3BH *tel:* 01603 612914 *fax:* 01603 624483 *email:* admin@scm-canterburypress.co.uk. *Hymn books.*

Impulse Edition. 18 Hillfield Park, Muswell Hill, London N10 3QS *tel:* 020 8444 8587 *fax:* 020 8245 0358 *email:* impulse@ impulse-music.co.uk. *Contemporary mus: solo, chmbr, orch, choral, liturgical, cross-cultural.*

International Music Publications Ltd. Griffin House, 161 Hammersmith Rd, Hammersmith, London W6 8BS *tel:* 020 8222 9222 *fax:* 020 8222 9260 *email:* imp.info@warnerchappell.com. *Pop, classical, educ mus, mus instruction videos, show mus.*

Isa Music. 27-29 Carnoustie Place, Scotland St, Glasgow G5 8PH *tel:* 0141 420 1881 *fax:* 0141 420 1892 *email:* lismor@lismor.co.uk. *Traditional Scottish pipe mus; all other styles.*

J P H Publications. Bridge View, Garrigill, Alston, Cumbria CA9 3DU *tel:* 01434 381583 *fax:* 01434 382877 *email:* j.edmonds@ jphbaroque.co.uk. *Facsimile of 17th and 18th C English mus.*

James Pass & Co Ltd. 71 Smallbrook Queensway, Birmingham B5 4HX *tel:* 0121 643 7623 *fax:* 0121 643 7623 *email:* info@euromusicweb.com. *Choral mus.*

Jazzwise Publications Limited. 2b Gleneagle Mews, Ambleside Ave, London SW16 6AE *tel:* 020 8769 7725 *fax:* 020 8677 7128 *email:* admin@jazzwise.com. *Publisher and distributor of printed mus and study materials for jazz.*

Jewish Music Distribution. PO Box 67, Hailsham BN27 4UW *tel:* 01323 832863; 0800 781 1686 *email:* orders@jewishmusic-jmd.co.uk. *Distributors and suppliers of Jewish and Israeli mus and recordings from around the world.*

John Fiddy Music. Production Music Library, Unit 3, Moorgate Business Centre, South Green, Dereham NR19 1PT *tel:* 01362 697922; 020 8367 2686; 07860 562558 *fax:* 01362 697923 *email:* info@ johnfiddymusic.co.uk. *Production mus library.*

John Trotter Books and Manor House Books. Sternberg Centre, 80 East End Rd, London N3 2SY *tel:* 020 8349 9484 *fax:* 020 8346 7430 *email:* jtrotter@freenetname.co.uk. John Trotter. *Suppliers of Jewish mus compilations, CDs and books on Jewish musicology, including cassettes.*

* **Josef Weinberger Ltd.** 12-14 Mortimer St, London W1T 3JJ *tel:* 020 7927 7304 *fax:* 020 7436 9616 *email:* general.info@jwmail.co.uk. *Mus theatre, orch, str and wind orch, choral, ens and solo (cats available).*

Jubilate Hymns. 4 Thorne Park Rd, Chelston, Torquay TQ2 6RX *tel:* 01803 607754 *fax:* 01803 605682 *email:* cpoyright@jubilate.co.uk. *Hymns, psalms and worship song material. Member of the Christian Music Publishers' Association.*

Just Accord Music. PO Box 224, Tadworth, Surrey KT20 5YJ *tel:* 01737 371631 *email:* information@justaccordmusic.com. *British mus.*

Kanon Editions. 4 Crosshills, Auchtermuchy, Cupar KY14 7AX *tel:* 01337 827507 *fax:* 01383 827507 *email:* dw@kanon.co.uk. D Watson, owner. *Specialising in classical gui, ens, school mus and children's songs.*

Kevin Mayhew Publishers. Buxhall, Stowmarket, Suffolk IP14 3BW *tel:* 01449 737978 *fax:* 01449 737834 *email:* info@ kevinmayhewltd.com. *Full range of org, choral and inst mus. Carefully edited and clearly set out including musicals, rcdr, str, w/wind, br, keyboard and vocal mus. UK distributor for Mel Bay Publications, Voggenreiter and AMA Verlag.*

Keyboard Konfections Music Publishing (KKOS). Ramshackles House, Nye Wood, Petersfield, Hants GU31 5JA *tel:* 01730 821030 *email:* fairytale.music@amserve.com. L K Robinson. *Keyboard, pno, ballet mus, stage songs.*

King's Music. Redcroft, Banks End, Wyton, Huntingdon, Cambs PE28 2AA *tel:* 01480 52076 *fax:* 01480 450821 *email:* clifford. bartlett@btopenworld.com. Clifford and Elaine Bartlett. *Facsimiles and editions of early mus.*

* **Kirklees Music.** 609 Bradford Rd, Bailiff Bridge, Brighouse HD6 4DN *tel:* 01484 722855 *fax:* 01484 722855/3591 *email:* sales@kirkleesmusic.co.uk. *Br and wind band, educ mus, rcdr, ens, church mus, ms paper/books.*

Kronos Press. Elmdale Cottage, Marsh, Aylesbury, Bucks HP17 8SP *tel:* 01296 613157. Philip Cannon. *S/publishing company for Philip Cannon (see Composers).*

Lathkill Music Publishers. 5 Shaftesbury Ave, Ashgate, Chesterfield, Derbys S40 1HN *tel:* 01246 233496 *email:* stevemarsh@ theguitarstudio.freeserve.co.uk. *Specialists in classical gui mus, solo and ens. Also small amount of orch and str quartet mus.*

Lazarus Edition. PO Box 14324, London W5 2YS *tel:* 020 8997 4300 *fax:* 020 8991 5982 *email:* lazarus@clarinet.demon.co.uk. Colin Bradbury, owner. *Freshly discovered masterpieces for wind insts.*

Leicestershire Music Publications. 1 Garth Heads, Beast Banks, Kendal LA9 4JL *tel:* 01539 736038 *fax:* 01539 736038 *email:* info@ lmp.net1.co.uk. *Materials for teachers: activities, schemes of work and policy documentation on ringbinder, booklets and/or discs, literacy and mus developed by advisers, inspectors and teachers in Leics, particularly for primary schools. Related INSET courses available.*

* **Lindsay Music.** 23 Hitchin St, Biggleswade, Beds SG18 8AX *tel:* 01767 316521 *fax:* 01767 317221 *email:* sales@lindsaymusic.co.uk. *Educ, inst, choral, songbooks, mus giftware.*

Lipkin, Malcolm. Penlan, Crowborough Hill, Crowborough, E Sussex TN6 2EA *tel:* 01892 652454 *email:* mail@malcolmlipkin.co.uk. *S/publishing company of Malcolm Lipkin (see Composers).*

Living Sound Presentations. 75 Greenleaf Gardens, Polegate, E Sussex BN26 6PQ *tel:* 01323 484058 *email:* maryhession@ livingsoundpresentations.com. *Production mus and spiritual and/or environmental works, meditation, relaxation and nature mus.*

Llonnod. Frogwy Fawr, Llangwyllog, Llangefni, Anglesey LL77 7PX *tel:* 01248 750418 *email:* gareth.glyn@ntlworld.com. *S/publishing company for Gareth Glyn.*

Lomond Music. 32 Bankton Park, Kingskettle, Fife KY15 7PY *tel:* 01337 830974 *fax:* 01337 830653 *email:* bruce.fraser@zetnet.co.uk. *Br band, wind band mus; educ.*

London Gabrieli Brass Edition. 22 Athenaeum Rd, London N20 9AE *tel:* 020 8445 3016 *fax:* 020 8446 9638 *email:* chrislarkinlgbe@ tesco.net. *Rare, mainly 19th C br.*

London Pro Musica Edition. PO Box 1088, Bradford BD1 3XT *tel:* 01274 728884 *fax:* 01274 728882 *email:* orders@londonpromusica.com. *Medieval, renaissance and baroque mus.*

Longship Music. Smidskot, Fawells, Keith Hall, Inverurie AB51 0LN *tel:* 01651 882274 *fax:* 01651 882274. *S/publishing company for John Hearne (see Composers).*

Lovely Music. 17 Westgate, Tadcaster, N Yorks LS24 9JB *tel:* 01937 832946 *fax:* 01937 835696 *email:* lovelymusic@supanet.com. *Educ mus and books. Agents for Holdstock & Mayflower publications.*

Lynwood Music. 2 Church St, West Hagley, Stourbridge, W Midlands DY9 0NA *tel:* 01562 886625 *fax:* 01562 886625 *email:* downlyn@globalnet.co.uk. *Mus of Andrew Downes and other selected 20th and 21st C compositions.*

* **MPL Communications Ltd.** 1 Soho Square, London W1D 3BQ *fax:* 020 7439 1492. *Big band, br band, military band, musicals, choral and vocal.*

McCrimmon Publishing Co Ltd. 10-12 High St, Great Wakering, Essex SS3 0EQ *tel:* 01702 218956 *fax:* 01702 216082 *email:* mccrimmons@dial.pipex.com. John McCrimmon. *Hymn books, psalm collections, mus for schools, etc.*

McTier Music. 106 Hounslow Rd, Twickenham, Middx TW2 7HB *tel:* 020 8894 5381 *fax:* 020 8898 4591 *email:* music@mctier.fsworld.co.uk. *Db mus.*

* **Maecenas Contemporary Composers Ltd** *see* **Maecenas Music Ltd.** *Educ, solo, ens, choral, wind band, orch, pno, org, gui, jazz, jazz ens, str, wind, perc, vocal.*

* **Maecenas Music Ltd.** 5 Bushey Close, Old Barn Lane, Kenley, Surrey CR8 5AU *tel:* 020 8660 3914 *fax:* 020 8668 5273 *email:* maecenasmusicltd@aol.com. *Educ, classical, gui, keyboard, perc, wind, jazz, str, br, orch, wind band, br band, marching band, jazz ens, choral, vocal, textbooks.*

Magick Musick Ltd. PO Box 17930, London SW19 7WA *tel:* c/o 020 8947 0484. *Educ mus.*

Magnificat Music. Park Place, Winchester Rd, Wickham, Hants PO17 5HA *tel:* 01329 835521 *fax:* 01329 833092 *email:* Magnimus@aol.com. *Liturgical mus and recordings; specialises in the mus of Paul Inwood (see Composers).*

Makepeace Music. 36 Kingsway, Coventry CV2 4FE *tel:* 024 7641 9592 *email:* straydog@robwoodward.fsnet.co.uk. *Pop and rock.*

Mansel Thomas Trust. Ty Cerbyd, Station Rd, Ponthir, Newport NP18 1GQ *tel:* 01633 421299 *email:* grace@manselthomas.org.uk. *Publishes the works of the late Mansel Thomas.*

Mapa Mundi. 15 Marvig, Lochs, Isle of Lewis HS2 9QP *tel:* 01851 880216 *fax:* 01851 880216 *email:* mapamundi@aol.com. *Renaissance choral mus.*

Margaret Carpenter Musicals. Out of the Ark Music, Sefton House, 2 Molesey Rd, Hersham, Walton-on-Thames KT12 4RQ *tel:* 01932 232250 *fax:* 01932 703010 *email:* music@outoftheark.com. M Johnson, partner; Jonathan Rogers, operations mgr. *Mus plays for primary schools. Titles include Pied Piper, David & Goliath (Giant Slayers) and various nativity plays for Christmas. Choice of book & tape and book & CD packages. Titles available on approval KS 1&2.*

Masterclass Music. 12 Kelso Place, Dundee DD2 1SL *tel:* 01382 667251 *fax:* 01382 640775 *email:* nigel@masterclassmusic.com. *Inst arrangements for secondary schools.*

Mautoglade Music Ltd. 1 Northfields Prospect, Putney Bridge Rd, London SW18 1PE *tel:* 020 8877 3366 *fax:* 020 8874 3131 *email:* stuart@hobro.co.uk.

Melody First Production Music Library *see* **Panama Music (Library).**

* **Memory Lane Music Limited.** c/o Independent Music Group, 54 Larkshall Rd, London E4 6PD *tel:* 020 8523 9000 *fax:* 020 8523 8888 *email:* ERich@independentmusicgroup.com.

* **Meriden Music.** Silverwood House, Woolaston, nr Lydney, Glos GL15 6PJ *tel:* 01594 529026 *fax:* 01594 529027 *email:* gdw.meriden@btclick.com. *S/publishing company for Graham Whettam (see Composers).*

Merton Music. 8 Wilton Grove, London SW19 3QX *tel:* 020 8540 2708 *fax:* 020 8540 2708 *email:* mertonmusic@argonet.co.uk. *Str chmbr mus.*

Methodist Publishing House. 4 John Wesley Rd, Werrington, Peterborough PE4 6ZP *tel:* 01733 325002 *fax:* 01733 384180 *email:* chief.exec@mph.org.uk. *Hymn books, choral mus, religious musical dramas.*

Middle Eight Music. 23 Garrick St, London WC2E 9RY *tel:* 020 7240 1612 *fax:* 020 7240 2639. *Solo, ens, classroom ens, mus courses, school orch (cat).*

Mister D Music (Publications). 57 Landsdowne Rd, Bournemouth BH1 1RN *tel:* 01202 551440 *email:* david@mdmusic.com. *Solo, ens, str orch, school orch; also electric keyboard mus. S/publishing company for David Hellewell (see Composers).*

Modrana Music Publishers Ltd. 41 Parklands Way, Poynton, Cheshire SK12 1AL *tel:* 01625 845389 *email:* info@modranamusicpromotions.com. David Golightly. *Contemporary classical mus.*

Modus Music. 21 Canonbury Rd, Enfield, Middx EN1 3LW *tel:* 020 8363 2663 *email:* enquiries@modusmusic.org. *Composers' publishing co-operative.*

Moeck UK. 38 Manningham Lane, Bradford BD1 3EA *tel:* 01274 721646 *fax:* 01274 393516 *email:* moeck@earlyms.demon.co.uk.

* **Moggie Music Ltd.** 101 Hazelwood Lane, London N13 5HQ *tel:* 020 8886 2801 *fax:* 020 8882 7380 *email:* info@halcarterorg.com. *Commercial popular mus.*

Mozart Edition (GB) Ltd. c/o Somerset & Co, 19 Woburn Place, London WC1H 0LU *tel:* 020 7278 3615 *fax:* 020 7837 6029. *Light orch mus and recorded mus library.*

Music Copyright Solutions Plc. 32 Lexington St, London W1F 0LQ *tel:* 020 7255 8777 *fax:* 020 7255 8778 *email:* info@mcsonline.com. *Incorporates Leosong Copyright Service Ltd, Screen Music Service Ltd, Copyright Online Services Ltd.*

Music Dynamics Ltd. Bishops Leys Business Park, Butts Lane, Woodmancote, Cheltenham, Glos GL52 9QH *tel:* 01242 679379 *fax:* 01242 663992 *email:* music@musicdynamics.co.uk. Sue Silverthorne, sales mgr. *Originator and producer of the 'ChoraLine' range of hi-tech rehearsal CDs and cassettes for choral singers (SATB); the Miller Keys scale and key signature learning kit. Also score supply and short-run audio and data CD duplication.*

* **Music Exchange (Manchester) Ltd.** Tayborn Publishing, Claverton Rd, Wythenshawe, Manchester M23 9ZA *tel:* 0161 946 1234 *fax:* 0161 946 1195 *email:* mail@music-exchange.co.uk. *Publishes educ, classical and pop mus; also distributors.*

Music for Television. Atlantic Studios, 65 Jeddo Rd, London W12 9ED *tel:* 020 8740 7727 *fax:* 020 8743 2523 *email:* guy@deepwaterblue.net. *Library mus publisher and s/publishing company for Guy Michelmore (see Composers).*

The Music Makers. 41 Sansom St, London SE5 7RD *tel:* 020 7207 5501 *fax:* 020 7207 5502 *email:* enquiries@themusicmakers.org. *Liturgical mus; original new compositions for sacred worship.*

* **Music Sales Ltd.** 8-9 Frith St, London W1D 3JB *tel:* 020 7434 0066 *fax:* 020 7287 6329 *email:* promotion@musicsales.co.uk. Chris Hargrave, mkt mgr; Claire Wheeler, mkt asst. *Distribution: Newmarket Rd, Bury St Edmunds, Suffolk IP33 3YB tel: 01284 702600 fax: 01284 768301. Contemporary, pop, classical and educ mus; books about mus.*

Music Works. 56 Hurdeswell, Long Hanborough, Oxford OX29 8DH *tel:* 01993 883117 *email:* trevor.davies@ukf.net. Trevor Davies. *Mus for orch, inst groups, voices, rcdrs and classroom. Specialise in resources that combine orch insts with classroom mus making and cater for a wide ability range. All publications produced as photocopiable resource packs.*

Musica Baltica Ltd. 16 Chase Court Gardens, Enfield, Middx EN2 8DH *tel:* 020 8363 4203 *fax:* 020 8363 4203 *email:* lilija.zobens1@btopenworld.com. Lilija Zobens, dir. *Latvian contemporary, choral, inst and educ mus.*

Musik' Image Music Library (GB) *see* **Panama Music (Library).**

* **Musisca Publishing.** 34 Strand, Topsham, Exeter EX3 0AY *tel:* 01392 877737 *fax:* 01392 877737; 01453 751911 *email:* musisca@printed-music.com. Philippe Oboussier. *Solo (vc), str quartet.*

Muskett Music. The Old Mill, Duntish, Dorchester, Dorset DT2 7DR *tel:* 01300 345412 *fax:* 01300 345412 *email:* mmuskett@beeb.net. *Teaching methods and early inst mus.*

Musography. 10 Carnaby, Kimbolton, Cambs PE28 0JB *tel:* 01480 861312 *fax:* 01480 861312 *email:* musography@cbmusic.freeserve.co.uk. *S/publishing company of Christopher Brown (see Composers). Practical performimg editions of baroque mus.*

* **Mute Song Ltd.** 429 Harrow Rd, London W10 4RE *tel:* 020 8964 2001 *fax:* 020 8968 6983 *email:* mutesong@mutehq.co.uk. *All types of mus.*

Nelson Thornes Ltd. Delta Place, 27 Bath Rd, Cheltenham, Glos GL53 7TH *tel:* 01242 267100 *fax:* 01242 221914 *email:* mail@nelsonthornes.com. *Complete range of primary curriculum materials.*

New Voices. British Music Information Centre, 10 Stratford Place, London W1C 1BA *tel:* 020 7499 8567 *fax:* 020 7499 4795 *email:* newvoices@bmic.co.uk. *Contemporary British classical mus.*

Niki Davies Musicals. Out of the Ark Music, Sefton House, 2 Molesey Rd, Hersham, Walton-on-Thames KT12 4RQ *tel:* 01932 232250 *fax:* 01932 703010 *email:* music@outoftheark.com. *Mus written specifically with the needs and abilities of nursery children in mind. Songs and nativities ideal for nurseries and KS 1 pupils.*

* **Novello & Co Ltd** *see* **Music Sales Ltd.**

* **Nymet Music.** 4 Pitt Court, Nymet Rowland, Crediton, Devon EX17 6AN *tel:* 01363 83515 *fax:* 01363 83936 *email:* lizbowdenmusic@talk21.com.

* **Obelisk Music.** 32 Ellerdale Rd, London NW3 6BB *tel:* 020 7435 5255 *fax:* 020 7431 0621. *Classical, inst, light mus.*

Oecumuse. 52a Broad St, Ely, Cambs CB7 4AH *tel:* 01353 663252 *fax:* 01353 663371. *Choral, org.*

Old Man Jobson's Music to Picture Ltd. 15 Cotham Vale, Cotham, Bristol BS6 6HS *tel:* 0117 946 6644 *fax:* 0117 946 6999 *email:* omjmusic@blueyonder.co.uk. James Barrett, head of production. *Publishing and promotion for film, TV and commercials. A Faber mus company.*

* **Orestes Music Publishing Ltd.** 112 Gunnersbury Ave, London W5 4HB *tel:* 020 8993 7441 *fax:* 020 8992 9993 *email:* orestes@dorm.co.uk. *Standard, classical, musicals, pop.*

Oriel Library. 32 The Burgage, Market Drayton TF9 1EG *tel:* 01630 653802 *email:* oriellibrary@aol.com. *Rcdr, viol and vocal consort mus.*

Ossian Music UK. 3 Waldron Court, Prince William Rd, Loughborough, Leics LE11 0GU *tel:* 01509 269629 *fax:* 01509 269206 *email:* sales@soarvalleymusic.demon.co.uk. David Ledsam. *Irish and Scottish traditional mus, recordings.*

Out of the Ark Music. Sefton House, 2 Molesey Rd, Hersham, Walton-on-Thames KT12 4RQ *tel:* 01932 232250 *fax:* 01932 703010 *email:* music@outoftheark.com. D Allen, sales mgr. *Songbook, cassette and CD packages. Resources for KS 1-2, including nursery and reception. Songs for Christmas, musicals and general songs available.*

Oxenford Imprint. c/o Cathedral Music (agent), King Charles Cottage, Racton, Chichester, W Sussex PO18 9DT *tel:* 01243 379968 *fax:* 01243 379859 *email:* enquiries@cathedral-music.co.uk. *Church mus.*

* **Oxford University Press Music Department.** Great Clarendon St, Oxford OX2 6DP *tel:* 01865 353349 *fax:* 01865 353749 *email:* music.enquiry.uk@oup.com. *Trade orders: Saxon Way West, Corby, Northants NN18 9ES. Contemporary, choral, orch, educ, easy and tutorial, opera, inst, church, etc.*

* **Oxford University Press/New Music Promotion.** 70 Baker St, London W1U 7DN *tel:* 020 7616 5900 *fax:* 020 7616 5901 *email:* repertoire.promotion@oup.co.uk. *20th C and contemporary composers.*

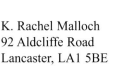
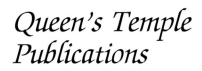

PSI Music Library (GB) *see* **Panama Music (Library).**

Pan Educational Music and Hunt Edition. 40 Portland Rd, London W11 4LG *tel:* 020 7727 5965 *fax:* 020 7727 7854 *email:* simonhunt@spartanpress.co.uk. *Specialists in wind mus.*

Panache Music Ltd. Regent House, 1 Pratt Mews, Camden, London NW1 0AD *tel:* 020 7267 6899 *fax:* 020 7267 6746 *email:* partners@newman-and.co.uk.

Panama Music (Library). Sovereign House, 12 Trewartha Rd, Praa Sands, Penzance, Cornwall TR20 9ST *tel:* 01736 762826; 07721 449477 *fax:* 01736 763328 *email:* Panamus@aol.com. *Inst mood mus library supplying TV, radio, film, audio-visual and advertising industries worldwide with library and commissioned mus.*

Paradisum Music. 19 Grove Hill, South Woodford, London E18 2JB *tel:* 020 8530 5454 *fax:* 020 8491 0898 *email:* paradisum@aol.com; info@paradisum.com. *Orch (including hire library material), vocal, choral, inst (including small ens and solo).*

Parish Publications. 28 Tom Price Close, Cheltenham, Glos GL52 2LF *tel:* 01242 230455 *fax:* 01242 230455 *email:* parish@lineone.net. *Ian and Janine Higginson. Church, choral, org, vocal, inst mus.*

Pathway Music. 8 Manor Rd, Tring, Herts HP23 5DA. *Pop and jazz. Spoken word. Meditation.*

* **Paul Rodriguez Music Ltd.** 61 Queen's Drive, London N4 2BG *tel:* 020 8802 5984 *fax:* 020 8809 7436 *email:* paul@paulrodriguezmus.demon.co.uk. *Classical, pop, jazz, dance.*

Peacock Press. Scout Bottom Farm, Mytholmroyd, Hebden Bridge, W Yorks HX7 5JS *tel:* 01422 882751 *fax:* 01422 886157 *email:* ruth@recordermail.demon.co.uk. *Publishers of rcdr and va da gamba mus.*

Peter R Birkby Publishing. PO Box 7, South Kirkby, Pontefract, W Yorks WF9 3XJ *tel:* 01977 648645 *fax:* 01977 648645 *email:* music@prbp.co.uk. Peter Birkby. *Mus for perc, solo, ens; choirs; ens for fls, guis, str quartet arrangements; br band, wind band, jazz orch, etc.*

* **Peters Edition Ltd.** Hinrichsen House, 10-12 Baches St, London N1 6DN *tel:* 020 7553 4000 *fax:* 020 7490 4921 *email:* sales@uk.edition-peters.com. *Pno, mus for exams, str, chmbr, ens, wind, org, vocal, choir, orch, br, opera, etc. Also, Edexcel New Anthology of Music, Music Partner 'play-along' CDs, Norton Music Books; Edexcel and AQA GCSE Anthologies of Music; Edexcel - Practice Papers; Language Through Music - Foundation Stages, KS1 and Lower KS2.*

Phaidon Press Ltd. Regent's Wharf, All Saints St, London N1 9PA *tel:* 020 7843 1234 *fax:* 020 7843 1111 *email:* esales@phaidon.com.

* **Phoenix Music.** Bryn Golau, Saron, Denbighshire LL16 4TH *tel:* 01745 550317 *fax:* 01745 550560 *email:* sales@phoenix-music.com. *Variable ens, inst ens, mus for schools.*

* **Phylloscopus Publications.** 92 Aldcliffe Rd, Lancaster LA1 5BE *tel:* 01524 67498 *email:* sales@phylloscopus.co.uk. *Chmbr mus for wind insts.*

Piano Bar Music Library (GB) *see* **Panama Music (Library).**

* **Piccolo Press.** 10 Clifton Terrace, Winchester, Hants SO22 5BJ *tel:* 01962 864755 *fax:* 01962 864755 *email:* PiccoWinch@aol.com. *Mainly mus for br and w/wind. Also books on insts.*

Piers Press. Overthorpe Hall, Banbury, Oxon *tel:* 01295 263733 *fax:* 01295 263733. *Rcdr/wind mus, classical sheet mus.*

Piper Publications. Dochroyle Farm, Barrhill by Girvan, Ayrshire KA26 0QG *tel:* 01465 821377 *email:* orders@piperpublications.co.uk. Pat Spence, dir. *Educ, vocal (including cantatas and mus plays), inst (solo and ens), orch; text books and mus linked project packs; steelpan handbook; Piper New Classics including the complete fl mus of James Hook.*

Power Music Co. 1 Station Rd, Harecroft, Wilsden, Bradford BD15 0BS *tel:* 01535 272905 *fax:* 01535 272905 *email:* power.music@btinternet.com. James Power. *Educ and w/wind mus specialists. Jazz, sax quartet, br quartet, fl/cl quartet.*

Primavera. 11 Langham Place, Highwoods, Colchester, Essex CO4 9GB *tel:* 01206 751522 *email:* julia.usher@lineone.net. *Contemporary mus. Also solo, str, orch, choir, ABRSM pieces.*

Prime Music. 3 The Square, Compton, W Sussex PO18 9HA *tel:* 023 9263 1369 *fax:* 023 9263 1786 *email:* primemusic@jonathanwillcocks.com. Peter Gordon, sales dir. *S/publishing company for Jonathan Willcocks (see Composers).*

Promo Sonor International (GB) *see* **Panama Music (Library).**

Quavers Rest Music. 22 Stephen's Rd, Tunbridge Wells, Kent TN4 9JE *tel:* 01892 537764 *fax:* 01892 511352 *email:* jacquesmusic@supanet.com. *Pno, choral, inst. S/publishing company for Michael Jacques (see Composers).*

Queen's Temple Publications. 15 Mallard Drive, Buckingham, Bucks MK18 1GJ *tel:* 01280 813144 *fax:* 01280 813144. *Educ, wind ens, minority wind insts.*

RG Editions. 23 The Croft, Hungerford, Berks RG17 0HY *tel:* 01488 682994 *email:* music@rgeditions.com. *Specialists in 17th and 18th C str chmbr mus, working from original editions and autograph manuscripts.*

* **RSCM Press.** Cleveland Lodge, Westhumble, Dorking, Surrey RH5 6BW *tel:* 01306 872811 *fax:* 01306 887240 *email:* press@rscm.com. *Choral mus, plus reference material for the church musician. Distributors for Editions Gheldar, Epiphany Music Press and White Light Music.*

RTL Music. White House Farm, Shropshire TF9 4HA *tel:* 01630 647374 *fax:* 01630 647612. *All types of mus.*

RTS Music Partnership. 17 Bradford Rd, St Johns, Wakefield, W Yorks WF1 2RF *tel:* 01924 370454 *fax:* 01924 370454 *email:* standford@rtsmusic.demon.co.uk. *Educ, light, publishers for Patric Standford (see Composers).*

RWM Music. PO Box 166, Northwood, Middx HA6 2FL *tel:* 01923 841645 *fax:* 01923 841785 *email:* info@rwmmusic.com. *Works of new composers. Keyboard; editions with corresponding CD; orch parts by arrangement; set mus for Williams-Morgan Piano Competition (see UK Competitions).*

Recital Music. PO Box 151, Aldershot, Hants GU12 6YQ *tel:* 01252 319610 *fax:* 01252 319610 *email:* doublebass@tiscali.co.uk. *Specialist publications for db.*

The Red Hedgehog. 45 Falsgrave Rd, Scarborough, Yorks *tel:* 01723 379897 *email:* gwemerson@argonet.co.uk. *Arrangements for wind of str and pno mus. Cat available.*

Redcliffe Edition. 68 Barrowgate Rd, London W4 4QU *tel:* 020 8995 1223 *fax:* 020 8995 1223 *email:* Redcliffe@frouth.freeserve.co.uk. D Mills, mgr. *British composers.*

Redgold Music. c/o Grand Union, 76 Wentworth St, London E1 7SA *tel:* 020 7375 1122 *fax:* 020 7426 0268 *email:* tony@grandunion.org.uk. *S/publishing company for Tony Haynes (see Composers) and Grand Union.*

Revelo Cornish Music. 35 Salisbury Rd, Harrow, Middx HA1 1NU *tel:* 020 8863 7180. *Oliver Hunt/Revelo Cornish Music publishes the works of the late Oliver Hunt. For archive and cat contact Mrs Jenny Hunt (address above).*

Reynard Music. 4 Reynard Way, Northampton NN2 8QX *tel:* 01604 845885 *email:* reynard@argonet.co.uk. Michael Watkins. *Sax and cl ens specialists, including Paul Harvey's 'El Torneo' for cl choir, Billy Goats Gruff for sax, cl or w/wind and transcription for 47 clarinets of Tallis's 'Spem in Alium'.*

Ricordi & Co (London) Ltd. Bedford House, 69-79 Fulham High St, London SW6 3JW *tel:* 020 7384 8180/95 *fax:* 020 7384 7858 *email:* Miranda.Jackson@bmg.com. *Opera, ballet, inst, ens, br band, orch, vocal, choral, school mus.*

Roanna Music. 141 Manor Rd North, Thames Ditton, Surrey KT7 0BQ *tel:* 020 8224 6493. *Easy listening.*

* **Roberton Publications.** The Windmill, Wendover, Aylesbury, Bucks HP22 6JJ *tel:* 01296 623107 *fax:* 01296 696536. *Standard classical, vocal, choral and inst mus.*

* **Rosehill Music Publishing Co Ltd.** PO Box 48, Aylesbury, Bucks HP17 8DW *tel:* 01844 290798 *fax:* 01844 290757 *email:* info@rosehillmusic.com. *Br.*

Rosewood Publications. Farthings, Rotten Row Hill, Bradfield, Berks RG7 6LL *tel:* 0118 974 4426 *email:* s.westmeath@virgin.net. Susanna Westmeath. *New works and previously unpublished or rare chmbr mus for wind and pno, wind, strs and pno, wind and strs and wind alone.*

Roy Chilton Music. 020 8777 6414 *email:* roy@roychiltonmusic.co.uk. *Tuition and graded repertoire books for elec gui, bs gui, gui and jazz ens.*

SGO Music Publishing Ltd. PO Box 34994, London SW6 6WF *tel:* 020 7385 9377 *fax:* 020 7385 0372 *email:* sgomusic@sgomusic.com. *Complete spectrum of pop mus.*

* **SJ Music.** 23 Leys Rd, Cambridge CB4 2AP *tel:* 01223 314771 *fax:* 01223 560353. *Str and chmbr mus.*

* **St Annes Music Ltd.** Kennedy House, 31 Stamford St, Altrincham, Cheshire WA14 1ES *tel:* 0161 941 5151 *fax:* 0161 928 9491 *email:* kse@kennedystreet.com.

St Gregory Publishing Co. 64 Pineheath Rd, High Kelling, Holt, Norfolk NR25 6RH *tel:* 01263 712288. *Church, org, vocal, educ mus.*

Salvi Publications/Lyon and Healy Publications. 58 Hopton St, London SE1 9JH *tel:* 020 7928 8451 *fax:* 020 7928 8284 *email:* holywell@holywell.co.uk. *Hp mus only.*

Samuel French Ltd. 52 Fitzroy St, London W1T 5JR *tel:* 020 7387 9373 *fax:* 020 7387 2161 *email:* theatre@samuelfrench-london.co.uk. *Musical plays and school mus.*

Satanic Mills Press. 4 Church St, Golcar, Huddersfield HD7 4AH *tel:* 01484 652762 *fax:* 01484 472656 *email:* m.l.wilkins@hud.ac.uk. *S/publishing company for Margaret Lucy Wilkins (see Composers). Orch, chmbr, solo, inst, vocal, choral.*

Saxtet Publications. 63 Witherford Way, Selly Oak, Birmingham B29 4AJ *tel:* 0121 472 2122 *fax:* 0121 472 2122 *email:* info@ saxtetpublications.com. Nigel Wood. *Sax, cl, fl mus.*

Scamp Music *see* **Panama Music (Library).**

Sceptre Publishers. 97 Elton Rd, Stibbington, Peterborough PE8 6JX *tel:* 01780 782093 *fax:* 01780 783159 *email:* grant@ sceptre-promotions.co.uk. *Solo elec org publications. Monthly magazine Organ and Keyboard Cavalcade (direct subscription only).*

* **Schauer & May Ltd** *see* **Boosey & Hawkes Music Publishers Ltd.**

Schirmer (G) Ltd *see* **Music Sales Ltd.**

* **Schott & Co Ltd.** 48 Great Marlborough St, London W1F 7BB *tel:* 020 7437 1246 *fax:* 020 7437 0263 *email:* promotions@schott-music.com; marketing@schott-music.com. *Mkt & Sales Dept: PO Box 411, Ashford, Kent TN27 0YF tel: 01233 714741 fax: 01233 714744. Solo, ens, wind band, str orch, school orch, choir; also rcdr, Orff-Schulwerk; contemporary.*

Scottish Music Information Centre. 1 Bowmont Gardens, Glasgow G12 9LR *tel:* 0141 334 6393 *fax:* 0141 337 1161 *email:* info@smic.org.uk. *Main supplier of the mus of Beamish, Cresswell, McGuire, Geddes, Sweeney, MacIlwham, Boyle, Matheson, Yeats, Robb, Weeks, Blake, Gourlay, Whyte, Wordsworth and many more Scottish composers.*

Seresta Music Ltd. c/o William Elkin Music Services, Station Rd Industrial Estate, Salhouse, Norwich NR13 6NS *tel:* 01603 721302 *fax:* 01603 721801 *email:* sales@elkinmusic.co.uk. *Sullivan, Burgess, Villa-Lobos, McQuattie, Ashbridge, songs, chmbr, orch.*

Shawnee Press *see* **Music Sales Ltd.**

Sin e Publications. 3 Waldron Court, Prince William Rd, Loughborough, Leics LE11 6GU *tel:* 01509 269629 *fax:* 01509 269206 *email:* sine@soarvalleymusic.com. *Celtic folk mus, perc tutors.*

* **Sing For Pleasure.** Unit 10a, Nortonthorpe Mills, Wakefield Rd, Scissett, Huddersfield HD8 9LA *tel:* 01484 860404 *fax:* 01484 860404 *email:* admin@singforpleasure.org.uk. *Mus for young singers.*

Snell & Sons. 68 West Cross Lane, West Cross, Swansea SA3 5LU *tel:* 01792 405727 *email:* snells@welshmusic.demon.co.uk. *Welsh sheet mus.*

Sound Music. 25 Turners Croft, Heslington, York YO10 5EL *tel:* 01904 410298 *email:* peterharrison@beeb.net. *Specialising in musicals for primary schools.*

Sounds Write. 56 Baswich Crest, Stafford ST17 0HJ *tel:* 01785 250405 *fax:* 01785 250405 *email:* soundswrite@supanet.com. *Offers a lively set of theory books written for young beginners to gr 3. Music Fun follows the ABRSM Theory of Music syllabus and gives a structured and fun approach through its child-centred method of teaching. It is applicable to any inst and does not require keyboard skills. Free brochure available.*

The Sparta Florida Music Group *see* **Music Sales Ltd.**

Spartan Press Music Publishers Ltd. Strathmashie House, Laggan by Newtonmore, Inverness-shire PH20 1BU *tel:* 01528 544770 *fax:* 01528 544771 *email:* mail@spartanpress.co.uk. Sandra Grant, sales. *Solo, duets, flexible ens, str orch, br ens, pno, group teaching.*

* **Stainer & Bell Ltd.** PO Box 110, Victoria House, 23 Gruneisen Rd, Finchley, London N3 1DZ *tel:* 020 8343 3303 *fax:* 020 8343 3024 *email:* post@stainer.co.uk. *Solo, ens, wind band, str orch, school orch, choral.*

Stanley Thornes (Publishers) Ltd *see* **Nelson Thornes Ltd.**

Stanza Music. 11 Victor Rd, Harrow, Middx HA2 6PT *tel:* 020 8863 2717 *fax:* 020 8863 8685 *email:* bill.ashton@virgin.net. *Big band and small jazz ens; also standard-type songs. Full cat available.*

State Music Ltd. 6 Kerick Place, London W1U 6HD *tel:* 020 7486 9994 *fax:* 020 7486 9934 *email:* songs@statemusic.co.uk. Wayne Bickerton.

Studio G. Cedar Tree House, Main St, Farthingstone, Northants NN12 8EZ *tel:* 01327 360820 *fax:* 01327 360821. *Library mus.*

* **Studio Music Co.** PO Box 19292, London NW10 9WP *tel:* 020 8459 6194/8830 0110 (sales) *fax:* 020 8451 6470 *email:* sales@ studio-music.co.uk. *General educ (inst and vocal); br, wind, jazz band, orch.*

Studium Classica. Brynreithin, Ffair Rhos, Ceredigion SY25 6BS *tel:* 01974 831391 *fax:* 01974 831391 *email:* studium_classica@ lineone.net. *Pno mus.*

Sun Pacific Music (London) Ltd. PO Box 5, Hastings, E Sussex TN34 1HR *tel:* 01424 721196 *fax:* 01424 717704 *email:* aquarius.lib@ clara.net. *Stage and film musicals.*

Sutton Elms Publications. 56 Arbor Rd, Croft, Leics LE9 3GD *tel:* 01455 284096 *fax:* 0870 133 1412 *email:* suttonelms@ukonline.co.uk. *Mus of Nigel Deacon (see Composers).*

* **Sweet 'n' Sour Songs Ltd.** 3 Warren Mews, London W1T 6AN *tel:* 020 7383 7767 *fax:* 020 7383 3020. *Musicals, pop.*

Take Note Publishing Ltd. 54 Lincolns Mead, Lingfield, Surrey RH7 6TA *tel:* 01342 836689 *email:* editor@takenote.co.uk. *Mus for w/wind, strs, gui, pno and keyboard; theory, mus educ software.*

Tecla Editions. PO Box 7567, London NW3 2LJ *tel:* 020 7435 5077 *fax:* 020 7435 5077 *email:* tecla@tecla.com. *Solo.*

* **Television Music Ltd.** Television Centre, Kirkstall Rd, Leeds LS3 1JS *tel:* 0113 243 8283 *fax:* 0113 222 7166.

Thames Publishing. c/o William Elkin Music Services, Station Rd Industrial Estate, Salhouse, Norwich, Norfolk NR13 6NS *tel:* 01603 721302 *fax:* 01603 721801 *email:* sales@elkinmusic.co.uk. Richard Elkin. *Specialist English mus publisher. Serious solo vocal, choral and inst mus. Also books.*

Thankyou Music Ltd. PO Box 75, Eastbourne, E Sussex BN23 6NW *tel:* 01323 437700 ext 316 *fax:* 01323 411970 *email:* tym@ kingsway.co.uk. *Christian mus.*

Tinderbox Music. 93 Stradella Rd, London SE24 9HL *tel:* 020 7274 5314 *fax:* 020 7274 3116 *email:* tinderbox_music@lineone.net. *Resource material for specialist and non-specialist teachers; primary and secondary, rcdr, classroom insts, song books. Jazz, rock, classical, ethnic and world mus.*

Tobin Music/Helicon Press. The Old Malthouse, Knight St, Sawbridgeworth, Herts CM21 9AX *tel:* 01279 726625 *email:* candida@tobinmusic.co.uk. *Tobin system of mus educ. Books on classroom teaching/infants, pno, rcdr, classical gui, theory. Also CD-ROM.*

Tomus Publications. 17 Kensington Rd, Earlsdon, Coventry CV5 6GG *tel:* 024 7667 0211 *fax:* 024 7667 0211 *email:* colintouchin@aol.com. *Rcdr and wind mus.*

Tristan Music Ltd. 1 Northfields Prospect, Putney Bridge, London SW18 1PE *tel:* 020 8877 3366 *fax:* 020 8874 3131 *email:* stuart@hobro.co.uk.

Tyalgum Press. 114 Histon Rd, Cambridge CB4 3JP *tel:* 01223 529218 *email:* administrator@tyalgumpress.com. *Opera, mus theatre, choral, orch, windband (s/publishing for Will Todd).*

Tyne Music.UK. 22 Forth Goods Yard, Forth Banks, Newcastle upon Tyne NE1 3PG *tel:* 0191 232 2479 *fax:* 0191 232 2479 *email:* dennis@ tynemusic.com. *Mus plays (8-15 yrs); also modern original musicals for 16-18 yrs.*

* **United Music Publishers Ltd (UMP).** 42 Rivington St, London EC2A 3BN *tel:* 020 7729 4700 *fax:* 020 7739 6549 *email:* info@ump.co.uk. Zoe Roberts, hire library mgr; Rebecca Bright, retail sales; Max Plummer, trade sales. *UK distributors of all major French Publishers, Ricordi and Theodore Presser, Play Percussion, Crash Bang Wallop!, CD Sheet Music and Piano Discoveries. School orch, choral, scores, hire library, retail, m/order service. Classical mus.*

* **Universal Edition (London) Ltd.** 48 Great Malborough St, London W1F 7BB *tel:* 020 7439 6678 *fax:* 020 7437 6115 *email:* handley@ universaledition.com. *Solo, ens, wind band, school orch, choir, school mus, orch, vocal, books (cat).*

* **Universal Music Publishing Ltd.** Bond House, 347-353 Chiswick High Rd, London W4 4HS *tel:* 020 8742 5600 *fax:* 020 8742 5607.

* **University of York Music Press Ltd.** Dept of Music, University of York, Heslington, York YO10 5DD *tel:* 01904 432434 *fax:* 01904 432450 *email:* uymp@york.ac.uk. *Contemporary mus.*

Useful Music. c/o Spartan Press, Strathmashie House, Laggan, Inverness-shire PH20 1BU *tel:* 01528 544770 *fax:* 01528 544771 *email:* useful@spartanpress.co.uk.

* **Valentine Music Select.** 7 Garrick St, Covent Garden, London WC2E 9AR *tel:* 020 7240 1628 *fax:* 020 7497 9242 *email:* valentine@ valentinemusic.co.uk. *Mus for bands and ens. AV Music, Cinque Port Music, Valentine Music. Distributes Bandleader Publications, Bardic Edition (wind mus), Herald Music Service and Southern Music Company (USA).*

* **Vanderbeek & Imrie Ltd.** 15 Marvig, Lochs, Isle of Lewis HS2 9QP *tel:* 01851 880216 *fax:* 01851 880216 *email:* mapamundi@aol.com. *Renaissance choral mus and 20th C mus.*

Virgo Music Publishers. Virgo House, 47 Cole Bank Rd, Hall Green, Birmingham B28 8EZ *tel:* 0121 778 5569 *fax:* 0121 778 5569 *email:* virgo@printed-music.com; virgohouse@aol.com. *Specialists in br, sax, easy jazz, educ mus and orch excerpt series.*

Visible Music. 43 The Marina, Deal, Kent CT14 6NN *tel:* 01304 382294 *email:* info@visible-music.com. *S/publishing company for Jean Hasse (see Composers). Choral, inst, ens, orch, film scores.*

Voicebox. 16 Teddington Park Rd, Teddington, Middx TW11 8ND *tel:* 020 8977 0924 *fax:* 020 8404 2414 *email:* info@fretwork.co.uk. *Vocal mus by Purcell, Blow and contemporaries.*

Ward Lock Educational Co Ltd. BIC Ling Kee House, 1 Christopher Rd, E Grinstead, W Sussex RH19 3BT *tel:* 01342 318980 *fax:* 01342 410980 *email:* orders@wleducat.freeserve.co.uk. Eileen Parsons. *Mus and songbooks for young children (cat).*

* **Warner-Chappell Music Ltd.** 3rd Floor, Griffin House, 161 Hammersmith Rd, London W6 8BS *tel:* 020 8563 5800 *fax:* 020 8563 5801. Matthew Crossey; Chris Statham. *Pop, standard and show, classical, educ mus.*

* **Warwick Music Ltd.** 1 Broomfield Rd, Coventry, W Midlands CV5 6JW *tel:* 08080 927942 (sales); 024 7671 2081 (admin) *fax:* 024 7671 2550 *email:* info@warwickmusic.com. *Specialists in all br mus.*

* **Josef Weinberger Ltd.** 12-14 Mortimer St, London W1N 7RD *tel:* 020 7580 2827 *fax:* 020 7436 9616 *email:* generalinfo@jwmail.co.uk. *Mus theatre, classical, light, educ and religious mus.*

Welsh Music Information Centre. Ty Cerdd, 15 Mount Stuart Square, Cardiff CF10 5DP *tel:* 029 2046 2855 *fax:* 029 2046 2733/5700 *email:* wmic@tycerdd.org. *Mus by Welsh composers (limited editions) otherwise unavailable.*

Westfield Music. Malt Shovel Cottage, 76 Old Walkergate, Beverley, E Yorks HU17 9ER *tel:* 01482 860580 *email:* ahedges@westfieldmusic.karoo.co.uk. *S/publishing company for Anthony Hedges (see Composers).*

* **William Elkin Music Services.** Station Rd Industrial Estate, Salhouse, Norwich, Norfolk NR13 6NS *tel:* 01603 721302 *fax:* 01603 721810 *email:* sales@elkinmusic.co.uk. *Distributers for A.I.M. Music Gifts,*

Allans of Australia, Arcadia, Aureole Editions, Braydeston Press, Chappell - choral, Christian Music Ministries, C.I.S. - Soviet Publishing, Classical Vocal Reprints, Colin, Coppenrath, Creative Concepts, Curci, Delrieu, Duettino Publications, EC Schirmer, Ensemble Publications, Freeman Easy Series, Galaxy - choral, Gehrmans, Goldfeder, Grafton Classics, Hargail Press, Hammond Textbooks, Hinshaw, Hoffnung Cards, Hofmeister, Joad Press, Karamar, Kahn and Averill, Kendor Music Inc, Lorenz Music Group, Margaux, Melodie, Minstrel Press, Music Box Dancer, Novello Brief Biographies, PP Music, Paraclete Press, Patelson, Peer Music Classical, Pickboy Music Accessories, Plymouth Music Co, Santorella, Seresta Music, Sing'N'Learn, Sikorski, Spratt, Tecla, Thames Publishing, Toccata Press, Tonos, UCCP, Walton Music Corp, Warner Bros - choral and organ, Zerboni, Zimmermann.

Wilson Editions. 1st & 2nd Floors, 7 High St, Cheadle, Cheshire SK8 1AX *tel:* 0161 491 6655 *fax:* 0161 491 6688 *email:* dimus@aol.com. *Mainly classical.*

Woodwind Plus. 42 St Mary's Park, Louth, Lincs LN11 0EF *email:* jeff@wwplus.freeserve.co.uk. *Chmbr mus for w/wind, saxes, hns, strs, with and without pno. Mus for concert band. Tutorial publications; AB and Trinity publications.*

* **Woza Music.** 46 Weigell Rd, Lee, London SE12 8HE *tel:* 020 8852 1997 *fax:* 020 8318 7417 *email:* lizglasser@lineone.net. *S/publishing company for Stanley Glasser (see Composers).*

Wright & Round Ltd. The Cornet Office, PO Box 157, Gloucester GL1 1LW *tel:* 01452 523438 *fax:* 01452 385631 *email:* wright-and-round@interactive-sciences.co.uk. *Br band, solo, ens.*

* **Yorke Edition.** The Bothy, Grove Cottage, Southgate, South Creake, Norfolk NR21 9PA *tel:* 01328 823501 *fax:* 01328 823502 *email:* enquiries@yorkedition.co.uk. R Slatford, dir; T Bigwood, asst. *Db only.*

Youngsong Music *see* **Music Sales Ltd.**

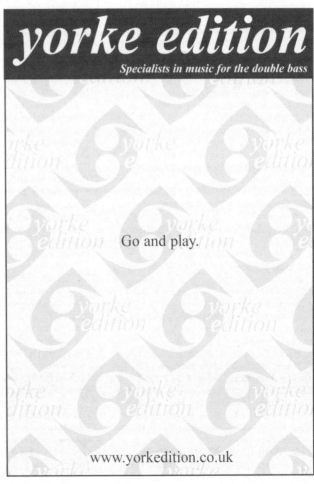

Subsidiary Music Publishers

Certain major foreign editions are available through publishers in the United Kingdom. These are listed below along with some UK editions that are represented by another publisher.

A Piacere (UK) – *Boosey & Hawkes Music Publishers Ltd*
ABRSM – *Oxford University Press Music Department (distributors)*
AMA Verlag (UK distribution) – *Kevin Mayhew Publishers*
Albert House Press – *Lindsay Music*
Alfred Lengnick & Co – *Faber Music Ltd*
Alfred Publishing Co (UK) Ltd – *Faber Music Ltd*
Alkor-Edition (Kassel) – *Bärenreiter Ltd*
Allans (Australia) – *William Elkin Music Services*
Alphonse Leduc & Cie (Paris) – *United Music Publishers Ltd (UMP)*
Amadeus Verlag (Switzerland) – *Schott & Co Ltd*
Amphion Editions Musicales (Paris) – *United Music Publishers Ltd (UMP)*
Amstel Music (Holland) – *De Haske Music (UK) Ltd*
Anglo Music Press – *De Haske Music (UK) Ltd*
Anglo-Soviet Music Press Ltd – *Boosey & Hawkes Music Publishers Ltd*
Anton J Benjamin – *Schauer & May Ltd*
Artemis Editions – *Faber Music Ltd*
Aug Zurfluh (Paris) – *United Music Publishers Ltd (UMP)*
Augener Edition Ltd – *Stainer & Bell Ltd*
Bardic Edition – *Schott & Co Ltd*
Bärenreiter (UK) Ltd – *Faber Music Ltd*
Belmont Music Publishers (LA) – *Alfred A Kalmus Ltd*
Bèrben, Edizioni (Italy) – *De Haske Music (UK) Ltd*
Bessel, W (Germany) – *Breitkopf & Härtel*
Boelke-Bomart Inc (New York) – *Alfred A Kalmus Ltd*
Bold Strummer – *William Elkin Music Services*
Bornemann, Editions (Paris) – *United Music Publishers Ltd (UMP)*
Bosse Verlag (Regensburg) – *Bärenreiter Ltd*
Boston Music Co – *Music Sales Ltd*
Bosworth – *Music Sales Ltd*
Bote & Bock (Berlin) – *Boosey & Hawkes Music Publishers Ltd*
Bourne Music (USA) – *Alfred A Kalmus Ltd*
Braydeston Press – *William Elkin Music Services*
British Standard Music Company – *Schauer & May Ltd*
C F Kahnt – *Peters Edition Ltd*
CD Sheet Music (USA) – *United Music Publishers Ltd (UMP)*
CIS Soviet Publishing – *William Elkin Music Services*
California University Press – *Peters Edition Ltd*
Camden Music – *Spartan Press Music Publishers Ltd*
Carisch SA – *William Elkin Music Services/ Boosey & Hawkes Music Publishers Ltd*
Carl Fischer (USA) – *Schott & Co Ltd*
Carl Fischer Publications – *Concord Partnership*
Carl Gehrmans Musikförlag – *William Elkin/ Boosey & Hawkes Music Publishers Ltd*
Carte Rudall & Co – *Boosey & Hawkes Music Publishers Ltd*
Carus-Verlag (Germany) – *United Music Publishers Ltd (UMP)/Peters Edition Ltd*
Cavendish Music Ltd – *Boosey & Hawkes Music Publishers Ltd*

Chant du Monde, Editions (France) – *United Music Publishers Ltd (UMP)*
Chanterelle (Germany) – *Guitarnotes*
Chantraine (Belgium) – *United Music Publishers Ltd (UMP)*
Chappell (Choral) – *William Elkin Music Services*
Chester Music Ltd – *Music Sales Ltd*
Chiltern Music – *Cathedral Music*
Choudens, Editions (Paris) – *United Music Publishers Ltd (UMP)*
Christian Music Ministries – *William Elkin Music Services*
Church Music Society – *Oxford University Press Music Department (distributors)*
Classic Editions – *Wilson Editions*
Colin – *William Elkin Music Services*
Columbia University Press – *Peters Edition Ltd*
Combre, Editions (Paris) – *United Music Publishers Ltd (UMP)*
Cool Music – *De Haske Music (UK) Ltd*
Coppenrath – *William Elkin Music Services*
Copperplate Music (UK) – *Bardic Edition*
Costallat, Editions (Paris) – *United Music Publishers Ltd (UMP)*
Creative Concepts – *William Elkin Music Services*
Curci, Edizioni (Italy) – *William Elkin Music Services*
Curnow Music Press – *De Haske Music (UK) Ltd*
D Rahter – *Schauer & May Ltd*
Daehn Publications (USA) – *Bardic Edition*
Daminus Edition (Germany) – *Guitarnotes*
De Haske Publications (Holland) – *De Haske Music (UK) Ltd*
Deutscher Verlag für Musik (Germany) – *Breitkopf & Härtel*
Dilia – *Boosey & Hawkes Music Publishers Ltd (operas and ballets)*
Doberman-Yppan (Canada) – *Guitarnotes*
Doblinger Musikverlag (Vienna) – *Alfred A Kalmus Ltd*
Dolce Edition – *Spartan Press Music Publishers Ltd*
Dominis Music (Canada) – *United Music Publishers Ltd (UMP)*
Dover Music (Distribution) – *Music Sales Ltd*
Drumblade Music (UK) – *Bardic Edition*
Duettino Publications – *William Elkin Music Services*
Durand, Editions (Paris) – *United Music Publishers Ltd (UMP)*
E C Schirmer Music Co (Boston, Mass, USA) – *William Elkin Music Services*
EFM (Paris) – *United Music Publishers Ltd (UMP)*
EMC (Holland) – *Spartan Press Music Publishers Ltd*
EME (Paris) – *United Music Publishers Ltd (UMP)*
Earlham Press Ltd – *De Haske Music (UK) Ltd*
Early English Church Music – *Stainer & Bell Ltd*
Editio Barenreiter Praha – *Bärenreiter Ltd*
Edition DeHaDe – *De Haske Music (UK) Ltd*
Edition HH (Oxford) – *Schott & Co Ltd*
Edition Margaux (Germany) – *Guitarnotes*
Editio Musica Budapest – *Boosey & Hawkes Music Publishers Ltd*

Edition Schwann (Germany) – *Peters Edition Ltd*
Edition Wilhelm Hansen – *Music Sales Ltd*
Editions Mario Bois – *Josef Weinberger Ltd*
Edizioni Curci Srl – *Josef Weinberger Ltd*
Edwin Ashdown – *Music Sales Ltd*
Elisabeth Thomi-Berg (Germany) – *De Haske Music (UK) Ltd*
Elkan-Vogel (USA) – *United Music Publishers Ltd (UMP)*
Enoch & Cie (Paris) – *United Music Publishers Ltd (UMP)*
Eschig, Editions Max (Paris) – *United Music Publishers Ltd (UMP)*
Eurobeat (UK) – *Wilson Editions*
European Music Archive – *Spartan Press Music Publishers Ltd*
European Music Centre – *Spartan Press Music Publishers Ltd*
Fenette Music – *De Haske Music (UK) Ltd*
Fennica Gehrman (Fazer) – *Boosey & Hawkes Music Publishers Ltd*
Fentone Music Ltd – *De Haske Music (UK) Ltd*
Forberg, Robert – *Peters Edition Ltd*
Freeman Easy – *William Elkin Music Services*
Fretful (Australia) – *United Music Publishers Ltd (UMP)*
Friedrich Hofmeister (Leipzig) – *William Elkin Music Services*
Furstner, Edition – *Boosey & Hawkes Music Publishers Ltd*
G Delrieu – *William Elkin Music Services*
G Schirmer Inc – *Music Sales Ltd*
GIA (education publications) – *Lindsay Music*
GIA Publications Inc – *Concord Partnership*
GS Publications – *Spartan Press Music Publishers Ltd*
Galliard Ltd – *Stainer & Bell Ltd*
Garden Music (UK) – *Guitarnotes*
Gendai Guitar (Japan) – *Guitarnotes*
Gérard Billaudot (Paris) – *United Music Publishers Ltd (UMP)*
Gitarre & Laute Verlag (Germany) – *Guitarnotes*
Glocken Verlag Ltd – *Josef Weinberger Ltd*
Golden Apple Productions – *Music Sales Ltd*
Goldfeder – *William Elkin Music Services*
Goodwin & Tabb (Music Hire) – *Music Sales Ltd*
Grafton Classics – *William Elkin Music Services*
Grainger Society Edition (UK) – *Bardic Edition*
Guildhall School of Music & Drama (UK) – *Boosey & Hawkes Music Publishers Ltd*
Gutheil, Edition – *Boosey & Hawkes Music Publishers Ltd*
Hal Leonard (Choral) – *William Elkin Music Services/Music Sales Ltd*
Hamelle (Paris) – *United Music Publishers Ltd (UMP)*
Hammond Publications – *William Elkin Music Services*
Hans Gerig (Germany) – *Breitkopf & Härtel*
Hargail Press – *William Elkin Music Services*
Hawkes & Son (London) Ltd – *Boosey & Hawkes Music Publishers Ltd*
Heinrichshofen Edition (Germany) – *Peters Edition Ltd*
Heinrichshofen Edition (USA) – *Peters Edition Ltd*

Hendon Music – *Boosey & Hawkes Music Publishers Ltd*
Henle Verlag (Munich) – *Schott & Co Ltd*
Henmar Press – *Peters Edition Ltd*
Henn, Editions (Switzerland) – *United Music Publishers Ltd (UMP)*
Henry Lemoine, Editions (Paris) – *United Music Publishers Ltd (UMP)*
Heugel & Cie (Paris) – *United Music Publishers Ltd (UMP)*
Hinnenthal Verlag (Germany) – *Bärenreiter Ltd*
Hinrichsen – *Peters Edition Ltd*
Hinshaw – *William Elkin Music Services*
Hortensia (Paris) – *United Music Publishers Ltd (UMP)*
Hunt Edition – *Spartan Press Music Publishers Ltd*
IMP (International Music Publishers) – *Music Sales Ltd*
Imprints of Theodore Presser Co – *Lindsay Music*
International Music Co (New York) – *Alfred A Kalmus Ltd*
Iota Music Publishers (UK) – *Amphonic Music Ltd*
Itchy Fingers Publications – *Boosey & Hawkes Music Publishers Ltd*
J Curwen & Sons Ltd – *Music Sales Ltd*
Joad Press – *William Elkin Music Services*
Joaquin Rodrigo Ediciones (Spain) – *Guitarnotes/Schott*
Jobert, Editions (Paris) – *United Music Publishers Ltd (UMP)*
Joel Rothman – *William Elkin Music Services*
John Lewis – *Wilson Editions*
Josef Weinberger – *Faber Music Ltd*
Joseph Patelson – *William Elkin Music Services*
Joseph Williams Ltd – *Stainer & Bell Ltd*
Jot-a-Note Publications – *Spartan Press Music Publishers Ltd*
Kahn & Averill – *William Elkin Music Services*
Kalmus (wind band) – *Concord Partnership*
Karamar – *William Elkin Music Services*
Karg-Elert Archive – *Cathedral Music*
Karthause - Schm‚lling (Germany) – *Hardie Press*
Kendor Music – *William Elkin Music Services*
Klavier CDs – *Concord Partnership*
Kneusslin (Switzerland) – *Peters Edition Ltd*
Koussevitzky Editions – *Boosey & Hawkes Music Publishers Ltd*
Kunzelmann, Edition (Switzerland) – *Peters Edition Ltd*
LCT Publications – *Schauer & May Ltd*
LSO Explorer – *Concord Partnership*
Lafleur Music Ltd – *Boosey & Hawkes Music Publishers Ltd*
Latham Music Enterprises (USA) – *De Haske Music (UK) Ltd*
Lathkill Music Publications – *Guitarnotes*
Lawson Gould – *William Elkin Music Services*
Lengnick – *Schauer & May Ltd (Simrock Editions)*
Leonard, Gould and Bolttler – *Music Exchange (Manchester) Ltd*
Les Productions d'Oz (Canada) – *Guitarnotes*
Leslie Music Supply (Ontario) – *Roberton Publications*
Lienau, Robert – *Peters Edition Ltd*
Litolff Henry Verlag (Frankfurt) – *Peters Edition Ltd*
London Orchestral Series – *De Haske Music (UK) Ltd*
Lorenz Music Corp – *William Elkin Music Services*
Lucks Music Library (USA) – *De Haske Music (UK) Ltd*
Lyche (Norway) – *Peters Edition Ltd*
M P Belaieff Editions – *Peters Edition Ltd*

MSM Publications – *Music Exchange (Manchester) Ltd*
Maecenas Contemporary Composers Ltd – *Concord Partnership*
Maecenas Music Ltd – *Concord Partnership*
Mannel de Falla Ediciones, SL (Distribution) – *Music Sales Ltd*
Mannheimer Musikverlag – *Schauer & May Ltd*
Mansem Music (UK) – *Wilson Editions*
Marais, Editions (Paris) – *United Music Publishers Ltd (UMP)*
Margaux – *William Elkin Music Services*
Margun Music– *Music Sales Ltd*
Masters Music Inc – *Concord Partnership*
Max Brockhaus (Germany) – *Schauer & May Ltd*
Mel Bay (UK distribution) – *Kevin Mayhew Publishers*
Melodie – *William Elkin Music Services*
Meredith – *William Elkin Music Services*
Mimram – *De Haske Music (UK) Ltd*
Minster Music – *Cathedral Music*
Minstrel Press – *William Elkin Music Services*
Mitropa Music (Switzerland) – *De Haske Music (UK) Ltd*
Molenaar – *William Elkin Music Services*
Montague Music (UK) – *Guitarnotes*
Möseler Verlag (Germany) – *Schott & Co Ltd*
Music 70 – *William Elkin Music Services*
Music Box Dancer – *William Elkin Music Services*
Music Concepts (Aural in Practice) – *De Haske Music (UK) Ltd*
Music Exchange Publications – *Music Exchange (Manchester) Ltd*
Music Unlimited Ltd – *Concord Partnership*
Musica Britannica – *Stainer & Bell Ltd*
Musica Rara (Germany) – *Breitkopf & Härtel*
Musica Russica – *Boosey & Hawkes Music Publishers Ltd*
Musicland Publications – *Peters Edition Ltd*
Musicus (Edition) (USA) – *Schauer & May Ltd*
Musikverlag City – *Schauer & May Ltd*
Musikwissenschaftlicher Verlag (Vienna) – *Alfred A Kalmus Ltd*
N Simrock – *Schauer & May Ltd*
Nagels Verlag (Germany) – *Bärenreiter Ltd*
Neil A Kjos Music Co (San Diego) (Distribution) – *Music Sales Ltd*
No Boyfriend Music Library (USA) – *Amphonic Music Ltd*
Nordiska Musikforlaget AB (Music Hire) – *Music Sales Ltd*
Norsk Musikforlag A/S (Norway) – *De Haske Music (UK) Ltd*
Norton Books – *William Elkin Music Services*
Notre Dame Choir Editions – *Peters Edition Ltd*
Nova Music – *Spartan Press Music Publishers Ltd*
Novello & Co Ltd – *Music Sales Ltd*
OGM/Professional Line (USA) – *Amphonic Music Ltd*
Octava Music Australia Ltd – *Josef Weinberger Ltd*
Opera Rara – *Josef Weinberger Ltd*
Opera Tres Ediciones Musicales (Spain) – *Guitarnotes*
Orchard Music – *Guitarnotes*
Orphée Editions (USA) – *Guitarnotes*
Out of the Ark Music – *Music Exchange (Manchester) Ltd*
Ouvrières (Paris) – *United Music Publishers Ltd (UMP)*
Oxenford Imprint – *Cathedral Music*
PP Music – *William Elkin Music Services*
PWM (Warsaw/Kraków) – *Alfred A Kalmus Ltd*
Pan Educational Music – *Spartan Press Music Publishers Ltd*
Panton (Prague) – *Schott & Co Ltd*

Papagrigoriou, C - H Nakas Co (Greece) – *Guitarnotes*
Paraclete Press – *William Elkin Music Services*
Patersons Publications Ltd – *Music Sales Ltd*
Penguin Cafe Orchestra – *Peters Edition Ltd*
Peters Edition Ltd – *Faber Music Ltd*
Philharmonia Miniature Scores – *Alfred A Kalmus Ltd*
Plymouth Music Co – *William Elkin Music Services*
Power Music – *Music Sales Ltd*
Prim - Musikverlag (Germany) – *Guitarnotes*
Princeton University Press – *Peters Edition Ltd*
Puffit Publications – *De Haske Music (UK) Ltd*
Queen's Temple Publications – *Spartan Press Music Publishers Ltd*
Real Musical (Spain) – *De Haske Music (UK) Ltd*
Red House (Australia) – *United Music Publishers Ltd (UMP)*
Redhead Music – *Faber Music Ltd*
Regina Music Publishing – *Music Exchange (Manchester) Ltd*
Richard Schauer – *Schauer & May Ltd*
Ricordi (London, Milan, Munich, Paris) – *United Music Publishers Ltd (UMP)*
Ricordi/BMG – *Boosey & Hawkes Music Publishers Ltd*
Rideau-Rouge (Paris) – *United Music Publishers Ltd (UMP)*
Robert King Music for Brass (USA) – *United Music Publishers Ltd (UMP)*
Robert Martin, Editions (France) – *United Music Publishers Ltd (UMP)*
Rodrigo (Spain) – *United Music Publishers Ltd (UMP)*
Roger Dean – *William Elkin Music Services*
Russe de Musique, Edition – *Boosey & Hawkes Music Publishers Ltd*
Sacred Music Press – *William Elkin Music Services*
Salabert, Editions (Paris) – *United Music Publishers Ltd (UMP)*
Saltire Music – *Hardie Press*
Sam Fox – *William Elkin Music Services*
Samfundet til Udgave af Dansk Music – *Music Sales Ltd*
Santorella – *William Elkin Music Services*
Scherzando (Belgium) – *De Haske Music (UK) Ltd*
Schola Cantorum (Switzerland) – *United Music Publishers Ltd (UMP)*
Schott Freres (Brussels) – *Schott & Co Ltd*
Seresta Music – *William Elkin Music Services*
Shawnee Press – *Music Sales Ltd*
Sher – *William Elkin Music Services*
Sikorski (Germany) – *William Elkin Music Services*
Sound Stage Production Music (UK) – *Amphonic Music Ltd*
Sound-Uision – *William Elkin Music Services*
Spratt – *William Elkin Music Services*
Staff Music Publishing – *William Elkin Music Services*
Star Nine Publishing – *William Elkin Music Services*
Subject Publications – *Music Exchange (Manchester) Ltd*
Süddeutscher Musikverlag Willy Müller – *Bärenreiter Ltd*
Suivini Zerboni, Editions – *William Elkin Music Services*
Sunshine Music Company – *Spartan Press Music Publishers Ltd*
TRO – *William Elkin Music Services*
Tayborn Publishing – *Music Exchange (Manchester) Ltd*

Tecla – *William Elkin Music Services*
Thames – *William Elkin Music Services*
Theodore Presser Comapny (USA) – *United Music Publishers Ltd (UMP)*
Toccata Press – *William Elkin Music Services*
Transatlantiques, Editions Musicales (Paris) – *United Music Publishers Ltd (UMP)*
Trinity College London – *Faber Music Ltd*
UCCP – *William Elkin Music Services*
UME (Union Musical Ediciones - Spain) – *Music Sales Ltd*
Universal Edition (London, Vienna) – *Alfred A Kalmus Ltd*
Useful Music – *Spartan Press Music Publishers Ltd*
Varney Music HB (Sweden) – *Guitarnotes*

Verlag Hubertus Nogatz (Germany) – *Guitarnotes*
Verlag Neue Musik (Germany) – *Guitarnotes*
Viola World Publications (Distribution) – *Music Sales Ltd*
Voggenreiter Verlag (UK distribution) – *Kevin Mayhew Publishers*
W W Norton Music Books – *Peters Edition Ltd*
F & R Walsh – *De Haske Music (UK) Ltd*
Walton Music Corp – *William Elkin Music Services*
Warner Bros (Choral and Organ) – *William Elkin Music Services*
Warner Bros Publications – *Concord Partnership/Schott*
West Wind Music (USA) – *Bardic Edition*

Wiener Urtext Edition – *Alfred A Kalmus Ltd*
William Grant Still Music (USA) – *Bardic Edition*
Willis Music Company – *Music Sales Ltd*
Winthrop Rogers Ltd – *Boosey & Hawkes Music Publishers Ltd*
Wollenweber (Switzerland) – *Peters Edition Ltd*
World Music Press (USA) – *Lindsay Music*
Yorke Edition – *Spartan Press Music Publishers Ltd*
Youngsong Musical – *Music Sales Ltd*
Zen-on – *Boosey & Hawkes Music Publishers Ltd*
Zimmermann (Germany) – *William Elkin Music Services*

International Music Publishers

The following list includes major international publishers of scores and sheet music.

Australia

Allans Publishing (Division of Allans Music Group Pty Ltd). PO Box 4072, Richmond East, Victoria 3121, Australia *tel:* +61 3 8415 8000 *fax:* +61 3 8415 8088 *email:* sales@allanspublishing.com.au. Richard Snape, general manager; Catherine Gerrard, publications and copyright manager. *Exclusive publisher of the Australian Music Examinations Board publications catalogue, approx 300 titles.*

Australian Music Centre. AMC, PO Box N690, Grosvenor Place NSW 1220, Australia *tel:* +61 2 9247 4677 *fax:* +61 2 9241 2873 *email:* info@amcoz.com.au. John Davis, general manager; Judith Foster, music resources manager; Anna Cerneaz, marketing manager. *Also at: Level 4, The Arts Exchange, 18 Hickson Rd, The Rocks, Sydney. Publishes 'Sounds Australian' journal twice a year, plus specialised music resource kits and books for secondary education. Through its facsimile score service the centre makes available facsimile copies of unpublished scores by Australian composers.*

Holborne Australasia Pty. PO Box 282, Alexandria NSW 1435, Australia *tel:* +61 2 9519 9066 *fax:* +61 2 9519 3622 *email:* info@holborne.com.au. Gary Jones, managing director; Sally Jones, PA; Nigel York, sales manager.

Red House Editions. PO Box 2123, Footscray VIC 3011, Australia *tel:* +61 3 9650 7432 *fax:* +61 3 9687 7785 *email:* musik@redhouse.com.au. Ross Hazeldine, manager; Alex Leslie, admin. *Distribution in UK through UMP.*

Austria

Josef Weinberger GmbH. Neulerchenfelderstr 3-7, Wien A-1160, Austria *tel:* +43 1 403 599125 *fax:* +43 1 403 599113 *email:* musik@weinberger.co.at. Christian Kobel, managing director.

Musikwissenschaftlicher Verlag. Dorotheergasse 10, Vienna A-1010, Austria *tel:* +43 1 515 0343 *fax:* +49 1 515 0351 *email:* office@mwv.at. Mathilde Eder, general manager; Angela Pachovsky, publishing director.

traunmusik Wien. Postfach 300, Vienna A-1021, Austria *tel:* +43 1 216 575510 *fax:* +43 1 216 575513 *email:* office@traunmusik.at. Josef P Traun, general manager. *Scores and sheet music of contemporary Austrian composers. Music for education and concerts. No. of publications: 200.*

Wiener Urtext Edition-Musikverlag. Bösendorferstr 12, Wien A-1010, Austria *tel:* +43 1 337 23 226 *fax:* +43 1 337 23 425 *email:* reutter@wiener-urtext.com. Jochen Reutter, editorial director. *No. of publications: 170.*

Belgium

Alamire Music Publishers. Toekomstlaan 5B, Neerpelt 3910, Belgium *tel:* +32 11 610510 *fax:* +32 11 610511 *email:* info@alamire.com. Herman Baeten, managing director. *Facsimile editions of early musical sources; scientific publications; short studies.*

Centre Belge de Documentation Musicale. Rue d'Arlon 75-77, Bruxelles B-1040, Belgium *tel:* +32 2 230 9430/7 *fax:* +32 2 230 9430/7 *email:* music-centre@cebedem.be. Alain Van Kerckhoven, director. *Belgian mus of the 20th C. No. of publications: 1500.*

Canada

Diffusion i Média. 4580 Ave de Lorimier, Montréal QC H2H 2B5, Canada *tel:* +1 514 526 4096 *fax:* +1 514 526 4487 *email:* info@electrocd.com. Jean-François Denis, president. *Electroacoustic music CD label 'empreintes DIGITALes'. Electronic/experimental music CD label 'No Type'. No. of publications: 82.*

Doberman-Yppan (Les Editions). PO Box 2021, St-Nicholas PQ G7A 4X5, Canada *tel:* +1 418 831 1304 *fax:* +1 418 836 3645 *email:* doberman.yppan@videotron.ca. Paul Gerrits, president; Marie Lévesque, vice president. *260 classical guitar, 180 Canadian concert music. No. of publications: 440.*

Gamelon Music Publications. PO Box 525, Station P, Toronto Ont M5S 2T1, Canada *email:* gamelon_music@hotmail.com. Michael Kleniec, manager. *No. of publications: 3.*

Leslie Music Supply Inc. 198 Speers Rd, Oakville Ont L6K 2E9, Canada *tel:* +1 905 844 3109 *fax:* +1 905 844 7637 *email:* sales@lesliemusicsupply.com. E Joan Leslie, secretary; Pat Leslie VanderHeyden, president; Anthony VanderHeyden, treasurer. *Selling agent: Roberton Publications, The Windmill, Wendover, Aylesbury, Bucks HP22 6JJ, UK. No. of publications: 900.*

Sound Ideas. 105 West Beaver Creek Rd, Suite No 4, Richmond Hill Ont L4B 1C6, Canada *tel:* +1 905 886 5000 *fax:* +1 905 886 6800 *email:* info@sound-ideas.com. Brian Nimens, president; Michael Bell, vice-president. *No. of publications: 4.*

Westar Music. 105 West Beaver Creek Rd, Suite No 4, Richmond Hill Ont L4B 1C6, Canada *tel:* +1 905 886 5000 *fax:* +1 905 886 6800 *email:* info@westarmusic.com. *No. of publications: 2.*

Czech Republic

Hudebni Informacni Stredisko (Music Information Centre). Sirotkova 67, Brno CZ-616 00, Czech Republic *tel:* +420 6 031 49923 *email:* medek@jamu.cz. *No. of publications: 2.*

Konvoj spol. s r.o. Berkova 22, Brno 612 00, Czech Republic *tel:* +420 5 4924 0233 *fax:* +420 5 4924 0233 *email:* konvoj@konvoj.cz. *Music publisher and bookseller, typesetting. No. of publications: 500.*

Denmark

Edition Wilhelm Hansen. Bornholmsgade 1, 1, Copenhagen K DK-1266, Denmark *tel:* +45 33 117888 *fax:* +45 33 148178 *email:* ewh@ewh.dk. Tine Birger Christensen, managing director; Eline Sigfusson, promotion. *Scores, songbooks, educational music books, etc. Music Sales Ltd, 8/9 Frith St, London W1D 3JB, UK.*

Finland

Modus Musiikki OY. PL 206, Kokkola FIN-67101, Finland *tel:* +358 6 8329 810 *fax:* +358 6 8329 811 *email:* modus.musiikki@saunalahti.fi. Matti Murto, manager. *No. of publications: 130.*

Sulasol. Fredrikinkatu 51-53 B, Helsinki FIN-00100, Finland *tel:* +358 9 4136 1100 *fax:* +358 9 4136 1122 *email:* info@sulasol.fi. Reijo Kekkonen, publications manager. *Mostly choral scores. No. of publications: c 800.*

France

Alphonse Leduc Editions Musicales. 175 Rue Saint-Honoré, Paris Cedex 01 F-75040, France *tel:* +33 1 42 96 89 11 *fax:* +33 1 42 86 02 83 *email:* AlphonseLeduc@wanadoo.fr. François Leduc, sales; Basile Crichton, promotion; Anna Le Tiec, sales. *Includes Hamelle, Heugel and Robert King. US affiliate and distributor: Robert King Music Sales Inc, 140 Main Street, North Easton, MA 02356, USA. No. of publications: 8950.*

Combre Editions. 24 Blvd Poissonnière, Paris F-75009, France *tel:* +33 1 48 24 89 24 *fax:* +33 1 42 46 98 82 *email:* info@editions_combre.com. Colette Geneste, manager; Demergers Odile, catalogue director. *Representatives: UMP, 42 Rivington St, London EC2A 3BN, UK. Theodore Presser Company, USA. No. of publications: 6450.*

DSCH-Shostakovich. Les Eversins du Presle, Chambost-Allières F-69870, France *tel:* +33 6 16 11 16 89 *fax:* +33 4 74 60 14 77 *email:* opus147@free.fr. A Mercer, editor. *No. of publications: 2.*

Editions Henry Lemoine. 41 Rue Bayen, Paris F-75017, France *tel:* +33 1 56 68 86 65 *fax:* +33 1 56 68 90 66 *email:* info@editions-lemoine.fr. Pierre H Lemoine, president. *No. of publications: 10,000.*

makemusic. Coda Music Technologies, 20c Boulevard Eugène Deruelle, Lyon Cedex 03 69432, France *tel:* +33 4 78 14 28 15 *fax:* +33 4 78 14 28 00 *email:* sdonikian@makemusic.com. Stéphane Donikian, European sales manager. *Music software manufacturer. Head office: 6210 Bury Drive, Eden Prairie, MN55346-1718, USA.*

Germany

Anton Böhm & Sohn. Lange Gasse 26, Augsburg D-86152, Germany *tel:* +49 821 502840 *fax:* +49 821 502 8433 *email:* boehmundsohn@freenet.de. Thomas Ballinger-Amtmann, manager. *Sacred and secular choral and organ music. No. of publications: c 8000.*

Breitkopf & Härtel. Walkmühlstr 52, Wiesbaden D-65195, Germany *tel:* +49 611 450080 *fax:* +49 611 450 0859 *email:* info@breitkopf.com. Lieselotte Sievers, general manager; Gottfried Möckel, general manager. *Deutscher Verlag für Musik, Leipzig GmbH; Bessel; Musica Rara. No. of publications: 15,000.*

Breitkopf & Härtel (Sales). Obere Waldstr 30, Taunusstein D-65232, Germany *tel:* +49 612 896 6321 *fax:* +49 612 896 6350 *email:* sales@breitkopf.com.

Edition Schultheiss. Pasinger Str 38a, Planegg b München D-82152, Germany *tel:* +49 89 859 9944 *fax:* +49 89 859 3323 *email:* Thomi-Berg@t-online.de. Elisabeth Thomi-Berg, managing director. *No. of publications: c 400.*

Firmament-Musik. Wittelsbacher Str 18, Berlin D-10707, Germany *tel:* +49 30 88 414143 *fax:* +49 30 88 15978 *email:* firmament@meiselmusic.de.

Furore Verlag. Naumburger Str 40, Kassel D-34127, Germany *tel:* +49 561 89 73 52 *fax:* +49 561 83 472 *email:* info@furore-verlag.de. *Sheet music, books and CDs; music by women composers. No. of publications: 1000.*

G Henle Verlag. Forstenrieder Allee 122, München D-81476, Germany *tel:* +49 897 598230 *fax:* +49 897 598240 *email:* rossbach@henle.de. Wolf-Dieter Seiffert, managing director; Ulrike Lucht-Lorenz, head of sales and marketing. *Urtext editions for piano, chamber music, solo instruments. Piano reductions, musicological editions. Overseas address: G Henle USA Inc, 1897 Craig Rd, St Louis, MO 63146, USA. No. of publications: 800.*

Gehann-Musik-Verlag. Lamperter Flur 2, Kludenbach D-55481, Germany *tel:* +49 676 32195 *fax:* +49 676 32175 *email:* Gehann-Musik@freenet.de. Horst Gehann. *No. of publications: 96.*

Heinrichshofen's Verlag GmbH & Co KG. Liebigstr 16, Wilhelmshaven D-26389, Germany *tel:* +49 4421 92670 *fax:* +49 4421 202007 *email:* heinrichshofen@t-online.de. Juergen Etzold, president. *Also at: C F Peters Corporation, 70-30 80th St, Glendale, NY 11385, USA. No. of publications: 2500.*

KGA Verlags-Service GmbH & Co KG. Postfach 10 21 80, Kassel D-34131, Germany *tel:* +49 561 3105 320 *fax:* +49 561 3105 310 *email:* kga@baerenreiter.com. *Distributor for Bärenreiter and other publishers.*

Karl Heinrich Möseler Verlag. Hoffmann-von-Fallersleben-Str 8, Wolfenbüttel D-38304, Germany *tel:* +49 5331 95970 *fax:* +49 5331 959720 *email:* info@moeseler-verlag.de. Jutta Möseler; Dietrich Möseler. *No. of publications: c 1500.*

Kistner & C F W Siegel & Co. Wippinger Weg 26, Niederkassel D-53859, Germany *fax:* +49 2208 770481 *email:* kistnerundsiegel@web.de. Annette Valder, owner. *No. of publications: 1000.*

Kurt Maas Music Distribution. Röntgenstr 5, Martinsried D-82152, Germany *tel:* +49 89 856 2477 *fax:* +49 89 856 2478 *email:* info@maas-noten.de. Kurt Maas, manager.

Leu-Verlag Wolfgang Leupelt. Herweg 34, Bergisch Gladbach D-51429, Germany *tel:* +49 220 498 1141 *fax:* +49 220 498 1143 *email:* leuverlag@aol.com. *Music education books.*

Melodie der Welt. Gr Friedberger Str 23-27, Frankfurt D-60313, Germany *tel:* +49 692 998 670 *fax:* +49 692 998 6710 *email:* melodie-der-welt@mdw-ffm.de. Pamela Georgi-Michel, general manager.

Moeck Musikinstrumente + Verlag. Lückenweg 4, Celle D-29227, Germany *tel:* +49 5141 88530 *fax:* +49 5141 885342 *email:* info@moeck-music.de. Sabine Haase-Moeck, publishing director; Andrea Höntsch-Bertram, hire material. *Overseas address: Magna Music Distributors Inc, PO Box 338, 74 Amenia Union Rd, Sharon, CT 06069, USA email: magnamusic@magnamusic.com. No. of publications: c 500.*

Otto Wrede Regina-Verlag e.k. Schumannstr 35, Wiesbaden D-65193, Germany *tel:* +49 611 523118 *fax:* +49 611 520773 *email:* otto.wrede@t-online.de. Edda Wrede, owner. *No. of publications: 100.*

PJ Tonger Musikverlag GmbH & Co. Auf dem Brand 10, Köln D-50996, Germany *tel:* +49 221 93 55640 *fax:* +49 221 93 556411 *email:* musikverlag@tonger.de. Peter Tonger, managing director. *Instrumental and choral. No. of publications: 7000.*

Peermusic Classical Europe. Mühlenkamp 45, Hamburg D-22303, Germany *tel:* +49 40 278 3790 *fax:* +49 40 2783 7940 *email:* classicaleur@peermusic.com. Reinhard Flender, vice-president classical music Europe; Arnt Nitschke, rental material, product management. *No. of publications: c 2500.*

Ries & Erler, Berlin Musikverlag. Wandlenallee 8, Berlin D-14052, Germany *tel:* +49 30 825 1049 *fax:* +49 30 825 9721 *email:* verlag@rieserler.de. Andreas Meurer, general manager. *No. of publications: 3000.*

Robert Lienau Musikverlag. Strubbergstr 80, Frankfurt D-60489, Germany *tel:* +49 699 782866 *fax:* +49 699 782 8679 *email:* info@lienau-frankfurt.de. Cornelia Grossmann, managing director; Saskia Bieber, hire department; Judith Picard, production manager. *No. of publications: 2000.*

Schott Musik International. Weihergarten 5, Mainz D-55116, Germany *tel:* +49 613 12460 *fax:* +49 613 124 6211 *email:* info@schott-musik.de. Peter Hanser-Strecker, president; Rainer Mohrs, head of editorial department; Andreas Pawlenka, sales manager; Michael Petry, managing director; Jochen Hillesheim, publishing director. *Also at: European American Music Distributors LLC, PO Box 4340, Miami FL 33014; Schott Japan Company Ltd, Kasuga Bldg, 2-9-3 Iidabashi, Chiyoda-ku, Tokyo 102-0072; Schott Music Publishers (Canada) Ltd, 2 Bloor St West,*

Toronto, Canada; Schott China Ltd, 111 Connaught Rd Central, Hong Kong. No. of publications: 30,000.

Sikorski, Internationale Musikverlage. Johnsallee 23, Hamburg D-20148, Germany *tel:* +49 40 41 41 000 *fax:* +49 40 41 41 00 40; +49 40 44 94 68 *email:* contact@sikorski.de. Dagmar R Sikorski, president; Axel Sikorski, president; Hans-Ulrich Duffek, director/head of classical music; Karl-Hermann Adrio, director/head of light music; Helmut Peters, PR manager; Reinhold Seyboth, librarian; Volker Kneller, sales manager.

Stockhausen-Verlag. Kettenberg 15, Kürten D-51515, Germany *fax:* +49 2268 1813. *All works of Karlheinz Stockhausen, books, scores and CDs.*

Thomi-Berg Publisher & Sheet Music Distributor. Pasinger Straße 38a, Planegg D-82152, Germany *tel:* +49 89 859 9944 *fax:* +49 89 859 3323 *email:* Thomi-Berg@t-online.de. Elisabeth Thomi-Berg, managing director. *No. of publications: c 5000.*

Tonos Musikverlags GmbH. Robert Edler Haus, Darmstadt D-64295, Germany *tel:* +49 6151 39040 *fax:* +49 6151 39 0490 *email:* mail@tonos-online.de. Marian Golf, director; Peter Bauer, director. *Argentinean Tango, sheet music for choirs, contemporary music. No. of publications: 4000.*

Tre Media Musikverlage. Amalienstr 40, Karlsruhe D-76133, Germany *tel:* +49 721 26023 *fax:* +49 721 26044 *email:* tremedia@aol.com. Friederike Zimmermann, manager. *No. of publications: 1500.*

Trio Musik Edition. Gewerbestrasse 2, Mettenheim D-84562, Germany *tel:* +49 8631 164160 *fax:* +49 8631 164162 *email:* trio.bme@t-online.de. Martin Lamprecht, manager; Michael Nowotny, manager; Friedemann Strube, manager. *Distributed in UK by: Harlequin Music, 69 Eversden Rd, Harlton, Cambridge CB3 7ET tel/fax: +44 1223 263795. No. of publications: 150.*

Zimmermann GmbH + Co. Strubbergstr 80, Frankfurt D-60489, Germany *tel:* +49 699 782866 *fax:* +49 699 782 8679 *email:* info@zimmermann-frankfurt.de. Cornelia Grossmann, managing director; Saskia Bieber, hire department; Michael Henne, sales manager. *No. of publications: 4000.*

Hungary

Editio Musica Budapest Music Publisher Ltd. Victor Hugo ucta 11-15, Budapest H-1132, Hungary *tel:* +36 12361 100 *fax:* +36 1 2361 101 *email:* emb@emb.hu. István Homolya, managing director. *No. of publications: 5000.*

Republic of Ireland

An Gúm. 27 Sráid Fhreidric Thuaidh, Dublin 1, Republic of Ireland *tel:* +353 1 889 2800 *fax:* +353 1 873 1140 *email:* angum@forasnagaeilge.ie. Seosamh Ó Murchú, senior editor. *Traditional, choral and instrumental music.*

Association of Irish Choirs. Drinan St, Cork, Republic of Ireland *tel:* +353 21 431 2296 *fax:* +353 21 496 2457 *email:* info@cnc.ie. Margaret O'Sullivan, executive director. *Choral music, especially Irish. No. of publications: 37.*

Melrose Music MM. 7 The Willows, Gort an Óir, Castlemartyr County Cork, Republic of Ireland *tel:* +353 21 464 6399 *email:* dg@melrosemusic.ie. *Contemporary and early music and recordings including numerous works by Irish composers. No. of publications: 60.*

Israel

Samuel Lewis Agency. PO Box 446, Herzlia B 46103, Israel *tel:* +972 9 955 3017 *email:* samlewis@zahav.net.il. Samuel Lewis. *Agent in Israel for hire of symphonic and stage works of Boosey & Hawkes, Faber Music, Schott Musik, OUP, Music Sales Group, Universal Edition, Peters Edition, Schirmer Inc, Dilia.*

Italy

Bèrben (Edizioni Musical). Via Redipuglia 65, Ancona I-60100, Italy *tel:* +39 071 204428 *fax:* +39 071 57414 *email:* info@berben.it.

Boccaccini & Spada Editori Srl. Via Arezzo 17, 00040 Pavona di, Albano Laziale (RM), Italy *tel:* +39 06 93 10 217/516 *fax:* +39 06 93 11 903 *email:* bsmusica@tiscali.it; Pietro Spada, admin. *No. of publications: 300.*

Mexico

Ediciones Mexicanas de Musica AC. Avda Juarez 18, Despacho 206 06050 D F, Mexico *tel:* +52 5 521 5855 *fax:* +52 5 521 5855. Isolda Acevedo Jiménez, manager. *No. of publications: 350.*

Netherlands

Albersen & Co BV. 182 Groot Hertoginnelaan, Den Haag NL-2517 EV, Netherlands *tel:* +31 70 345 6000/0865 (sales/hire) *fax:* +31 70 345

7110/361 4528 (sales/hire) *email:* sales@albersen.nl. Herman Albersen, general manager. *No. of publications: 50,000.*

Amstel Music BV. Middenweg 213, Amsterdam NL-1098 AN, Netherlands *tel:* +31 20 668 0232 *fax:* +31 20 692 2027 *email:* amsmusic@euronet.nl. Johan de Meij, director; Chris Abelen, chief editor. *Overseas offices: Hal Leonard Corporation, 7777 West Bluemound Rd, Milwaukee, Wisconsin 53213 USA tel: +1 414 774 3630 fax: +1 414 774 3259 email: info@halleonard.com. Also at: De Haske Publications BV, Business Park Friesland West 15, NL-8440 AS Heerenveen, Netherlands tel: +31 513 653 053 fax: +31 513 653 291 email: music@deheske.com. No. of publications: 16.*

XYZ International. Ambachtsweg 42, Am Huizen NL-1271, Netherlands *tel:* +31 35 69 58599 *fax:* +31 35 69 58999 *email:* info@emcmusic.nl. Frank Wymenga, manager. *UK distribution: Spartan Press. No. of publications: 1000+.*

New Zealand

Promethean Editions Ltd. PO Box 10-143, The Terrace, Wellington 6036, New Zealand *tel:* +64 4 473 5033 *fax:* +64 4 473 5066 *email:* info@promethean-editions.com. Ross Hendy, publisher; Thomas Liggett, music editor; Aaron Lloydd, legal and copyright. *Publisher of contemporary music by composers from New Zealand and Australia, specialising in instrumental and chamber music and works for percussion. Composers include John Psathas, Gareth Farr and Matthew Hindson. No. of publications: 100.*

Trust Records. PO Box 10-143, The Terrace, Wellington 6036, New Zealand *tel:* +64 4 473 5033 *fax:* +64 4 473 5066 *email:* info@trustcds.com. Ross Hendy, executive producer. *HRL Morrison Music Trust is a charitable trust established to support New Zealand performers and composers considered to be of international calibre. Its record label, Trust Records, releases up to 7 CDs a year.*

Norway

Norsk Noteservice AS. Breivollveien 25a, Box 5 Alnabru, Oslo N-0614, Norway *tel:* +47 2303 9555 *fax:* +47 2303 9559 *email:* post@noteservice.no. Odd Steenberg, print manager; Bjørn Morten Kjærnes, chairman, editor; Carl Svae, sales manager, Norway; Thomas Wettergreen, shop manager; Eva Kristen Kjæreng, international sales; Vegard Schaug, warehouse manager; Morten Steenberg, print assistant. *No. of publications: 40-50.*

Poland

PWM Edition Polskie Wydawnictwo Muzyczne. Al Krasinskiego 11a, Kraków, PL-31111, Poland *tel:* +48 12 422 0174 *fax:* +48 12 422 7171 *email:* pwm@pwm.com.pl. Andrzej Kosowski, editor-in-chief; Grazyna Adamczyk, deputy director, publishing; Wieslaw Olkuski, deputy director, economy; Stawomir Tabkowski, chairman of the managing board. *No. of publications: 13,000.*

Slovak Republic

Hudobny Fond Bratislava. Medená 29, Bratislava 1 811 02, Slovak Republic *tel:* +421 2 5443 1110 *fax:* +421 2 5443 1110 *email:* hfv@hfv.sk. Ing Milos Kocian, director; Ivan Valenta, head of publishing department; Helena Matasova, head of Musica Slovaca, CD editor; Lenka Plencznerova, head of hire library. *CD catalogue, sheet music catalogue, hire music catalogue. No. of publications: 1450.*

Music Centre Slovakia. Publishing Department, Michalska 10, Bratislava 815 36, Slovak Republic *tel:* +421 2 5920 4841 *fax:* +421 2 9520 4842 *email:* slovedit@hc.sk. Peter Zagar, head of department; Elena Kmetová, distribution. *Major project is an edition of 'The Complete Works of Jan Levoslav Bella'. Monthly periodical 'Musical Life'. No. of publications: 33.*

South Africa

Peermusic (Pty) Ltd. 9 Hoopoe Ave, Camps Bay, Cape Town 8005, South Africa *tel:* +27 21 438 8890 *fax:* +27 21 438 8894 *email:* kthompson@peermusic.com. Kate Thompson, senior director; Jane Mitchell, office manager; Morne Blignaut, admin assistant.

Spain

Arte Tripharia. Villamanin 50, b 70, Madrid E28011, Spain *tel:* +34 917 550 250 *fax:* +34 917 550 251 *email:* info@artetripharia.com. Rudesindo Soutelo, director.

Multimusic SL. Abdón Terradas 3, Madrid E-28015, Spain *tel:* +34 91 544 7880 *fax:* +34 91 544 6554 *email:* clif@sintonia.es. Bartolomé Espadalé, president; Clifton Williams, director.

Sintonia SA. Abdón Terradas 3-5, Madrid E-28015, Spain *tel:* +34 91 549 2350 *fax:* +34 91 543 9690 *email:* sintonia@sintonia.es. Bartolomé Espadalé, president, managing director; Clifton Williams, publishing

director. *Overseas address: 28 Rua Amilcar Cabral, P-1750-020 Lisbon, Portugal.*

Sweden

Edition Suecia. PO Box 27327, Stockholm S-102 54, Sweden *tel:* +46 8 783 8800 *fax:* +46 8 783 9510 *email:* swedmic@stim.se. Karin Heurling, editor. *No. of publications: c 300.*

Gehrmans Musikförlag. Box 6005, Hälsingegatan 1, Stockholm S-102 31, Sweden *tel:* +46 8 610 0610 *fax:* +46 8 610 0626 *email:* order@gehrmans.se; orkester@gehrmans.se. *Choir music, orchestral music, chamber music, educational material.*

TRUMPH. Horngaddevagen 5, Trelleborg S-231 92, Sweden *tel:* +46 410 334 186 *fax:* +46 410 334 316 *email:* order@trumph.se. Mats Frendahl, manager. *Publisher of organ music. No. of publications: 200.*

Switzerland

Amadeus. Vertrieb, Hermannstrasse 7, Winterthur CH-8400, Switzerland *tel:* +41 52 233 2866 *fax:* +41 52 233 5401 *email:* info@amadeusnet.ch.

Guild GmbH. Wiesholz 42b, Ramsen 8262, Switzerland *tel:* +41 52 743 1600 *fax:* +41 52 743 1553 *email:* s.guildmusic@bluewin.ch. Silvia Lalkaka, director; Kaikoo C Lalkaka, managing director. *No. of publications: 150.*

The White Prince Edition. PO Box 84, Vacallo CH-6833, Switzerland *email:* thewhiteprincestudio@hotmail.com. *Sheet music, educational books.*

Turkey

Muzikotek Ltd. 4 Gazeteciler Sitesi A 17-4, Levent 80620, Istanbul, Turkey *tel:* +90 212 282 8194 *fax:* +90 212 282 8195 *email:* muzikotek@muzikotek.com.tr. D Baydur, president; F Bezmen, general manager; Hande Twfekgi, copyright; B Erol, music resources. *No. of publications: 5.*

USA

Alliance Software Corporation. 1505 N Capitol St NE, Washington DC 20002, USA *tel:* +1 202 529 6730 *fax:* +1 202 318 3026 *email:* info@alliance.biz. Aspen Olmsted, president. *Publishes integrated box office management, fundraising, memberships, group and tour scheduling capabilities and accounting management software. Clients include representatives from the performing arts, museums and universities.*

Alry Publications Etc Inc. PO Box 36542, Charlotte NC 28236, USA *tel:* +1 704 334 3413 *fax:* +1 704 334 1143 *email:* amyblu@aol.com. Amy Rice Blumenthal, president; Susan Price, assistant. *Publishes music for woodwind and chamber music. No. of publications: 500+.*

Anglo-American Music Publishers. PO Box 161323, Altamonte Springs FL 32716-1323, USA *tel:* +1 407 464 9454 *email:* wwm32712@yahoo.com. Eric Fletcher, president. *No. of publications: c 500.*

A-R Editions Inc. Suite 180, 8551 Research Way, Middleton WI 53562, USA *tel:* +1 608 836 9000 *fax:* +1 608 831 8200 *email:* info@areditions.com. Patrick Wall, president. *No. of publications: 400.*

Bourne Co. 5 West 37 St, New York NY 10018, USA *tel:* +1 212 391 4300 *fax:* +1 212 391 4306 *email:* Bourne@bournemusic.com. Beebe Bourne, president. *Also at: 86 Windham Trail, Aurora, Ontario L4G 5L5, Canada, tel: +1 905 841 3094 fax: +1 905 727 0218; 27 Boulevard Beaumarchais, 75004 Paris, France, tel: +33 1 44 54 36 04 fax: +33 1 44 54 36 20; Second Floor Offices, 207-209 Regent St, London W1B 4ND, UK, tel: +44 20 7734 3454 fax: +44 20 7734 3385.*

C L Barnhouse Company. PO Box 680, 205 Cowan Avenue West, Oskaloosa Iowa 52577, USA *tel:* +1 641 673 8397 *fax:* +1 641 673 4718 *email:* questions@barnhouse.com. Robert Barnhouse Jr, chief executive officer; Andrew Clark, editorial; Andrew Glover, editorial. *Distributed in UK by: Harlequin Music, 69 Eversden Rd, Harlton, Cambridge CB3 7ET tel/fax: +44 1223 263795.*

Carl Fischer LLC. 65 Bleecker St, 8 Fl, New York NY 10012, USA *tel:* +1 212 777 0900 *fax:* +1 212 477 6996/3382 *email:* laurenk@carlfischer.com. Lauren Keiser, chief executive; William Heese, vice-president special projects; Larry Clark, vice-president instrumental music; Chris Scialfa, vice-president sales. *No. of publications: 6000.*

European American Music Distributors LLC. PO Box 4340, 15800 NW 48th Ave, Miami FL 33014, USA *tel:* +1 305 521 1604 *fax:* +1 305 521 1638 *email:* eamdc@eamdc.com. James Kendrick, acting president. *See also Schott, Germany; Universal Edition, Vienna. No. of publications: 500.*

G Schirmer Inc. 257 Park Ave South, 20th Floor, New York NY 10010, USA *tel:* +1 212 254 2100 *fax:* +1 212 254 2013 *email:* schirmer@schirmer.com.

Hal Leonard Corporation. PO Box 13819, 7777 West Bluemound Rd, Milwaukee WI 53213, USA *tel:* +1 414 774 3630 *fax:* +1 414 774 3259

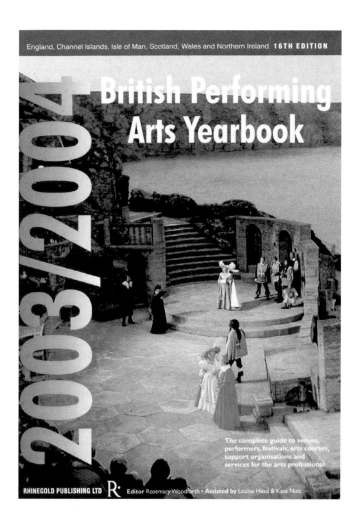

email: halinfo@halleonard.com. Keith Mardak, chief executive officer; Larry Morton, president; Sally Grant, vice president international sales admin; Phillip Burn, general manager (Australia). *Also at: Hal Leonard, Australia Pty Ltd, 22 Tauton Drive, Cheltenham East, Vic 3192. No. of publications: 8000.*

Herman and Apter. 5748 West Brooks Rd, Shepherd MI 48883-9202, USA *tel:* +1 989 828 6987 *email:* hermanapter@earthlink.net. Mark Herman, chief administrator; Ronnie Apter. *14 dual-language piano-vocal scores. No. of publications: 14.*

Hildegard Publishing Co. Box 332, Bryn Mawr PA 19010, USA *tel:* +1 610 667 8634 *fax:* +1 610 667 8635 *email:* sglickman@hildegard.com. Sylvia Glickman, president; Martha Furman Schleifer, senior editor. *Music by women composers. No. of publications: 545.*

Hinshaw Music Inc. PO Box 470, Chapel Hill NC 27514-0470, USA *tel:* +1 919 933 1691 *fax:* +1 919 967 3399. Roberta M Van Ness, president. *No. of publications: 2500.*

International Music Co. 5 West 37 St, New York NY 10018, USA *tel:* +1 212 391 4200 *fax:* +1 212 391 4306 *email:* IMC@internationalmusicco.com. Beebe Bourne, president.

Jazzmuze Inc. 80 Rumson Pl, Little Silver NJ 07739, USA *tel:* +1 732 747 5227 *fax:* +1 732 747 7822 *email:* wmtodt@aol.com. Joe Utterback, president; William E Todt, vice-president, secretary; Mary Todt, treasurer. *Jazz-influenced compositions for classical artists. No. of publications: 120.*

Joseph Patelson MusicHouse Ltd. 160 West 56 St, New York NY 10019, USA *tel:* +1 212 757 5587 *fax:* +1 212 246 5633 *email:* info@patelson.com. Dan Patelson, president; Carlos Vasquez, business manager; Scott Shade, buyer. *No. of publications: 50,000.*

Kendor Music Inc. PO Box 278, Delevan NY 14042, USA *tel:* +1 716 492 1254 *fax:* +1 716 492 5124 *email:* mmoland@kendormusic.com. Craig Cornwall, president; Jeff Jarvis, chief executive officer; Melinda Moland, copyright admin. *No. of publications: 2500.*

Mel Bay Publications Inc. #4 Industrial Dr, Pacific MO 63069, USA *tel:* +1 636 257 3970 *fax:* +1 636 257 5062 *email:* email@melbay.com. William Bay, president; Doug Witherspoon, purchasing and facilities manager. *No. of publications: 776.*

MJQ Music Inc. 1697 Broadway, New York NY 10019, USA *tel:* +1 212 582 6667 *fax:* +1 212 582 0627. Paul Schwartz, general manager.

MMB Music Inc. Contemporary Arts Building, 3526 Washington Ave, St Louis MO 63103-1019, USA *tel:* +1 314 531 9635 *fax:* +1 314 531 8384 *email:* MLG@mmbmusic.com. Norman A Goldberg, president; Marcia Lee Goldberg, vice-president, sales/marketing. *Publisher/distributor of*

the *'Music of our Time' for orchestra, opera, chamber ensemble and concert band, as well as books and videos. No. of publications: 2900.*

Neil A Kjos Music Co. 4380 Jutland Dr, San Diego CA 92117, USA *tel:* +1 858 270 9800 *fax:* +1 858 270 3507 *email:* email@kjos.com. Neil A Kjos, chairman.

Routledge Inc. 29 West 35th St, New York NY 10001, USA *tel:* +1 917 351 7123 *email:* rcarlin@taylorandfrancis.com. Richard Carlin, executive editor; Robert Bryne, editorial assistant. *Publishes Garland and Gordon & Breach/Harwood Academic Press titles. Also at: 11 New Fetter Lane, London EC4P 4EE, UK. No. of publications: 150.*

Seesaw Music Corp. 2067 Broadway, New York NY 10023, USA *tel:* +1 212 874 1200. Raoul R Ronson, president. *No. of publications: 4230.*

Smith Publications/Sonic Art Editions. 2617 Gwynndale Ave, Baltimore MD 21207, USA *tel:* +1 410 298 6509 *fax:* +1 410 944 5113. Sylvia Smith, editor. *No. of publications: 400.*

Southern Music Co. PO Box 329, San Antonio TX 78292, USA *tel:* +1 210 226 8167 *fax:* +1 210 223 4537 *email:* info@southernmusic.com. Arthur Gurwitz, president. *No. of publications: 5000.*

Themes and Variations. 39 Danbury Ave, Westport CT 06880-6822, USA *tel:* +1 203 227 5709 *fax:* +1 203 227 5715 *email:* tnv@tnv.net. John W Waxman, chief administrator.

Viola World Publications. 2 Inlander Rd, Saratoga Springs NY 12866, USA *tel:* +1 518 583 7177 *fax:* +1 518 583 7177 *email:* info@violaworldpublications.com. Alan Arnold, director. *UK office: Yvonne Dorsay, Music Sales Ltd, Bury St Edmunds, Newmarket Rd, Suffolk IP33 3YB. No. of publications: 100+.*

Visible Music. 1755 East 236, Euclid OH 44117, USA *tel:* +1 216 486 8211 *email:* info@visible-music.com. Jean Hasse, owner. *Choral, chamber, instrumental, orchestral and film music.*

William Grant Still Music. 1109 S Univ Plaza Way, Suite 109, Flagstaff AZ 86001-6317, USA *tel:* +1 928 526 9355 *fax:* +1 928 526 0321 *email:* wgsmusic@bigplanet.com. Judith Anne Still, proprietor; Lisa M Huffman, marketing; Daniel Headlee, accounting; Celeste Anne Headlee, operations. *UK office: African to American Music Society, c/o Mike Wright, 49 Waltham Ave, Guildford, Surrey GU2 6QF, UK. No. of publications: 199.*

Willis Music Co. 7380 Industrial Rd, Florence KY 41042, USA *tel:* +1 859 283 2050 *fax:* +1 859 283 1784 *email:* orderdpt@willis-music.com. Gary Abston, sales and marketing; Kevin Cranley, president. *Composers Thompson, Burnam, Gillock Morris, Campbell. No. of publications: 3000.*

Wiscasset Music Publishing Co. 10 Mason St, Cambridge MA 02138, USA *tel:* +1 617 492 5720 *fax:* +1 617 492 4031 *email:* information@wiscassetmusicpublishing.com. Betsy Warren-Davis, president; Natalie Palme, librarian; Sue Mundell, business manager. *No. of publications: 89.*

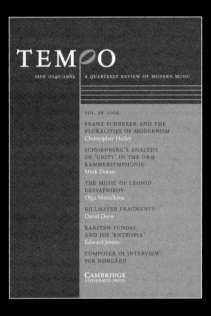

Book Publishers

Listed below are the publishers of academic, educational and general interest books about music. Information on the publications available is shown after each entry; for educational publishers the education level is specified.

A & C Black (Publishers) Ltd. Music Dept, 37 Soho Square, London W1D 3QZ *tel:* 020 7758 0200 *fax:* 020 7758 0222/0333 *email:* enquiries@acblack.com. Sheena Roberts, head of mus; Jane Sebba, commissioning ed; Marie Penny, asst ed; Katherine Davies, commissioning ed. *Primary, secondary, songbooks, musicals, mus scheme, classroom mus, inst tutors and repertoire.*

Albion Music Ltd. 65 Marathon House, 200 Marylebone Rd, London NW1 5PL *tel:* 01728 454820 *fax:* 020 7935 8678 *email:* cynthia. cooper@dial.pipex.com. Stephen Connock MBE, chmn. *Publications include Paradise Remembered by Ursula Vaughan Williams and Ralph Vaughan Williams in Perspective (ed Lewis Foreman).*

Amadeus Press. 2-4 Station Rd, Swavesey, Cambridge CB4 5QJ *tel:* 01954 204704 *fax:* 01954 206040 *email:* amadeuspressuk@btinternet.com. Carole A Green. *Specialist books on classical mus and musicians. Biographies of major figures such as Jussi Björling, Rosa Ponselle, Beethoven, Boulez, Korngold, Pierre Monteux, CALLAS, Mario Lanzo, Wagner, etc.*

Ashgate Publishing Ltd. Gower House, Croft Rd, Aldershot, Hants GU11 3HR *tel:* 01252 331551 *fax:* 01252 344405 *email:* info@ ashgatepub.co.uk. Sarah Noble, mkt mgr; Heidi May, commissioning ed. *Academic studies in mus, biographies, bibliographies and monographs. U/grad and p/grad level. Orders should be addressed to Bookpoint Ltd, 130 Milton Park, Abingdon, Oxon OX13 4SB tel: 01235 827730 email: ashgate@bookpoint.co.uk; enquiries@bookpoint.co.uk.*

Backbeat UK. Unit 2.1a, Union Court, 20-22 Union Rd, Clapham, London SW4 6JP *tel:* 020 7720 3581 *fax:* 020 7819 3998 *email:* info@backbeatuk.com. Nigel Osborne, mgr dir; Mark Brend, promotions and mkt co-ord; Tony Bacon, ed; Phil Richardson, producer. *Books on mus, musicians and insts. Incorporates Balafon Music Books.*

Blackwell Publishing. 9600 Garsington Rd, Oxford OX4 2DQ *tel:* 01865 476255 *fax:* 01865 476155 *email:* DUNCAN.HUMPHREY@ oxonblackwellpublishing.co.uk. Duncan Humphrey, mkt mgr (journals). *Publishers of Music Analysis.*

The British Library. Publishing Office, 96 Euston Rd, London NW1 2DB *tel:* 020 7412 7704 *fax:* 020 7412 7768 *email:* blpublications@bl.uk. Catherine Brittan, publishing mgr; Lara Speicher, mgr ed. *Wide range of mus publications.*

Cambridge University Press. Edinburgh Building, Shaftesbury Rd, Cambridge CB2 2RU *tel:* 01223 312393 *fax:* 01223 315052 *email:* information@cambridge.org. Victoria Cooper, commissioning ed, academic group; Susan Taylor, commissioning ed, educ group. *Primary and secondary educ mus books; gen mus books; books for scholars and students on the history of mus, mus performance, theory and analysis, popular mus and opera. Books series include Cambridge Companions to Music, Cambridge Music Handbooks, Musical Lives, Music in the Twentieth Century, Cambridge Studies in Opera and Cambridge Opera Handbooks. Also publishes a range of mus journals including British Journal of Music Education, Cambridge Opera Journal, Popular Music, Early Music History.*

Continuum. The Tower Building, 11 York Rd, London SE1 7NX *tel:* 020 7922 0880 *fax:* 020 7922 0881 *email:* jjoyce@continuumbooks.com. Philip Sturrock, mgr dir; Janet Joyce, ed dir, humanities division.

Cork University Press. Crawford Business Park, Crosses Green, Cork *tel:* 00 353 (0) 21 490 2980 *fax:* 00 353 (0) 21 431 5329 *email:* corkunip@ucc.ie. Mike Collins, sales/mkt mgr. *Selection of books covering Irish mus, traditions and culture.*

Duke University Press *see* **Indiana University Press.**

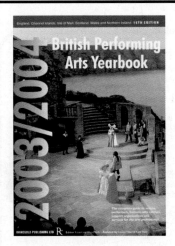

Europa Publications. Taylor & Francis Group, 11 New Fetter Lane, London EC4P 4EE *tel:* 020 7842 2110 *fax:* 020 7842 2249 *email:* sales.europa@tandf.co.uk. Paul Kelly, editorial dir; Mary Sweny, mkt mgr. *The International Who's Who in Classical Music (annual); The International Who's Who in Popular Music (annual).*

Evans Brothers Ltd. 2a Portman Mansions, Chiltern St, London W1U 6NR *tel:* 020 7487 0920 *fax:* 020 7487 0921 *email:* sales@ evansbrothers.co.uk. S Pawley, mgr dir; B Jones, international publishing dir; S Swallow, UK publishing dir. *World of Music (book and CD), Tell Me About Mozart and Tell Me About Chopin.*

Faber & Faber Ltd. 3 Queen Square, London WC1N 3AU *tel:* 020 7465 0045 *fax:* 020 7465 0034. Belinda Matthews, mus ed. *General mus books, including Composers Remembered series, biographies and letters, history, criticism, theory, reference, popular mus titles.*

First and Best in Education Ltd. Earlstrees Court, Earlstrees Rd, Corby, Northants NN17 4HH *tel:* 01536 399005 (orders)/399004 (editorial) *fax:* 01536 399012 *email:* sales@firstandbest.co.uk. Tony Attwood, mgr dir; Anne Cockburn, ed. *Books geared towards schools' mus depts including Listening to Music for GCSE and Music: The Perfect Classroom.*

Gresham Books Ltd. The Gresham Press, 46 Victoria Rd, Oxford OX2 7QD *tel:* 01865 513582 *fax:* 01865 512718 *email:* greshambks@ btinternet.com. Paul Lewis, publisher; Mary Lewis, school liaison; Jane Beeson, copyrights. *Approx 30 hymn books (standard, special, school) pa. Words only, melody and full mus editions; prayer books (special), orch and choir portfolios.*

Grove's Dictionaries of Music/Grove Music Online. Oxford University Press, Great Clarendon St, Oxford OX2 6DP *tel:* 01865 353796 *fax:* 01865 353308 *email:* david.towsey@oup.com. David Towsey, sales and mkt co-ord. *The New Grove Dictionary of Music and Musicians, 2nd edition (29 vols, hardback and online); The New Grove Dictionary of Jazz, 2nd edition (3 vols, hardback and online).*

Heinemann Educational. Halley Court, Jordan Hill, Oxford OX2 8EJ *tel:* 01865 314130 *fax:* 01865 314140 *email:* orders@heinemann.co.uk. Elizabeth Tyler, mus publisher. *Curriculum materials for primary and secondary schools.*

Hodder Arnold. 338 Euston Rd, London NW1 3BH *tel:* 020 7873 6000 *fax:* 020 7873 6299 *email:* hayley.lewis@hodder.co.uk. Philip Walters,

mgr dir; Hayley Lewis, head of trade mkt. *Hodder & Stoughton Educational, Essential Guide To Music (GNVQ/BTEC) and What Primary Teachers Should Know About Music. Teach Yourself series.*

Hollis Publishing. Harlequin House, Teddington, Middx TW11 8EL *tel:* 020 8977 7711 *fax:* 020 8977 1133 *email:* orders@hollis-pr.com. Gillie Mayer, ed; Jane Ireland, ad dir. *Showcase International Music Book (formerly 'Kemps International Music Book'). Showcase - the International Music Business Guide.*

Indiana University Press. CAP Ltd, 15a Lewin's Yard, East St, Chesham, Bucks HP5 1HQ *tel:* 01494 581601 *fax:* 01494 581602 *email:* nickesson@combinedacademic.demon.co.uk. Nick Esson, dir; Julia Monk, mrkt mgr. *Academic books for students, academics and professionals.*

International Music Publications Ltd. Griffin House, 161 Hammersmith Rd, London W6 8BS *tel:* 020 8222 9200 *fax:* 020 8222 9260 *email:* enquiries@music-at-school.co.uk. Robin Norman, educ specialist, ed; Matt Crossey, mkt and creative mgr; Chris Statham, sales mgr. *Classical, jazz, pop and rock publications, tutors, mus for schools. Series include 'In Session With', 'Take the Lead', 'Jam With'. Educ range includes 'Music About Us' (KS1,2), 'Sing It And Say It' (KS2), 'Key Club', 'Team' and 'Let's Make Music Fun'. Early years songbooks 'Class Act Musicals' (KS1), 'Box Office Productions' (KS2,3), Schaum, Aaron and Suzuki methods. Plus mus for orch, br band, concert band and jazz ens.*

Jessica Kingsley Publishers. 116 Pentonville Rd, London N1 9JB *tel:* 020 7833 2307 *fax:* 020 7837 2917 *email:* post@jkp.com. Jaishree Parmar, mkt mgr; Jessica Kingsley, mgr dir; Amy Lankester-Owen, ed dir. *Mus therapy, mus for children with special needs, mus and health. Mus therapy and palliative care.*

Kahn & Averill. 9 Harrington Rd, London SW7 3ES *tel:* 020 8743 3278 *fax:* 020 8743 3278 *email:* kahn@averill23.freeserve.co.uk. Morris Kahn, dir. *Bach: Chorale Harmonization/Instrumental Counterpoint. Editorial enquiries to: 21 Pennard Mansions, Goldhawk Rd, London W12 8DL. Distributors: BR & D Ltd, Hadleigh Hall, London Rd, Hadleigh, Essex SS7 2DE.*

Nelson Thornes Ltd. Delta Place, 27 Bath Rd, Cheltenham, Glos GL53 7TH *tel:* 01242 267100 *fax:* 01242 221914 *email:* primary@

nelsonthornes.com. *A complete range of primary curriculum materials and the following resources for music: 'Sounds of Music', a balanced, structured programme ensuring careful year on year progression through the whole of primary. 'Sounds of Singing' (new), available in the Autumn term. A wealth of ideas to develop and nurture children's voices. Both resources cover all UK curricula.*

Ominibus Press. Music Sales Ltd, 8-9 Frith St, London W1D 3JB *tel:* 020 7434 0066 *fax:* 020 7743 9718 *email:* music@musicsales.co.uk. Guy Lloyd, home and export sales mgr; Lucy Grant, sales admin. *Part of the Music Sales group. Biographies (pop and classical), studies of popular culture, technical guides.*

Open University Press. McGraw Hill House, Shoppenhangers Rd, Maidenhead, Berks SL6 2QU *tel:* 01628 502500 *fax:* 01628 770224 *email:* enquiries@openup.co.uk. *Books for students, academics and professionals. Cultures of Popular Music is a new title in the Issues in Cultural and Media Studies series, plus there are books on Supporting Musical Development in the Early Years.*

Oxford University Press (OUP). Music Books, Great Clarendon St, Oxford OX2 6DP *tel:* 01865 556767 *fax:* 01865 267741 *email:* jacqueline.smith@oup.com. Jacqueline Smith, asst ed. *Academic, general, reference, college, paperbacks and Master Musicians series. Education/Trade: Saxon Way West, Corby, Northants NN18 9ES tel: 01536 741519 fax: 01536 746337.*

Pendragon Press. Crag House, Witherslack, Grange-over-Sands, Cumbria LA11 6RW *tel:* 01539 552286 *fax:* 01539 552013 *email:* musicbks@rdooley.demon.co.uk. Rosemary Dooley, European distributor. *Aesthetics, dance and mus, Liszt, French opera, analysis, Czech mus, performance guides, thematic catalogues, mus history.*

Penguin Press. 80 Strand, London WC2R 0RL *tel:* 020 7010 3000 *fax:* 020 7010 6701. Jenny Todd, mkt dir; Rachel Salvidge, mkt mgr. *Reference books on mus, including Penguin Guide to Compact Discs and DVDs, Penguin Guide to Compact Discs Yearbook, Penguin Opera Guide, Penguin Price Guide for Record and CD Collectors, Penguin Guide to Jazz on CD.*

Phaidon Press. Regent's Wharf, All Saints St, London N1 9PA *tel:* 020 7843 1234 *fax:* 020 7843 1111. *20th C composers series of biographies and other titles, including a new translation and commentary of Der Ring des Nibelungen by Rudolph Sabor.*

Rhinegold Publishing Ltd. 241 Shaftesbury Ave, London WC2H 8TF *tel:* 01832 270333 *fax:* 01832 275560 *email:* booksales@rhinegold.co.uk. Tony Gamble, mgr dir; Keith Diggle, mkt dir; Sarah Williams, gen mgr. *Publishes magazines and reference books for the performing arts and educ. The company began with the magazine Classical Music and has expanded to include Music Teacher, Piano, Early Music Today, The Singer and Opera Now. Works of reference include the British and International Music Yearbook, Music Education Yearbook and British Performing Arts Yearbook. Other books include Arts Marketing, Study Guides for GCSE, AS, A2 level Music for AQA, OCR and Edexcel exam boards and Music Technology Study Guide for AS/A2 Edexcel, Religious Studies Guides for AS and A2 level and The Rhinegold Dictionary of Music in Sound.*

Robert Hale Ltd. 45-47 Clerkenwell House, Clerkenwell Green, London EC1R 0HT *tel:* 020 7251 2661 *fax:* 020 7490 4958 *email:* enquire@halebooks.com. Martin Kendall, mkt dir. *Various books including reference, Christmas carols, classical mus guides, vn-making, etc.*

Robson Books. 64 Brewery Rd, London N7 9NT *tel:* 020 7697 3000 *fax:* 020 7697 3007 *email:* Jrobson@chrysalisbooks.co.uk. Jeremy Robson, publisher; Jo Brooks, snr ed; Jane Donovan, snr ed; Sharon Benjamin, head of publicity. *Secondary and above. Books include the Contemporary Composers series, biographies of Placido Domingo, Luciano Pavarotti, Toscanini and Bernard Haitink, and Opera Lover's Guide to Europe.*

Routledge. Taylor & Francis Books, 11 New Fetter Lane, London EC4P 4EE *tel:* 020 7842 2410 *fax:* 020 7842 2303 *email:* tom.church@tandf.co.uk. Tom Church, mkt co-ord. *Publishes a wide range of titles on contemporary, classical and early mus as well as popular mus and musicians, scores and mus research.*

Sounds Write. 56 Baswich Crest, Stafford ST17 0HJ *tel:* 01785 250405 *fax:* 01785 250405 *email:* soundswrite@supanet.com. Keith Baskett, mkt and sales mgr. *Theory work books for young beginners to gr 3 following the ABRSM syllabus. Material offers a structured and fun approach through its child-centred method of teaching. Applicable to any inst and does not require keyboard skills. Free brochure available.*

Taylor & Francis. 4 Park Square, Milton Park, Abingdon, Oxon OX14 4RN *fax:* 01235 829003 *email:* Victoria.Lincoln@tandf.co.uk.

Thomson Learning. High Holborn House, 50-51 Bedford Row, London WC1R 4LR *fax:* 020 7067 2600. *Schirmer list covering mus theory and teaching methods.*

Toccata Press. 16 Dalkeith Court, Vincent St, London SW1P 4HH *tel:* 020 7821 5020 *fax:* 020 7834 5020 *email:* martin@toccatapress.com. Martin Anderson, proprietor. *Publishes studies of composers, other books on mus and the following series: Musicians on Music, Symphonic Studies, Musicians in Letters and Other Operas. Trade enquiries to: Gazelle, White Cross Mills, High Town, Lancaster LA1 4XS tel: 01524 68765 fax: 01524 63232 email: Sales@gazellebooks.co.uk.*

University of Nebraska Press *see* **Indiana University Press.**

WW Norton & Company Ltd. Castle House, 75-76 Wells St, London W1T 3QT *tel:* 020 7323 1579 *fax:* 020 7436 4553 *email:* office@wwnorton.co.uk. Alan Cameron, mgr dir; Victoria Keown-Boyd, mkt mgr. *Norton Introduction to Music History, Norton History of Music, musicology titles, Norton Critical Scores series and Grout: History of Western Music.*

Ward Lock Educational Co Ltd. BIC Ling Kee House, 1 Christopher Rd, East Grinstead, W Sussex RH19 3BT *tel:* 01342 318980 *fax:* 01342 410980 *email:* wle@lingkee.com. Eileen Parsons. *Mus and song books for young children.*

Woodwind Plus. 42 St Mary's Park, Louth, Lincs LN11 0EF *tel:* 01507 605244 *email:* jeff@wwplus.freeserve.co.uk. *Tutorial publications. Chmbr mus for w/wind, hn, str and pno. AB and Trinity exam publications. Mus for concert band.*

Orchestral Hire Libraries

Listed below are the main commercial libraries that deal in the hire of orchestral scores and parts. The works of most well-known composers are available from nearly all the libraries, and the information after each entry indicates the specific composers and editions which are only available from that library. Some orchestral sets of works that are no longer in copyright may be available from larger music libraries.

Banks Music Publications Hire Library. The Old Forge, Sand Hutton, York YO41 1LB *tel:* 01904 468472 *fax:* 01904 468679 *email:* banksramsay@cwcom.net. Jeremy Warnes, hire library mgr. *Mus of James Brown, Gerald Finzi, Francis Jackson, Philip Marshall.*

Bardic Edition. 6 Fairfax Cres, Aylesbury, Bucks HP20 2ES *tel:* 01296 428609 *fax:* 01296 581185 *email:* hire@bardic-music.com. *Mus of Percy Grainger, Christopher Headington, John Pickard, Alan Gibbs, Bernard Stevens, Dana Paul Derna, Thomas Pitfield, Antoinette Kirkwood.*

Baroque Publications Ltd Hire Library. Treadam Farm, Llantilio-Crossenny, Abergavenny, Gwent NP7 8TA *tel:* 01600 780233 *fax:* 01600 780233. Sally Felps, hire library mgr. *Mainly mus of Handel with libretto in English (orch parts and vocal scores of operas, separate arias available). Reduced orchestration (10 insts) of some Mozart and Rossini operas. Also Hansel and Gretel (Humperdinck) and Falstaff (Verdi). 18th and 19th C ballet mus with pno scores and orch parts.*

Boosey & Hawkes Music Publishers Ltd Hire Library. 295 Regent St, London W1B 2JH *tel:* 020 7580 2060 *fax:* 020 7580 5815 *email:* hirelibrary.uk@boosey.com. Bruce MacRae, hire library mgr. *Mus of John Adams (since 1986), Louis Andriessen, Bartók (some), Bernstein, Blacher, Britten (until 1963), Birtwistle (since 1994), Carter (since 1981), Copland, Dean, Delius (some), Druckman, von Einem, Finzi, Firsova, Floyd, Gerhard (until 1960), Ginastera, Glanert, Goldschmidt, Górecki (some), Gubaidulina, HK Gruber, Holloway, Höller (since 1983), Karl Jenkins, Kodály (some), Kurtág, Lindberg (since 1996), MacMillan, Mackey, Martinu (some), Maxwell Davies (some), Panufnik, Prokofieff, Rachmaninoff, Rautavaara, Reich, Rouse, Schnittke, Schwertsik, Shostakovich, Richard Strauss, Stravinsky, Torke, Xenakis (until 1969), Yun. Editions: Boosey and Hawkes/London, New York, Berlin, Sydney; Anton Benjamin/Berlin; Bote & Bock/Berlin; Carisch/Milan; Dilia/Prague; DSCH/Moscow; EMB/Budapest; Fazer Music/Scandinavia; Fennica Gehrmans Oy/Scandinavia; Gehrmans/Scandinavia; Moscow Musical Publishing House (VAAP/RAO/MMI); Rahter/Berlin; Senff/Berlin; Simrock/Berlin; Zen-on Music/Japan.*

Chandos Music Ltd. Chandos House, Commerce Way, Colchester, Essex CO2 8HQ *tel:* 01206 225200 *fax:* 01206 225201 *email:* shogger@chandos.net. *Mus of Takashi Yoshimatsu, Gordon Langford, J N Hummel, Ernest Tomlinson, Sir Thomas Armstrong and Jack Byfield.*

Chester Music Ltd Hire Library. Newmarket Rd, Bury St Edmunds, Suffolk IP33 3YB *tel:* 01284 705705 *fax:* 01284 703401 *email:* hire@musicsales.co.uk. Adam Harvey, snr hire librarian; Janet Atkinson, Rebecca Johnson, hire librarians. *Editions: Associated Music Publishers, Chester Music, J Curwen & Sons Ltd, Dunvagen, Edwin Ashdown Ltd, A Lengnick & Co, Alain Boublil Overseas Ltd, MCA, Ongaka No Tomo Edition, Really Useful Group Ltd, G Schirmer Inc, G Schirmer (Australia) Pty Ltd, Union Musical Ediciones, Wilhelm Hansen Edition.*

Clyde, R. 6 Whitelands Ave, Chorleywood, Rickmansworth, Herts WD3 5RD *tel:* 01923 283600 *fax:* 01923 283600 *email:* r.clyde@dial.pipex.com. Roger Harris, proprietor. *Works for orch, voices and orch, operas by Sullivan.*

Concord Music Hire Library. 5 Bushey Close, Old Barn Lane, Kenley, Surrey CR8 5AU *tel:* 020 8660 4766 *fax:* 020 8668 5273 *email:* concordmusichire@aol.com. Ray Lee, hire library mgr. *Mus of Judith Bingham, Arthur Bliss, Nigel Clarke, Martin Ellerby, Nicola LeFanu, Philip Grange, Edward Gregson, Piers Hellawell, Daniel Jones, Constant Lambert, Kenneth Leighton, Clark McAlister, Roger Marsh, Janet Owen Thomas, Geoffrey Poole, Matthew Taylor, Robert Walker, Philip Wilby, Gareth Wood. Editions: Carl Fischer Rental Library, Maecenas Music, Maecenas Contemporary Composers Ltd, Warner Chappell Music Hire Library.*

D'Oyly Carte Music Library. The Powerhouse, 6 Sancroft St, London SE11 5UD *tel:* 020 7793 7700/7100 *fax:* 020 7793 7300 *email:* ronant@doylycarte.org.uk. Ronan Tighe, mus library mgr. *Gilbert & Sullivan operettas, Sullivan & Co, J Strauss, Offenbach.*

Faber Music Hire Library. FM Distribution, Burnt Mill, Elizabeth Way, Harlow CM20 2HX *tel:* 01279 828907/8 *fax:* 01279 828902 *email:* hire@fabermusic.com. Chris Norris, performance and hire library mgr; James McCarthy, asst hire librarian. *Mus of T Adès, J Anderson, M Arnold (some), G Benjamin, H Blake (The Snowman), A Boyd (some), F Bridge (some), Britten (some), M Daugherty, C Davis, J Harvey, M Hindson, Holst (some), O Knussen, P McCartney (some), C Matthews, D Matthews, N Maw (later works), D Muldowney (some), P Sculthorpe, H Searle (some), R Simpson (some), R Smalley (some), R Vaughan Williams (some), C Vine (later works), J Woolrich. Editions: Alkor, Bärenreiter, Peermusic, Threefold Music, Supraphon.*

Fentone Music Ltd Hire Library. Fleming Rd, Earlstrees, Corby, Northants NN17 4SN *tel:* 01536 260981 *fax:* 01536 401075 *email:* music@fentone.com. Mark Coull, hire library mgr. *Editions: Berben, London Orchestral Series, Norsk Musikforlag, Real Musical.*

Josef Weinberger Ltd Hire Library. 12-14 Mortimer St, London W1T 3JJ *tel:* 020 7927 7312 *fax:* 020 7436 9616 *email:* hirelibrary@jwmail.co.uk. Christopher Moss, hire library mgr; Timothy Seddon, asst. *Music Theatre International and Rodgers and Hammerstein Concert Library, Kurt Weill Foundation (some), mus of Emmérich Kálmán, Wilfred Josephs (some), Mahler (some), Paul Patterson (some), Morris Pert (some), André Tchaikovsky, Ernst Von Dohnanyi (some), Malcolm Williamson (some), Ermanno Wolf-Ferrari (some).*

MDS Ltd. Hire & Copyright Administration, 48 Great Marlborough St, London W1F 7BB *tel:* 020 7734 6622 *fax:* 020 7439 2897 *email:* hire@mdslondon.co.uk. Rod Taylor, head of hire admin. *Mus of Birtwistle, Bryars, Casken, Duddell, Goehr, Henze, Hesketh, Ligeti, Orff, Roxanna Panufnik, Sawer, Takemitsu, Tippett, Turnage. Editions: Boelke Bomart, Breitkopf & Härtel, Casa Musicale Sonzogno, Czech Music Fund, European American Music/Helicon Inc, Israel Music Institute, PWM, Schott London/Mainz/Japan, Universal Edition London/Vienna.*

Novello & Co Ltd Hire Library. Newmarket Rd, Bury St Edmunds, Suffolk IP33 3YB *tel:* 01284 705705 *fax:* 01284 703401 *email:* hire@musicsales.co.uk. Adam Harvey, snr hire librarian; Janet Atkinson, Rebecca Johnson, hire librarians. *Mus of Malcolm Arnold (some), Arthur Bliss, Richard Rodney Bennett, Herbert Howells, Tristan Keuris, John McCabe, Thea Musgrave, Stephen Oliver, Aulis Sallinen, Giles Swayne, Judith Weir (some). Editions: Arnold, Belwin Mills, Bosworth & Co Ltd, Donemus, Elkin, EMI, Goodwin & Tabb, Paterson, Paxton.*

Oxford University Press Hire Library. Great Clarendon St, Oxford OX2 6DP *tel:* 01865 353699 *fax:* 01865 353767 *email:* music.hire.uk@oup.com. Iain MacKinlay, mus hire mgr; Will Harriss, mus hire asst; *Mus of Gerald Barry, Michael Berkeley, John Buller, Martin Butler, Andrew Carter, Richard Causton, Bob Chilcott, Gordon Crosse, Gabriel Erkoreka, Michael Finnissy (from 1988), Edward Harper, Alun Hoddinott, Constant Lambert (some), William Mathias, Anthony Powers, Alan Rawsthorne, John Rutter, Robert Sherlaw Johnson, Howard Skempton, Michael Thomas, Ralph Vaughan Williams (from 1926), William Walton.*

Peters Edition Ltd Hire Library. 10-12 Baches St, London N1 6DN *tel:* 020 7553 4020 *fax:* 020 7490 4921 *email:* hire@uk.edition-peters.com. Fiona Flower, dir, hire and copyright; Pascal Fallas, hire library mgr. *Mus of John Cage, George Crumb, James Dillon, Jonathan Dove, Morton Feldman (some), Brian Ferneyhough, Alan Hovhaness, Mauricio Kagel, György Ligeti (some), Roger Reynolds, Rebecca Saunders, Erkki-Sven Tüür, Grrollyn Wallen. Editions: M P Belaieff, Edition Kunzelmann, Edition Schwann, Heinrichshofen, Henry Litolff, Hinrichsen Edition, C F Kahnt, F E C Leuckart, Robert Lienau, Lyche, C F Peters/London/New York/Frankfurt/Leipzig, Robert Forberg Musikverlag, Tischer & Jagenberg, Thomi-Berg, Christian Vieweg, Zimmermann.*

Queensgate Music Hire Library. 120 Downhill St, Glasgow G12 9DN *tel:* 0141 339 1699 *fax:* 0141 339 1699 *email:* queensgatemusic@btopenworld.com. *Mus of Thomas Wilson only.*

Scottish Music Information Centre. 1 Bowmont Gardens, Glasgow G12 9LR *tel:* 0141 334 6393 *fax:* 0141 337 1161 *email:* info@smic.org.uk. *Extensive hire library of Scottish composers' works, including: Beamish, Blake, Boyle, Creswell, Dalby, Dare, Gardner, Gourlay, Hearne, Nicolson, McGuire, McLeod, McPherson, MacIlwham, Sweeney, Whyte, etc.*

Stainer & Bell Ltd Hire Library. PO Box 110, Victoria House, Gruneisen Rd, London N3 1DZ *tel:* 020 8343 3303 *fax:* 020 8343 3024 *email:* post@stainer.co.uk. Caroline Holloway, hire library mgr. *Agents for UK and rest of Europe for the hire library of ECS Publishing, Boston, USA.*

United Music Publishers Ltd Hire Library. 42 Rivington St, London EC2A 3BN *tel:* 020 7827 8106 *fax:* 020 7739 6549 *email:* hire@ump.co.uk. Zoe Roberts, hire library mgr; Shirley Ranger, mgr dir. *Mus of Simon Bainbridge (some), Richard Barrett, Havergal Brian, Diana Burrell, Edward Cowie, Chris Dench (some), Petr Eben (some), Michael Finnissy (some), Naji Hakim (some), George Lloyd (some), Stephen Montague (some), Edwin Roxburgh (some). Editions (all France unless otherwise stated): Amphion, Billaudot, Bornemann, Carus-Verlag (Germany), Chant du Monde, Chantraine (Belgium), Choudens, Combre, Costallat, Dominis (Canada), Durand, EFM, EME, Elkan-Vogel (USA), Enoch, Eschig, Hamelle, Henn (Switzerland), Heugel, Jobert, Leduc, Lemoine, Marais, R Martin, Ouvrières, Ricordi (France, Germany, Italy, UK), Rideau-Rouge, Salabert, Schola Cantorum, Transatlantiques, UMP (UK), Zurfluh.*

Warner Chappell Music Ltd Hire Library. 5 Bushey Close, Old Barn Lane, Kenley, Surrey CR8 5AU *tel:* 020 8660 4766 *fax:* 020 8668 5273 *email:* concordmusichire@aol.com. Ray Lee, librarian. *Administered by the Concord Music Hire Library. Mus of Arnold Bax, Eric Coates, George Gershwin. Editions: Asherberg Hopwood and Crew, Chappell, Warner Brothers.*

William Elkin Music Services Hire Library. Station Rd Industrial Estate, Salhouse, Norwich NR13 6NS *tel:* 01603 721302 *fax:* 01603 721801 *email:* sales@elkinmusic.co.uk. Cindy Hazard, hire library mgr. *Editions: Braydeston Press, Hofmeister, Lawson-Gould, Seresta, Sikorski, Thames Publishing.*

Yorke Edition. Grove Cottage, Southgate, South Creake, Norfolk NR21 9PA *tel:* 01328 823501 *fax:* 01328 823502 *email:* info@yorkedition.co.uk. Twiggy Bigwood. *Orch parts for concertos, concert pieces and ens for the db, including Bottesini, Dittersdorf and Capuzzi.*

Copyright Organisations

Listed below are the main organisations concerned with musical copywright in the UK. The Copyright Laws are extremely complex and details should be checked carefully with the institution concerned.

Copyright Online Royalties Services Ltd. 32 Lexington St, London W1F 0LQ *tel:* 020 7255 8777 *fax:* 020 7255 8778 *email:* info@mcsmusic.com. Guy Fletcher; Tim Hollier; Brian Scholfield. *Specialises in the registration of mus copyrights and the speedy repatriation of funds from overseas; quick processing of UK royalties and online royalty statements and payments.*

International Federation of the Phonographic Industry. IFPI Secretariat, 54 Regent St, London W1B 5RE *tel:* 020 7878 7900 *fax:* 020 7878 7950 *email:* info@ifpi.org. *Represents the recording industry worldwide. Promotes and defends the copyright interests of its members and undertakes anti-piracy initiatives.*

MCS Music Ltd. 32 Lexington St, London W1F 0LQ *tel:* 020 7255 8777 *fax:* 020 7255 8778 *email:* info@mcsonline.com. Brian Scholfield; Guy Fletcher; Tim Mollier. *Administers and exploits the rights of mus publishers and writers. The service includes songwriters' agreements, registering the copyrights with societies all over the world and preparing writers' royalties on behalf of publishing companies.*

Music Copyright Solutions Plc. 32 Lexington St, London W1F 0LQ *tel:* 020 7255 8777 *fax:* 020 7255 8778 *email:* info@mcsmusic.com. Guy Fletcher; Tim Hollier; Brian Scholfield.

Music Publishers Association Ltd. 3rd Floor, Strandgate, 20 York Buildings, London WC2N 6JU *tel:* 020 7839 7779 *fax:* 020 7839 7776 *email:* info@mpaonline.org.uk. *Exists to safeguard the interests of mus publishers and the writers signed to them. Provides members with a forum and a collective voice, and aims to inform and to educate the wider public in the importance and value of copyright.*

Phonographic Performance Ltd (PPL). 1 Upper James St, London W1F 9DE *tel:* 020 7534 1000 *fax:* 020 7534 1111 *email:* performer.info@ppluk.com. *Represents over 3000 record companies, 13,000 labels and licenses the broadcast and public performance of their repertoire and recordings in every genre of mus. Collect and distribute revenues from radio stations, pubs, clubs and thousands of users of sound recordings on behalf of member companies as well as some 25,000 performers.*

Music Journalism

Newspapers

The following list of major newspapers all carry regular coverage of classical music. The editor, the chief music critics and additional music and arts critics are listed below.

Evening Express. PO Box 43, Lang Stracht, Mastrick, Aberdeen AB15 6DF *tel:* 01224 690222 *fax:* 01224 699575 *email:* ee.news@ajl.co.uk. Donald Martin, ed; Scott Begbie, features ed. *35p.*

The Evening Standard. Northcliffe House, 2 Derry St, Kensington, London W8 5EE *tel:* 020 7938 6000 *fax:* 020 7937 2648. Norman Lebrecht, asst ed (arts); Fiona Hughes, arts ed.

The Financial Times. 1 Southwark Bridge, London SE1 9HL *tel:* 020 7873 3000 *fax:* 020 7873 3929. Andrew Gowers, ed; Richard Fairman, mus critic; Lorna Dolan, arts ed; Andrew Clark, mus and opera critic. *90p. Arts section daily plus in the FT magazine.*

The Guardian. 119 Farringdon Rd, London EC1R 3ER *tel:* 020 7278 2332 *fax:* 020 7837 2114. Alan Rusbridger, ed; Dan Glaister, arts ed; Charlotte Higgins, classical mus ed; Andrew Clements, chief mus and opera critic; Adrian Searle, art critic.

The Independent. 191 Marsh Wall, London E14 9RS *tel:* 020 7005 2000. David Lister, arts ed.

The News (Mon-Sat). The News Centre, Hilsea, Portsmouth, Hants PO2 9SX *tel:* 023 9266 4488 *fax:* 023 9267 3363. Mike Gilson, ed; Mike Allen, mus critic; Barry Rutter, pop mus. *32p.*

The Times Educational Supplement (weekly). Admiral House, 66-68 East Smithfield, London E1W 1BX *tel:* 020 7782 3000 *fax:* 020 7782 3200 *email:* friday@tes.co.uk. Bob Doe, ed; Heather Neill, arts ed; Geraldine Brennan, books ed. *£1.20.*

Music Periodicals

Periodicals devoted to classical music or of specific music interest are listed alphabetically, followed by the number of issues per annum and the name of the editor.

BBC Music Magazine (12). Room A1004, Woodlands, 80 Wood Lane, London W12 0TT *tel:* 020 8433 3283 (ed)/3590 (ad) *fax:* 020 8433 3292 *email:* music.magazine@bbc.co.uk. Helen Wallace, ed. *£3.99; £47.88 pa (UK).*

BM Magazine (3). The Baptist Music Network, 4 Broughton Cres, Wyke Regis, Weymouth, Dorset DT4 9AR *email:* editor@baptistmusicnetwork.org.uk. Ian Garland, ed. *£2.50, 3 times pa. Articles, letters, book and CD reviews to help musicians with worship and leading worship.*

Braille Music Magazine (12). Royal National Institute of the Blind, Dalesbury, 2 Station Rd, Milbourne Port, Sherbourne DT9 5EQ *tel:* 01963 250656 *email:* roger.firman@rnib.org.uk. Roger Firman, ed. *75p per issue. Original commissioned articles including CD reviews and items from print magazines. Specialises in classical mus. Also available on computer disk for PC.*

Brass Band World (10). Caron Publications, Peak Press Building, Eccles Rd, Chapel-en-le-Frith, High Peak SK23 9RQ *tel:* 01298 812816 *fax:* 01298 815220 *email:* info@brassbandworld.com. Robert Mulholland, ed; Liz Winter, ad mgr; Lisa Puddle, head of subs. *£3.85; £35.50 pa (UK), £42.50 (Europe), £42 (rest of world including USA). Illustrated magazine with informative coverage of the br band scene; includes articles by leading authorities, and features up-to-date news.*

Brio (2). The Library, Royal Northern College of Music, 124 Oxford Rd, Manchester M13 9RD *tel:* 0161 907 5245 *fax:* 0161 273 7611 *email:* Geoff.Thomason@rncm.ac.uk. Geoffrey Thomason, ed; Marian Hogg, reviews ed; Mrs Alex Garden, ad ed. *Membership: national: £32 (individual), £45 (institutions), sub £30; international: £46/60. Journal of International Association of Music Libraries, Archives and Documentation Centres UK and Ireland Branch. Articles on musicology, mus bibliography/librarianship. Reviews of books and mus.*

British Bandsman (52). 64 London End, Beaconsfield, Bucks HP9 2JD *tel:* 01494 674411 *fax:* 01494 670932 *email:* info@britishbandsman.com. Nicola Bland, editorial dir. *90p; £39.50 pa (UK subscriptons).*

British Journal of Music Therapy (2). 61 Church Hill Rd, E Barnet, Herts EN4 8SY *tel:* 020 8441 6226 *fax:* 020 8441 4118 *email:* info@bsmt.org. Julie Sutton, ed; Simon Procter, asst ed. *£60 (corporate bodies), £40 (individuals).*

British Performing Arts Yearbook (1). Rhinegold Publishing Ltd, 241 Shaftesbury Ave, London WC2H 8TF *tel:* 01789 209281 (ed); 020 7333 1733 (ad) *fax:* 01789 264009 (ed); 020 7333 1736 (ad) *email:* bpay@rhinegold.co.uk. Rosemary Woodforth, ed. *£26.95. Annual directory of performing arts in Britain. Includes venues, companies, solo performers, symphony and chmbr orchs, arts festivals, educ and training, arts councils, regional arts boards, support associations, local authorities, suppliers and services for the arts professional.*

The Bruckner Journal (3). 2 Rivergreen Close, Beeston, Nottingham NG9 3ES *tel:* 0115 928 8300 (ed/ad); 01384 566383 (sub) *fax:* 0161 275 4994; 0115 928 8300 *email:* raymond@cox269.freeserve.co.uk. Peter Palmer, ed; Crawford Howie, associate ed; Raymond Cox, mgr ed. *News, concert, CD and book reviews and articles by and for scholars and enthusiasts. £9 (UK), £10 (Europe), £12 (world) pa.*

Choir & Organ (6). Orpheus Publications Ltd, 3 Waterhouse Square, 138-142 Holborn, London EC1N 2NY *tel:* 020 7882 1040 *fax:* 020 7882 1020 *email:* choirandorgan@orpheuspublications.com. Matthew Power, ed; Maggie Hamilton, asst ed; Shirley Ratcliffe, choral ed. *£3.50. Features and news on choral mus and singing, orgs and org mus.*

Church Music Quarterly (4). Cleveland Lodge, Westhumble, Dorking RH5 6BW *tel:* 01306 872800 *fax:* 01306 887260 *email:* cmq@rscm.com. Esther Jones, ed; Julian Elloway, reviews ed; Anne Hastings, ad mgr. *No cover price; issued to Royal School of Church Music members only.*

Classic FM Magazine (13). Haymarket Publishing, 38-42 Hampton Rd, Teddington, Middx TW11 0JE *tel:* 020 8267 5180 *fax:* 020 8267 5150 *email:* classicfm@haynet.com. John Evans, ed. *£3.99.*

Classical Guitar (12). 1-2 Vance Court, Trans Britannia Enterprise Park, Blaydon on Tyne NE21 5NH *tel:* 0191 414 9000 *fax:* 0191 414 9001 *email:* mail@ashleymark.co.uk. Macer Hall, ed. *£2.95; £40.95 pa.*

Classical London (12). 39 Bushwood, London E11 3BW *email:* editor@classical-london.com. Malcolm Galloway, ed. *Free. Email classical mus news letter; CD reviews, news, concerts, opportunities, etc.*

Classical Music (26). Rhinegold Publishing Ltd, 241 Shaftesbury Ave, London WC2H 8TF *tel:* 020 7333 1742 (ed)/1733 (ad) *fax:* 020 7333 1769 (ed)/1736 (ad) *email:* classical.music@rhinegold.co.uk. Keith Clarke, ed; Clare Stevens, deputy ed. *£3.25; £66 pa.*

The Conductor (4). Marrey, 7 Carr View Rd, Hepworth, Holmfirth HD9 1HX *tel:* 01484 683793 *fax:* 01484 686209 *email:* jeffrey.turner7@virgin.net. Jeffrey Turner, ed. *£2.50. Journal of the NABBC.*

The Consort (Journal of the Dolmetsch Foundation) (1). 2 Parkfields, High St, Butleigh, nr Glastonbury, Somerset BA6 8SZ *tel:* 01458 851561 *email:* elizabethrees_ocv@hotmail.com. Elizabeth Rees, ed. *£22 pa (overseas), £17.50 (UK), £7 (student) including general membership and newsletter 'Dolmetsch Foundation Bulletin' (3).*

Early Music (4). Oxford University Press, 70 Baker St, London W1U 7DN *tel:* 020 7616 5902 *fax:* 020 7616 5901 *email:* earlymusic@oxfordjournals.org. Tess Knighton, ed; David Roberts, asst ed. *£10.50; £47 pa (individuals), £103 (institutions). Articles on medieval,* *renaissance, baroque and pre-classical mus with special reference to performance practice. Book, mus and recording reviews; colour illustrations and extensive advertising.*

Early Music Review (10). Redcroft, Bank's End, Wyton, Huntingdon PE28 2AA *tel:* 01480 52076 *fax:* 01480 450821 *email:* clifford.bartlett@btopenworld.com. Clifford Bartlett, ed; Brian Clark, associate ed; Elaine Bartlett, admin. *£2; £15 pa. For all concerned with the performance, study and enjoyment of early mus throughout the world. Includes international diary of concerts and events.*

Early Music Today (6). Rhinegold Publishing Ltd, 241 Shaftesbury Ave, London WC2H 8TF *tel:* 020 7333 1744 (ed)/1733 (ad) *fax:* 020 7333 1769 (ed)/1736 (ad) *email:* emt@rhinegold.co.uk. Lucien Jenkins, ed. *£2.70; £16 pa. News magazine reporting on performers, insts, broadcasting, events, books, mus, CDs and the early mus scene in the UK and abroad.*

Early Music Yearbook (1). Ruxbury Publications Ltd, Scout Bottom Farm, Mytholmroyd, Hebden Bridge HX7 5JS *tel:* 01422 882751 *fax:* 01422 886157 *email:* emyb@recordermail.demon.co.uk. *£18. Oct. List of individuals and ens, directory of useful addresses, buyers' guide.*

English Dance and Song (4). English Folk Dance and Song Society, 2 Regents Park Rd, London NW1 7AY *tel:* 020 7485 2206 *fax:* 020 7284 0534 *email:* felicity.greenland@efdss.org. Paul Davenport, ed; Felicity Greenland, publications mgr. *£2.50 per issue, £26 including individual membership of EFDSS.*

Ensemble (The Music Masters' and Mistresses' Association) (3). Wayfaring, Smithers Lane, E Peckham, Tonbridge, Kent TN12 5HT *tel:* 01622 872758 *fax:* 01622 872758 *email:* editormma@btopenworld.com. Katharine Le Page, admin; Gary Beauchamp, ed (tel: 029 2045 9098). *£3.50. Members and general sale.*

Flutewise (4). 9 Beaconsfield Rd, Portslade by Sea, E Sussex BN41 1XA *tel:* 01273 702367 *fax:* 01273 888864 *email:* mail@flutewise.com. James Galway, president; Liz Goodwin, ed. *£15 pa. Quarterly magazine for all fl players, especially the young, featuring articles, quizzes, competitions and events.*

Folk Music Journal (1). English Folk Dance and Song Society, 2 Regents Park Rd, London NW1 7AY *tel:* 020 7485 2206 *fax:* 020 7284 0534 *email:* michael.heaney@ulib.ox.ac.uk. Michael Heaney, ed. *£7.50, £26 including individual membership of EFDSS.*

The Full Score (3). Chester Music Ltd, 8-9 Frith St, London W1D 3JB *tel:* 020 7434 0066 *fax:* 020 7287 6329 *email:* promotion@musicsales.co.uk. Nick Kimberley, ed; Kate Johnson, co-ord. *Free. Tri-annual newsletter of the Music Sales Group of companies.*

The Galpin Society Journal (1). 4 Princes Ride, Woodstock, Oxford OX20 1UP *tel:* 01993 810035 *fax:* 01993 810035 *email:* cmm@chalkface.net. Charles Mould, ed; Maggie Kilbey, admin; Graham Wells, chmn; Margaret Birley, reviews ed. *Editorial: Charles Mould, above address. Membership, Journal Distribution and all other matters: Maggie Kilbey, administrator of the Galpin Society, 37 Townsend Drive, St Albans, AL3 5RF. £18 (UK), £24 (Europe), £28 (elsewhere), £30 (institutions and non-members), inclusive of Journal and Newsletters (study of mus insts).*

Hallé (4). Hallé Concerts Society, Manchester M1 5HA *tel:* 0161 237 7000 *fax:* 0161 237 7029 *email:* info@halle.co.uk. Patsy Lawler, ed. *Free to members and sponsors. News of fundraising, sponsorship, educ and other activities.*

Haydn Society Journal (1). 2 Aldcliffe Mews, Aldcliffe, Lancaster LA1 5BT *tel:* 01524 61553 *fax:* 01524 61553 *email:* d.mccaldin@lancaster.ac.uk. Denis McCaldin, ed. *£5 pa. Articles, reviews, forthcoming events concerning Joseph Haydn and his circle.*

Hi-Fi News (12). Focus House, Link House, Dingwall Ave, Croydon CR9 2TA *tel:* 020 8774 0846 *fax:* 020 8774 0940 *email:* hifinews@ipcmedia.com. Steve Harris, ed; Christopher Breunig, mus ed; Andrew Harrison, deputy ed. *£43.20 pa (UK) (euros) 91.20 (Western Europe) £76.70 (rest of world) $122.70 (USA). Cover price £3.60. Reviews of hi-fi equipment and mus.*

The Horn Magazine (3). Neuschel Publications, 15 Hailey Croft, Chinnor, Oxon OX39 4TS *tel:* 01844 353025 *fax:* 01844 353025 *email:* ian@wagstaff.fsbusiness.co.uk. Ian Wagstaff, publisher and ed. *A magazine for hn players by hn players, published for the British Horn Society.*

ISM Register of Musicians in Education (1). Incorporated Society of Musicians, 10 Stratford Place, London W1C 1AA *tel:* 020 7629 4413 *fax:* 020 7408 1538 *email:* membership@ism.org. Kim Davenport Gee, production; Alison Pickard, ed; Fiona MacLeod, listings ed. *£10. Directory and classified lists of ISM members working in or for educ establishments.*

ISM Register of Professional Private Music Teachers (1). Incorporated Society of Musicians, 10 Stratford Place, London W1C 1AA *tel:* 020 7629 4413 *fax:* 020 7408 1538 *email:* membership@ism.org. Kim Davenport Gee, production; Alison Pickard, ed; Fiona MacLeod, listings ed. *£16. Classified directory, by insts and geographical location, of ISM registered private teachers.*

ISM Yearbook (1). Incorporated Society of Musicians, 10 Stratford Place, London W1C 1AA *tel:* 020 7629 4413; 01376 563811 (ad) *fax:* 020 7408 1538; 01376 562453 (ad) *email:* membership@ism.org. Neil Hoyle, chief exec and ed; Kim Davenport Gee, production; PRN Media Ltd, ad sales. *£35. Gives contact details for the ISM's 5000 members, reports on the previous year's activities and describes the society's services.*

ISSTIP Journal (1). School of Music, Kingston University, c/o 28 Emperor's Gate, London SW7 4HS *tel:* 020 7373 7307 *fax:* 020 7373 5440 *email:* carogrindea@yahoo.com. Carola Grindea, ed. *£3.50 (including p&p); free to ISSTIP members. Articles on musicians' physical and psychological problems by specialists in the field as well as various techniques for coping with stress and anxiety in performance.*

International Arts Manager (10). Arts Publishing International Ltd, A402A Tower Bridge Business Complex, 100 Clements Rd, London SE16 4DG *tel:* 020 7232 5806 *fax:* 020 7294 8753 *email:* iam@api.co.uk. Martin Huber, publishing dir; Eva Johansson, mgr ed; Femke Colbourne, editorial asst. *Business magazine for the performing arts. £50 pa, or £80 for two years (UK); £60 pa, or £95 for two years (outside UK).*

International Journal of Music Education (IJME) (1). ISME International Office, PO Box 909, Nedlands, WA 6909, Australia *tel:* 00 61 8 9386 2654 *fax:* 00 61 8 9386 2658 *email:* isme@isme.org. Judy Thönell, sec gen; Jo-anne Todd, admin. *Articles covering a wide range of issues concerning mus educ worldwide and book reviews. Subscription includes one IJME and one MEI. $40 (two copies) full price, $30 (two copies) agents price, $24 (two copies) members price. Single copies only available as back copies, not during current subscription year.*

International Record Review (12). 1 Haven Green, London W5 2UU *tel:* 020 8810 9050 *fax:* 020 8810 9081 *email:* info@recordreview.co.uk. Máire Taylor, ed; Barry Irving, publisher/ad mgr. *£3.80; £38 pa. Monthly magazine for record enthusiasts. Up-to-date, authoritative comment on new and historic classical recordings released worldwide.*

International Trombone Association Journal (4). PO Box 305338, Denton TX 76203, USA *fax:* 00 940 891 3435 *email:* vern@kagarice.com. Vern Kagarice, ed. *Quarterly publication for trombonists. £6 per issue or free to ITA members.*

Jazzwise Magazine (11). Jazzwise Publications, 2b Gleneagle Mews, London SW16 6AE *tel:* 020 8664 7222 *fax:* 020 8677 6128 *email:* magazine@jazzwise.com. Charles Alexander, mgr dir; Stephen Graham, ed; Jon Newey, publishing and editorial dir. *£3.20; £32 pa (UK). Covers all styles and periods of jazz, with emphasis on current activity. Includes features, news, CD reviews, concert reviews, DVD and book reviews.*

Journal into Melody (4). Stone Gables, Upton Lane, Seavington St Michael, Ilminster, Somerset TA19 0PZ *tel:* 01460 242226 *fax:* 01460 242226 *email:* david@rfsoc.freeserve.co.uk. *£13 pa (Robert Farnon Society).*

London Organ Concerts Guide (2). 19 Pandora Rd, London NW6 1TS *tel:* 020 7435 8649 *fax:* 020 7794 3608 *email:* jcommon@csma-netlink.co.uk. James Common, sec; Catherine Ennis, chmn. *Educ articles about the org as well as editorial comment. Also includes listings of org concerts in all venues all over Greater London and beyond. Mailing list £4 pa.*

The Lute (1). c/o The Lute Society, Southside Cottage, Brook Hill, Albury, Guildford, Surrey GU5 9DJ *tel:* 01483 202159 *fax:* 01483 203088 *email:* lutesoc@aol.com. Christopher Goodwin, sec and ed. *£30. Subscribers also receive the quarterly magazine 'Lute News'. Covers all aspects of the lute and related insts and their mus.*

MI Pro (12). 35 High St, Marlow, Bucks SL7 1AU *tel:* 01628 487820 (ed); 01799 520900 (ad) *fax:* 01799 520734 (ad) *email:* news@mi-pro.com; ads@mi-pro.co.uk. Gez Kahan, ed; Phil Johnston, ad mgr. *£36 pa. Business magazine for mus inst and pro audio industries, including annual directory (available separately - cost option).*

MOD - Music, Opera, Dance and Drama in Asia, the Pacific and North America. Alain Charles Arts Publishing Ltd, A402A Tower Bridge Business Complex, 100 Clements Rd, London SE16 4DG *tel:* 020 7232 5800 *fax:* 020 7394 8753 *email:* mod@api.co.uk. Martin Huber, publisher; Wiebke Morgan, ed; Marion Qazi, admin. *£46.*

Music and Liturgy (4). Society of Saint Gregory, 70 Haddon Rd, Lillington, Leamington Spa, Warks CV32 7QY *tel:* 01926 741995 *fax:* 0117 924 1311 *email:* editor@ssg.org.uk. Paul Wellicome, mus ed; Patrick Geary, liturgy ed. *£30 pa (concessions £20); Europe: £34; Rest of*

World: £38. Journal of the Society of Saint Gregory, registered in the UK as a charity.

Music Education International (MEI) (1). ISME International Office, PO Box 909, Nedlands, WA 6909, Australia *tel:* 00 61 8 9386 2654 *fax:* 00 61 8 9386 2658 *email:* isme@isme.org. Judy Thönell, sec gen; Jo-anne Todd, admin. *Articles covering a wide range of issues concerning mus educ worldwide and book reviews. Subscription includes one ISME and one MEI. $40 (two copies) full price, $30 (two copies) agents price, $24 (two copies) members price. Single copies only available as back copies, not during current subscription year,*

Music Education Yearbook (1). Rhinegold Publishing Ltd, 241 Shaftesbury Ave, London WC2H 8TF *tel:* 01789 209281 (ed); 020 7333 1733 (ad) *fax:* 01789 264009 (ed); 020 7333 1736 (ad) *email:* meyb@rhinegold.co.uk. Louise Head, ed. *£17.50. Guide to mus in educ for parents, teachers, students and musicians. Provides contact information, course details, scholarship policy and entry requirements for independent schools, colleges and universities in Britain. Also sections on world mus, publishers, exam syllabuses, youth orchs and choirs, teachers' resources and others.*

Music Journal (12). Incorporated Society of Musicians, 10 Stratford Place, London W1C 1AA *tel:* 020 7629 4413; 01376 563811 (ad) *fax:* 020 7408 1538; 01376 562453 (ad) *email:* membership@ism.org. Neil Hoyle, ed; Kim Davenport Gee, production; PRN Media Ltd, ad sales. *£3, £30 pa. Details of ISM members' activities and the ISM's work, plus news and views from the world of professional mus.*

Music Teacher (12). Rhinegold Publishing Ltd, 241 Shaftesbury Ave, London WC2H 8TF *tel:* 020 7333 1747 (ed)/1733 (ad) *fax:* 020 7333 1769 (ed)/1736 (ad) *email:* music.teacher@rhinegold.co.uk. Lucien Jenkins, ed. *£3.75; £40 pa. News and features on mus technology, A-level and GCSE topics and set works, classroom lesson suggestions, insts and teaching choices; book, mus and video reviews. Regular special topic guides.*

Musical Opinion (6). 2 Princes Rd, St Leonards-on-Sea, E Sussex TN37 6EL *tel:* 01424 715167 *fax:* 01424 712214 *email:* musicalopinion2@aol.com. Denby Richards, ed; Judith Monk, deputy ed. *£4.50; £28 pa (UK), £40 pa (overseas). Contains news and reviews of live concerts, ballets, operas, festivals, books, CDs, DVDs, etc.*

The Musical Times (4). 7 Brunswick Mews, Hove, E Sussex BN3 1HD *email:* mustimes@aol.com. Antony Bye, ed; Anne Hastings, ad mgr. *Scholarly journal, est 1844, containing articles of academic and general mus interest and book reviews. Annual subscription; rates available on request, tel: 01442 879097.*

NODA National News (4). NODA House, 58-60 Lincoln Rd, Peterborough PE1 2RZ *tel:* 0870 770 2480 *fax:* 0870 770 2490 *email:* everyone@noda.org.uk. Mark Pemberton, mgr ed. *£2.50; free to members of National Operatic and Dramatic Association.*

New Music News (3). Irish Contemporary Music Centre, 19 Fishamble St, Temple Bar Dublin 8, Ireland *tel:* 00 353 1 673 1922 *fax:* 00 353 1 648 9100 *email:* info@cmc.ie. Eve O'Kelly, ed. *Free.*

new notes (11). c/o spnm, 4th Floor, 18-20 Southwark St, London SE1 1TJ *tel:* 020 7407 1640 *fax:* 020 7403 7652 *email:* spnm@spnm.org.uk. Shoël Stadlen, promotions and publications offr. *Free to spnm members. New mus concerts listings, articles and spnm news.*

Nineteenth-Century Music Review *formerly* **Music Review** (2). Ashgate Publishing Ltd, Gower House, Croft House, Aldershot, Hants GU11 3HR *tel:* 01252 331551 *fax:* 01252 344405 *email:* info@ashgatepub.co.uk. Nicola Staskiewicz, subscriptions mgr. *£60 pa.*

Opera (13). 36 Black Lion Lane, London W6 9BE *tel:* 020 8563 8893 *fax:* 020 8563 8635 *email:* editor@operamag.clara.co.uk. John Allison, ed; Alice Lindsay, mkt dir; Erica Jeal, asst ed. *£3.70; £49.95 pa.*

Opera Now (6). Rhinegold Publishing Ltd, 241 Shaftesbury Ave, London WC2H 8TF *tel:* 020 7333 1740 (ed)/1733 (ad) *fax:* 020 7333 1769 (ed)/1736 (ad) *email:* opera.now@rhinegold.co.uk. Ashutosh Khandekar, ed; Antonia Couling, deputy ed. *£4.95; £29.70 pa. Covers every aspect of opera, from live performances, festivals and recitals to recordings and broadcasts from around the world.*

The Organ (4). 2 Princes Rd, St Leonards-on-Sea, E Sussex TN37 6EL *tel:* 01424 715167 *fax:* 01424 712214 *email:* musicalopinion2@aol.com. Brian Hick, ed. *£4.50; £20 pa UK, £28 pa overseas. Contains dates of events, reviews of live concerts, CDs, books, etc.*

Organ Club Newletter (3). Trinity Flat, Bremner Rd, London SW7 2QU *fax:* 01727 810453. Alec Dingwall, ed; Tim Roe, ed. *Features on insts, composers and repertoire, news and reviews, reports of club activities. Distributed free to members of The Organ Club. Bi-monthly newsletter, also on website.*

Organ and Keyboard Cavalcade (12). Sceptre Promotions, 97 Elton Rd, Stibbington, Peterborough PE8 6JX *tel:* 01780 782093 *fax:* 01780 783159. Grant Neal, ed. *£19.50 pa. Monthly magazine covering all things*

electronic org and home keyboard: tutorial, news, reviews, concerts, classifieds, etc.

Organists' Review (4). 4 Vicars' Court, Southwell, Notts NG25 0HP *tel:* 01636 812228; 01245 609294 *fax:* 01636 812228 *email:* OrganistsReview@diaphone.clara.net. Paul Hale, ed; Steve Knight, ad mgr; Roger Fisher, features ed; James Parsons, educ ed. *£4.95. Articles on orgs, org and choral mus, org playing. Major review section.*

Piano (6). Rhinegold Publishing Ltd, 241 Shaftesbury Ave, London WC2H 8TF *tel:* 020 7333 1724 (ed)/1733 (ad) *fax:* 020 7333 1769 (ed)/1736 (ad). Jeremy Siepmann, ed. *£2.70; £16.00 pa. Explores the endlessly varied and fascinating world of pianism, performance, interpretation and repertoire. Includes discussions, profiles, reviews and news.*

Piano Journal. 28 Emperor's Gate, London SW7 4HS *tel:* 020 7373 7307 *fax:* 020 7373 5440 *email:* carogrindea@yahoo.com. Malcolm Troup, ed; Carola Grindea, consultant/ed. *£2.70 3 times a year. Free European Piano Teachers Associations and associate members. Interviews, articles on repertoire, pno teaching, technique, etc; book, mus and CD reviews. Available by subscription: UK £7.00, Europe £8.00.*

Piano Tuners' Quarterly (4). RNIB, PO Box 173, Peterborough PE2 6WS *tel:* 01733 375000 *fax:* 01733 375001 *email:* joanna.franks@rnib.org.uk. Joanna Franks, publications ed. *£1.54 (UK); £3.00 (overseas). News and articles about pno tuning.*

The Record Collector (4). 111 Longshots Close, Broomfield, Chelmsford CM1 7DU *tel:* 01245 441661 *fax:* 01245 443642 *email:* larry.lustig@btinternet.com. Larry Lustig, ed. *£21 by subscription.*

The Recorder Magazine (4). Scout Bottom Farm, Mytholmroyd, Hebden Bridge, W Yorks HX7 5JS *tel:* 01422 882751 *fax:* 01422 886157 *email:* ruth@recordermail.demon.co.uk. Andrew Mayes, ed. *£20 pa.*

The Ringing World (52). Ringing World Ltd, 7-9 Chantry St, Andover SP10 1DE *tel:* 01264 366620 *fax:* 01265 360594 *email:* rw@ringingworld.co.uk. Robert Lewis, ed; Paul Trend, gen mgr. *£1.60 weekly, £52 pa.*

Royal Musical Association Research Chronicle (1). Dept of Music, University of York, Heslington, York YO10 5DD *tel:* 01904 488722 *fax:* 01904 432450 *email:* jpw6@york.ac.uk. Jonathan Wainwright, ed. *Approx £35. Emphasis on the raw materials of musicology; indexes, categories, inventories, etc.*

Scottish Folk Directory (1). Scottish Folk Arts Group, Blackfriars Music, 49 Blackfriars St, Edinburgh EH1 1NB *tel:* 0131 557 3090 *fax:* 0131 557 3090 *email:* blackfriarsmusic@btinternet.com. Willie Haines, ed. *£3.50. A contact resource for folk and traditional arts in Scotland.*

Sheet Music (4). John Catt Educational Ltd, Great Glemham, Saxmundham, Suffolk IP17 2DH *tel:* 01728 663666 *fax:* 01728 663415 *email:* editor@sheetmusicmag.co.uk. Gay Pirrie-Weir, ed; Catherine Travers, asst ed; Jonathan Evans, mrg dir; Derek Bingham, ed-in-chief. *£5 per issue. One year subscription (4 issues) £19.95. Two year subscription (8 issues) £34.95. Specialising in printed mus and everything for the musician.*

Showcase International Music Book (1). Hollis Publishing Ltd, Harlequin House, 7 High St, Teddington, Middx TW11 8EL *tel:* 020 8977 7711 *fax:* 020 8977 0482 *email:* Jane@hollis-pr.com. Jane Ireland, sales dir; Gillie Mayer, ed. *Cover price £60 (2003 edn). The professional users' guide to the mus business covering all PR support services, studios, producers, suppliers, etc.*

The Singer (6). Rhinegold Publishing Ltd, 241 Shaftesbury Ave, London WC2H 8TF *tel:* 020 7333 1746 (ed)/1733 (ad) *fax:* 020 7333 1769 (ed)/1736 (ad) *email:* the.singer@rhinegold.co.uk. Antonia Couling, ed. *£2.70; £16 pa. For anyone with a serious, wide-ranging enthusiasm for vocal mus, from choral to mus theatre, opera, jazz and cabaret.*

Singers Legacy (10). Rondo Music, 2 Willow Close, Horncastle, Lincs LN9 5BH *tel:* 020 7681 3309 *fax:* 020 7681 3309 *email:* maria@singerslegacy.com. James Anderson, ed; Maria Barbera Martinez, asst ed. *£30 pa. Exploring the singing styles of the past for the benefit of today.*

Sounding Board (4). Sound Sense, 7 Tavern St, Stowmarket, Suffolk IP14 1PJ *tel:* 01449 673990 *fax:* 01449 673994 *email:* info@soundsense.org. Kathryn Deane, ed; Sarah Bennett-Day, mus and disability ed. *Quarterly journal for those interested in participatory mus-making. Subscription ranges from £10 to £65 pa and includes membership of Sound Sense.*

Sounds Great! (10). Bright Horizons Publications, PO Box 1572, Ascot, Berks SL5 0PF *tel:* 01344 291398 *fax:* 01344 621021 *email:* jb@soundsgreat.co.uk. Joan Brightwell, ed. *£22.50 pa. Comprehensive guide (hard copy and online) to live classical events in over 800 venues in London and the home counties.*

The Stage (52). Stage House, 47 Bermondsey St, London SE1 3XT *tel:* 020 7403 1818 *fax:* 020 7403 1418 *email:* info@thestage.co.uk. Brian Attwood, ed. *£1.*

The Strad (12). Orpheus Publications Ltd, 3 Waterhouse Square, 138-142 Holborn, London EC1N 2NY *tel:* 020 7882 1040 *fax:* 020 7882 1020 *email:* thestrad@orpheuspublications.com; advertising@ orpheuspublications.com. Naomi Sadler, ed; Ariane Todes, deputy ed. *£3.75; £40.95 pa (UK). For performers, teachers, students, makers and enthusiasts of bowed str insts.*

Tempo (4). PO Box 171, Herne Bay, Kent CT6 6WD *tel:* 01223 312393 (subscriptions); 020 7352 6400 (advertising) *email:* macval@ compuserve.com. Calum MacDonald, ed; Arthur Boyars, ad mgr. *£4.99, £20.00 pa (individuals); £40 (institutions). Journals subscriptions: Cambridge University Press, The Edinburgh Building, Shaftesbury Rd, Cambridge CB2 2RU.*

Welsh Music (2). 17 Penyrheol Drive, Llanelli, Carmarthenshire SA15 3NX *tel:* 01554 774188. A J Heward Rees, ed. *£5.*

The White Book (1). Bank House, 23 Warwick Rd, Coventry CV1 2EW *tel:* 024 7657 1171 *fax:* 024 7657 1172 *email:* michelle_ tayton@mm.co.uk. Michelle Tayton, group sales mgr. *£80 (UK). Production directory for the event industry.*

Winds (4). Wayfaring, Smithers Lane, E Peckham, Tonbridge TN12 5HT *tel:* 01622 871576 *fax:* 01622 871576 *email:* editor@winds.org.uk. Charles Hine, chmn; Brendon Le Page, ed. *£3; £10 pa. Articles on repertoire analysis, conducting, inst teaching, jazz, plus news and reviews. Incorporating the journal of the British Association of Symphonic Bands and Wind Ensembles (BASBWE).*

Instrument Manufacturers

Listed here are the principal manufacturers and repairers of modern instruments, with their area of expertise given in italics after each entry. A list of early musical instrument makers will be found under **Early Music Instrument Manufacturers**. For repairs of standard instruments, refer to the manufacturers listed below or to the **Retailers** section. Specialist repairers can be found under **Instrument Technicians.**

Aitchison & Mnatzaganian. 7 Cambridge Rd, Ely, Cambs CB7 4HJ *tel:* 01353 668559 *fax:* 01353 612264 *email:* info@aitchisoncellos.com. Robin Aitchison, proprietor; Sarah Mnatzaganian, customer contact. *Vc specialists, baroque, classical and modern vcs made to commission. Stock of fine vcs. Annual contemporary bow exhibition: 'Take a Bow'.*

Allen Organ Studios (London) Ltd. Trada Business Campus, Stocking Lane, Hughenden Valley, High Wycombe, Bucks HP14 4ND *tel:* 01494 563833 *fax:* 01494 563546 *email:* sales@allenorgans.co.uk. Richard Goodall, UK sales mgr; Giles Williams, UK sales mgr.

Andrew Wooderson Early Keyboard Instruments. 5 Bourne Rd, Bexley, Kent DA5 1LG *tel:* 01322 558326 *fax:* 01322 525558 *email:* andrew.wooderson@btinternet.com. *All types of hpds, spinets, virginals, clvds; also tuning, maintenance, restoration, repairs and hire. Sale of tools and accs. Second-hand insts for sale.*

Arbiter Group plc. Wilberforce Rd, London NW9 6AX *tel:* 020 8202 1199 *fax:* 020 8202 7076 *email:* info@arbitergroup.com. Nick Sharples, mkt mgr. *UK distributers of Fender guis and amps, Sabian, Remo, Steinberg, AKG, JBL, Digitech, Gretsch, Guild, Akai, Jackson/Charvel, Vic Firth and many others.*

Ardival Harps Ltd. Orchard House, Castle Leod, Strathpeffer, Ross-shire IV14 9AA *tel:* 01997 421260 *fax:* 01997 421260 *email:* info@ardival.com. *Historical and traditional Scottish hps.*

Batchelar, Timothy. 28 Colbert Drive, Leicester LE3 2JB *tel:* 0116 286 2511/289 9798; 07710 204303 *fax:* 0116 286 2511/289 9798 *email:* tim@batchelar.com. *Dealer, restorer and maker of stringed insts of the vn family. Accredited member of the Institute of Musical Instrument Technology.*

Beare & Son. 18 Tavistock Place, Tavistock St, Dunstable, Beds LU6 1NG *tel:* 01582 477130 *fax:* 01582 477130. *Vns, vas, vcs and dbs; bows, cases, strs, fittings and accs. Also manufacturers and wholesale distributors of Beare-Tertis vas and Michael Poller insts.*

Bexley Harpsichord Workshops Ltd. 5 Bourne Rd, Bexley, Kent DA5 1LG *tel:* 01322 557147 *fax:* 01322 527366 *email:* edmund.handy@btinternet.com. Edmund Handy, dir; Andrew Wooderson, dir. *All types of hpds, spinets, virginals, clvds; also tuning, maintenance, restoration, repairs and hire. Sale of tools and accs. Second-hand insts for sale.*

Bigio, Robert. 1 Doveridge Gardens, London N13 5BJ *tel:* 020 8882 2627 *fax:* 020 8882 2728 *email:* Robert@bigio.com. *Boehm system fls and piccs (wood and silver).*

Bishop and Son. 38 Bolton Lane, Ipswich, Suffolk IP4 2BT *tel:* 01473 255165 *fax:* 01473 255165. E J Bailey, mgr. *Org builders; new pipe orgs; also org restoration, repair and tuning.*

Blüthner Piano Centre Ltd. 1 Davies St, Berkeley Square, London W1K 3DB *tel:* 020 7753 0533 *fax:* 020 7753 0535 *email:* bluthner@globalnet.co.uk. Rodney Vaughn, gen mgr. *Distributor for Blüthner, Haessler and Irmler pnos.*

Boardman, Peter. 33a Hogstown Rd, Donaghadee, Co Down BT21 0NH *tel:* 028 9188 3474. *Vns, vas and vcs.*

Bolton, Tarquin. 33 Quebec St, Langley Park, Durham DH7 9UU *tel:* 0191 373 4906. *Vns and bows.*

Besson Musical Instruments Ltd. 1 Blackmoor Lane, Croxley Business Park, Watford WD18 8GA *tel:* 01923 659500 *fax:* 01923 659600 *email:* besson@musicgroup.com. *Br, w/wind, strs, guis, accs.*

Border Harps. Waterloo Cottages, Letton, Hereford HR3 6DN *tel:* 01544 327352 *fax:* 01544 327352 *email:* borderharps@hotmail.com. *Hps, hp kits, parts and strs.*

The Bridge Fiddler. Riverside House, Chapel Milton, Chapel-en-le-Frith, High Peak SK23 0QQ *tel:* 01298 813813. *Str insts, bows and accs supplied; repairs and restoration.*

Canter, Kenneth J. 54 Maltings Garth, Thurston, Bury St Edmunds, Suffolk IP31 3PP *tel:* 01359 230694. *Orgs.*

Centrepiece Music. PO Box 1601, Newport Pagnell, Bucks MK16 8PD *tel:* 01908 218003 *fax:* 01908 211828 *email:* centrepiece. music@virgin.net. Glenda Smith, partner. *Distributor of speciality accs for w/wind and gui; cl and sax mouthpieces (Portnoy and Beechler), Winslow ligs, etc; Neotech sax and gui slings and straps.*

The Clarke Tin Whistle Co Ltd. The Old Joinery, Whetsted Rd, Five Oak Green, Kent TN12 6RS *tel:* 01892 837433 *fax:* 01892 837434 *email:* michael@clarketinwhistle.com. *Manufacturers of the 'Clarke' tin whistle.*

Clive Morley Harps Ltd. Goodfellows, Filkins, Nr Lechdale, Glos GL7 3JG *tel:* 01367 860493 *fax:* 01367 860659 *email:* harps@ morleyharps.com.

Cohen, Brian. Soundpost, The Old Glassworks, Alexandra Place, Guildford, Surrey GU1 3QH *tel:* 01483 456422 *fax:* 01483 456422 *email:* strings@soundpost.co.uk. *Guis, vns, vcs, db, bows, accs.*

Comus (UK) Ltd. 12 Churchill Way, Lomeshaye Industrial Estate, Nelson, Lancs BB9 6RT *tel:* 01282 606600 *fax:* 01282 606660 *email:* info@bontempi.co.uk. *Elec keyboards, educ insts, mus toys.*

Copeman Hart & Company Ltd. Finedon Rd, Irthlingborough, Northants NN9 5TZ *tel:* 01933 652600 *fax:* 01933 652288 *email:* info@ copemanhart.co.uk. *Church org builders.*

David R Ouvry Violin Maker. Southwood, Burchetts Green, Maidenhead, Berks SL6 6QS *tel:* 01628 823340 *email:* davidouvry@ violin-maker.co.uk. *Vns and vas.*

David Wells Organ Builders Ltd. Cathedral Works, 52 Westminster Rd, Kirkdale, Liverpool L4 4LT *tel:* 0151 207 9200 *fax:* 0151 207 9201 *email:* davidwells@dwob.co.uk. *Pipe org builder and restorer.*

Derek Roberts Violins. 185 Leam Terrace, Leamington Spa, Warks CV31 1DW *tel:* 01926 428313 *fax:* 01926 428313 *email:* mail@ derekroberts.co.uk. *Modern and baroque vn, va, vc maker and restorer.*

Dolmetsch Musical Instruments. Unicorn Trading Estate, Weydown Rd, Haslemere, Surrey GU27 1DN *tel:* 01428 643235 *fax:* 0870 056 0190 *email:* brian@dolmetsch.com. Brian Blood, sales mgr. *Viols, rcdrs in wood and plastic, hpds, clvds and spinets.*

Eaton, Peter. Woodside, Orestan Lane, Effingham, Surrey KT24 5SN *tel:* 01372 452513 *fax:* 01372 451416 *email:* Peter@eatonclarinets.com. *Cls and cl mouthpieces.*

Edgar, Alan. 43 Beverley Rd, Hessle, E Yorks HU13 9AE *tel:* 01482 640330 *email:* sue@jaracanda.f9.co.uk. *Hpds, hps.*

Edmund Handy. Early Keyboard Instruments, 5 Bourne Rd, Bexley, Kent DA5 1LG *tel:* 01322 527366 *fax:* 01322 527366 *email:* edmund. handy@btinternet.com. Edmund Handy, dir. *All types of hpds, spinets, virginals, clvds; also tuning, maintenance, restoration, repairs and hire. Sale of tools and accs. Second-hand insts for sale.*

Elysian Pianos. Robert Morley & Co Ltd, 34 Engate St, London SE13 7HA *tel:* 020 8318 5838 *email:* jvm@morley-r.u-net.com. *Grand and upright pnos; also stools.*

Ertz, Neil. 4 Cowper Rd, Cambridge CB1 3SN *tel:* 01223 513257 *fax:* 01223 513257 *email:* neil@ertz-violins.com. Neil Ertz, owner. *Maker of vns, vas and vcs in both modern and baroque form.*

F H Browne & Sons (Organ Builders) Ltd. The Old Cartwright School, The Street, Ash, Canterbury, Kent CT3 2AA *tel:* 01304 813146 *fax:* 01304 812142 *email:* brownefh@aol.com. R J Greensted. *Orgs.*

FCN Music. Melody House, Wealdon Business Park, Farningham Rd, Crowborough, E Sussex TN6 2JJ *tel:* 01892 603733 *fax:* 01892 613220 *email:* sales@fcnmusic.co.uk. Julia Thompson. *Aulos rcdrs, Larrivee and Westone guis, K&M inst stands, Meinl and Dixon perc, Fishman pickups, Lee Oscar harmonicas, Meinl cymbals, Ayrs guis, Lorenzo and Kimbara.*

Farfisa (UK) Ltd. 12 Churchill Way, Lomeshaye Industrial Estate, Nelson, Lancs BB9 6RT *tel:* 01282 606600 *fax:* 01282 606660 *email:* farfisa@comus-uk.demon.co.uk. *Elec keyboards.*

Gordon Stevenson Violins. 6 Barclay Terrace, Bruntsfield, Edinburgh EH10 4HP *tel:* 0131 229 2051 *fax:* 0131 229 9298. *Vns.*

Green, Miranda. 26 Plasturton Gardens, Cardiff CF11 9HF *tel:* 029 2066 6166. *Vns and vas.*

Grotrian-Steinweg Pianos. Robert Morley & Co Ltd, 34 Engate St, London SE13 7HA *tel:* 020 8318 5838 *email:* jvm@morley-r.u-net.com. *Grand and upright pnos.*

Hanson International. Globe Crossroads, 5 Huddersfield Rd, Liversedge WF15 7EN *tel:* 0800 542 9524 *fax:* 0870 744 2742 *email:* info@hanson-music.co.uk. Steve Parker. *Makers of cls and acoustic designers for br and w/wind insts.*

Harrison & Harrison Ltd. St John's Rd, Meadowfield, Durham DH7 8YH *tel:* 0191 378 2222 *fax:* 0191 378 3388 *email:* h.h@btinternet.com. *Pipe orgs.*

Henry Willis & Sons Ltd. 160 Triumph Way, Speke Hall Rd, Liverpool L24 9GQ *tel:* 0151 486 1845 *fax:* 0151 486 1926 *email:* dw@willis-organs.com. David Wyld. *Pipe orgs. IBO accredited.*

Hibernian Violins. 67 Somers Rd, Malvern, Worcs WR14 1JA *tel:* 01684 562947 *fax:* 01684 562947. *Vn and viol family insts, bows.*

Holywell Music Ltd. 58 Hopton St, London SE1 9JH *tel:* 020 7928 8451 *fax:* 020 7928 8284 *email:* holywell@holywell.co.uk. *Salvi and Lyon & Healy concert and non-pedal hps.*

Huggett, Martin. The Old Library, Stour St, Manningtree, Essex CO11 1BE *tel:* 01206 396354 *fax:* 01206 396354 *email:* martin@ huggett.co.uk. *Artcase pno restoration and rebuilding including all decorative work. Carving, gilding, painting, marquetry, and all associated areas of expertise.*

Impact Percussion. 7 Goose Green Trading Estate, 47 East Dulwich Rd, London SE22 9BN *tel:* 020 8299 6700 *fax:* 020 8299 6704 *email:* sales@impactpercussion.com. *Tubular bells, bs bells, bs drums, custom manufacture of perc insts and touring trolleys.*

Irish Organ Co Ltd. Steeple Rd Industrial Estate, Antrim, Co Antrim BT41 1AB *tel:* 028 9446 7954 *fax:* 028 9446 7954 *email:* colin@davidsonc.freeserve.co.uk. *Pipe orgs.*

J P Guivier & Co Ltd. 99 Mortimer St, London W1W 7SX *tel:* 020 7580 2560 *fax:* 020 7436 1461 *email:* violins@guivier.com. *Restorers and dealers of insts, bows and accs of the vn family.*

J W Walker & Sons Ltd. Wimbledon Ave, Brandon, Suffolk IP27 0NF *tel:* 01842 810296 *fax:* 01842 813124 *email:* organs@jwwalker.co.uk. David Wilson, tonal dir. *Pipe orgs.*

J Wood & Sons Ltd. 38 Manningham Lane, Bradford BD1 3EA *tel:* 01274 307636 *fax:* 01274 393516 *email:* sales@earlyms.demon.co.uk. *Orgs, celestas, pnos, keyboards, early w/wind insts.*

Jeremy Lowe. 102 Greenwich South St, London SE10 8UN *tel:* 020 8691 6868; 07950 466199 *email:* jlowe@dircon.co.uk. Jeremy Lowe, proprietor. *Cl mouthpieces, barrels; cl design.*

John Hornby Skewes & Co Ltd. Salem House, Parkinson Approach, Garforth, Leeds LS25 2HR *tel:* 0113 286 5381 *fax:* 0113 286 8515 *email:* info@jhs.co.uk. John H Skewes, chmn, mgr dir; Dennis J Drumm, sales dir, mgr dir designate. *Manufacturer, wholesaler and distributor of mus insts, associated accs, inst amplification and pro-audio equipment.*

KGB Musical Instruments. Pacific Rd Arts Centre, Pacific Rd, Birkenhead, Merseyside CH41 1LJ *tel:* 0151 647 3268 *email:* keith@kgb-music.co.uk. *Guis and fretted insts; parts and accs.*

Keith S Bance. 72 Waverley Rd, Rayners Lane, Harrow, Middx HA2 9RD *tel:* 020 8866 4158 *fax:* 020 8866 4158. *Org builders, tonal consultants, voicers.*

Kemble & Co Ltd. Mount Ave, Bletchley, Milton Keynes MK1 1JE *tel:* 01908 371771 *fax:* 01908 270448 *email:* brian.kemble@ gmx.yamaha.com. Brian Kemble, joint mgr dir; Peter Corney, sales mgr. *Upright pnos, silent pnos.*

Langer International Ltd. Stapleford Rd, Trowell, Notts NG9 3QE *tel:* 0115 932 1214 *fax:* 0115 932 1215 *email:* dmartin@ langer-piano.com. *Pno actions, keys, spare parts.*

Lyons Musicale Ltd. Homecroft, Sun Lane, Harpenden, Herts AL5 4GJ *tel:* 01582 460978 *fax:* 01582 767343 *email:* HMusicale@aol.com. David Johnston, mgr dir. *Lyons 'c' cl, lightweight easy stretch cl for the young beginner.*

Makin Organs Ltd. Sovereign House, 30 Manchester Rd, Shaw, Oldham, Lancs OL2 7DE *tel:* 01706 888100 *fax:* 01706 888109 *email:* davidc@makinorgans.co.uk. *Classical orgs, MIDI expanders. Also distributors and nationwide hire service.*

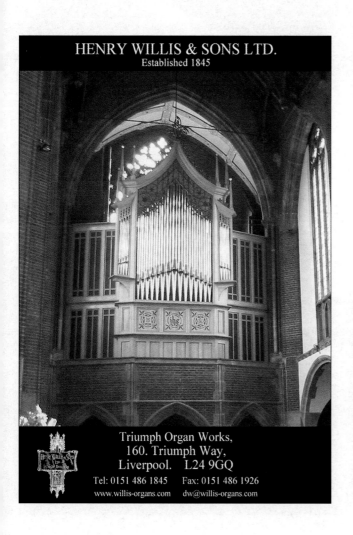

The waiting is over!

new

VIOLIN | VIOLA
No. 203

THOMASTIK-INFELD
V I E N N A

www.thomastik-infeld.com

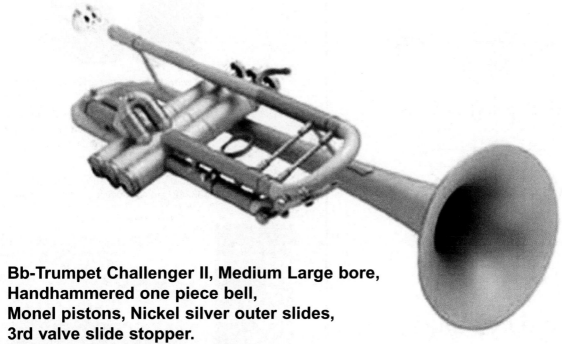
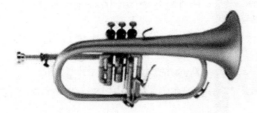

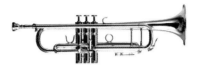

Mander Organs. St Peter's Organ Works, St Peter's Square, Warner Place, Hackney Rd, London E2 7AF *tel:* 020 7739 4747 *fax:* 020 7729 4718 *email:* manderuk@mander-organs.com. *Pipe orgs.*

Mark Norris Harps. The Old School, Stobo, Peebles, Peeblesshire EH45 8NU *tel:* 01721 760298 *fax:* 01721 760298 *email:* norris.harps@virgin.net. Mark Norris. *Non-pedal hps with professional semitone levers.*

Martyn Booth Guitar Services. Unit 4, Old Brickworks, Chapel Lane, Little Cornard, Sudbury, Suffolk CO10 0PB *tel:* 01787 370192 *fax:* 01787 370192 *email:* mboothguitar@yahoo.co.uk. *Custom manufacture and repair of guis.*

The Midland Organ Company. 17 Belvoir St, Melton Mowbray, Leics LE13 1QA *tel:* 01664 566348 *fax:* 01664 569208 *email:* midorgco@telinco.com. Christopher Gray, mgr dir. *Manufacture of chmbr and continuo pipe orgs. Supplier of quality restored historic insts.*

Moeck UK. 38 Manningham Lane, Bradford, W Yorks BD1 3EA *tel:* 01274 721646 *fax:* 01274 393516 *email:* moeck@earlyms.demon.co.uk. *Rcdrs and historical w/wind.*

Monington and Weston Pianos. Robert Morley & Co Ltd, 34 Engate St, Lewisham, London SE13 7HA *tel:* 020 8318 5838 *email:* jvm@morley-r.u-net.com. *Upright and grand pnos; also stools.*

Norman Hall & Sons Organ Builders. 39 Sturton St, Cambridge CB1 2QG *tel:* 01223 350516 *fax:* 01223 350516.

Nowak, Steffen. 75 Sylvia Ave, Bristol BS3 5BU *tel:* 0117 977 7141 *email:* sn@nowakviolins.co.uk. *Modern and baroque vn, va and vc.*

Oakwood Instruments. 8 Ladywood Rd, Leeds LS8 2QF *tel:* 0113 265 8585 *fax:* 0113 293 3011 *email:* workshop@oakwoodinstruments.co.uk. *Electric vns, mandolins, mandolas, bouzoukis, citterns, guis, banjos, hammer dulcimers, hps, melodeons.*

Ocarina Workshop. PO Box 56, Kettering, Northants NN15 5LX *tel:* 01536 485963 *fax:* 01536 485051 *email:* ocarina@compuserve.com. *Ocarinas, duet ocarinas, poly-oc school ocarinas, card-oc, ocarina mus (also m/order).*

Paxman Musical Instruments Ltd. Linton House, 164-180 Union St, London SE1 0LH *tel:* 020 7620 2077 *fax:* 020 7620 1688 *email:* info@paxman.co.uk. *Hns.*

Percussion Plus. The Mill, Great Bowden Rd, Market Harborough, Leics LE16 7DE *tel:* 01858 433124 *fax:* 01858 462218 *email:* jdean@percussionplus.co.uk. *Perc inst manufacturer and distributor.*

Peter Collins Ltd. 42 Pate Rd, Melton Mowbray, Leics LE13 0DG *tel:* 01664 410555 *fax:* 01664 410535 *email:* pd.collins@lineone.net. *Pipe org builders and restorers.*

Peter Conacher & Co. Smith Steads, Cragg Vale, Hebden Bridge HX7 5SQ *tel:* 01422 885846 *email:* info@conacher.co.uk. R A Sinclair Willis. *Orgs, harmoniums, reed orgs; repair, restoration repair, tuning and supply of spare parts.*

Phil Parker Ltd (Wholesale). 106a Crawford St, London W1H 2HZ *tel:* 020 7723 6909 *fax:* 020 7935 6686 *email:* sales@philparker.co.uk. *W/wind, br, gig bags and accs.*

Phil Rees Music Tech. Unit 1a, Garcia Trading Estate, Canterbury Rd, Worthing BN13 1AL *tel:* 01903 691160 *fax:* 01903 691170 *email:* info@philrees.co.uk. Sheila Cantlay, sales mgr; Philip Rees. *Manufacturers of electronic mus accs. Specialists in MIDI. Builders of custom audio laptops and PCs particularly for use with recording mus.*

Philip Brown Violins. 85a Northbrook St, Newbury, Berks RG14 1AE *tel:* 01635 35465 *email:* philip@philipbrown-violins.co.uk. Philip Brown. *Sale and manufacture of vns, vcs and vas.*

Piano Warehouse. 30 Highgate Rd, London NW5 1NS *tel:* 020 7267 9229 *fax:* 020 7284 0083 *email:* enquiries@piano-warehouse.co.uk. *Distributor of Young Chang, Weber, Steinmater, Gors and Kallmann pnos; pno stools.*

Pilgrim Harps. Stansted House, Tilburstow Hill Rd, S Godstone, Surrey RH9 8NA *tel:* 01342 893242 *fax:* 01342 892646 *email:* info@pilgrimharps.co.uk. *Concert grand, pedal and non-pedal hps. Restoration, servicing, str, mus, insurance, accs.*

Premier Percussion Ltd. Blaby Rd, Wigston, Leics LE18 4DF *tel:* 0870 160 3121 *fax:* 0870 160 3122 *email:* info@premier-percussion.com. Keith Mann, UK & European sales dir; Julie Firmager, mkt co-ord. *Perc insts and accs. UK based manufacturers of drum sets, marching, orch and pipeband perc insts.*

R A J Bower & Co. Wellgrove Organ Manufactory, Weston Longville, Norwich NR9 5JJ *tel:* 01603 881189 *fax:* 01603 881222 *email:* rbower@albatross.co.uk. *Orgs, pedal pnos.*

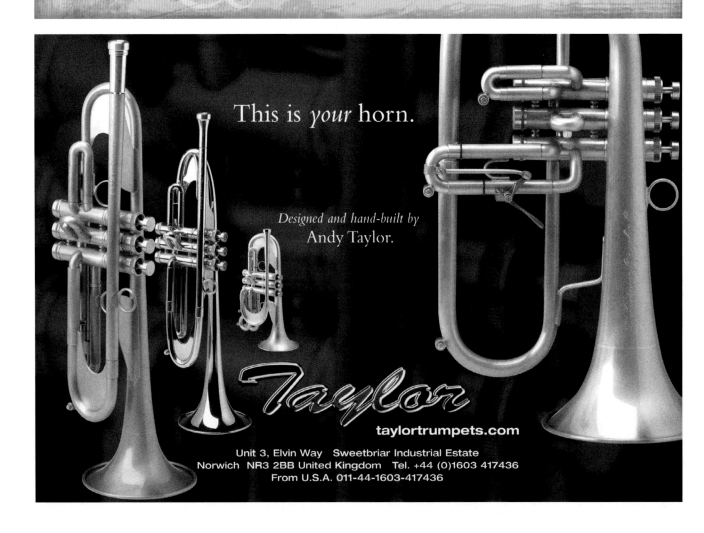

Renaissance Workshop Company Ltd. 38 Manningham Lane, Bradford BD1 3EA *tel:* 01274 201752 *fax:* 01274 201753 *email:* sales@renwks.com. *Early mus insts, inst kits and inst plans.*

Richard Smith Musical Instruments. 110 The Vale, London N14 6AY *tel:* 020 8882 1580 *fax:* 020 8447 8567 *email:* info@smithwatkins.com. *Designers and makers of Smith-Watkins tpts, cornets and flugel hns.*

Robert Morley & Co Ltd. 34 Engate St, Lewisham, London SE13 7HA *tel:* 020 8318 5838 *email:* jvm@morley-r.u-net.com. *Pnos, hpds, spinets, clvds, virginals and celestes.*

Roger Hansell Violins. The Violin Making Workshop, Leyburn Business Park, Leyburn, N Yorks DL8 5QA *tel:* 01969 624643/3048 *fax:* 01969 623048 *email:* roger@hansellviolins.com. Roger Hansell. *Finest pegs and inst fittings, also collector insts.*

Roland (UK) Ltd. Atlantic Close, Swansea Enterprise Park, Swansea, W Glamorgan SA7 9FJ *tel:* 01792 702701 *fax:* 01792 700130; 01792 799644 (sales) *email:* info@roland.co.uk. *Distributor and manufacturer of elec mus insts inc digital pnos, synthesizers, keyboards and hard disk rcdrs.*

Rosetti Ltd. 4 Tamdown Way, Springwood Industrial Estate, Braintree, Essex CM7 2QL *tel:* 01376 550033 *fax:* 01376 550042 *email:* music@rosetti.co.uk. *Str, br, w/wind, guis, perc, gui accs, amps.*

Rotosound Manufacturing Ltd. Unit 3b, Morewood Close, Sevenoaks, Kent TN13 2HU *tel:* 01732 450838 *fax:* 01732 458994 *email:* jason@rotosound.co.uk. *Strs for gui, bs gui, vn and db and all other str insts. Rotosound USA Inc, City National Bank Building, Suite 208/4605 Lankershim Blvd, N Hollywood CA 91602, USA tel: 001 818 505 0158 fax: 001 818 505 0582 email: rsusa@gateway.net.*

Schimmel Pianos. Forsyth Bros Ltd (Distributor), 126 Deansgate, Manchester M3 2GR *tel:* 0161 834 3281 ext 227 *fax:* 0161 834 0630 *email:* schimmel@forsyths.co.uk. Simon Loat, gen mgr. *Upright and grand pnos.*

Simon Watkin Violins. 2 North Green, Coates, Peterborough, Cambs PE7 2BQ *tel:* 01733 840235 *fax:* 0870 1342652 *email:* scdw@cix.co.uk. *Vns, vas, vcs.*

Smith-Watkins Brass. 110 The Vale, Southgate, London N14 6AY *tel:* 020 8882 1580 *fax:* 020 8447 8567 *email:* info@smithwatkins.com. *Designers/makers of tpts, cornets and flugel hns.*

Soar Valley Music. 3 Waldron Court, Prince William Rd, Loughborough, Leics LE11 5GU *tel:* 01509 269629 *fax:* 01509 269206 *email:* sales@soarvalleymusic.com. *Brazilian and African perc specialist and Folk inst wholesaler (w/wind, perc).*

Solid State Organ Systems. 25 Putney Close, Brandon, Suffolk IP27 0PA *tel:* 01842 813813 *fax:* 01842 813802 *email:* salesuk@ssosystems.com. *Elec switching and piston capture systems for the pipe org.*

Stagg, John W. 10 Christmas Steps, Bristol BS1 5BS *tel:* 0117 925 4538 *fax:* 0117 925 4538 *email:* johnstagg.bows@tesco.net. *Master bowmaker, restoration, repairs, fine bows bought and sold.*

Starfish Designs. Units 1 & 2, Old Ferry Rd, North Ballachulish, by Fort William, Inverness-shire PH33 6SA *tel:* 01855 821429 *fax:* 01855 821062 *email:* info@starfishdesigns.co.uk. *Makers and repairers of Celtic hps (26, 31 and 34 str models) and electric bowed insts (Stingray electric vns, vas; Dolphin electric vcs; Orca electric dbs).*

Steinway & Sons (UK). Steinway Hall, 44 Marylebone Lane, Wigmore St, London W1U 2DB *tel:* 020 7487 3391 *fax:* 020 7935 0466 *email:* pianosales@steinway.co.uk. *Pnos.*

Stentor Music Co Ltd. Albert Rd North, Reigate, Surrey RH2 9EZ *tel:* 01737 240226 *fax:* 01737 242748 *email:* stentor@stentor-music.com. *Str inst manufacturer, br, w/wind and gui wholesaler.*

Stephen Wessel. Millbrook House, Alhampton, Shepton Mallet, Somerset BA4 6PX *tel:* 01749 860047 *fax:* 01749 860047 *email:* wessel@ntlworld.com. *Fl maker, repairs and alteration.*

Stoppani, George. 6 Needham Ave, Chorlton cum Hardy, Manchester M21 8AA *tel:* 0161 256 1173 (home)/860 7386 (w/shop) *fax:* 0161 860 7386 (w/shop) *email:* george.stoppani@talk21.com. *Str family insts, db.*

Strings & Things Ltd. Unit 3, 202-210 Brighton Rd, Shoreham-by-Sea, W Sussex BN43 6RJ *tel:* 01273 440442 *fax:* 01273 440278 *email:* strings@stringsandthings.co.uk. *Str, accs.*

Summerfield. 1-2 Vance Court, Trans Britannia Enterprise Park, Blaydon on Tyne NE21 5NH *tel:* 0191 414 9000 *fax:* 0191 414 9001 *email:* summerfield@ashleymark.co.uk. *Guis and fretted insts.*

T W Howarth & Co Ltd. 31-35 Chiltern St, London W1U 7PN *tel:* 020 7935 2407 *fax:* 020 7224 2564 *email:* sales@howarth.uk.com. *Cls, obs, ob d'am, ehs, bsns.*

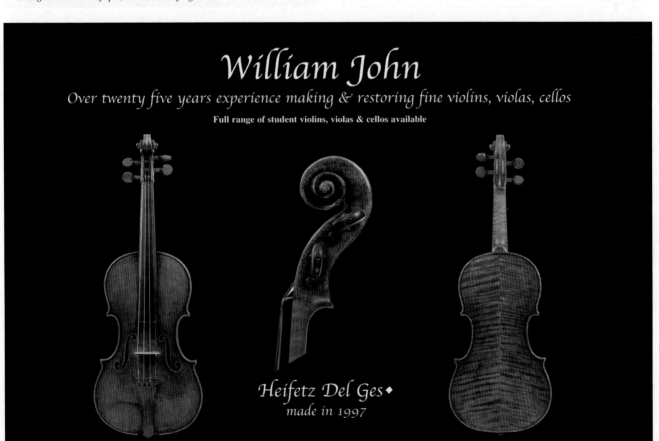

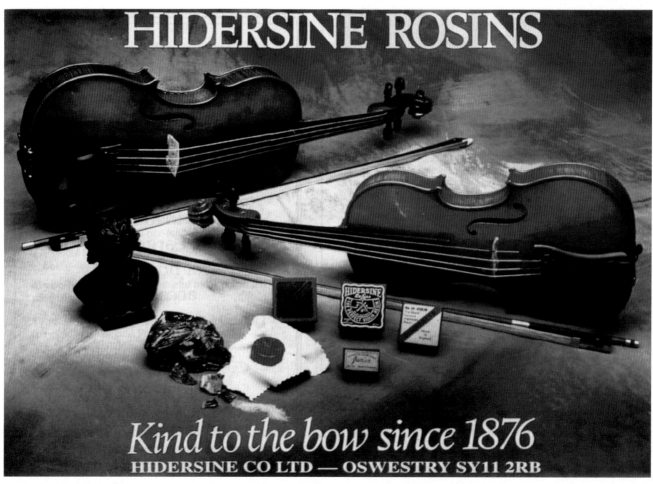

Technics Musical Instruments. Panasonic UK Ltd, Panasonic House, Willoughby Rd, Bracknell, Berks RG12 8FP *tel:* 01344 853177/858 (helpline) *fax:* 01344 853389 *email:* technics.helpline@panasonic.co.uk. *Digital pnos, keyboards.*

Terry Riley Vessel Flute Maker. 183 Glen Rd, Oadby, Leicester LE2 4RJ *tel:* 0116 271 9784. *Concert ocarinas and vessel fls using English fingering system.*

Thibouville-Lamy & Co Ltd. Gilbert House, 406 Roding Lane South, (off Woodford Ave), Woodford Green, Essex IG8 8EY *tel:* 020 8551 1282 *fax:* 020 8550 8377 *email:* sales@jtlamy.co.uk. *Importer and wholesaler of mus insts and accs.*

Trevor J James & Co. Worldwind House, Ashmill Park, Ashford Rd, Lenham, Maidstone, Kent ME17 2GQ *tel:* 01622 859590 *fax:* 01622 859596 *email:* tjj@worldwind.co.uk. *W/wind and accs manufacture and distribution.*

Violectra/Unison Strings Ltd. 113 The Custard Factory, Gibb St, Birmingham B9 4AA *tel:* 0121 693 0933 *fax:* 0121 693 0933 *email:* info@violectra.co.uk. *Makers of electric vns, vas, vcs and dbs. Also bows, cases and accs. Acoustic vn sales, makers and restorers. Valuations, appraisals and bow rehairing.*

W P Williams & Co (Est 1863). 2 Boscombe Mews, Boscombe Rd, Southend on Sea SS2 5JD *tel:* 01702 610981 *fax:* 01702 325049. Robin Stannard, master craftsman. *Pipe orgs, br shallots.*

Ward, Alan. St Andrews, 27 Plomer Hill, Downley, High Wycombe, Bucks HP13 5JG *tel:* 01494 523371. *Modern and baroque vn, va, vc maker, commissions handmade to order, restorer, repairer.*

Ward & Winterbourn. 75 Alexandra Rd, London NW4 2RX *tel:* 020 8203 2678. *W/wind.*

Wells-Kennedy Partnership. 85-87 Gregg St, Lisburn, Co Antrim BT27 5AW *tel:* 028 9266 4257 *fax:* 028 9260 3722 *email:* wellskennedy@dnet.co.uk. *Orgs.*

Whone, Adam. 86 Mill Hill Rd, Acton, London W3 8JJ *tel:* 020 8992 0619 *fax:* 020 8992 8891 *email:* info@adamwhone.co.uk. Adam Whone. *Dealer, restorer and maker of fine vns, vas, vcs and bows. Also valuations and sales.*

William John. 56 Lammas Park Rd, Ealing, London W5 5JB *tel:* 020 8567 3464 *email:* wjohnviolins@aol.com. *Maker and restorer of vns, vas, vcs; also old vns.*

Wood of Huddersfield. St Andrews Rd, Huddersfield, W Yorks HD1 6RZ *tel:* 01484 533374 *fax:* 01484 533374 *email:* woodorgan@huddersfield11.freeserve.co.uk. *Org builders.*

Yamaha-Kemble Music (UK) Ltd. Sherbourne Drive, Tilbrook, Milton Keynes MK7 8BL *tel:* 01908 369259 *fax:* 01908 368872. Mike Ketley. *Br, w/wind, digital keyboards, hi-tech, pro audio, pnos, guis, cymbals and drums.*

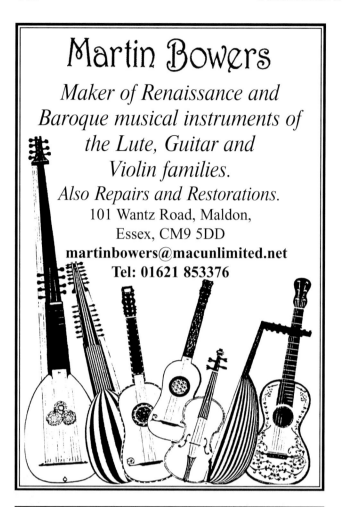

Early Music Instrument Manufacturers

This list of manufacturers of instruments for early music and authentic performance is divided into five broad categories: strings (bowed and plucked instruments); wind (woodwind and brass); keyboard (harpsichord, organ, etc); percussion; materials. Different manufacturers often use different spellings for particular instruments. To avoid confusion, spelling has been standardised in the entries below.

Strings

Attwood, Merion David *email:* instruments@merion.co.uk. *Viols, vns, bows.*

Baker, Paul. 21 Oakfield Ave, Kingswinford, W Midlands DY6 8HJ *tel:* 01384 295210 *email:* paul@diabolus.org. Paul Baker. *Medieval and renaissance plucked and bowed strs, hurdy-gurdies.*

Border Harps. Waterloo Cottages, Letton, Hereford HR3 6DN *tel:* 01544 327352 *fax:* 01544 327352 *email:* borderharps@hotmail.com. M C Saunders, partner; S R Saunders, partner. *Non-pedal hps, hp kits, parts and strs.*

Bowers, Martin. 101 Wantz Rd, Maldon, Essex CM9 5DD *tel:* 01621 853376. Martin Bowers, proprietor. *Chitarrones, theorbos, archlutes, liuto attiorbato, renaissance and baroque lutes, guis, vn family, oud. Repairs and restorations.*

Bridgewood, Gary D. 146 Stoke Newington Church St, London N16 0UA *tel:* 020 7249 9398 *fax:* 020 7275 9330 *email:* violinsbn@btclick.com. *Vas da gamba, violones, baroque vns, vcs, etc.*

Cohen, Brian. Soundpost, The Old Glasshouse, Alexandra Place, Guildford GU1 3QH *tel:* 01483 456422 *fax:* 01483 456422 *email:* strings@soundpost.co.uk. *Guis, lutes, vas da gamba, vns, vcs, dbs.*

Crumpler, Alan. 12 Buttercross Arcade, Leominster, Herefords HR6 8BN *tel:* 01568 613477 *fax:* 01568 613477 *email:* alan@capriole.fsnet.co.uk. *Early str insts: medieval fiddles, organistrum; symphony, renaissance and earlier hps; early bows.*

Early Music Shop. 38 Manningham Lane, Bradford BD1 3EA *tel:* 01274 393753 *fax:* 01274 393516 *email:* sales@earlyms.demon.co.uk. *Viol family, lutes, psalteries (bowed, plucked), medieval fiddles, hourglass dulcimers, hps, hurdy-gurdies; also available in kit form.*

Edgar, Alan. Northwood, 43 Beverley Rd, Hessle, E Yorks HU13 9AE *tel:* 01482 640330 *email:* sue@jacaranda.f9.co.uk. Alan Edgar, proprietor. *Small hps, mus stands.*

Edwards, David Van. The Smokehouse, 6 Whitwell Rd, Norwich, Norfolk NR1 4HB *tel:* 01603 629899 *email:* david@vanedwards.co.uk. *Medieval, renaissance and baroque lutes, chitarrones and theorbos, renaissance and baroque bows for vn, va da gamba inst families.*

Fleming, Michael. 13 Upland Park Rd, Oxford OX2 7RU *tel:* 01865 512807 *fax:* 01865 512807 *email:* viols@flemingoxford.co.uk. *Viols (wide range, especially early 17th C English), vn family (16th-17th C), fixed-frog and other bows.*

Forrester, Peter S. Sunflower House, 20 Beechwood Ave, Aylmerton, Norfolk NR11 8QQ *tel:* 01263 837711 *email:* peterforrester@waitrose.com. *Citterns, bandoras, orpharions and associated plucked strs.*

Jones, Lewis. 18 Mare St, London E8 4RT *tel:* 020 8533 6404 *fax:* 020 8533 6404. *Hps, other medieval and renaissance str insts.*

Julier, Jane. Old Trickey's Farmhouse, Blackborough, Cullompton, Devon EX15 2HZ *tel:* 01823 681012 *fax:* 01823 681012 *email:* rossclocks@clara.co.uk. *Vas da gamba.*

Maynard, Bryan. Teviot House, Fishers Brae, Coldingham, Berwickshire TD14 5NJ *tel:* 01890 771235 *email:* bryolin@hotmail.com. *Renaissance and baroque vns, vas, vcs, viols and violones.*

Northern Renaissance Instruments. 6 Needham Ave, Chorlton cum Hardy, Manchester M21 8AA *tel:* 0161 881 8134 *fax:* 0161 881 8134 *email:* post@nrinstruments.demon.co.uk. E and Y Segerman, partners. *Strs and varnish materials, lutes, viols, guis, citterns, bandoras, orpharions and rebecs.*

Nowak, Steffen. 75 Sylvia Ave, Bristol BS3 5BU *tel:* 0117 977 7141 *email:* sn@nowakviolins.co.uk. Steffen Nowak. *Vn, va, vc, baroque and modern.*

O'Kelly, Joseph M. 2 Middleton Rd, London E8 4BL *tel:* 020 7254 7074 *fax:* 0870 125 7669 *email:* lute@hygra.com. *Baroque lutes and guis, ouds, theorbos, vihuelas, chitarrones, calasciones. Also restoration.*

Oakwood Instruments. 8 Ladywood Rd, Leeds LS8 2QF *tel:* 0113 265 8585 *fax:* 0113 293 3011 *email:* workshop@oakwoodinstruments.co.uk. Martyn Banks, dir. *Hps, hammer dulcimers, guis, citterns, mandolins, banjos, bouzoukis, mandolas, electric insts.*

Pilgrim Harps. Stansted House, Tilburstow Hill Rd, South Godstone, Surrey RH9 8NA *tel:* 01342 893242 *fax:* 01342 892646 *email:* info@pilgrimharps.co.uk. *Non-pedal and pedal hps, accs, strs, mus, hire and servicing. Insurance.*

Renaissance Workshop Company Ltd. 38 Manningham Lane, Bradford BD1 3EA *tel:* 01274 201752 *fax:* 01274 201753 *email:* sales@renwks.com. *Medieval, renaissance and baroque insts; kits and plans.*

Rose, Roger. West Dean Musical Inst Workshop, c/o West Dean College, Chichester, W Sussex PO18 0QZ *tel:* 01243 811301/8235 *email:* roger.rose@westdean.org.uk. *Viols, baroque vns, vcs and bows.*

Stoppani, George. 6 Needham Ave, Chorlton cum Hardy, Manchester M21 8AA *tel:* 0161 860 7386 (w/shop)/256 1173 (home) *fax:* 0161 860 7386 (w/shop) *email:* george.stoppani@talk21.com. *Period vns, vas, vcs, bs vns, violones. Gut str for period insts.*

Tunnicliffe, Brian. Bow Brook Cottage, Marsh Lane, Horsington, Templecombe BA8 0ER *tel:* 01963 370904 *fax:* 01963 370904 *email:* Brian.Tunnicliffe@ukgateway.net. Brian Tunnicliffe, sole proprietor. *Bowmaker for vn, va, vc and db, and the baroque family of bows. Restoration and rehairing.*

Ward, Alan. St Andrews, 27 Plomer Hill, Downley, High Wycombe, Bucks HP13 5JG *tel:* 01494 523371. *Baroque and modern vns, vas, vcs. Commissions handmade to order. Also restoration and repairs.*

Wind

Ackerman, Brian. 70 Portland Rd, Hove, E Sussex BN3 5DL *tel:* 01273 702444 *fax:* 01273 702222 *email:* info@ackermanmusic.co.uk. *Cls (also mouthpieces), fls, chalumeaux.*

All Flutes Plus. 60-61 Warren St, London W1T 5NZ *tel:* 020 7388 8438 *fax:* 020 7388 7438 *email:* afp@allflutesplus.co.uk. Polly Bowden, early fl specialist. *Early fls: Baroque, Classical, 19th C (original and reproduction). Also folk fls and whistles.*

Christopher Monk Instruments. Perkwood, Station Rd, Yaxham NR19 1RD *tel:* 01362 691198 *fax:* 01362 691198 *email:* info@jeremywest.co.uk. Jeremy West, partner; Keith Rogers, partner; Dick Earle. *Cornetts, serpents, historical obs.*

Dart, Mathew. 45 Bonnington Square, London SW8 1TF *tel:* 020 7735 0479 (home); 020 7787 2614 (w/shop) *email:* mathdart@aol.com. *Baroque fls, bsns, classical bsns.*

Dolmetsch Musical Instruments. Unicorn Trading Estate, Weydown Rd, Haslemere, Surrey GU27 1DN *tel:* 01428 643235 *fax:* 08700 560190 *email:* brian@dolmetsch.com. Brian Blood, mgr and sales dir. *Rcdrs.*

Early Brass. 25 Church Path, Merton Park, London SW19 3HJ *tel:* 020 8542 4942 *fax:* 020 8287 9528 *email:* earlybrass@hotmail.com. Frank Tomes. *English and German baroque and medieval tpts; sackbutts.*

Early Music Shop. 38 Manningham Lane, Bradford BD1 3EA *tel:* 01274 393753 *fax:* 01274 393516 *email:* sales@earlyms.demon.co.uk. *Crumhorns, cornamuse, racketts, bagpipes (also available in kit form), sordunes, curtals, baroque bsns, shawms, rauschpfeife.*

Gruar, Philip. Brook Cottage, Burton Rd, Holme, via Carnforth, Lancs LA6 1QN *tel:* 01524 781601 *email:* philip@gruar.clara.net. *Northumbrian and Scottish smallpipes.*

Harding, David. 56 Netherton Rd, Appleton, Abingdon, Oxon OX13 5JZ *tel:* 01865 863673. *Serpents.*

Heriot & Allan. 28 Fairfield Green, West Monkseaton, Whitley Bay, Tyne and Wear NE25 9SD *tel:* 0191 251 3845 *email:* heriotandallan@tiscali.co.uk. R A Greensitt, owner; A H Sessoms, asst. *Northumbrian and Scottish smallpipes.*

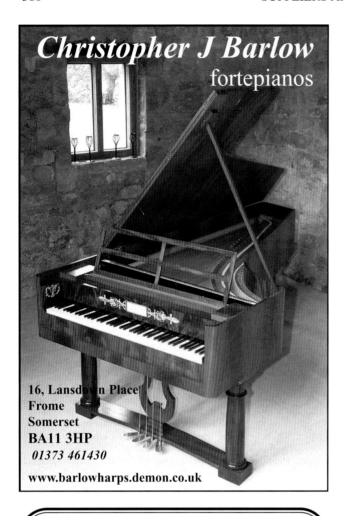

Jones, Lewis. 18 Mare St, London E8 4RT *tel:* 020 8533 6404 *fax:* 020 8533 6404. *Renaissance transverse fls.*

Julian Goodacre - Bagpipe Maker. 4 Elcho St, Peebles EH45 8LQ *tel:* 01721 722539 *email:* julian@goodbagpipes.co.uk. Julian Goodacre, bagpipe maker. *Historical and folk bagpipes: English medieval bagpipes and Leicestershire smallpipes, Cornish double pipes, Scottish bellows, smallpipes, Border bagpipes. Also repairs and restores.*

Lewin, Greg. The Hawthorns, Hawthorn Drive, Wheaton Aston, Staffs ST19 9NQ *tel:* 01785 840186 *fax:* 01785 840476 *email:* greg@hawthornsmusic.co.uk. *Crumhorns, cornamuse, kortholts, racketts, schreierpfeifen (schryarii), sordunes.*

Moulder, A Eric. 30 King St, Leek, Staffs ST13 5NW *tel:* 01538 386867 *fax:* 01538 386867 *email:* eric@renaissancewoodwinds.co.uk.

Renaissance reed insts, chorist-fagotts, cornamuse, crumhorns, dulcians (curtals), shawms, rauschpfeifen, baroque bsns, etc.

Renaissance Workshop Company Ltd. 38 Manningham Lane, Bradford BD1 3EA *tel:* 01274 201752 *fax:* 01274 201753 *email:* sales@renwks.com. *Medieval, renaissance and baroque insts; kits and plans.*

Saunders Recorders. 205 Whiteladies Rd, Blackboy Hill, Clifton, Bristol BS8 2XT *tel:* 0117 973 5149 *fax:* 0117 973 5149 *email:* john@saundrecs.co.uk. John Everingham, mgr. *Specialist rcdr dealer.*

Wells, Charles. Early Woodwinds, 32 Manor Rd, Hatfield, Doncaster, S Yorks DN7 6SD *tel:* 01302 846492 *fax:* 01302 846492 *email:* charlie@kawells.fsnet.co.uk. *Renaissance, baroque and classical fls, cls, flageolets, tabor pipes, restoration, repairs.*

Keyboard

Andrew Wooderson Early Keyboard Instruments. 5 Bourne Rd, Bexley, Kent DA5 1LG *tel:* 01322 558326 *fax:* 01322 525558 *email:* andrew.wooderson@btinternet.com. *All types of hpds, spinets, virginals, clvds handbuilt to order; also tuning, maintenance, restoration, repairs and hire. Sale of tools and accs. Second-hand insts for sale.*

Barlow, Christopher. 16 Lansdown Place, Frome, Somerset BA11 3HP *tel:* 01373 461430 *email:* chris@barlowharps.demon.co.uk. *Maker of early keyboard insts, particularly f-pnos (including Stein, Walter, Schantz and Graf models) and hpds (including late 18th C English Kirkman). Some insts available for concert hire in the West Country.*

Bavington, Peter. 291 Sprowston Mews, London E7 9AE *tel:* 020 8519 1170 *fax:* 020 8519 1170 *email:* peterbav@nildram.co.uk. *Clvds and hpds.*

Bexley Harpsichord Workshops Ltd. 5 Bourne Rd, Bexley, Kent DA5 1LG *tel:* 01322 557147 *fax:* 01322 527366 *email:* edmund.handy@btinternet.com. Edmund Handy and Andrew Wooderson. *All types of hpds, spinets, virginals and clvds. Tuning, repair and restoration of hpds, spinets, virginals, clvds, celestes and square pnos. Inst hire, tools and accs. Second-hand insts for sale.*

Bolton, D H. 44 Church Lane, Acklam, Middlesbrough TS5 7EB *tel:* 01642 817097 *fax:* 01642 284178 *email:* dhbolton@ntlworld.com. *Custom-built hpds, spinets, virginals, clvds, also in kit form with many components sold separately. Chmbr orgs (finished insts only).*

Booth, Colin. Mount Pleasant, Westbury-sub-Mendip, Wells BA5 1HU *tel:* 01749 870516 *fax:* 01749 870516 *email:* colin@harpsichords.demon.co.uk. *Hpds, virginals.*

Coad, Lucy. Workshop 3, Greenway Farm, Bath Rd, Wick, nr Bristol BS30 5RL *tel:* 0117 937 4949 *email:* lucy@squarepiano.co.uk. *Square pno conservation and repairs; wound bs strs.*

Deegan (Robert) Harpsichords. Tonnage Warehouse, St Georges Quay, Lancaster LA1 1RB *tel:* 01524 60186 *fax:* 01524 60186 *email:* harpsichords@hotmail.com. Robert Deegan, proprietor. *Hpds, virginals, spinets, clvds. Also concert hire, transport, tuning, maintenance, restoration and repairs, strs, spares.*

Dolmetsch Musical Instruments. Unicorn Trading Estate, Weydown Rd, Haslemere, Surrey GU27 1DN *tel:* 01428 643235 *fax:* 08700 560190 *email:* brian@dolmetsch.com. Brian Blood, mgr and sales dir. *Hpds, clvds, spinets.*

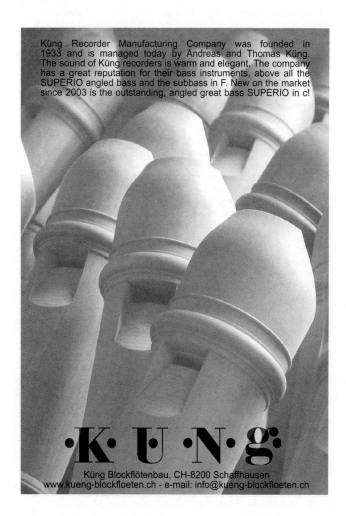

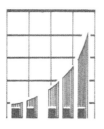

Early Keyboard Agency. Heyford Galleries, High St, Upper Heyford, Oxon OX25 5LE *tel:* 01869 232282. Martin Robertson, proprietor; Stuart Robertson, proprietor; Barry Robertson, proprietor. *Hpds, virginals, spinets, clvds, f-pnos, square pnos, restoration, tuning; specialists in all types of early and modern overspun strs. Humidifiers and dehumidifiers.*

Early Music Shop. 38 Manningham Lane, Bradford BD1 3EA *tel:* 01274 393753 *fax:* 01274 393516 *email:* sales@earlyms.demon.co.uk. *Spinets, clvds, hpds (also in kit form).*

Edgar, Alan. Northwood, 43 Beverley Rd, Hessle, E Yorks HU13 9AE *tel:* 01482 640330 *email:* sue@jaracanda.f9.uk. *Mus stands, hpds.*

Garlick, Andrew. Madgeon Wood House, Buckland St Mary, Chard, Somerset TA20 3QF *tel:* 01460 234221 *fax:* 01460 234782. *Hpds, spinets, virginals.*

George Veness Workshop. Stanhope Studio, Donald Way, Winchelsea, E Sussex TN36 4NH *tel:* 01797 225878. Marcus Weeks, pno tuner, technician, restorer. *Clavichord maker and restorer. Also makes traditional mus stands.*

Goetze, Martin and Dominic Gwynn. 1-2 East Workshops, Welbeck Abbey Estate, Worksop, Notts S80 3LW *tel:* 01909 485635 *fax:* 01909 485635 *email:* dominic@goetzegwynn.co.uk. *Church and chmbr orgs in period styles; also restoration work.*

Gotto, Alan. 5 Bessemer Rd, Norwich NR4 6DQ *tel:* 01603 620102 *fax:* 01603 620102 *email:* agotto@dsn.co.uk. *Hpds, virginals, spinets.*

Handy, Edmund. 5 Bourne Rd, Bexley, Kent DA5 1LG *tel:* 01322 527366 *fax:* 01322 527366 *email:* edmund.handy@btinternet.com. *Clvd maker. Tuning, repair and restoration of hpds, spinets, virginals, clvds, celestes and square pnos. Inst hire, tools and accs. Second-hand insts for sale.*

Hollick, Douglas. 4 Station Cottages, Harby Lane, Stathern, Leics LE14 4HJ *tel:* 01949 861347 *fax:* 01949 861347 *email:* dwh@globalnet.co.uk. *Hpds, virginals, clvds, also restoration work.*

Huggett, Martin. The Old Library, Stour St, Manningtree, Essex CO11 1BE *tel:* 01206 396354 *fax:* 01206 396354 *email:* martin@huggett.demon.co.uk. *Hpds, clvds, spinets; mus stands, chmbr orgs and harmoniums. Also materials. Specialist artcase pno restorations, including carving, gilding, all art and decorative work, recreated and restored.*

Hugh Craig Harpsichords. Sugarcroft, Lower Southfield Lane, Bosbury, Ledbury, Herefords HR8 1NH *tel:* 01531 640069 *fax:* 01531 640069 *email:* enquiries@harpsichord.co.uk. *Hpds, spinets, clvds.*

Jennings, Robin. 81 Gordon Rd, Buxted, Uckfield, E Sussex TN22 4LJ *tel:* 07770 851950 *email:* robin@jennings-organs.co.uk. *Chmbr and continuo orgs including keyed glockenspiel.*

John Storrs Workshop. 169 Clifton Rd, Rugby, Warks CV21 3QN *tel:* 01788 567613 *fax:* 01788 567613 *email:* StephenRobinson@johnstorrsworkshop.co.uk. Stephen Robinson, proprietor. *Hpds, spinets, clvds; kits or finished insts. Also mus stands and cabinets.*

Jones, Lewis. 18 Mare St, London E8 4RT *tel:* 020 8533 6404 *fax:* 020 8533 6404. *Hpds, spinets, virginals, clvds, clavicytheria, lute-hpds, also specialist restoration work.*

Julia Morley, Robert Morley and Co Ltd. 34 Engate St, London SE13 7HA *tel:* 020 8318 5838 *email:* jvm@morley-r.u-net.com. Julia Morley, mgr. *Hpds, clvds, spinets, virginals, celestes. Also repairs, rentals, sales and restoration work.*

Leigh-Flanders, Xavier. 44 Seaward Ave, Southbourne-on-Sea, Dorset BH6 3SH *tel:* 01202 428835 *fax:* 01202 428835 *email:* xlf@harpsichords.co.uk. *Hpds, virginals.*

Mander Organs. St Peter's Organ Works, St Peter's Square, London E2 7AF *tel:* 020 7739 4747 *fax:* 020 7729 4718 *email:* manderuk@mander-organs.com. John Pike Mander, mgr dir. *Portatives, regals, chmbr orgs, pipe orgs.*

Minns, Michael. 22a Davenant Rd, Oxford OX2 8BX *tel:* 01865 556368 *fax:* 01865 316876 *email:* michael@minnsox.freeserve.co.uk. *Hpds, spinets, virginals.*

Mitchell, William. 44 Seaward Ave, Southbourne-on-Sea, Dorset BH6 3SH *tel:* 01202 428835 *fax:* 01202 428835 *email:* william.mitchell@harpsichords.co.uk. *Hpds, virginals, claviorganum.*

Nimblejack Ltd. 67 Old Rd, Studley, Calne, Wilts SN11 9NF *tel:* 01249 817283 *email:* alan@thewhears.freeserve.co.uk. Alan Whear. *Portable clavicytheria, hpd maintenance, gen inst repairs.*

Peter Collins Ltd. 42 Pate Rd, Melton Mowbray, Leics LE13 0DG *tel:* 01664 410555 *fax:* 01664 410535 *email:* pd_collins@lineone.net. Peter Collins, mgr dir. *New pipe orgs of all sizes, restoration; continuo org for hire.*

R A J Bower & Co. Wellgrove Organ Manufactory, Weston Longville, Norwich NR9 5JJ *tel:* 01603 881189 *fax:* 01603 881222 *email:* rbower@albatross.co.uk. *Early orgs, practice orgs, continuo orgs, church and chmbr orgs, pipe orgs.*

Ransom, Mark. 130 Westbourne Terrace Mews, London W2 6QG *tel:* 020 7723 9650 *fax:* 020 7723 9650 *email:* markransom@harpsichord-workshop.co.uk. *Hpds, virginals, spinets.*

Renaissance Workshop Company Ltd. 38 Manningham Lane, Bradford BD1 3EA *tel:* 01274 201752 *fax:* 01274 201753 *email:* sales@renwks.com. *Medieval, renaissance and baroque insts; kits and plans.*

Richter, Karin. The Workshop, English Passage, Lewes, E Sussex BN7 2AP *tel:* 01273 481010 *fax:* 01273 481010 *email:* clavichords@k-richter.fsnet.co.uk. Karin Richter. *Clvds, restoration of keyboard insts.*

Robert Goble & Son. Greatstones, Kiln Lane, Headington, Oxford OX3 8HQ *tel:* 01865 761685 *fax:* 01865 761685. Edward Goble, dir. *Hpds, spinets.*

Robert Shaftoe Organbuilder. 58 High St, Pavenham, Bedford MK43 7PE *tel:* 01234 823609 (evenings). Robert Shaftoe. *Orgs, spinets.*

Rose, Malcolm. The Workshop, English Passage, Lewes, E Sussex BN7 2AP *tel:* 01273 481010 *fax:* 01273 481010 *email:* info@malcolm-rose.com. Malcolm Rose. *Hpd maker, repairer and conservator. Maker of iron and brass wires for keyboard insts up to 1850.*

Temple, Alex. Platt Lodge, 61 Barton Rd, Worsley, Manchester M28 2GX *tel:* 0161 794 3717 *fax:* 0870 120 8401 *email:* alextemple@supanet.com. *Hpds, clvds; also hire and maintenance.*

W P Williams & Co (est 1863). 2 Boscombe Mews, Boscombe Rd, Southend-on-Sea, Essex SS2 5JD *tel:* 01702 610981 *fax:* 01702 352049. Robin Stannard, master craftsman. *Pipe orgs, reeds and shallots; established 1863.*

Wells-Kennedy Partnership. 85-87 Gregg St, Lisburn, Co Antrim BT27 5AW *tel:* 028 9266 4257 *fax:* 028 9260 3722 *email:* wellskennedy@dnet.co.uk. David H McElderry, dir. *Chmbr orgs and pipe orgs.*

Percussion

Early Music Shop. 38 Manningham Lane, Bradford BD1 3EA *tel:* 01274 393753 *fax:* 01274 393516 *email:* sales@earlyms.demon.co.uk. *Timbrels, tabors, nakers, drums and timpani (also in kit form).*

Glover, Marcel. Norton Cottage, Colchester Rd, Wivenhoe, Colchester, Essex CO7 9HT *tel:* 01206 826342 *email:* marcelg@aspects.net. *Nakers, tabors, triangles.*

Renaissance Workshop Company Ltd. 38 Manningham Lane, Bradford BD1 3EA *tel:* 01274 201752 *fax:* 01274 201753 *email:* sales@renwks.com. *Medieval, renaissance and baroque insts; kits and plans.*

Materials

Bexley Harpsichord Workshops Ltd. 5 Bourne Rd, Bexley, Kent DA5 1LG *tel:* 01322 557147 *fax:* 01322 527366 *email:* edmund.handy@btinternet.com. Edmund Handy, dir; Andrew Wooderson, dir. *Hpd tools, spares and accs.*

Handy, Edmund. Early Keyboard Instruments, 5 Bourne Rd, Bexley, Kent DA5 1LG *tel:* 01322 527366 *fax:* 01322 527366 *email:* edmund.handy@btinternet.com. Edmund Handy, dir. *Hpd tools, spares and accs.*

Huggett, Martin. The Old Library, Stour St, Manningtree, Essex CO11 1BE *tel:* 01206 396354 *fax:* 01206 396354 *email:* martin@huggett.demon.co.uk. *All early keyboard insts, clvd, hpd, spinet, org and harmonium. Specialist inlaying and marquetry, high-class cabinet making, mus stands.*

Woolrich, A P. Canal Side, Huntworth, Bridgwater, Somerset TA7 0AJ *tel:* 01278 663020 *fax:* 01278 663913 *email:* apw@ap-woolrich.co.uk. *Ironmongery; tuning hammers, wrest pins, itch pins, hpd stop levers, stop mechanisms, etc.*

Retailers

This list is arranged by county, with Greater London first, followed by England, Scotland, Wales and Northern Ireland. Shops listed consist of dealers in printed music and musical instruments. The list does not claim to be exhaustive and excludes multiple stores whose larger branches occasionally stock instruments or accessories. A list of record shops specialising in classical recordings will be found under **Specialist Record Dealers**. Many **Music Publishers** also have a retail counter.

Greater London

ASM Music. 318a Kennington Rd, London SE11 4LD *tel:* 020 7735 1932 *fax:* 020 7582 6128 *email:* asmmusic@btinternet.com. *Keyboards, hi-tech, home recording, PA equipment.*

All Flutes Plus. 60-61 Warren St, London W1T 5NZ *tel:* 020 7388 8438 *fax:* 020 7388 7438 *email:* afp@allflutesplus.co.uk. *Fl specialists; mus, repairs, rentals, second-hand fls.*

Argent's Printed Music. 20 Denmark St, London WC2H 8NA *tel:* 020 7379 3384 *fax:* 020 7240 4159. *Classical sheet mus and scores; also jazz, pop and rock.*

Barbican Chimes Music. Cromwell Tower, Silk St, Barbican, London EC2Y 8DD *tel:* 020 7588 9242 *fax:* 020 7628 1080 *email:* barbican@chimesmusic.com. *Books, mus, insts, CDs, accs.*

Bell Percussion Ltd. 6 Greenock Rd, Acton, London W3 8DU *tel:* 020 8896 1200 *fax:* 020 8896 0100. *Mallet specialist. Perc retail, hire and repairs. Yamaha 5.5 octave celeste. West London Sibelius Software dealer.*

Blackburn Stringed Instruments. 75 Harrington Gardens, London SW7 4JZ *tel:* 020 7373 2474 *fax:* 020 7373 5141 *email:* blackburn@stringed-instruments.freeserve.co.uk. *Buying and selling of str insts; also restoration and evaluation. Vns, vas, bows, vcs.*

Blanks Music Store. 271-273 Kilburn High Rd, London NW6 7JR *tel:* 020 7624 7777 *email:* sales@blanksmusic.co.uk. *Guis, amps, drums and perc, br and w/wind, keyboards, vns, Irish and traditional insts, books, etc, vintage insts, accordians and hire; also servicing (within 24 hrs)*

Blüthner Piano Centre Ltd. 1 Davies St, Berkeley Square, London W1K 3DB *tel:* 020 7753 0533 *fax:* 020 7753 0535 *email:* bluthner@globalnet.co.uk. Roger Willson, sales dir. *Upright and grand pianos (Blüthner, Irmler, Haessler).*

Books Etc. Royal Festival Hall, Belvedere Rd, South Bank, London SE1 8XX *tel:* 020 7620 0403 *fax:* 020 7620 0426 *email:* booksetc@rfh.org.uk. *Biographies, analyses, histories, libretti, scores.*

Boosey & Hawkes Music Shop. 295 Regent St, London W1B 2JH *tel:* 020 7291 7255; 0800 731 4778 (freephone) *fax:* 020 7436 2850 *email:* musicshop@boosey.com. *Books, mus, accs; m/order (cat), credit cards. Boosey & Hawkes, Peters Edition, ABRSM and all other major suppliers.*

Bridgewood and Neitzert. 146 Stoke Newington Church St, London N16 0UH *tel:* 020 7249 9398 *fax:* 020 7275 9330 *email:* violinsbn@btclick.com. *Vn, va, vc, db, bows; maker, restorer and dealer. Strs for period insts. Baroque and classical specialists. M/order.*

Chappell of Bond Street. 50 New Bond St, London W1S 1RD *tel:* 020 7491 2777 *fax:* 020 7491 0133 *email:* enquiries_bs@chappell-bond-st.co.uk. George Clayton. *Insts, mus, pnos, keyboards, books, school mus, mus software.*

The Drum Cellar. 21 Denmark St, London WC2H 8NA *tel:* 020 7240 3483 *fax:* 020 7379 3398 *email:* info@wom.co.uk. *Acoustic and electric drums, wide range of ethnic perc.*

Ealing Strings. 4 Station Parade, Uxbridge Rd, London W5 3LD *tel:* 020 8992 5222/3993 *fax:* 020 8992 3544 *email:* mail@ealingstrings.info. *Books, str insts, accs. Suppliers and restorers.*

Music for Musicians

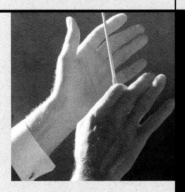

printed music

syllabus material

instrument hire

books

repairs

accessories

staffed by qualified musicians

prompt mail order

free delivery for schools and libraries

free fax order hot-line for schools

**Open:
Mon-Fri 9-5.30
Sat 9-4**

A specialist service

As one of Britain's leading music retailers
we stock a vast range of printed music, a comprehensive range of syllabus material for all the main examination boards, and a wide range of books. We offer an instrument hire scheme, a fast repair service, and an extensive supply of accessories.

Our staff are qualified musicians, with substantial trade experience, we offer a prompt mail order service, free delivery to schools and libraries, and a special free fax order hot-line for schools.

Phone today for details of our latest special offers and discounts. We believe our prices are competitive and will beat any price quoted.

Kensington Chimes Music 9 Harrington Rd South Kensington London SW7 3ES
tel: 020 7589 9054 fax: 020 7225 2662 e-mail: kensington@chimesmusic.com

Barbican Chimes Music Cromwell Tower Barbican London EC2Y 8DD
tel: 020 7588 9242 fax: 020 7628 1080 e-mail: barbican@chimesmusic.com

www.chimesmusic.com

Kensington Chimes
music
Barbican Chimes
SHEET MUSIC • BOOKS • INSTRUMENTS • ACCESSORIES

Electrohill. 124-126 Green Lanes, London N13 5UN *tel:* 020 8886 9426 *fax:* 020 8886 9356 *email:* sales@electrohill.co.uk. *Specialists in guis, amps, effects and PA equipment.*

Eric Lindsey Ltd. 20 Rushey Green, Catford, London SE6 4AS *tel:* 020 8690 8621 *fax:* 020 8690 7064. *Guis, drums, keyboards, recording and PA equipment.*

Fazioli Pianos. 142 Edgware Rd, London W2 2DZ *tel:* 020 7935 7378 *fax:* 020 7224 8692 *email:* info@jspianos.com. Daniel Thomas, hire mgr. *Pno sales, hire, tuning, servicing, practice rooms.*

Florian Leonhard Fine Violins. 3 Frognal Lane, London NW3 7DY *tel:* 020 7813 3307 *fax:* 020 7813 3308 *email:* violins@florianleonhard.com. Florian Leonhard, dir. *Vn makers, restorers, dealers, consultants. Advice given on buying and selling vns, investment quality insts, bow rehairs, restoration, sound adjustments; strs by m/order and in stock; wholesalers of Pirastro strs.*

Frederick Phelps Ltd, Dealers in Fine Violins. 67 Fortess Rd, London NW5 1AG *tel:* 020 7482 0316 *fax:* 020 7813 4589 *email:* fpviolin@dircon.co.uk. *Vns, vas, vcs, accs; also restoration and bow repairs.*

Hampstead Pianos. 131-133 Abbey Rd, London NW6 4SL *tel:* 020 7624 8895 *email:* info@hampsteadpianos.co.uk. *Acoustic and digital pnos, restoration, tuning, removals, hire and unique pno designs.*

Harpsichord Workshop. 130 Westbourne Terrace Mews, London W2 6QG *tel:* 020 7723 9650 *fax:* 020 7723 9650 *email:* markransom@harpsichord-workshop.co.uk. *Tuning, repair and renovation, short and long-term hire, insts for sale. Agent for well-known makers.*

Hobgoblin Music. 24 Rathbone Place, London W1T 1JA *tel:* 020 7323 9040 *fax:* 020 7323 1606 *email:* london@hobgoblin.co.uk. *Specialists in traditional, folk and acoustic insts: fretted, str, pipes, w/wind, free reed, perc. Books, accs, spares and strs. Acoustic and electric guis.*

Holywell Music Ltd. 58 Hopton St, London SE1 9JH *tel:* 020 7928 8451 *fax:* 020 7928 8284 *email:* holywell@holywell.co.uk. *Salvi and Lyon & Healy concert and lever hps, hp mus, strs, recordings and accs.*

Impact Percussion. 7 Goose Green Trading Estate, 47 East Dulwich Rd, London SE22 9BN *tel:* 020 8299 6700 *fax:* 020 8299 6704 *email:* sales@impactpercussion.com. Paul Hagen, proprietor. *Orch and latin perc and kits; also repairs and hire.*

Islington Music. 6 Shillingford St, off Cross St, London N1 2DP *tel:* 020 7354 3195 *fax:* 020 7354 3195. Mrs P M Cottle, owner. *Sheet mus, books, tapes, accs, gifts; insts (sales and hire); m/order.*

Ivor Mairants Musicentre. 56 Rathbone Place, London W1T 1JT *tel:* 020 7636 1481 *fax:* 020 7580 6272 *email:* info@ivormairants.co.uk. Mak Ogawa, mgr. *Acoustic, classical and jazz guis, folk insts, second-hand insts, accs; tutorials, videos, repairs, m/order.*

J & A Beare Ltd. 30 Queen Anne St, London W1G 8HX *tel:* 020 7307 9666 *fax:* 020 7307 9651 *email:* violins@beares.com. Simon Morris; Frances Gillham. *Dealers, restorers and makers of vn, va, vc.*

J P Guivier & Co Ltd. 99 Mortimer St, London W1W 7SX *tel:* 020 7580 2560/7636 6499 *fax:* 020 7436 1461 *email:* violins@guivier.com. *Dealers and restorers of insts and bows of the vn family. Also cases, accs and valuations.*

J Reid Pianos. 184 St Annes Rd, Tottenham, London N15 5RP *tel:* 020 8800 6907 *fax:* 020 8809 0767 *email:* jreidpianos@ukonline.co.uk. *Pnos, repairs, restoration, educ discounts, retail and wholesale supplier.*

Jaques Samuel Pianos Ltd. 142 Edgware Rd, London W2 2DZ *tel:* 020 7723 8818 *fax:* 020 7224 8692 *email:* info@jspianos.com. *Pnos, repairs, removals, sale and hire. Practice rooms.*

Kensington Chimes Music. 9 Harrington Rd, London SW7 3ES *tel:* 020 7589 9054 *fax:* 020 7225 2662 *email:* kensington@chimesmusic.com. *Mus, books, insts, accs.*

Len Stiles Musical Instruments Ltd. 268 Lewisham High St, London SE13 6JX *tel:* 020 8690 2958/7771 *fax:* 020 8690 2958/7771 *email:* lenstilesmusic@aol.com. *Mus, keyboards, digital pnos, synths, orch, group gear, accs, repairs.*

Les Aldrich Music Shop. 98 Fortis Green Rd, London N10 3HN *tel:* 020 8883 5631 *fax:* 020 8444 9805 *email:* music@lesaldrich.co.uk. *Books, insts, mus, classical CDs, DVDs, opera videos, sheet mus, inst repairs.*

The London Recorder Centre. 34 Chiltern St, London W1U 7QH *tel:* 020 7486 9101 *fax:* 020 7486 9109 *email:* london@earlyms.demon.co.uk. *Rcdrs, sheet mus, CDs, accs. See also* **W Yorkshire** *The Early Music Shop.*

The London PA Centre. 24 Denmark St, London WC2H 8NA *tel:* 020 7497 1178 *fax:* 020 7379 3398 *email:* info@wom.co.uk. *Public address systems, microphones, amplifiers, public address installations and recording equipment.*

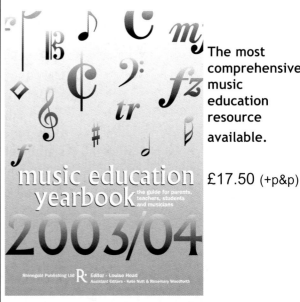

M and J Healey Violins. 12 Rosehill, London, Surrey SM1 3EU *tel:* 020 8644 4700 *fax:* 020 8644 4700 *email:* Malcolm@Healeyviolins.f9.co.uk. *Str insts, accs, repairs, makers.*

MDC Classic Music Ltd. 473 The Strand, London WC2R 0QN *tel:* 020 7240 2157 *fax:* 020 7240 5848 *email:* classic@mdcmusic.co.uk. Kevin McDermott, mgr. *Classical mus CDs and DVDs; selection of musical and film soundtracks; world cinema DVDs.*

MDC Classic Music Ltd. 46 Thurloe St, London SW7 2LT *tel:* 020 7584 3338 *fax:* 020 7584 9179 *email:* classic@mdcmusic.co.uk. *Classical mus CDs and DVDs.*

MDC Classic Music Ltd. Royal Festival Hall, London SE1 8XX *tel:* 020 7620 0198 *fax:* 020 7620 0197. *Classical, world and jazz CDs and DVDs; world cinema DVDs.*

MDC Classic Music Ltd - Mail Order. 31 St Martin's Lane, London WC2N 4ER *tel:* 020 7240 0273 *fax:* 020 7379 5231 *email:* classic@mdcmusic.co.uk. *Classical mus CDs, DVDs and videos.*

MDC Classic Music Ltd - Opera Shop. 31 St Martin's Lane, London WC2N 4ER *tel:* 020 7240 0270 *fax:* 020 7379 5231. *Opera and classical vocal mus, including historical recordings on CD, DVD and video. Opera guides and opera and ballet magazines.*

Macari's Ltd. 92-94 Charing Cross Rd, London WC2H 0JB *tel:* 020 7836 9149 *fax:* 020 7379 8762 *email:* info@macaris.co.uk. *Acoustic and elec guis, amps, br, w/wind, accs. Theremins, didges, banjos, mandolins, ukelele, shakers and bongos, Suzuki Q-Chord.*

Markson Pianos Ltd. 8 Chester Court, Albany St, London NW1 4BU *tel:* 0800 074 8980 *fax:* 020 7224 0957 *email:* sales@pianosuk.co.uk. Simon Markson, mgr dir. *Pno sales, hire, tuning, maintenance, repairs, restoration, transport; acoustic and digital; educ and student discounts. 24-hr concert hire service. Teaching and practice studios. Also at 36-38 Artillery Place, Woolwich, London SE18 4AB tel: 0800 298 7384.*

Media Tools PLC. 12 Flitcroft St, London WC2H 8DL *tel:* 020 7692 6611 *fax:* 020 7692 7619 *email:* sales@mediatools.co.uk. *Professional and audio-visual equipment.*

Michael White. 11 Queens Parade, Queens Drive, Ealing, London W5 3HU *tel:* 020 8997 4088 *fax:* 020 8566 9379. *W/wind and br sales and repairs.*

The Music Studios Ltd. 29 Marylebone Lane, London W1U 2NQ *tel:* 020

7486 0025 *fax:* 020 7935 8454. *Steingraeber, Gors & Kallmann, Steinmayer, Weber and other fine new and used pnos.*

New Notations Computer Services Ltd. 7 Duncombe Hill, London SE23 1QY *tel:* 07968 312032 *fax:* 0870 706 4795 *email:* sales@newnotations. co.uk. *Consultancy and hardware/software sales. Mus notation. Custom-built computer workstations.*

New Notations London. 93 Wellmeadow Rd, London SE6 1HL *tel:* 020 8697 6351 *fax:* 020 8697 0038 *email:* info@newnotations.com. Stephen Gibson, proprietor. *Mus software: Score, Sibelius, Finale. Sequencers; audio; software synths.*

Paxman Musical Instruments Ltd. Unit B4, Linton House, 164-180 Union St, London SE1 0LH *tel:* 020 7620 2077 *fax:* 020 7620 1688 *email:* info@paxman.co.uk. *Hns, mus, repairs, accs.*

Peter Vel Fine String Instruments and Bows. 164 Camden Rd, London NW1 9HJ *tel:* 020 7813 7981 *fax:* 020 7267 3418 *email:* v@vstrings.co.uk. *Sales and repairs.*

Peters Music Shop. c/o Boosey & Hawkes, 295 Regent St, London W1B 2JH *tel:* 020 7291 7244 *fax:* 020 7436 2850 *email:* peters.edition@ boosey.com. *Stocks mus in Peters Edition and agencies (in the Boosey & Hawkes Music Shop).*

Phelps Pianos. 49 Fortess Rd, London NW5 1AD *tel:* 020 7485 2042; 0800 298 7385 *fax:* 020 7284 1404 *email:* info@phelpsmusic.co.uk. *Specialists in acoustic and digital pnos (uprights and grands, new and second-hand). Sales, hire, tuning, repairs, restoration and free advice. Educ discounts. Also a range of mus insts and accs, practice rooms, teaching facilities.*

Phil Parker. 106a Crawford St, London W1H 2HZ *tel:* 020 7486 8206 *fax:* 020 7935 6686 *email:* sales@philparker.co.uk. *Br insts, accs, repairs and mus.*

Piano Warehouse Ltd. 30 Highgate Rd, London NW5 1NS *tel:* 0800 018 7671 *fax:* 020 7284 0083 *email:* sales@piano-warehouse.co.uk. Martin Weedon, sales dir. *Specialists in upright and grand pnos both new and second-hand. Dealers for Yamaha, Kemble, Young Chang, Weber and Steinmayer. Also extensive range of digital pnos by Yamaha and Technics.*

Professional Percussion. 205 Kentish Town Rd, London NW5 2JU *tel:* 020 7485 0822/4434 *fax:* 020 7485 9745 *email:* sales@propercussion.co.uk. *All areas of perc: drum kits and accs, cymbals, electric drums, tuned, latin and marching perc.*

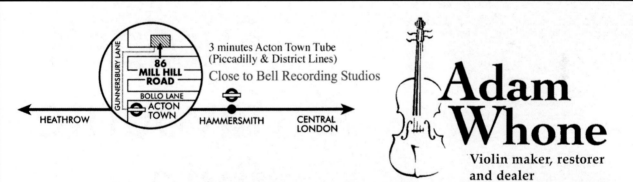

Ransom, Mark. 130 Westbourne Terrace Mews, London W2 6QG *tel:* 020 7723 9650 *fax:* 020 7723 9650 *email:* markransom@ harpsichord-workshop.co.uk. *Hpds, virginals.*

Ray Man. 54 Chalk Farm Rd, London NW1 8AN *tel:* 020 7692 6261 *email:* rayman@raymaneasternmusic.co.uk. *World mus insts, recordings, tuition, workshops, hire.*

Reid-Sohn Pianos. 184 St Ann's Rd, Tottenham, London N15 5RP *tel:* 020 8800 6907 *fax:* 020 8809 0767 *email:* jreidpianos@ukonline.co.uk. *Pno repairs, restoration, educ discounts, retail and wholesale supplier.*

Rhodes Music Ltd. 21 Denmark St, London WC2H 8NA *tel:* 020 7240 4656 *fax:* 020 7379 3398 *email:* info@wom.co.uk. *Electric guis, acoustic guis, amplifiers, effects and accs.*

Richmond Music Shop Ltd. 16 Red Lion St, Richmond TW9 1RW *tel:* 020 8332 6220 *fax:* 020 8332 0552 *email:* richmondmusic@compuserve.com. *Strs, w/wind, br, perc, printed mus, repairs on site.*

Robert Morley & Co Ltd. 34 Engate St, London SE13 7HA *tel:* 020 8318 5838 *email:* jvm@morley-r.u-net.com. *J Morley. Spinets, virginals, clvds, hpds, pnos, antique hps; stools, cabinets, mus stands; sales and rental, tuning, repairs (cat).*

Salvationist Publishing and Supplies Ltd. 1 Tiverton St, London SE1 6NT *tel:* 020 7367 6570 *fax:* 020 7367 6589 *email:* trevor.cassull@sp-s.co.uk. *Salvation Army vocal and inst mus.*

Schott/Universal Edition. 48 Great Marlborough St, London W1F 7BB *tel:* 020 7437 1246 *fax:* 020 7437 6115 *email:* retail@mdslondon.co.uk. *Publishers retail shop, classical mus.*

Spanish Guitar Centre. 36 Cranbourn St, London WC2H 7AD *tel:* 020 7240 0754 *fax:* 020 7240 0754 *email:* info@spanishguitarcentre.com. *Classical, acoustic and flamenco guis, accs, mus CDs, videos, tuition.*

Steinway & Sons. 44 Marylebone Lane, London W1U 2DB *tel:* 020 7487 3391 *fax:* 020 7935 0466 *email:* pianosales@steinway.co.uk. Ron Losby, mgr dir. *New and refurbished pnos, tuning, rebuilds and repairs; concert hire.*

T W Howarth & Co Ltd. 31 Chiltern St, London W1U 7PN *tel:* 020 7935 2407 *fax:* 020 7224 2564 *email:* sales@howarth.uk.com. *W/wind, inst repairs and accs, inst hire, sheet mus m/order.*

Top Wind. 2 Lower Marsh, London SE1 7RJ *tel:* 020 7401 8787 *fax:* 020 7401 8788 *email:* topwind@topwind.com. *Fl specialists. Also repairs and suppliers to schools and colleges. Full range of student and professional insts, sheet mus, rentals, books, accs and expert advice.*

Total Music. Suite 2000, 16-18 Woodford Rd, London E7 0HA *tel:* 01206 271710 *fax:* 01206 273706 *email:* info@total-music.com. Steve Smith, dir. *Offers mus inst resale, rental and repair.*

Turnkey. 114-116 Charing Cross Rd, London WC2H 0DT *tel:* 020 7419 9999 *fax:* 020 7379 0093 *email:* sales@turnkey.co.uk. *Hi-tech insts, recording equipment, PC and Macintosh computer mus hardware and software, PA systems, guis, amps, bs, home keyboards and digital pnos.*

Walthamstow Music. 2 Greenleaf Rd, Walthamstow, London E17 6QQ *tel:* 020 8520 2163 *fax:* 020 8509 3005 *email:* sales@walthamstowmusic. com. A Jonns, mgr dir. *Br, w/wind, str, keyboard and hi-tech insts. Repairs, hire.*

Whone, Adam. 86 Mill Hill Rd, London W3 8JJ *tel:* 020 8992 0619 *fax:* 020 8992 8891 *email:* info@adamwhone.co.uk. *Vn restorers, makers and dealer; valuations and sales. Also vas, vcs and bows.*

World of Pianos. 8 Denmark St, London WC2H 8LP *tel:* 020 7240 5555 *fax:* 020 7379 3398 *email:* info@wom.co.uk. *Digital pnos, mus software, home keyboards, br and w/wind insts.*

England

Bath & North East Somerset
Bath

Bath Music Centre Ltd. 20-22 Monmouth Place, Bath BA1 2AY *tel:* 01225 335154 *fax:* 01225 335154. *Insts, perc, drum kits, guis, sheet mus, repairs.*

Bedfordshire
Biggleswade

Lindsay Music. 23 Hitchin St, Biggleswade, Beds SG18 8AX *tel:* 01767 316521 *fax:* 01767 317221 *email:* sales@lindsaymusic.co.uk. *Books, mus, accs (strs, reeds, etc), mus gifts.*

Dunstable

Beare & Son. 18 Tavistock Place, Tavistock St, Dunstable, Beds LU6 1NG *tel:* 01582 477130 *fax:* 01582 477130. *Vns, vas, vcs, bs, bows, cases, strs, fitting and accs. Manufacturers and wholesale distributors of Beare-Tertis vas plus Michael Poller insts.*

Kempston

Tema Music. 34-36 High St, Kempston, Beds MK42 7AL *tel:* 01234 856465 *fax:* 01234 856480 *email:* music@temamusic.co.uk. *Insts, mus, accs.*

Berkshire

Maidenhead

Just Woodwind. Basement, 40 Queen St, Maidenhead, Berks SL6 1HZ *tel:* 01628 674707/621488. *Mus, insts, ABRSM exam mus, US jazz educ books and CDs.*

Sheargold Pianos Ltd. 53 King St, Maidenhead, Berks SL6 1DU *tel:* 01628 771400 *fax:* 01628 771483 *email:* pianos@sheargold.com. *New and second-hand pnos, digital pnos, pno hire, sheet mus. Removals, tuning, part-exchange.*

Windcraft Ltd. The Woodwind & Brass Warehouse, Reform Rd, Maidenhead, Berks SL6 8BT *tel:* 01628 778377 *fax:* 01628 777466 *email:* sales@windcraft.co.uk. *Wind inst spares, accs (m/order), repair materials and tools.*

Reading

Hickies Ltd. 153 Friar St, Reading RG1 1HG *tel:* 0118 957 5771 *fax:* 0118 957 5775. *Insts, pnos, restorations, mus, CDs.*

Sandhurst

In Tune Music. 410-412 Yorktown Rd, College Town, Sandhurst, Berks GU47 0PR *tel:* 01276 34800 *fax:* 01276 34800 *email:* intunemusic@virgin.net. *Guis, amps, all types of traditional insts. Exam mus and mus albums.*

Slough

Guitar Centre. 126 Meadfield Rd, Langley, Slough, Berks SL3 8JF *tel:* 01753 542720 *email:* sales@guitarcentre.demon.co.uk. *All mus insts, recording equipment and rehearsal studio, PA and mus hire service, pnos.*

Bristol, City of
Bristol

Arnolfini/Bristol. 16 Narrow Quay, Bristol BS1 4QA *tel:* 0117 929 9191 *fax:* 0117 925 3876 *email:* arnolfini@arnolfini.demon.co.uk. *Books, art magazines, jewellery, cards. In autumn 2003 Arnolfini plans to undertake a major development programme to refurbish its premises. Although this means the building will be closed to the public for 18 months, Arnolfini hope to keep the bookshop open throughout the project. Please phone ahead to confirm details.*

Bristol Musical. 581 Gloucester Rd, Horfield Common, Horfield, Bristol BS7 0BW *tel:* 0117 929 2758 *fax:* 0117 929 2758. *New and used electric guis, basses; accs, equipment, PA systems.*

Bristol Piano Co. 85 Bristol Rd, Whitchurch, Bristol BS14 0PS *tel:* 01275 834141. *New and reconditioned pnos, repairs, rebuilds, tuning, polishing.*

The Bristol Violin Shop. 12 Upper Maudlin St, Bristol BS2 8DJ *tel:* 0117 925 9990 *fax:* 0117 925 0033 *email:* sales@bristol-violin-shop.co.uk. *Makers and repairers of bowed str insts; insts bought and sold; accs and specialist str mus. Also m/order and comprehensive internet cat of mus and accs.*

Cremona House Violin Shop. 7 Perry Rd (Park Row), Bristol BS1 5BQ *tel:* 0117 926 4617 *fax:* 0117 926 4617 *email:* violins@bigfoot.com. Richard Bristow; Ken Green; Mae Morrison. *Vns, vcs, vas; repairs; valuations, old insts bought and sold; bows, accs; advice, insurance. Also m/order and sheet mus service (cat). Online shop.*

The Drumstore. 125 St Georges Rd, Hotwells, Bristol BS1 5UW *tel:* 0117 929 8540. *Specialists in drums and perc.*

Hobgoblin Music. 30 College Green, Bristol BS1 5TB *tel:* 0117 929 0902 *fax:* 0117 929 3431 *email:* Bristol@hobgoblin.co.uk. *Specialists in traditional, folk and acoustic insts: fretted, str, pipes, w/wind, free reed, perc. Books, accs, spares and strs. Acoustic and electric guis.*

John W Stagg - Bowmaker. 10 Christmas Steps, Bristol BS1 5BS *tel:* 0117 925 4538 *fax:* 0117 925 4538 *email:* johnstagg.bows@tesco.net. *Master bowmaker, restoration, repairs, fine bows bought and sold.*

Mickleburgh Ltd. 1-9 Stokes Croft, Bristol BS1 3PL *tel:* 0117 924 1151 *fax:* 0117 924 4158 *email:* mail@mickleburgh.co.uk. *Insts, pnos, keyboards, mus, pno hire for concerts, pno repairs and tuning.*

Saunders Recorders. 205 Whiteladies Rd, Blackboy Hill, Clifton, Bristol

BS8 2XT *tel:* 0117 973 5149 *fax:* 0117 973 5149 *email:* john@saundrecs.co.uk. *Insts, mus, rcdr specialist.*

Spanish Guitar Centre. 103 Coldharbour Rd, Westbury Park, Bristol BS6 7SD *tel:* 0117 942 0479 *fax:* 0117 914 6685 *email:* bristolspanishguitar@compuserve.com. *Insts, mus, tuition.*

Trevor Jones Brass and Woodwind Ltd. 13 Christmas Steps, Bristol BS1 5BS *tel:* 0117 922 7402 *fax:* 0117 922 7402. *Insts, mus, accs, rentals, repairs, m/order.*

Buckinghamshire
Aylesbury
R Smith & Co. PO Box 367, Aylesbury, Bucks HP22 4JJ *tel:* 01296 682220 *fax:* 01296 681989 *email:* info@rsmith.co.uk.

Beaconsfield
Rosehill Instruments Ltd. 64 London End, Beaconsfield, Bucks HP9 2JD *tel:* 01494 671717 *fax:* 01494 676428 *email:* rosehill@percypriors.co.uk. *Insts, accs, mus, electronic pnos.*

Chesham
Perfect Pitch. 72 The Broadway, Chesham, Bucks HP5 1EG *tel:* 01494 774826 *fax:* 01494 778353 *email:* perfectpitchmus@cs.com. *Mus, insts, repairs, rental scheme, accs.*

High Wycombe
Countrywide Piano Centre Ltd. 194 Penn Rd, Hazlemere, High Wycombe, Bucks HP15 7NU *tel:* 01494 813388 *fax:* 01494 813994 *email:* info@countrywidepianos.co.uk. *Pnos (new and second-hand), repairs, tuning, restorations. School, churches, educ discount.*

Allen Organ Studios (London) Ltd. Trada Business Campus, Stocking Lane, Hughenden Valley, High Wycombe HP14 4ND *tel:* 01494 563833 *fax:* 01494 563546 *email:* sales@allenorgans.co.uk. *Allen classical and theatre orgs.*

Percy Prior's Music. 31 The Octagon Arcade, High Wycombe, Bucks HP11 2HT *tel:* 01494 443418/465733 (sheet mus) *fax:* 01494 463353 *email:* highwycombe@percypriors.co.uk. *Insts, sheet mus, hi-tech, repairs.*

Milton Keynes
Chappell of Bond St. 21 Silbury Arcade, thecentre:mk, Milton Keynes MK9 3AG *tel:* 01908 663366 *fax:* 01908 606414 *email:* david_meek@chappell-bond-st.co.uk. *Insts, keyboards, studio, PA, mus, CDs, tuning, repairs, hire, pnos, DVDs, CD-ROMs.*

Suzuki Europe Ltd. 7 Drakes Mews, Crownhill, Milton Keynes MK8 0ER *tel:* 01908 263990 *fax:* 01908 265955 *email:* hojo@suzukimusic.co.uk. *Suzuki harmonicas, digital pnos, guis, vns, rcdrs and general educ insts.*

Cambridgeshire
Cambridge
Cambridge Pianoforte Centre. 10-12 Kings Hedges Rd, Cambridge CB4 2PA *tel:* 01223 424007 *fax:* 01223 425599 *email:* info@cambridgepianoforte.co.uk. *Full range of new and previously owned grand and upright pnos.*

Digital Village. 86 Mill Rd, Cambridge CB1 2AS *tel:* 01223 316091/324536 *fax:* 01223 353857 *email:* cambridge@digitalvillage.co.uk.

Ken Stevens Music and Instruments. 12 Sussex St, Cambridge CB1 1PW *tel:* 01223 367758 *fax:* 01223 362480 *email:* info@kenstevens.co.uk. *All insts, pnos and keyboards, sheet mus, classical CDs, accs. Educ specialists. Est 1856.*

MDC Classic Music. 8 Rose Cres, Cambridge CB2 3LL *tel:* 01223 506526 *email:* akashadeva@manju5.freereserve.co.uk. David Earl, co mgr; Simon Hassala, co mgr. *Classical and jazz CDs, books, videos, gifts.*

The Music Gallery - Cambridge. 10-12 Kings Hedges Rd, Cambridge CB4 2PA *tel:* 01223 424999 *fax:* 01223 425599 *email:* sales@musicgallery.org.uk. *Full range of orch insts and mus. Special emphasis on vns, vas, vcs and classical guis.*

Reeds Direct Cambridge. Freepost CB914, Cambridge CB2 1YA *tel:* 0800 096 9440 (orders) *fax:* 01223 576231 *email:* shop@reeds-direct.co.uk. *M/order cl and sax reeds.*

Wood, Wind and Reed. Russell St, Cambridge CB2 1HU *tel:* 01223 500442 *fax:* 01223 576231 *email:* shop@wwr.co.uk. *W/wind and br insts and accs, sheet mus; valuations, repairs and restoration, m/order.*

Ely
Aitchison & Mnatzaganian. 7 Cambridge Rd, Ely, Cambs CB7 4HJ *tel:* 01353 668559 *fax:* 01353 612264 *email:* info@aitchisoncellos.com. *Vc specialists: stocks of vcs and bows, antique and contemporary. Annual contemporary bow exhibition: 'Take a Bow'.*

The Four Seasons

From The Sound Post

Violin ~ Viola ~ Cello ~ Bass

Now in our tenth year

The UK Specialist Distributor of Bowed
String Instruments, Strings & accessories

Exclusive distributors of Primavera™ & Rainbow™ Violins

Cheshire
Cheadle
Sounds Great. 182 Wilmslow Rd, Heald Green, Cheadle, Cheshire SK8 3BG *tel:* 0161 436 4799 *fax:* 0161 498 6468 *email:* soundsgreat@btinternet.com. *Insts, br, w/wind, guis, amps, keyboards, digital and acoustic pnos, mus.*
Chester
Curzon Music (Mail Order). 82b Hough Green, Chester CH4 8JW *tel:* 01244 683457 *fax:* 01244 683457. *Educ and classical mus, m/order.*
Hyde
Harry Ash. 133 Knott Lane, Gee Cross, Hyde, Cheshire SK14 5BS *tel:* 0161 366 0195 *email:* tarisio@postmaster.co.uk. *Vns, vas, vcs, all accs, repairs, valuations, bow repairs, insurance facilities, strs by m/order.*
Knutsford
Mostly Music. 28 Carlisle Close, Mobberley, Knutsford, Cheshire WA16 7HD *tel:* 01565 872650 *fax:* 01565 872650 *email:* mostlymusic@btinternet.com. *M/order books, mus, recordings, tapes, CDs.*
Swans Music. The Belan, Moss Lane, Mobberley, Knutsford, Cheshire WA16 7BS *tel:* 01565 873044 *fax:* 01565 873044 *email:* hire@swansmusic.co.uk. *Pno, inst and backline hire. Pno tuning, maintenance and removal.*
Warrington
Dawsons Music Ltd. 65 Sankey St, Warrington, Cheshire WA1 1SU *tel:* 01925 582420 *fax:* 01925 582422 *email:* education@dawsons.co.uk. *Books, insts, mus, hi-tech equipment, pnos.*

Cornwall
Camborne
Trevada Music. 9-11 Chapel St, Camborne, Cornwall TR14 8EF *tel:* 01209 714353 *fax:* 01209 718708 *email:* sales@trevadamusic.co.uk. *Pnos, keyboards, br, w/wind, perc, str, sheet mus, repairs, rental scheme. Also at: 18 Wind St, Ammanford SA18 3DN tel: 01269 596607 fax: 01269 596608.*
Launceston
Tottle's Music Shop. 30 Westgate St, Launceston, Cornwall PL15 7AE *tel:* 01566 772512 *email:* tottlesmusic@btconnect.com. *Mus; w/wind, br, str, perc insts; gui, amps, orgs, keyboards, pnos.*
Redruth
John Oliver. 33 Fore St, Redruth, Cornwall TR15 2AE *tel:* 01209 216494 *fax:* 01209 213999. *CDs, DVDs, cassettes, accs, videos.*
Wadebridge
Hobgoblin Music. Polmorla House, Polmorla Walk, Wadebridge, Cornwall PL27 7NS *tel:* 01208 812230 *fax:* 01208 814593 *email:* wadebridge@hobgoblin.co.uk. *Specialists in traditional, folk and acoustic insts: fretted, str, pipes, w/wind, accordians, perc. Books, accs, spares and strs. Acoustic and electric guis.*

Cumbria
Alston
Jacks, Pipes & Hammers. Bridge View, Garrigill, Alston, Cumbria CA9 3DU *tel:* 01434 381583 *fax:* 01434 382877 *email:* j.edmonds@jphbaroque.co.uk. *Mus for keyboard, org, vocal, trio sonatas, quadros, solos. Specialists in 17th-18th C mus and books. Publishers of 17th-18th C mus in facsimile.*
Brampton
Omega Music (UK) Ltd. Townfoot Estate, Brampton, Cumbria CA8 1SW *tel:* 01697 73067 *fax:* 01697 741018 *email:* sales@omegamusic.co.uk. *Insts, perc, pno showroom.*

Derbyshire
Derby
Chas Foulds & Son (Derby) Ltd. 40 Irongate, Derby DE1 3GA *tel:* 01332 344842/2654 *fax:* 01332 294415 *email:* info@fouldsmusic.co.uk. *Pnos, insts, sheet mus, guis.*
Neville Bros. 74 Babington Lane, Derby DE1 1SX *tel:* 01332 290762 *fax:* 01332 290762 *email:* nevillebrothers@btinternet.com. *Guis, amps, br, w/wind, repairs.*

Devon
Barnstaple
Soundpad. Rolle Quay House, Rolle Quay, Barnstaple, Devon EX31 1JE *tel:* 01271 323686 *fax:* 01271 323686 *email:* info@soundpad.co.uk. *Guis, amplification, perc, keyboards, disco, lighting, recording equipment.*
Exeter
Bill Greenhalgh Ltd. 125-127 Fore St, Exeter EX4 3JQ *tel:* 01392 430008. *Insts, keyboards, mus, pnos, amps.*
LMS Music Supplies. PO Box 7, Exeter EX1 1WB *tel:* 01392 428108 *fax:* 01392 412521 *email:* LMSmusic@compuserve.com. *Educ m/order mus insts and books.*
Music Lines. 1 Bartholomew St West, Exeter EX4 3AJ *tel:* 01392 433748 *fax:* 01392 433748. *Sheet mus and m/order.*
South Molton
Studio Music Shop. 5 East St, S Molton, Devon EX36 3BU *tel:* 01769 574346 *email:* studiomusicdev@aol.com.

Dorset
Poole
Achille Roma. 456 Ashley Rd, Parkstone, Poole, Dorset BH14 0AD *tel:* 01202 743654 *fax:* 01202 743654. *All insts, sheet mus, accs, MIDI, PA equipment.*
Poole Music Centre. Unit 14 Towngate Centre, High St, Poole, Dorset BH15 1ER *tel:* 01202 682700 *fax:* 01202 660755 *email:* poole@mip5.dircon.co.uk. *Printed mus, Yamaha keyboards pnos and guis, Technics pnos, keyboards, Casio keyboards, Fender guis and amps; Zoom, Fostek, Gibson, Epiphone, Tanglewood and Jackson guis.*

East Riding of Yorkshire
Beverley
Beverley Music Centre. 14 Norwood, Beverley, E Riding Of Yorks HU17 9EZ *tel:* 01482 881584 *fax:* 01482 867653 *email:* shop@beverleymusiccentre.co.uk. *Vns, vas, vcs, dbs, bows and accs. Br, w/wind, guis. Educ insts. Printed mus. Postal service. Insts for sale/hire. Restorers and valuers.*
Hull
Antone's Guitars. 326 Beverley Rd, Hull HU5 1BA *tel:* 01482 445733 *fax:* 01482 343007 *email:* info@antonesguitars.com. *Guis, amps, vintage section, repairs, home recording, acoustic insts.*

East Sussex
Battle
Amadeus Performance Equipment Ltd. Great Beech Barn, Kane Hythe Rd, Battle, E Sussex TN33 9QU *tel:* 01424 775867 *fax:* 01424 775866 *email:* info@amadeus-equipment.co.uk. *Mus stands, musician posture chairs, inst racks, portable staging, acoustically designed rehearsal rooms, other performing arts furniture, accs.*
Bexhill
Marten's Music. 15 London Rd, Bexhill, E Sussex TN39 3JR *tel:* 01424 222560 *fax:* 01424 222542 *email:* martensmusic@btconnect.com. *New and reconditioned pnos, tuning, repairs, w/wind, br, strs, mus.*
Eastbourne
Brittens Music Ltd. 24 Pevensey Rd, Eastbourne, E Sussex BN21 3HP *tel:* 01323 732553 *fax:* 01323 417455 *email:* mail@seaford-music.co.uk. *Mus, educ books, inst accs, classical CDs and DVDs.*
Hailsham
Jewish Music Distribution. PO Box 67, Hailsham, E Sussex BN27 4UW *tel:* 01323 832863; 0800 7811 686 *email:* orders@jewishmusic-jmd.co.uk. *Suppliers of Jewish and Israeli mus from around the world. CDs, books and sheet mus.*
Hove
Ackerman Music. 70 Portland Rd, Hove, E Sussex BN3 5DL *tel:* 01273 702444 *fax:* 01273 702222 *email:* info@ackermanmusic.co.uk. *Specialists in wind and str sales and repairs.*
Fab Music. 4 Westbourne Place, Hove, E Sussex BN3 4GN *tel:* 01273 777743 *fax:* 01273 777743 *email:* kate@fabmusic.freeserve.co.uk. *W/wind, br, orch strs, sales, on-site repairs, sheet mus, accs, m/order, inst rental scheme with option to buy.*
Winchelsea
George Veness. Stanhope Studio, Donald Way, Winchelsea, E Sussex TN36 4NH *tel:* 01797 225878. *Mus stands, clvd and hpd maker.*

Essex
Chelmsford
James Dace & Son Ltd. 33 Moulsham St, Chelmsford, Essex CM2 0HX *tel:* 01245 352133 *fax:* 01245 262841 *email:* shop@jamesdace.co.uk. *Insts, mus, accs, CDs.*
Colchester
Axe Music. 95 High St, Colchester, Essex CO1 1TH *tel:* 01206 765652 *fax:* 01206 764110 *email:* sales@axemail.com. *Guis, amps, recording equipment, accs, cassettes.*
Mann's Music. 123 High St, Colchester, Essex CO1 1SZ *tel:* 01206 572783 *fax:* 01206 572783 *email:* enquiries@mannsmusic.co.uk. *Br, w/wind, str, perc, keyboards, pnos, guis, sheet mus. Repairs, hire and m/order.*
Hornchurch
Advance Music Ltd. 79 Station Lane, Hornchurch, Essex RM12 6JU *tel:* 01708 442748 *fax:* 01708 452727 *email:* music@advancemusic.co.uk. *Insts, mus, pnos, classical CDs.*

Leigh-on-Sea

Clive Cowan Recording (CCR). 27 Stirling Ave, Leigh-on-Sea, Essex SS9 3PP *tel:* 01702 460451 *pager:* 07625 397858 *email:* info@ ccr.euromarques.com. Clive Cowan. *Location recording, especially for broadcast and video. Professional audio equipment sales including Steinberg Nuendo authorised dealer. Full member of the Institute of Broadcast Sound.*

Southend-on-Sea

Tim Gentle Music. 39-45 Grainger Rd Ind Estate, Southend-on-Sea, Essex SS2 5DD *tel:* 070 7171 7777; 0870 740 6282 *fax:* 0870 740 6283. *Mus insts and accs. Mail order: PO Box 154, Stockton-on-Tees TS20 1XJ.*

Gloucestershire

Cheltenham

Musical Instruments (Cheltenham) Ltd. 52 Winchcombe St, Cheltenham, Glos GL52 2ND *tel:* 01242 517635 *fax:* 01242 250794. *Pnos, insts, mus, accs.*

Sounds Good. 26 Clarence St, Cheltenham, Glos GL50 3NU *tel:* 01242 234604 *fax:* 01242 253030 *email:* cds@soundsgoodonline.co.uk. *CDs (classical, folk, world, jazz); videos (opera, ballet); DVDs (opera, ballet).*

Soundhouse. 295a High St, Cheltenham, Gloucester, Glos GL50 3HL *tel:* 01452 417429. *Drums, guis, amps, keyboards, br, w/wind, mus.*

Gloucester

Duck Son & Pinker Ltd. 52-56 Southgate St, Gloucester GL1 2DR *tel:* 01452 521061 *fax:* 01452 313693. *Insts, pnos, keyboards, mus.*

Soundhouse. 49 Westgate St, Gloucester GL1 2NW *tel:* 01452 417429. *Drums, guis, amps, keyboards, br, w/wind, mus.*

Lechlade

Clive Morley Harps Ltd. Goodfellows, Filkins, nr Lechlade, Glos GL7 3JG *tel:* 01367 860493 *fax:* 01367 860659 *email:* harps@morleyharps.com. *Concert and folk hps, antique insts, restorations, hp strs, mus, sales/rentals, repairs.*

Ruardean

Frank Fidler. Rosehill Instruments, The Old Dairy, The Square, Ruardean, Glos GL17 9TJ *tel:* 01594 544053 *email:* framaur@aol.com. *Br, w/wind sales and repairs, accs.*

Stroud

Musisca Ltd. Piccadilly Mill, Lower St, Stroud, Glos GL5 2HT *tel:* 01453 751911 *fax:* 01453 751911 *email:* marc@musisca.co.uk. *Mus stands and lighting, cond stands, desk stands, pno stools and pno wheels. Cat available on request.*

Tewkesbury

Goodmusic. PO Box 100, Tewkesbury, Glos GL20 7YQ *tel:* 01684 773883 *fax:* 01684 773884 *email:* sales@goodmusic-uk.com. *M/order only. Mus, books.*

Greater Manchester

Cadishead

Woodwind & Co. 208 Liverpool Rd, Cadishead, Manchester M44 5DB *tel:* 0161 775 1842 *fax:* 0161 775 4149 *email:* woodwindco@ntlworld.com. *W/wind specialists.*

Fallowfield

Alan Gregory Music & Musical Instruments. 196 Moseley Rd, Fallowfield, Manchester M14 6PB *tel:* 0161 224 8915. *Str insts, bows, w/wind, br, guis, sales and repairs, accs, mus.*

Manchester

Forsyth Brothers Ltd. 126 Deansgate, Manchester M3 2GR *tel:* 0161 834 3281 *fax:* 0161 834 0630 *email:* info@forsyths.co.uk. *Mus, books, orch insts, guis, perc, accs, keyboards, digital pnos, grand and upright pnos (new and second-hand), automated pnos, etc. Tuning, repair, hire. CDs, cassettes, videos, DVDs, talking books, m/order.*

Hampshire

Aldershot

George Potter & Co (Musical Instruments) Ltd. 26 Grosvenor Rd, Aldershot, Hants GU11 3DP *tel:* 01252 323226 *fax:* 01252 342921 *email:* pottersdrums@aol.com. *Books, insts, mus.*

Basingstoke

Modern Music (Basingstoke) Ltd. 3-4 Chelsea House, Festival Place, Basingstoke, Hants RG21 7JR *tel:* 01256 464663 *fax:* 01256 818113 *email:* modernmusicbas@hotmail.com. *Insts, mus, pnos, orgs, hi-tech.*

Fareham

Kimbers Keyboards and Musical Instruments. 179-179a West St, Fareham, Hants PO16 0EF *tel:* 01329 286535 *fax:* 01329 285826. *Keyboards, elec pnos, orgs, guis, amps, accs, mus.*

Portsmouth

Nevada Music. 189 London Rd, North End, Portsmouth PO2 9AE *tel:* 023 9266 0036 *fax:* 023 9269 0626 *email:* music@nevada.co.uk. *Guis, amps, keyboards. PA effects, repairs and hire.*

Ringwood

Chris Venables Pianos. 1 Monmouth Court, Ringwood, Hants BH24 1HE *tel:* 01425 476644 *fax:* 01425 476645 *email:* pianos@chrisvenables.co.uk. *Award winning top dealer. Yamaha grand pno centre and main dealer. Free nationwide delivery. Massive discounts on new and second-hand grands, uprights and digitals. Publishers of 'The Good Piano Guide'.*

Southampton

Beckett's Music Ltd. 56 Commercial Rd, Southampton SO15 1GD *tel:* 023 8022 4827 *fax:* 023 8032 2046 *email:* admin@beckettsmusic.co.uk. *W/wind, br, guis, keyboards, perc, repairs, mus, computer software, accs, educ insts, rental scheme, m/order.*

Fret Music Co Ltd. 11-13 Church St, Southampton SO15 5LG *tel:* 023 8077 4433 *fax:* 023 8070 4116 *email:* sales@fretmusic.co.uk. *Guis, drums, amps, accs, effects, 4-track recording, hire service, PA.*

Note-Ability Music Ltd. 5 Premier Parade, Forest Hills Drive, Townhill Park, Southampton, Hants SO18 2GA *tel:* 023 8055 8024 *fax:* 023 8058 5398 *email:* info@note-ability.com. *Printed mus m/order service available, w/wind, br, perc, keyboards, stringed inst specialist. Yamaha authorised dealers, repairs and restoration.*

Southsea

Courtney and Walker Ltd. 82-86 Elm Grove, Southsea, Hants PO5 1LN *tel:* 023 9282 2036 *fax:* 023 9278 0799 *email:* sales@courtneyandwalker. co.uk. *Br, w/wind, strs, pno, perc, sheet mus.*

Winchester

Martin Restall Violins. Stonemasons Court, Parchment St, Winchester, Hants *tel:* 01962 841514. *Vns, vas, vcs, accs, also repairs.*

Herefordshire

Hay-on-Wye

Hancock & Monks. 6 Broad St, Hay-on-Wye, Herefords HR3 5DB *tel:* 01497 821784 *fax:* 01591 610778 *email:* jerry@hancockandmonks.co.uk. *Classical CDs, DVDs, second-hand books on mus, sheet mus.*

Leominster

Syrinx Records. 12 Buttercross, Leominster, Herefords HR6 8BN *tel:* 01568 613477 *fax:* 01568 613477 *email:* alan@syrinxrecords.fsnet.co.uk. *Location recording, editing and production. Early mus speciality. CD sales and mkt.*

Trevor Davies Music. 87 Etnam St, Leominster, Herefords HR6 8AE *tel:* 01568 613611. *Insts, amps, mus, accs.*

Hertfordshire

Cockfosters

Make Music. 109 Cockfosters Rd, Cockfosters, Herts EN4 0DA *tel:* 020 8441 1050 *fax:* 020 8441 8254. *Digital pnos, keyboards, hi-tech, guis, drums, PA, software, br and w/wind, printed sheet mus and accs. Keyboard mus tuition.*

Harpenden

Musicale Ltd. Homecroft, Sun Lane, Harpenden, Herts AL5 4GJ *tel:* 01582 769712 *fax:* 01582 767343 *email:* info@musicale.co.uk. *Books, nationwide inst trial and purchase scheme, mus, accs, m/order, repairs. Commission for teachers and mus depts.*

Hitchin

Evans-Pughe Strings of Hitchin Ltd. 24 Bucklersbury, Hitchin, Herts SG5 1BG *tel:* 01462 426012 *fax:* 01462 426013 *email:* sales@strings.co.uk. *Specialists in str insts of the vn family. Vns, vas, vcs and dbs and their bows bought and sold. Range of insts and accs; repairs and restoration.*

Myatt (John) Woodwind and Brass. 57 Nightingale Rd, Hitchin, Herts SG5 1RQ *tel:* 01462 420057 *fax:* 01462 435464 *email:* shop@myatt.co.uk. *New and second-hand wind insts, accs, CDs, T-shirts, repairs. UK distributor of Fox bsns and JM tpts, fls and cases. M/order specialist.*

Richard Reason Pianos. 94 Tilehouse St, Hitchin, Herts SG5 2DW *tel:* 01462 454244 *email:* enquiries@richardreasonpianos.co.uk. *New and reconditioned pnos, restorations, second-hand mus.*

St Albans

Britannia Music Shop. 156 Hatfield Rd, St Albans, Herts AL1 4JD *tel:* 01727 846055 *fax:* 01727 838435 *email:* britanniamusicshop@btinternet.com. *W/wind, br, str insts, sheet mus, reeds, accs. Second-hand inst list available.*

St Albans Music Centre. 20 Holywell Hill, St Albans, Herts AL1 1DD *tel:* 01727 852717 *fax:* 01727 853045 *email:* stalbansmusic@hotmail.com. *Mus, insts, accs, books, sheet mus and m/order.*

Ware

3J Cantata. 60 High St, Puckeridge, Ware, Herts SG11 1RX *tel:* 01920 822435 *fax:* 01920 821479. *Choral mus and folders for choirs.*

Make Music Ltd. 31 Baldock St, Ware, Herts SG12 9DH *tel:* 01920 460646 *fax:* 01920 464601 *email:* ware@makemusic.co.uk. *Keyboards, orgs, digital pnos. Hi-tech, br, w/wind.*

Edmund Handy
Early Keyboard Instruments

New & secondhand instruments.
Tuning, repair and restoration of harpsichords,
clavichords, early pianos & celestes

5 Bourne Road, Bexley, Kent DA5 1LG, England
Tel / fax: +44 (0)1322 527366
email: edmund.handy@btinternet.com

19 Bitteswell Road,
Lutterworth,
Leics, LE17 4EL
Tel: 01455 552306
Fax: 01455 559448
E-mail: griff@accusound.com
Web: http://www.accusound.com

The latest microphone system for fiddles from Accusound incorporates an interchangeable system of capsules. This means that, for recording, an omni-directional capsule is used, but for performing live you can use a uni-directional capsule. Thus feedback and spill from other instruments can be avoided. The illustration is for a fiddle, but the same system can be adapted, with appropriate mounting systems, for any acoustic instrument.

The system is in use by Aidan O'Rourke of Blazin' Fiddles and by Caroline Lavelle, with the Chieftains.

Watford

Thwaites Fine Stringed Instruments. 33 Chalk Hill, Oxhey, Watford WD19 4BL *tel:* 01923 232412 *fax:* 01923 232463 *email:* sales@thwaites.com. *Str insts, repairs, restoration. Vns, vas, vcs, dbs; bows; strs, cases and other accs.*

Viscount Organs Ltd. 5 Caxton Way, Watford Business Park, Watford WD18 8UA *tel:* 01923 247437 *fax:* 01923 249345 *email:* sales@viscount-organs.co.uk. *Classical (digital) church and theatre orgs.*

Isle of Man
Douglas

Peter Norris Music. Villa Marina Arcade, Douglas, Isle of Man IM1 2HN *tel:* 01624 661794 *fax:* 01624 622540 *email:* info@peternorrismusic.co.im. *Insts, mus, amplification.*

Isle of Wight
Newport

W Teague & Co Ltd. 34 Orchard St, Newport, Isle Of Wight PO30 1AU *tel:* 01983 523460 *fax:* 01983 525171 *email:* music@teagues.sagehost.co.uk. *Mus, pnos (electric and acoustic), keyboards, br, w/wind, str insts, perc, accs.*

Kent
Bexley

Bexley Harpsichord Workshops Ltd. 5 Bourne Rd, Bexley, Kent DA5 1LG *tel:* 01322 557147 *fax:* 01322 527366 *email:* andrew.wooderson@btinternet.com. *Hpds, spinets, virginals, clvds. New insts built to order and fully-overhauled second-hand insts for sale. Also tuning, maintenance, repairs and restoration; hpd hire for concerts, recordings, tours and festivals. Comprehensive range of spares and accs available by m/order. Specialist advice. Courses in tuning and maintenance.*

Handy, Edmund. Early Keyboard Instruments, 5 Bourne Rd, Bexley, Kent DA5 1LG *tel:* 01322 527366 *fax:* 01322 527366 *email:* edmund.handy@btinternet.com. *Hpds, clvds, spinets and virginals individually handbuilt to order. New and fully-overhauled second-hand hpds, clvds and other early keyboard insts. Hpd spares and accs. Also tuning, maintenance repairs and restoration; hpd hire for concerts and recordings.*

Andrew Wooderson Early Keyboard Instruments. 5 Bourne Rd, Bexley, Kent DA5 1LG *tel:* 01322 558326 *fax:* 01322 525558 *email:* andrew.wooderson@btinternet.com. *Hpds, spinets and virginals individually handbuilt to order. New and fully-overhauled second-hand hpds, clvds and other early keyboard insts. Hpd spares and accs. Also tuning, maintenance repairs and restoration; hpd hire for concerts and recordings.*

Bromley

Unisound. 171 Widmore Rd, Bromley, Kent BR1 3AX *tel:* 020 8313 1161. *Guis, drums, amps, br, w/wind, mus.*

Canterbury

Crowthers of Canterbury. 10 Longport, Canterbury, Kent CT1 1PE *tel:* 01227 763965 *fax:* 01227 788865 (plus m/order hotline) *email:* ian@crowthersofcanterbury.co.uk. *W/wind, str and br specialists. Lorée obs, mus, repairs.*

Maidstone

Sharon Music. 65 High St, Maidstone, Kent ME14 1SR *tel:* 01622 761649 *fax:* 01622 685935 *email:* info@sharonmusic.co.uk. *Insts, w/wind, br, guis, educ supplies, accs, mus, pnos, keyboards.*

Rochester

Discurio Ltd. 46 High St, Rochester, Kent ME1 1LD *tel:* 01634 845222 *fax:* 01634 845222 *email:* Discurio1@aol.com. *Books, records, videos, CDs and LPs; military mus.*

Sevenoaks

Bösendorfer.UK, Main Distributor. Hurstwood Farm, The Hurst, Crouch, Borough Green, Sevenoaks, Kent TN15 8TA *tel:* 01732 885050 *fax:* 01732 883030 *email:* pianos@boesendorfer.uk.com; info@bosendorferpianos.co.uk. *The company is located at the Concert Hall and Piano venue of Hurstwood Farm where there is a display of over 20 new Bösendorfer pnos including the new generation of SE reproducing pnos. A comprehensive national service is available at Bosendorfer.UK including recording studio, concert hall, spares stock, repairs, servicing, artist support and hire insts.*

Tonbridge

Beat 'N' Track Music Co. 7 Quarry Hill Parade, Tonbridge, Kent TN9 2HR *tel:* 01732 366455. *Group insts, keyboards, drums, br, w/wind, PA systems, amps, mus.*

Tunbridge Wells

Brittens Music. Grove Hill Rd, Tunbridge Wells, Kent TN1 1RZ *tel:* 01892 526659 *fax:* 01892 540611 *email:* sales@brittensmusic.co.uk. *Pnos (acoustic and electric), keyboards, insts, restoration and repair, accs, mus, books, CDs, videos, m/order.*

Classic Violins. 1 Northfields, Speldhurst, Tunbridge Wells, Kent TN3 0PL *tel:* 01892 870319 *fax:* 01892 870966 *email:* stringinvest@supanet.com. *Vns, vas, vcs, dbs, bows (baroque, classical and modern). Also restorers, valuers.*

Westerham

Culver Music. 17 High St, Brasted, Westerham, Kent TN16 1JA *tel:* 01959 561109 *fax:* 0870 125 4441 *email:* culvermusic@which.net. *M/order mus service specialising in choral and org mus.*

Lancashire
Accrington

Music Box. 16 Whalley Rd, Accrington, Lancs BB5 1AA *tel:* 01254 383571 *email:* Beegee444@aol.com. *Insts, mus, repairs, amps.*

Ashton-under-Lyne

The Music Corner. Unit 40 & 49 Ashton Market Hall, Bow St, Ashton-under-Lyne, Lancs OL6 6BZ *tel:* 0161 830 0880; 0800 328 5294 (order line) *fax:* 0161 830 0880 *email:* sales@musiccorner.co.uk. *Suppliers of insts, inst accs, sheet mus, award systems, rosettes, etc. Also free worldwide mus teacher listings, ens listings, practice challenge, pupils pages, musicians forum and teacher resources online. Secure on-line store.*

Blackburn

Time and Tune (Blackburn). Eldon Place, 53 Preston New Rd, Blackburn, Lancs BB2 6AY *tel:* 01254 697460 *fax:* 01254 696570 *email:* sales@timeand_tune_music.co.uk. *Mus, pnos, keyboards, str, w/wind, br insts, repairs, tuning, rentals.*

Blackpool

Tower Music. 46-48 Topping St, Blackpool, Lancs FY1 3AQ *tel:* 01253 627359 *fax:* 01253 627359. *Electric and acoustic guis, amps, PA, keyboards, mus, educ, br, w/wind, drums.*

Bolton

Booth's Music. 17 Churchgate, Bolton, Lancs BL1 1HU *tel:* 01204 522908 *fax:* 01204 380008 *email:* info@boothsmusic.co.uk. *Insts, mus, repairs, hire.*

Harker & Howarth (Music) Ltd. Folds Rd, Bolton, Lancs BL1 1UN *tel:* 01204 526623 *fax:* 01204 364220. *Pnos, keyboards, insts, mus. Mus school.*

Bury

Read Franklin and Heywood Ltd. 11 Broad St, Bury, Lancs BL9 0DA *tel:* 0161 764 4624 *fax:* 0161 764 9424 *email:* info@musicshopuk.co.uk. *Keyboards, guis, insts, mus, tuition, elec pnos.*

Oldham

Keys Musical Instruments Ltd. 71 Henshaw St, Oldham, Lancs OL1 2AA *tel:* 0161 627 0614 *fax:* 0161 620 0614 *email:* peter@keysmusic.co.uk. *Keyboards, hi-tech, pnos, orgs, guis, PA, br, w/wind.*

Preston

A & C Hamilton. 946-950 Blackpool Rd, Preston, Lancs PR2 1XN *tel:* 01772 722468 *email:* sales@achamilton.co.uk. *Keyboards, pnos, digital pnos, orgs, guis, amplification, mus, accs.*

Music Cellar, Preston. 12 Fox St, Preston, Lancs PR1 2AB *tel:* 01772 251407 *fax:* 01772 251412. *Orch insts, pnos, clavinovas, keyboards, mus, perc, guis, repairs.*

Leicestershire
Leicester

Batchelar, Timothy. 28 Colbert Drive, Leicester LE3 2JB *tel:* 0116 286 2511/289 9798; 07710 204303 *fax:* 0116 286 2511/289 9798 *email:* tim@batchelar.com. *Dealer, restorer and maker of stringed insts of the vn family. Accredited Fellow of the Institute of Musical Instrument Technology.*

City Music. 66 London Rd, Leicester LE2 0QD *tel:* 0116 254 4441 *fax:* 0116 254 4441. *Printed mus specialists; m/order.*

Sheehan's Music Services. 50-52 London Rd, Leicester LE2 0QD *tel:* 0116 255 7492 *fax:* 0116 285 5932 *email:* music@sheehans.com. *Acoustic mus insts. Electric guis and amplifiers.*

Templar Pianos. 5 Woodgate Rothley, Leicester LE7 7LL *tel:* 0116 230 2638 *fax:* 0116 230 2638. *New pnos: Steinway, Bechstein, Collard & Collard, Yamaha, Kemble, Reid-Sohn, Boston, Seiler; free delivery and stool. Also second-hand pnos and mus giftware.*

Lutterworth

Accusound. 19 Bitteswell Rd, Lutterworth, Leics LE17 4EL *tel:* 01455 552306 *fax:* 01455 559448 *email:* griff@accusound.com. *Microphone systems for acoustic insts.*

Melton Mowbray

Mel-Tone The Music Centre. 58 King St, Melton Mowbray, Leics LE13 1XB *tel:* 01664 568000 *fax:* 01664 480722 *email:* tony@mel-tone.co.uk. *Insts, mus, guis, amps, drums, br, w/wind, strs, digital pnos, keyboards, mus books, tuition, repairs.*

Lincolnshire
Boston
Harmony Music. 17-17a West St, Boston, Lincs PE21 8QE *tel:* 01205 355366 *fax:* 01205 354433 *email:* sales@harmony-music.co.uk. *Br and w/wind specialists, orgs, pnos, keyboards, perc, sheet mus, repairs.*
Lincoln
Counterpoint Music Shop. 38 Grantham St, Lincoln LN2 1LW *tel:* 01522 560065 *email:* eileen@counterpointmusic.co.uk. *Sheet mus, books, CDs, educ specialist, m/order.*
Spalding
Portass & Carter Music Shop. 26 Bridge Rd, Sutton Bridge, Spalding, Lincs PE12 9UA *tel:* 01406 350266/407 *fax:* 01406 350266/407. *New, second-hand insts. (Est 40 yrs.)*
Stamford
Stamford Music Shop. 11 St Mary's Hill, Stamford, Lincs PE9 2DP *tel:* 01780 751275 *fax:* 01780 752245 *email:* stamfordmusicshop@hotmail.com. *Mus, insts, CDs, second-hand insts and pnos.*
Stringed Instruments. The Cedars, New Rd, Ryhall, Stamford, Lincs PE9 4HL *tel:* 01780 756806 *email:* info@rutlandstrings.com. dir. *Antique French, Italian, German and English vns, vas, vcs, dbs and bows. Bought, sold and exchanged. Free valuations.*

Merseyside
Liverpool
JAM Percussion Ltd. Queens Dock Business Centre, Jordan St, Liverpool L1 0BG *tel:* 0151 709 9709 *fax:* 0151 709 7092 *email:* mail@jampercussion.com. *Retailing specialists of classical perc insts. Large stock of timpani, xylophones, marimbas, sticks, mallets, cymbals, educ perc insts. M/order welcome.*
Music Notes. 6 South John St, Liverpool L1 8BJ *tel:* 0151 707 9123 *email:* musicnotes@btopenworld.com. *Specialise in printed mus. Mus gifts, accs and insts also stocked.*
Richard Behrend. 8 Greenbank Rd, off Smithdown Rd, Liverpool L18 1HN *tel:* 0151 733 2213. *Mus, br and w/wind insts, accs, repairs.*

Middlesex
Harrow
Harrow Music Centre. 52 Greenhill Way, Harrow HA1 1LE *tel:* 020 8427 2250 *fax:* 020 8863 1167. *Insts, mus, amps, PA.*
Herga Music. 2a-4 High St, Wealdstone, Harrow HA3 7AA *tel:* 020 8861 1590 *fax:* 020 8861 5501 *email:* retail@hergamusic.co.uk. *Sheet mus, br, w/wind, str insts, guis, pnos, keyboards, educ products, mus books, gifts, hire, m/order.*
Shaftesbury Music. 2 Shaftesbury Ave, Kenton, Harrow, Middx HA3 0QX *tel:* 020 8907 1376 *fax:* 020 8933 6282. *Sheet mus (m/order).*
Twickenham
Albert's Music Shop Ltd. 138-140 Heath Rd, Twickenham, Middx TW1 4BN *tel:* 020 8892 7634 *fax:* 020 8891 1781 *email:* albertsmusic@btconnect.com. *Insts, mus, keyboards.*

Norfolk
Great Yarmouth
Soundgear Music. 11 Southdown Rd, Great Yarmouth, Norfolk NR31 0HU *tel:* 01493 603746 *fax:* 01493 603746. *Guis, drums, amplification, br, w/wind, etc.*
Norwich
Aldens Pianos. 107 Gloucester St, Norwich NR2 2DY *tel:* 01603 625331 *fax:* 01603 610865. *Pnos (new, re-conditioned, second-hand and as traded in), Korg electric pnos, pno stools, accs. Tuning, polishing, repairs, hire.*
Elkin Music. 31 Exchange St, Norwich NR2 1DP *tel:* 01603 666332 *fax:* 01603 666332 *email:* sales@elkinmusic.co.uk. *Books, mus, mus gifts.*
Gibson Music. 5 St John Maddermarket, Norwich, Norfolk NR2 1DN *tel:* 01603 663262 *fax:* 01603 663262 *email:* sales@gibsonmusic.co.uk. *Orch insts, guis, sheet mus, accs, repairs, rentals.*
Klef Music Ltd. 118 Magdalen St, Norwich, Norfolk *tel:* 01603 612396. *New and second-hand guis, amps, repairs, accs.*
St George's Music Shop. 17-19 St George's St, Norwich NR3 1AB *tel:* 01603 626414 *fax:* 01603 618811 *email:* sales@stgeorgesmusic.co.uk. *Comprehensive selection of classical sheet mus, books, accs and insts, supplying many schools and colleges. Also m/order.*
William Elkin Music Services. Station Rd Industrial Estate, Salhouse, Norwich, Norfolk NR13 6NS *tel:* 01603 721302 *fax:* 01603 721801 *email:* sales@elkinmusic.demon.co.uk. *Books, mus, mus gifts, m/order.*

North Lincolnshire
Scunthorpe
Pauls Music Shop. 15 Laneham St, Scunthorpe, N Lincs DN15 6LJ *tel:* 01724 867650 *fax:* 01724 289359. *Sheet mus, books; guis, keyboards, amps, w/wind, br, str, perc insts; strs and accs; video, CD-ROMS.*

North Somerset
Clevedon
Clevedon Music Shop. 19 Alexandra Rd, Clevedon BS21 7QH *tel:* 01275 791181/342090 *fax:* 01275 791181/342090 *email:* sales@thatmusicshop.com. *Insts, pnos, mus, books, accs, repairs, CDs, sheet mus. Recording equipment, PAs. PC mus software.*

North Yorkshire
Ampleforth
June Emerson Wind Music. Windmill Farm, Ampleforth, York Y062 4HF *tel:* 01439 788324 *fax:* 01439 788715 *email:* juneemerson@compuserve.com. *Mus for wind insts.*
Harrogate
Arcadia Music. 27 Cheltenham Cres, Harrogate, N Yorks HG1 1DH *tel:* 01423 565110 *fax:* 01423 546840 *email:* arcadia@normus.com. *Insts, mus, accs, gifts, mus software, repairs.*
Knock on Wood. Unit 12, Glasshouses Mill, Harrogate, N Yorks HG3 5QH *tel:* 01423 712712 *fax:* 01423 712712 *email:* info@knockonwood.co.uk. *M/order multicultural supplies of insts, recordings, books and teaching resources.*
Skipton
Time and Tune (Skipton) Ltd. 14-16 Victoria St, Skipton, N Yorks BD23 1JE *tel:* 01756 798515. *Mus, pnos, str, w/wind, br insts, guis, harmonicas, keyboards (electronic), repairs, tuning, rentals.*
Tadcaster
Lovely Music. 17 Westgate, Tadcaster, N Yorks LS24 9JB *tel:* 01937 832946 *fax:* 01937 835696 *email:* lovelymusic@supanet.com. *Mus, educ mus and books, choral, orch, wind band.*

Northants
Brackley
Heritage Music. The Old Chapel, Banbury Rd, Brackley, Northants NN13 6BA *tel:* 01280 703111; 0800 169 6430. *Br, w/wind, str and pno. Sales, rental, on-site repair, sheet mus, m/order. Educ specialist.*
Peterborough
Oundle Music. 13 West St, Oundle, Peterborough PE8 4EJ *tel:* 01832 273669 *fax:* 01832 273669. *Mus, insts (rcdrs to guis), accs, repairs, m/order.*
Wellingborough
Keyboard Kavern. High St, Wellingborough, Northants NN8 4HT *tel:* 01933 227837 *fax:* 01933 227240 *email:* geoffkey@aol.com. *Keyboards, pnos, br, w/wind, perc, second-hand insts. M/order and online ordering service.*

Northumberland
Bedlington
Dennis Todd Music. 86 Front St, Bedlington, Northumberland NE22 5AE *tel:* 01670 822085 *fax:* 01670 820592 *email:* dtoddmusic@aol.com. *Br, w/wind, perc, elec keyboards, digital pnos, guis, sheet mus, educ insts and mus, rental plan, repairs, amplifiers, all accs.*
Corbridge
John Ross (Pianos). St Helen's St, Corbridge, Northumberland NE45 5BE *tel:* 01434 632968 *fax:* 01434 632245 *email:* johnross.pianos@ukonline.co.uk. *Insts, pnos, mus, accs.*

Nottinghamshire
Mansfield
Music Scene. 9a Albert St, Mansfield, Notts NG18 1EA *tel:* 01623 631174 *fax:* 01623 654544. *Keyboards, orgs, pnos, digital pnos, br, w/wind, guis, amps, mus, accs; tuition.*
Newark
The Music Shop. 20-22 Barnby Gate, Newark, Notts NG24 1PZ *tel:* 01636 610588 *fax:* 01636 610588 *email:* enquireys@themusicshopuk.com. *New and second-hand insts, accs, mus, repairs.*
Trent Music Centre. 1a Pelham St, Newark, Notts NG24 4XD *tel:* 01636 677626. *Guis, amps, keyboards, books, other insts, repairs, jazz guis, tuition, goods sold on behalf of clients.*
Nottingham
Farnsworth Musical Supplies Ltd. 126 Nottingham Rd, Sherwood Rise, Nottingham NG7 7AH *tel:* 0115 960 8955 *email:* sales@farnsworth-musical.co.uk. *Insts, mus, accs.*
Guitarnotes. Spanish Guitar Centre, 44 Nottingham Rd, New Basford, Nottingham NG7 7AE *tel:* 0115 962 2709 *fax:* 0115 962 5368

email: sales@spanishguitar.com; sales@guitarsales.co.uk. *Guis, gui mus, accs, m/order.*

Turner Violins Ltd. 1-5 Lily Grove, Beeston, Nottingham *tel:* 0115 943 0333 *fax:* 0115 943 0444 *email:* info@turnerviolins.co.uk. *Vns, db, vas, vcs, repairs, accs, valuations, rentals, export, commission.*

Windblowers. 75-77 Derby Rd, Nottingham NG1 5BA *tel:* 0115 941 0543 *fax:* 0115 947 4433 *email:* windblowers@btconnect.com. *Br and w/wind insts and accs; all types of sheet mus.*

Worksop

Berry's Music. 23 Bridge Place, Worksop, Notts S80 1DT *tel:* 01909 473532 *fax:* 01909 530609. *Mus, insts, accs.*

Oxfordshire
Oxford

Allegro Oxford Ltd. 404 Marston Rd, Marston, Oxford OX3 0JE *tel:* 01865 798165 *fax:* 01865 407662 *email:* enquiries@saxophoneheaven.com. *Sax specialists.*

Blackwell's Music Shop. 23-25 Broad St, Oxford OX1 3AX *tel:* 01865 333580 *fax:* 01865 728020 *email:* music@blackwell.co.uk. *New mus, new and second-hand books, CDs, gifts and accs; also m/order.*

Lighting and Sound Equipment. 118 Cowley Rd, Oxford OX4 1JE *tel:* 01865 722027 *fax:* 01865 202454. *PA, lighting, hire and sales.*

Oxford University Press Bookshop. 116-117 High St, Oxford OX1 4BZ *tel:* 01865 242913 *fax:* 01865 241701 *email:* bookshop.uk@oup.com. *Books, sheet mus.*

Witney

Shackell Pianos. 41 Kinsfield Cres, Witney, Oxon OX28 2JB *tel:* 01993 703375 *email:* info@shackellpianos.co.uk. *Yamaha and Steinway; sales, hire and repairs.*

Shropshire
Oswestry

Barnes & Mullins (Mfg) Ltd (inc Hidersine Co Ltd). Grays Inn House, Unit 14, Mile Oak Industrial Estate, Oswestry, Shropshire SY10 8GA *tel:* 01691 653970 *fax:* 01691 679403 *email:* mail@barnhide.co.uk. *Rosin and strs.*

Shifnal

Shifnal Music. Unit 3, 26 Bradford St, Shifnal, Shropshire TF11 8AU *tel:* 01952 463495 *fax:* 01952 463495 *email:* jimbomusic@lineone.net. *Guis, amps, effects, accs. Repairs a speciality.*

Shrewsbury

Salop Music Centre. St Michaels St, Shrewsbury, Shropshire SY1 2DE *tel:* 01743 365561/4111 *fax:* 01743 245127 *email:* sales@salopmusic.co.uk. *Keyboards, synths, guis, hi-tech, PA, DJ and nightclub dept; repairs, sheet mus, br, w/wind, orch str, educ perc. Schools discount.*

Windband. 9 Greyfriars Rd, Longden Coleham, Shrewsbury, Shropshire SY3 7EN *tel:* 01743 367482 *fax:* 01743 340412 *email:* Windinstruments@ aol.com. *W/wind and br specialist, mus and accs, inst hire schemes, repairs.*

Somerset
Frome

Peter Barnes. 46 Church Lane, Rode, Frome BA11 6PN *tel:* 01373 831498 *email:* Barnesbarndance@ukonline.co.uk. *W/shop drawings and information for builders of early keyboard insts, clvd kits (portable 18th C design), hpd and spinet kits. Covered strs for clvds and square pnos. Repairs and renovations. New insts made to order.*

Sounds of Frome. 5 Bath St, Frome, Somerset BA11 1DH *tel:* 01373 462083 *fax:* 01373 453164. *Pnos, keyboards, guis, amps, multi-track recorders, sheet mus.*

Milbourne Port

EOS Music Service (EMS). English Organ School, Chapel Lane, Milborne Port, Sherborne, Somerset DT9 5DL *tel:* 01963 250022 *fax:* 01963 250022 *email:* ems@davidhunt.demon.co.uk. *Org mus (m/order).*

Taunton

Gillian Greig Music. 44 Kingston Rd, Taunton, Somerset TA2 7SG *tel:* 01823 333317 *fax:* 01823 338454 *email:* gillian@ggmusic.co.uk. *Books, mus, cassettes, CDs. Mus gifts, str insts and accs, wind accs. Mus stands, cases, perc insts, rcdrs, metronomes, bodhrans, ocarinas.*

John Packer Ltd. 141 Staplegrove Rd, Taunton, Somerset TA2 6AF *tel:* 01823 282386 *fax:* 01823 337653 *email:* sales@johnpacker.co.uk. *Specialist supplier and repairer of wind and br insts. Educ contractor.*

Westside Music Centre. 24-26 Bridge St, Taunton, Somerset TA1 1UB *tel:* 01823 283307 *fax:* 01823 279353. *Elec orgs, keyboards, guis, amps, drums, hi-tech, elec pnos.*

South Yorkshire
Doncaster

E Smedley & Sons. 19 Printing Office St, Doncaster, S Yorks DN1 1TS

tel: 01302 323248 *fax:* 01302 323248. *Mus, portable keyboards, guis, accs.*

Sheffield

The Music Box. 30/31 The Lanes (by the Oasis), Meadowhall, Sheffield S9 1EP *tel:* 0114 256 9089 *email:* ask@themusicbox.co.uk. *Insts, mus, accs, gifts, etc.*

Staffordshire
Burton on-Trent

Normans Ltd. Third Ave, Centrum 100, Burton on-Trent, Staffs DE14 2WD *tel:* 0800 028 1415 *fax:* 01283 535340 *email:* sales@normans .co.uk. *Br, w/wind, strs, perc, keyboards, pnos. LEA contract specialist.*

Burton-on-Trent

Eric Reynolds Ltd. 88 High St, Burton-on-Trent, Staffs DE14 1LJ *tel:* 01283 565869/086 *fax:* 01283 534922 *email:* ereynolds@used-pianos.co.uk. *Specialises in restoration of upright and grand pnos, especially polyester cabinet work. Also fully-reconditioned Japanese pnos (Yamaha, Kawai, etc) for sale.*

Lichfield

S & J Music. 13 Dam St, Lichfield, Staffs WS13 6AE *tel:* 01543 268909 *fax:* 01543 417736. *Insts, mus, accs.*

Stoke-on-Trent

N J Tostevin & Son. 491 Hartshill Rd, Hartshill, Stoke-on-Trent, Staffs ST4 6AA *tel:* 01782 617081 *fax:* 01782 617081. *Pnos.*

Suffolk
Bury St Edmunds

Balaam's Music. 103 Risbygate St, Bury St Edmunds, Suffolk IP33 3AA *tel:* 01284 766933 *fax:* 01284 701605 *email:* info@balaamsmusic.co.uk. *Mus, insts, books, repairs, insurance.*

Music In Print (Head Office). Newmarket Rd, Bury St Edmunds, Suffolk IP33 3YB *tel:* 01284 767019 *fax:* 01284 723235. *Printed mus, insts and mus accs franchisers.*

Ipswich

Haven Keyboards. 486 Felixstowe Rd, Ipswich, Suffolk IP3 8SU *tel:* 01473 710051. *Keyboards, digital pnos, orgs, sheet mus. Hammond specialists.*

Jack White Music. 92 Fore Hamlet, Ipswich IP3 8AF *tel:* 01473 257223 *fax:* 01473 254070 *email:* music@jackwhite.co.uk. *Orgs, keyboards, pnos, synths, MIDI, modules, guis, accs, tuition.*

Music World. 16 Queen St, Ipswich *tel:* 01473 253666 *fax:* 01473 213091. *Insts, sheet mus.*

Lowestoft

Morlings Ltd. 149-151 London Rd North, Lowestoft, Suffolk NR32 1NG *tel:* 01502 565491/2 *fax:* 01502 530223 *email:* morlings.music@ btclick.com. *Insts, mus, keyboards, guis, amps, drums, karaoke.*

Surrey
Cobham

Sheargold Pianos Ltd. 162 Anyards Rd, Cobham, Surrey KT11 2LH *tel:* 01932 866577 *fax:* 01932 868178 *email:* sales@sheargold.com. *Uprights, grands (new and reconditioned); digital pnos, pno rental, removals, sheet mus, tuning, repairs. Also at 53 King St, Maidenhead, Berks SL6 1DU; tel: 01628 771400.*

Croydon

H Lane & Son Pianos. 326 Brighton Rd, S Croydon, Surrey CR2 6AJ *tel:* 020 8688 3513 *fax:* 020 8688 4804 *email:* abrizga@lanespianos.com. *New and reconditioned upright and grand pnos.*

Jonathan Myall Music/Just Flutes. 46 South End, Croydon, Surrey CR0 1DP *tel:* 020 8662 8424 *fax:* 020 8662 8404. *Mus, books, insts, recordings, cassettes, accs, m/order, repairs.*

Willson & Newman. High Bank, Hook Hill, Sanderstead, Croydon, Surrey CR2 0LA *tel:* 020 8657 5817. *Pno tuning and repairs.*

Dorking

Royal School of Church Music. Cleveland Lodge, Westhumble, Dorking RH5 6BW *tel:* 01306 872811 *fax:* 01306 887240 *email:* musicdirect@ rscm.com. *Org and choral mus.*

Esher

ABC Music Ltd. 85 High St, Esher, Surrey KT10 9QA *tel:* 01372 466195 *fax:* 01372 470445 *email:* info@abcmusic.co.uk. *Insts, mus, CDs, pnos, rentals. Branches at: 433-437 Great West Rd, Hounslow, Middx tel: 020 8570 4444, Station Approach, Kew Gardens, W London tel: 020 8940 1892 and 20 Ridgeway, Wimbledon Village, London SW19 tel: 020 8739 0202.*

Farnham

Lloyd & Keyworth Music. 6-7 Downing St, Farnham, Surrey GU9 7PE *tel:* 01252 710666 *fax:* 01252 711159 *email:* linda@landk.demon.co.uk. *New and reconditioned grand and upright pnos; w/wind, br, strs, printed mus; m/order service.*

Godalming

T Andrews & Co (Farncombe) Ltd. 62 Meadrow, Godalming, Surrey GU7 3HT *tel:* 01483 422459. *Pnos, pno stools.*

Godstone

Pilgrim Harps. Stansted House, Tilburstow Hill Rd, S Godstone, Surrey RH9 8NA *tel:* 01342 893242 *fax:* 01342 892646 *email:* info@pilgrimharps.co.uk. *Pedal and lever hps: new, second-hand and restoration. Hire, inst insurance, strs, mus, servicing and accs.*

Guildford

Albert's Music Shop Ltd. 9 Market St, Guildford, Surrey GU1 4LB *tel:* 01483 440188 *fax:* 01483 440823 *email:* albertsguildford@btconnect.com. *Mus insts, accs, sheet mus.*

Andertons Music Co. 58-59 Woodbridge Rd, Guildford, Surrey GU1 4RF *tel:* 01483 456777 (sales)/456888 (educ) *fax:* 01483 456722 *email:* info@andertons.co.uk. *Guis, keyboards, perc, computers, recording and educ equipment, PA, repairs, amps, accs.*

Haslemere

Chamberlain Music. Weyhill, Haslemere, Surrey GU27 1HN *tel:* 01428 658806 *fax:* 01428 658807 *email:* info@chamberlainmusic.com. *Educ m/order supplies, sheet mus specialists, UK distributors for Collegium and Hinshaw publications.*

Dolmetsch Musical Instruments. Unicorn Trading Estate, Weydown Rd, Haslemere, Surrey GU27 1DN *tel:* 01428 643235 *fax:* 08700 560190 *email:* brian@dolmetsch.com. *Rcdrs in wood and plastic, early keyboard insts, accs, viols, sheet mus, books.*

Merstham

David and Emma Newton Violins. 16 High St, Merstham, Surrey RH1 3EA *tel:* 01737 645065 *fax:* 01737 645808 *email:* enquiries@rainbowviolins.com. *Str insts, bows; sales, vns, electric vns and accs.*

Reigate

Stentor Music Co Ltd. Albert Rd North, Reigate, Surrey RH2 9EZ *tel:* 01737 240226 *fax:* 01737 242748 *email:* stentor@stentor-music.com. *Wholesale specialist str inst supplier; also br, w/wind and guis.*

Touchstone Tonewoods Ltd. 44 Albert Rd North, Reigate, Surrey RH2 9EZ *tel:* 01737 221064 *fax:* 01737 242748 *email:* info@touchstonetonewoods.co.uk. *Supplier to makers and repairers.*

Richmond

ABC Music Ltd. 9 Royal Parade, Station Approach, Richmond, Surrey TW9 3QD *tel:* 020 8940 1892 *fax:* 020 8948 2666 *email:* ben@abcmusic.fsbusiness.co.uk. *Insts, pnos, sheet mus, gifts, CDs, accs, software.*

Chandler Guitars. 300-302 Sandycombe Rd, Kew, Richmond, Surrey TW9 3NG *tel:* 020 8940 5874 *fax:* 020 8948 8203 *email:* sales@chandlerguitars.co.uk. *Elec and acoustic guis, amps and accs.*

Surbiton

Piano Warehouse. 111-113 Ewell Rd, Surbiton, Surrey KT6 6AL *tel:* 0800 018 4110 *fax:* 020 8390 1688 *email:* sales@piano-warehouse.co.uk. *Specialists in retailing upright and grand pnos, both new and second-hand. Dealers for Yamaha, Kemble, Young Chang, Weber and Steinmayer. Also extensive range of digital pnos by Yamaha and Technics.*

Sutton

Music Education Supplies. 101 Banstead Rd South, Sutton, Surrey SM2 5LH *tel:* 020 8770 3866 *fax:* 020 8770 3554 *email:* music.mes@btconnect.com. *Agents of Sonor school perc and suppliers of Suzuki handchimes and perc, Nordoff-Robbins reed hns, Aulos rcdrs, books, insts, etc.*

West Byfleet

Britten's Music Ltd. 3-4 Station Approach, W Byfleet, Surrey KT14 6NG *tel:* 01932 351165; 0800 0521 900 *fax:* 01932 350606 *email:* sales@brittensmusic.co.uk. *Sheet mus, insts, accs, digital pnos, keyboards, software, m/order, mus tuition (Yamaha mus school).*

Woking

The Drums & Percussion Centre. Studio 9, The Mayford Centre, Mayford Green, Woking, Surrey GU22 0PP *tel:* 01483 721100 *fax:* 01483 721100 *email:* philcorse@drumscentre.freeserve.co.uk. *Acoustic drums and perc, repairs and refurbishment, tuition.*

Surrey Music Store. 5 Central Buildings, Chobham Rd, Woking, Surrey GU21 6JH *tel:* 01483 776317 *fax:* 01483 763699 *email:* sales@surreymusic.co.uk. *Insts to rent or buy, accs, sheet mus, mus books including ABRSM exam mus and specialist vocal/choral mus books, classic CDs, m/order.*

Tyne And Wear
Gateshead
Williams the Music People. 16 Garden Walk, Metro Centre (Yellow Quadrant), Gateshead, Tyne And Wear *tel:* 0191 493 2244 *fax:* 0191 460 2422 *email:* enquiries@williams-music.co.uk. *Mus, insts, keyboards, pnos, orgs, sheet mus, guis, amps and electric.*

Newcastle upon Tyne
Newcastle Music. 71 Westgate Rd, Newcastle upon Tyne NE1 1SG *tel:* 0191 221 0595 *fax:* 01661 820755 *email:* sales@newcastlemusic.co.uk. *W/wind, br, strs, folk insts. Repairs and rental scheme.*

Warwickshire
Leamington Spa
Derek Roberts Violins. 185 Leam Terrace, Leamington Spa, Warks CV31 1DW *tel:* 01926 428313 *fax:* 01926 428313 *email:* mail@derekroberts.co.uk. *Orch strs, cases, bows, accs; also maker and restorer.*

Presto Classical. 11 Park St, Leamington Spa, Warks CV32 4QN *tel:* 01926 317025 *fax:* 01926 337032 *email:* info@prestoclassical.co.uk. *Sheet mus, insts, accs, classical CD specialist, plus DVDs, m/order, secure website.*

R B Mew. 1 Park St, Leamington Spa, Warks CV32 4QN *tel:* 01926 424949 *fax:* 01926 422311. *Pnos, keyboards, insts and accs, mus, tuning and repairs.*

Nuneaton
Abbey Music Studios. 114 Abbey St, Nuneaton, Warks CV11 5BX *tel:* 024 7664 1915 *fax:* 024 7664 1915 *email:* sales@abbeymusic.co.uk. *Orgs, pnos, keyboards, mus, insts, tuition.*

Leisure Music (Head Office). 32 Queens Rd, Nuneaton, Warks CV11 5JU *tel:* 024 7634 8702 *fax:* 024 7638 4602 *email:* office@leisuremusic.co.uk. *Pnos, keyboards, guis, w/wind, br; educ insts; m/order.*

Rugby
Freeman & Neale's Music Shop. 40-42 Lawford Rd, Rugby, Warks CV21 2DY *tel:* 01788 577064 *fax:* 01788 541612 *email:* sales@freemanandneale.co.uk. *Insts, mus.*

West Midlands
Birmingham
Allegro Music. 82 Suffolk St, Queensway, Birmingham B1 1TA *tel:* 0121 643 7553 *fax:* 0121 633 4773 *email:* sales@allegro.co.uk. *Books, mus, m/order.*

James Pass Music. 71 Smallbrook Queensway, Birmingham B5 4HX *tel:* 0121 643 7623 *fax:* 0121 643 7623 *email:* info@euromusicweb.com. *Books, insts, mus, educ videos, sheet mus, m/order.*

Midland Music. 1070 Stratford Rd, Hall Green, Birmingham B28 8AD *tel:* 0121 777 3188 *fax:* 0121 702 2683 *email:* music@midlandmusic.co.uk. *Mus, books, br, w/wind, str insts, guis, accs, novelties, educ mus; m/order; tuition centre.*

Unison Strings Ltd. 113 The Custard Factory, Gibb St, Birmingham B9 4AA *tel:* 0121 693 1214 *fax:* 0121 693 0933 *email:* info@unisonstrings.co.uk. *Vns, vas, vcs and dbs. Also bows, cases and accs. Vn makers and restorers. Valuations, appraisals and bow rehairing.*

Violectra. Unison Strings Ltd, 113 The Custard Factory, Gibb St, Birmingham B9 4AA *tel:* 0121 693 0933 *fax:* 0121 693 0933 *email:* info@violectra.co.uk. *Makers of electric vns, vas, vcs, dbs. Also bows, cases and accs. Acoustic vn sales, makers and restorers. Valuations, appraisals and bow rehairing.*

Turner Violins Ltd. 1 Gibb St, The Custard Factory, Digbeth High St, Birmingham B9 4AA *email:* info@turnerviolins.co.uk. *Vns, db, vas, vcs, repairs, accs, valuations, rentals, export, commission.*

Coventry
MB Sunderland Music. 62 Earlsdon St, Coventry CV5 6EJ *tel:* 024 7671 4272 *fax:* 024 7671 4272 *email:* sales@mbsunderlandmusic.co.uk. *Sheet mus, insts.*

Halesowen
Musical Instrument Repairs & Sales. Hereward Rise, Halesowen Industrial Park, Halesowen, W Midlands B62 8AN *tel:* 0121 550 9707 *fax:* 0121 501 3873 *email:* mirsales@aol.com. *New and second-hand insts, sale and repair.*

Solihull
The Music Store. 11 Forest Court, Dorridge, Solihull, W Midlands B93 8HN *tel:* 01564 773100. *Gui specialists. Insts, mus, m/order.*

Sutton Coldfield
Colbecks. 26-28 Chester Rd, New Oscott, Sutton Coldfield, Birmingham B73 5DA *tel:* 0121 321 3909 *fax:* 0121 321 1815 *email:* sales@colbecks-music.com. *Pnos, keyboards, guis, insts, sheet mus.*

Walsall
TR Music. 233-236 Stafford St, Walsall, W Midlands WS2 8DF *tel:* 01922 613101 *fax:* 01922 632597 *email:* info@trmusic.co.uk. *Guis, str insts, cl, fl, drums, PA, amps, electric repairs, mus books, accs, recording equipment, lighting, pyrotechnic, karaoke machines and CDs, backing tapes.*

Wolverhampton
One Way Music. 122-123 Salop St, Wolverhampton WV3 0RX *tel:* 01902 423060 *fax:* 01902 424094 *email:* info@one-way-music.co.uk.

West Sussex
Chichester
Berns Music. 42 West St, Chichester, W Sussex PO19 1RP *tel:* 01243 781844 *fax:* 01243 781844 *email:* info@bernsmusic.co.uk. *Sheet mus: classical, popular and educ. W/wind, br, str insts, rental with option to buy, repairs, accs, gifts.*

Cathedral Music Ltd. King Charles Cottage, Racton, Chichester, W Sussex PO18 9DT *tel:* 01243 379968 *fax:* 01243 379859 *email:* enquiries@cathedral-music.co.uk. *Mus (m/order); visitors by appointment.*

Crawley
Hobgoblin Music. 17 The Parade, Northgate, Crawley, W Sussex RH10 8DT *tel:* 01293 515858 *fax:* 01293 561602 *email:* Crawley@hobgoblin.co.uk. *Specialists in traditional, folk and acoustic insts: fretted, str, pipes, w/wind, free reed, perc. Books, accs, spares and strs. Acoustic and electric guis.*

Haywards Heath
Peter Voigt Ltd. 71 High St, Lindfield, Haywards Heath, W Sussex RH16 2HN *tel:* 01444 483206 *fax:* 01444 483206. *Vn family insts and accs.*

Horsham
Horsham Music. 36a East St, Horsham, W Sussex RH12 1HL *tel:* 01403 254880 *fax:* 01403 259800. *Sheet mus, accs, insts, repairs, hire, m/order.*

West Yorkshire
Bradford
Early Music Shop. 38 Manningham Lane, Bradford BD1 3EA *tel:* 01274 393753 *fax:* 01274 393516 *email:* sales@earlyms.demon.co.uk. *Insts, inst kits, rcdrs, mus, cds. See also London The London Recorder Centre.*

J Wood & Sons Ltd. 38 Manningham Lane, Bradford BD1 3EA *tel:* 01274 307636 *fax:* 01274 393516 *email:* sales@earlyms.demon.co.uk. *Insts, mus, pnos, orgs, keyboards, strs, sheet mus, CDs.*

Minstrels Music Shop. 37 Alexandra St, Queensbury, W Yorks BD13 2EH *tel:* 01274 411600 *fax:* 01274 411700 *email:* mail@minstrels-music.co.uk. *Acoustic, elec guis, vns, strs, w/wind. Harmonica specialist including books and accs. M/order/internet only.*

Renaissance Workshop Company Ltd. 38 Manningham Lane, Bradford BD1 3EA *tel:* 01274 201752 *fax:* 01274 201753 *email:* sales@renwks.com. *Early mus insts, inst kits and inst plans.*

The Woodwind Exchange. 38 Manningham Lane, Bradford BD1 3EA *tel:* 01274 721831 *fax:* 01274 393516. *New and second-hand w/wind and br insts.*

Halifax
Maestro Music. 25 The Piece Hall, Halifax HX1 1RE *tel:* 01422 349359 *email:* maestro.music@virgin.net. *Guis, harmonicas, keyboards, mus books, w/wind, br, accs, effects (zoom).*

Harrogate
Ian Edwards. The Old Chapel, 282 Skipton Rd, Harrogate HG1 3HE *tel:* 01423 500442 *fax:* 01423 705200. *Good quality handmade furniture. Wide range of furniture for mus lovers and bibliophiles.*

Huddersfield
Davies, Peter. The Woodwind Workshop, 2nd Floor, Byram Arcade, Westgate, Huddersfield HD1 1ND *tel:* 01484 533053 *fax:* 01484 359100 *email:* ENQUIRIES@TheWoodwindWorkshop.co.uk. *Repair and restoration of ob family of insts, plus repair of all other w/wind. New and used w/wind plus reeds and accs.*

Michael Rath Brass Musical Instruments Limited. Newsome Mill, Hart St, Huddersfield HD4 6LS *tel:* 01484 549600 *fax:* 01484 549400 *email:* info@rathtrombones.com. *Trb manufacturers. Br inst sales and repair.*

Hanson Clarinet Company. The Globe Crossroads, Huddersfield Rd, Millbridge, W Yorks WF15 7EN *tel:* 0800 542 9524 *fax:* 0870 744 2742 *email:* tradesales@hanson-music.co.uk. *Clarinet makers. W/wind and br specialists, makers/repairers. New and used sales.*

Ilkley
Grove Music. 10 The Grove, Ilkley, W Yorks LS29 9EG *tel:* 01943 817301 *fax:* 01943 817086. *Mus, CDs, insts.*

Leeds
Fox's Music. 97-99 Vicar Lane, Leeds LS1 6PJ *tel:* 0113 245 0350 *fax:* 0113 245 8897 *email:* foxsaver@foxmusic.co.uk. *Guis, PA, hi-tech, keyboards, accs, mus, pnos, digital pnos.*

John Scheerer & Sons. 88-90 Merrion Centre, Leeds LS2 8NG *tel:* 0113 244 9592 (insts); 0113 244 0444 (sheet mus) *fax:* 0113 245 0347 *email:* sales@scheerers.com. *Insts and sheet mus.*

Knock on Wood - The Multicultural Music Shop. 13 Eastgate, Leeds LS2 7LY *tel:* 0113 242 9146 *fax:* 0113 245 9878. *Insts, books and recordings from around the world. M/order dept: Unit 12, Glasshouses Mill, Harrogate HG3 5QH tel: 01423 712712 also fax; email: info@knockonwood.co.uk.*

S & E M Turner Violins. 39 Call Lane, Leeds LS1 7BT *tel:* 0113 244 6133 *fax:* 0113 244 3088 *email:* leeds@turnerviolins.co.uk. *Vns, db, vas, vcs, repairs, accs, valuations, rentals, export, commission.*

Wiltshire
Codford St Mary
The Sound Post Ltd. Mayflower Farm, New Rd, Codford St Mary, Wilts BA12 0NS *tel:* 01985 841244 *fax:* 01985 841266 *email:* bimy@ thesoundpost.co.uk. *Vns, vas, vcs, strs, bs, bows and cases. Wholesalers.*

Pewsey
Warblers. Embrook House, Hilcot, Pewsey, Wilts SN9 6LE *tel:* 01672 851317 *fax:* 01672 851317 *email:* sales@warblers.co.uk. *M/order vocal mus.*

Salisbury
Percy Prior's Music. 5 Catherine St, Salisbury SP1 2DF *tel:* 01722 322278/8181 (sheet mus dept) *fax:* 01722 337272 *email:* salisbury@percypriors.co.uk. *Electric pnos, keyboards, insts, sheet mus specialists, repairs. W/wind, br, str, gui, drums.*

Swindon
Duck Son & Pinker Ltd. 59-60 Bridge St, Swindon, Wilts SN1 1BT *tel:* 01793 522018/522220 *fax:* 01793 495848. *Mus, books, insts, guis, drums, pnos, orgs, folk insts, hire, educ mus, CDs.*

Holmes Music. 21-23 Faringdon Rd, Swindon, Wilts SN1 5AR *tel:* 01793 520948/534095 *fax:* 01793 542436 *email:* sales@holmesmusic.co.uk. *Mus, elec orgs, keyboards, digital pnos, synths, guis, amps, drums, educ insts, commercial sound, mus school.*

Kempster & Son (The Music Shop). 98 Commercial Rd, Swindon, Wilts SN1 5PL *tel:* 01793 535523 *fax:* 01793 526375. *Group and PA gear, multi-track recording, educ insts.*

Worcestershire
Evesham
Vine Music - Evesham. Vine Court, 7 Vine St, Evesham, Worcs WR11 4RE *tel:* 01386 442548 *fax:* 01386 422293 *email:* mikevine@aol.com; info@vinemusic.com. *Insts, amps, PA, sound enhancement, accs, lighting, installation, repairs, books, tutorials, recording and FX.*

Malvern
Hibernian Violins. 67 Somers Rd, Malvern, Worcs WR14 1JA *tel:* 01684 562947 *fax:* 01684 562947. *Vns, bows, accs, repairs, restoration.*

Jonathan Gibbs Books. The Lakes Cottages, Drake St, Welland, Malvern, Worcs WR13 6LN *tel:* 01684 593169 *fax:* 01684 591356 *email:* jona@malvernbooks.demon.co.uk. *Second-hand books, vocal scores, miniature and full scores, sheet mus.*

The Malvern Bookshop. 7 Abbey Rd, Malvern, Worcs WR14 3ES *tel:* 01684 575915 *fax:* 01684 575915 *email:* browse@malvern-bookshop.co.uk. *Second-hand scores, sheet mus and books; large general stock. Searches undertaken. Quality items bought.*

Worcester
Cranes Music. 26 New St, Worcester WR1 2DP *tel:* 01905 723073/23 *fax:* 01905 723073/23 *email:* info@cranesmusic.com. *Orgs, keyboards, pnos (including second-hand), digital pnos and Clavinovas. Also at 27 Comberton Hill, Kidderminster tel: 01562 825262.*

Musical Instrument Repairs and Sales. 57 Martley Rd, St John's, Worcester WR2 6HH *tel:* 01905 420241 *fax:* 01905 420241 *email:* music@ mirworcester.fsnet.co.uk. *Br, w/wind, str, guis, accs, printed mus, finance schemes.*

York, City of
York
Banks & Son (Music) Ltd. 18 Lendal, York YO1 8AU *tel:* 01904 658836 *fax:* 01904 629547 *email:* banksmusic@dial.pipex.com. *Printed mus, mus text books, classical CDs, mus insts, accs, software, mus gifts.*

Philip Martin Music Books. 38 Fossgate, York YO1 9TF *tel:* 01904 636111 *fax:* 01904 658889 *email:* musicbooks@philipmartin.demon.co.uk. *Books, mus (new and second-hand); m/order at 22 Huntington Rd, York YO31 8RL.*

Scotland

Dundee, City of
Dundee
Rainbow Music. 35 Cowgate, Dundee DD1 2JF *tel:* 01382 201405 *fax:* 01382 225183. *Insts, PA and recording equipment.*

Edinburgh, City of
Edinburgh
The Bagpipe Centre. Blackfriars Music, 49 Blackfriars St, Edinburgh EH1 1NB *tel:* 0131 577 3090 *fax:* 0131 577 3090 *email:* blackfriarsmusic@ btinternet.com. *Bagpipes, books, CDs, accs.*

Blackfriars Music. 49 Blackfriars St, Edinburgh EH1 1NB *tel:* 0131 577 3090 *fax:* 0131 577 3090 *email:* blackfriarsmusic@btinternet.com. *All folk mus insts, books and CDs.*

Edinburgh Organ Studio. 98 Canongate, The Royal Mile, Edinburgh EH8 8DD *tel:* 0131 556 3005 *fax:* 0131 556 8445 *email:* sales@organstudio.co.uk. *Orgs, church orgs, keyboards, digital pnos. Repairs, tuition.*

Gordon Stevenson Violin Maker and Restorer. 6 Barclay Terrace, Bruntsfield, Edinburgh EH10 4HP *tel:* 0131 229 2051 *fax:* 0131 229 9298. *Str insts for sale; restoration of vns.*

McAlister Matheson Music Ltd. 1 Grindlay St, Edinburgh EH3 9AT *tel:* 0131 228 3827 *fax:* 0131 228 4780 *email:* sales@mmmusic.co.uk. Anne McAlister, Sandy Matheson, dirs. *Classical CD and DVD retailer, also stocks wide range of Scottish folk CDs as well as books on composers and musicians. Discounts available to educ institutions. Advice willingly given on merits of different recordings.*

Scayles Music. 50 St Patrick Square, Edinburgh EH8 9EZ *tel:* 0131 667 8241 *fax:* 0131 667 0444. *Guis (elec, acoustic, bs), br, w/wind, drums, perc, bouzoukis, mandolas, mandolins, books, spares, repairs, PA hire, amplification, accordions, keyboards, hi-tech, software, PA sales, cymbals.*

Sheena McNeil Music. 7 Barclay Terrace, Edinburgh EH10 4HP *tel:* 0131 228 3666 *fax:* 0131 228 3966 *email:* sales@sheenamcneilmusic.co.uk. *Mus, m/order, specialists in educ titles.*

Stringers of Edinburgh. 13 York Place, Edinburgh EH1 3EB *tel:* 0131 557 5432 *fax:* 0131 557 6999 *email:* info@stringersmusic.com. *Str inst specialists, beginner to professional level. M/order service. Specialist childrens/educ dept. Restoration w/shops on site.*

Tapp Music. 7 Barclay Terrace, Edinburgh EH10 4HP *tel:* 0131 228 4050 *fax:* 0131 228 3966 *email:* sales@tappmusic.freeserve.co.uk. *Mus, m/order, specialist pno cat.*

Glasgow, City of
Glasgow
Band Supplies (Scotland). 13-15 Old Dumbarton Rd, Glasgow G3 8QY *tel:* 0141 339 9400 *fax:* 0141 334 8157 *email:* glasgow@bandsupplies.co.uk. *Sax specialists, insts (br, w/wind, perc), mus, recordings; also repairs.*

Biggars - Music for All. 273 Sauchiehall St, Glasgow G2 3HH *tel:* 0141 332 8676 *fax:* 0141 572 6963 *email:* martin@biggars.co.uk. *Orgs, pnos, digital pnos, keyboards, orch and band insts, mus, synthesizers, guis, sheet mus. Mus studio and rehearsal rooms available for hire also.*

Drum Shop Glasgow. 15 Blackie St, Glasgow G3 8TN *tel:* 0141 339 4497 *fax:* 0141 339 4497 *email:* info@drumshopglasgow.co.uk. *Perc.*

Highland
Beauly
Serenade for Strings. South Teavarran, Foxhole, Kiltarlity, Beauly, Inverness-shire IV4 7HT *tel:* 01463 741651 *fax:* 01463 741651 *email:* serenade.strings@virgin.net. *Specialises in sheet mus for strs, including current syllabuses for the exam boards. Post-free service for mus not in stock.*

Inverness
The Music Shop. 27 Church St, Inverness IV1 1DY *tel:* 01463 233374 *fax:* 01463 713983 *email:* themusicshop@lineone.net. *Wide range of insts, accs, sheet mus. M/order. Educ discount.*

Renfrewshire
Paisley
Music Centre. 8 Wellmeadow St, Paisley PA1 2EF *tel:* 0141 848 1033 *email:* paismusic@aol.com. *Keyboards, guis, mus, insts.*

Scottish Borders
Galashiels
Waverley Piano Co. 4 Chapel St, Galashiels, Selkirkshire TD1 1BU *tel:* 01896 752308. *Upright and grand pnos; also restoration, tuning and reconditioning.*

South Ayrshire
Ayr
Billy McEwen Organ Ltd. Keyboard and Piano Centre, 31-35 Fort St, Ayr KA7 1DG *tel:* 01292 269667 *fax:* 01292 289597 *email:* mcewensmusic@ tiscali.co.uk. *Orgs, pnos, digital pnos, keyboards, synths, guis, accs, amps.*

Mackay Music. 3 Cathcart St, Ayr KA7 1BJ *tel:* 01292 289562 *fax:* 01292 289562 *email:* mackaymusic@aol.com. *Books, insts, mus, accs, novelties, inst hire.*

South Lanarkshire
East Kilbride
Just Music. 246 Auldhouse Rd, Auldhouse, E Kilbride G75 9DX *tel:* 01355 245674 *fax:* 01355 231020 *email:* Just.Music.Scotland@zetnet.co.uk. *Mus (m/order), br and wind band specialist.*

Stirling
Stirling
Roadshow. 64 Upper Craigs, Stirling FK8 2DS *tel:* 01786 471323 *fax:* 01786 471323 *email:* tedchristopher@ukonline.co.uk. *PA, guis, amps, drums, lighting, sales, tuition, hire, repairs.*

Wales

Cardiff
Cardiff
Cardiff Music. 31-33 Castle Arcade, Cardiff CF10 1BW *tel:* 029 2022 9700 *email:* cardiff@abermusic.com. *CDs, DVDs, videos, gifts, sheet mus and books to order. M/order.*

Cranes Musical Instruments. 5a High St, Cardiff CF10 1AW *tel:* 029 2039 8215 *fax:* 029 2066 7017. *Pnos, guis, amps, keyboards, br, w/wind, str, drums, mus.*

G M Music. 2 Wharton St, Cardiff CF10 1AG *tel:* 029 2023 1606 *fax:* 029 2023 1612 *email:* enquiry@gmmusic.co.uk. *Orch and group insts, equipment.*

Gamlin's Music Centre. 56 St Mary St, Cardiff CF10 1FE *tel:* 029 2037 6630 *fax:* 029 2023 7616 *email:* info@gamlinsmusic.co.uk. *Sheet mus, br, w/wind, str, pno, keyboards, guis, amps, hire, repairs.*

San Domenico Stringed Instruments. 175 Kings Rd, Cardiff CF11 9DF *tel:* 029 2023 5881 *fax:* 029 2034 4510 *email:* hmorgan@ san-domenico.co.uk. *Fine vns, vcs, bows, accs. Bow repairs, restoration, insurance, expert appraisals.*

Speed Music plc. 7 Quay St, Cardiff CF10 1DZ *tel:* 029 2034 2211 *fax:* 029 2034 2299 *email:* cardiff@speedmusic.co.uk. *General mus inst store with PA dept, digital recording, school inst hire (everything except acoustic pno and org).*

Carmarthenshire
Newcastle Emlyn
Christian Savage Violins. Danyrhelyg Isaf, Danyrhelyg, Newcastle Emlyn, Carmarthenshire SA38 9RG *tel:* 01239 710036. *New and second-hand vns, vas, vcs, dbs. Also bows and accs. Vn maker and repairers.*

Newport
Abergavenny
Abergavenny Music. 23 Cross St, Abergavenny, Monmouthshire NP7 5EW *tel:* 01873 853394 *fax:* 01873 859525 *email:* angela@abermusic.com. *Sheet mus, books, CDs, tapes, videos, gifts, accs, m/order.*
Newport
Speed Music Plc. 177 Upper Dock St, Newport, Gwent NP20 1DY *tel:* 01633 220390 *fax:* 01633 266636 *email:* newport@speedmusic.co.uk. *General mus inst store with PA dept, digital recording, school inst hire (everything except acoustic pno and org).*

Speed Music Plc Head Office. 1 West St, Baneswell, Newport NP20 1DY *tel:* 01633 215577 *fax:* 01633 213214 *email:* info@speedmusic.co.uk. *Accounts and invoicing, internet and educ orders, PA systems supply and installation.*

Pembrokeshire
Haverfordwest
Swales Music Centre. 2-6 High St, Haverfordwest, Pembrokeshire *tel:* 01437 762059 *fax:* 01437 760872 *email:* musician@swalesmusic.co.uk. *Mus, books, CDs, insts, accs.*
Pembroke Dock
The Music Centre. 4 Meyrick St, Pembroke Dock, Pembrokeshire SA72 6UT *tel:* 01646 682811 *fax:* 01646 682811. *Insts, accs, mus.*

Swansea
Swansea
The Leading Note. 49 Eversley Rd, Sketty, Swansea SA2 9DE *tel:* 01792 207018 *fax:* 01792 207018 *email:* rjilewis@aol.com. *Str inst specialist (orch strs). Also acoustic/classical gui; w/wind, school supplies. Accs for all insts. Large stock of mus both new and second-hand. Importer of Peruvian insts.*

Snell & Sons. 68 West Cross Lane, West Cross, Swansea SA3 5LU *tel:* 01792 405727 *email:* snells@welshmusic.demon.co.uk. *Shirley Davies, proprietor. Welsh mus specialists.*

Speed Music Plc. 391 The Kingsway, Swansea SA1 5LQ *tel:* 01792 455456 *fax:* 01792 455457 *email:* swansea@speedmusic.co.uk. *General mus inst store with PA dept, digital recording, school inst hire (everything except acoustic pno and org).*

Wilks Music Stores Ltd. 1325 Camarthen Rd, Fforestfach, Swansea SA5 4BP *tel:* 01792 561861 *fax:* 01792 561861. *Insts; also restoration, repairs; pnos, large mus showroom. ABRSM examination centre.*

Wrexham
Wrexham
Music Place. 30 Brook St, Wrexham LL13 7LL *tel:* 01978 265308. *Digital pnos, keyboards, guis, str, br, w/wind, sheet mus.*

Northern Ireland

Co Antrim
Belfast
Marcus Musical Instruments Ltd. 125 Royal Ave, Belfast BT1 1FF *tel:* 028 9032 2871 (UK) 01 7080888 (ROI) *fax:* 028 9043 9955 *email:* musicman@ marcus.dnet.co.uk. *Northern Ireland's largest store with the lowest prices.*

Co Down
Newry
Kennedy's Music Mart. 26 Upper Water St, Newry, Co Down BT34 1DJ *tel:* 028 3026 6715.

Co Tyrone
Omagh
Gortin Music Wholesale *see* O'Neills of Gortin, Omagh. *Tel:* 028 816 4892 *fax:* 028 8164 8492 *email:* sales@boorinwoodmusic.com. *Accordian, melodeon, concertina, banjo, bodh, wood and metal fl and fife. Generation and Clarke whistle, gui, vn, spare parts, cases, accs.*

O'Neills of Gortin. 17 Main St, Gortin, Omagh BT79 8PQ *tel:* 028 8164 8492 *fax:* 028 8164 8492 *email:* oneillmusic@freezone.co.uk. *Accordian, melodeon, concertina, banjo, bodh, wood and metal fl and fife. Generation and Clarke whistle, gui, vn, spare parts, cases, accs.*

SUPPLIERS AND SERVICES

H. BARON

(Est. 1949)

**121 CHATSWORTH ROAD
LONDON NW2 4BH
ENGLAND**
(by appointment only)

tel & fax : 0208-459-2035

* * * * * *

**Old and New Music
Books on Music
Autograph Letters
Portraits**

Members: Antiquarian Booksellers Association
Provincial Booksellers Fairs Association.

Philip Martin Music Books

A treasure-trove of secondhand
scores at bargain prices

Wide-ranging display of books
both new and secondhand

Visit our shop at 38 Fossgate, York

Tuesday – Saturday, 10.00 – 5.30

··················

We can also supply all your new books
and scores

NO ONE DOES IT FASTER!

··················

Join our mailing list to receive catalogues

Send your name and address to us at:

22 Huntington Road, York YO31 8RL
Tel: (01904) 636111   Fax: (01904) 658889
musicbooks@philipmartin.demon.co.uk

The most influential opera magazine
in the world

Insight from the top people in the business on the design,
management, artistic direction and of course the
performance of opera.Profiles and Biographies.News and
reviews from the four corners of the globe and the most
comprehensive worldwide opera listings to be found
anywhere.

Annual UK Subscription £29.70 (6 issues)

Please send your order to: **Rhinegold Subscriptions,
FREEPOST LON20614, Peterborough, PE8 5BR**
(cheques payable to *Rhinegold Publishing Ltd*)
Tel: **01832 741941**
Fax: **01832 275560**
Email: **subs@rhinegold.co.uk**

www.rhinegold.co.uk

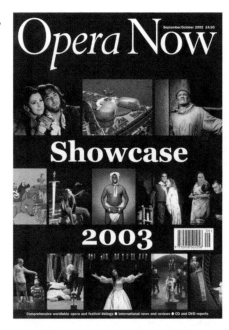

Antiquarian and Specialist Music Booksellers

Alba Secondhand Music. The Courtyard, 61 Otago St, Glasgow G12 8PQ *tel:* 01389 875996 *email:* robert@albamusick.fsnet.co.uk. Robert Lay, proprietor. *Inst and vocal printed mus, some antiquarian. Collections purchased. Mon-Sat, 11am-5.30pm.*

Austin Sherlaw-Johnson. Woodland View, Churchfields, Stonesfield, Oxon OX29 8PP *tel:* 01993 898223 *email:* austin. sherlaw-johnson@virgin.net. *Dealer in mus and books on mus. Cat issued. Wants welcome. Mus and books bought (any quantity). M/order only from given address but has retail outlets in Oxford and Malvern.*

Baron, H. 121 Chatsworth Rd, London NW2 4BH *tel:* 020 8459 2035 *fax:* 020 8459 2035. *Members ABA, PBFA. Antiquarian mus, books, autographs, mss, prints. M/order.*

Bingham, Tony. 11 Pond St, London NW3 2PN *tel:* 020 7794 1596 *fax:* 020 7433 3662 *email:* tbingham@easynet.co.uk. *Old and new insts, reference books.*

Books Etc. Royal Festival Hall, Belvedere Rd, South Bank, London SE1 8XX *tel:* 020 7620 0403 *fax:* 020 7620 0426 *email:* booksetc@ rfh.org.uk. *Biographies, analyses, histories, libretti, scores.*

Dooley, Rosemary M S. Crag House, Witherslack, Grange-over-Sands, Cumbria LA11 6RW *tel:* 01539 552286 *fax:* 01539 552013 *email:* musicbks@rdooley.demon.co.uk. *Second-hand books on mus. Cat available. European distributor for Pendragon Press (US).*

English Folk Dance and Song Society. Cecil Sharp House, 2 Regent's Park Rd, London NW1 7AY *tel:* 020 7485 2206 ext 17 *email:* info@efdss.org. *Educ resources for English and other traditional folk dances. Books, CDs, tapes, videos. Cat available by post or online.*

Gilham Books. 4 St Austell Rd, London SE13 7EQ *tel:* 020 8852 1905 *fax:* 020 8852 1905 *email:* mendel@gilhambooks.fsnet.co.uk. *Second-hand mus books. 2000 vols. 2 cats pa.*

Goodden, Peter. 7 Clarendon Villas, Widcombe Hill, Bath BA2 6AG *tel:* 01225 310986 *email:* peter.goodden@ukonline.co.uk. *Rare, second-hand and out-of-print books.*

Otto Haas. 49 Belsize Park Gardens, London NW3 4JL *tel:* 020 7722 1488 *fax:* 020 7722 2364. *Mss, rare mus books and eds. By appointment only.*

Paramor, C D. 25 St Mary's Square, Newmarket, Suffolk CB8 0HZ *tel:* 01638 664416 *fax:* 01638 664416 *email:* cdparamor@ btopenworld.com. *Gilbert & Sullivan, mus and theatre. Music hall, light entertainment.*

Travis & Emery Music Bookshop. 17 Cecil Court, off Charing Cross Rd, London WC2N *tel:* 020 7240 2129 *fax:* 020 7497 0790 *email:* bimy@travis-and-emery.com. *Antiquarian and second-hand mus, new and second-hand books, programmes, playbills. Cat available.*

Wood, Peter. 20 Stone Hill Rd, Great Shelford, Cambridge CB2 5JL *tel:* 01223 842419 *fax:* 01223 842419. *Specialist in books on performing arts including mus and opera and Stephen Sondheim.*

Woodlands Books. 65 Gledhow Wood Rd, Leeds LS8 4DG *tel:* 0113 266 7834. *W F and V W Astbury. Out-of-print and second-hand books on mus and musicians. Cat available. M/order only.*

Architects and Theatre/Acoustic Consultants

3 Design Partnership. 8 Park Rd, Whitchurch, Cardiff CF14 7BQ *tel:* 029 2052 0800 *fax:* 029 2052 2868 *email:* design@3design.co.uk. Bob James, partner; Mike Jones-Pritchard, partner. *Architectural partnership. Design of new theatres and restoration of existing theatre spaces. General construction detailing and design, new build and refurbishment.*

ACT Consultant Services. The Old Wood Mill, Church Lane, Madingley, Cambs CB3 8AF *tel:* 01954 210766 *fax:* 01954 211466 *email:* cbaldwin@ actconsultantservices.co.uk. Chris Baldwin, partner, theatre design consultancy; John Coffey, partner, audio-visual services (tel: 01323 491611 fax: 491612); Roger Tomlinson, partner, arts development studies (Cambridge office). *Offers a flexible approach to design planning and development of arts and conference spaces informed through practical management and operational experience. Ticketing and market place technology and analysis, collaborative marketing, audience development, feasibility studies and arts development strategies.*

Acoustic Dimensions. 24 Styvechale Ave, Coventry CV5 6DX *tel:* 024 7667 3645 *fax:* 024 7667 9820 *email:* nedwards@acousticdimensions. co.uk. Nicholas Edwards, partner; Craig Janssen, partner; David Kahn, partner. *Acoustics consulting for performing arts; auditorium design; sound and communications systems design.*

Adrian James Acoustics. 65 Yarmouth Rd, Blofield, Norwich NR13 4LG *tel:* 01603 717703 *fax:* 01603 713183 *email:* adrian@adrianjamesacoustics. co.uk. A James, consultant; A Thompson, consultant. *Independent acoustics consultancy specialising in buildings for mus, theatre, opera, dance and educ in the arts. Services include feasibility studies, design, advice on new build and refurbishment of buildings. Experts in modelling of auditorium acoustics, electronic design and specification.*

All Clear Designs Ltd. 3 Devonshire Mews, London W4 2HA *tel:* 020 8400 5093 *fax:* 020 8400 5094 *email:* allclear@easynet.co.uk. James Holmes-Siedle, dir. *Access audits for disabled people; feasibility studies to improve access; architectural work to improve access; finding guidance for the above; training: disability, equality training. Intended for all organisations to look at audience, employees and performers.*

Amadeus Acoustic Solutions Ltd. Great Beech Barn, Kane Hythe Rd, Battle, E Sussex TN33 9QU *tel:* 01424 775867 *fax:* 01424 775866 *email:* john@amadeus-equipment.co.uk. John Locke, dir; Robin Tyndale-Biscoe, principal acoustic consultant. *Acoustic consultancy. Advice and supply of acoustic mus rehearsal rooms, studios and sound booths. Installation into old and new buildings, any floor, subject to building construction. Acoustic wall panels and refurbishment.*

Armitage Associates. Fleming House, 134 Renfrew St, Glasgow G3 6ST *tel:* 0141 332 8011 *fax:* 0141 332 8374 *email:* architects@ armitage90.freeserve.co.uk. Jeremy Armitage, principal. *Architectural practice interested in new build and restoration.*

Arts Team @ Rhwl. 5th Floor, 133 Long Acre, London WC2E 9DT *tel:* 020 7379 7900 *fax:* 020 7836 4881 *email:* artsteam@rhwl.co.uk. Nick Thompson, snr partner; Barry Pritchard, snr partner. *Specialised large group of architects and designers working on arts, media and educ projects throughout the UK and overseas. Skills include theatre planning, brief writing, business planning, auditoria design, and Lottery applications.*

Arup Acoustics. Boston House, 36-38 Fitzroy Square, London W1T 6EY *tel:* 020 7636 2853 *fax:* 020 7755 3665 *email:* acoustics@arup.com. Rob Harris, dir (Winchester); Ian Knowles, associate (London); Raf Orlowski, associate (Cambridge); Nick Antonio, associate (Manchester). *Acoustic and venue design consultants. Offices also at: Parkin House, 8 St Thomas Street, Winchester, Hants SO23 9HE tel: 01962 829900 fax: 01962 867270; St Giles Hall, Pound Hill, Cambridge CB3 0AE tel: 01223 531100 fax: 01233 361258; 8th Floor, St James' Buildings, Oxford Street, Manchester M1 6EL tel: 0161 228 2331 fax: 0161 236 1057. Also in Los Angeles, New York, San Francisco, Melbourne, Sydney and Hong Kong.*

Bob Massey Associates (Consulting Engineers). 9 Worrall Ave, Arnold, Nottingham NG5 7GN *tel:* 0115 967 3969 *fax:* 0115 967 3969 *email:* bm.associates@virgin.net. R M Massey, projects dir; G Dudley, snr projects engineer; S Nickerson, projects engineer. *Independent consulting engineers, specialising in theatre and visual arts. Design, advice and specification on all aspects of technical services and specialist building requirements for architects, consultants and users both large and small.*

Burrell Foley Fischer LLP. York Central, 70-78 York Way, London N1 9AG *tel:* 020 7713 5333 *fax:* 020 7713 5444 *email:* mail@bff-architects.co.uk. Mark Foley, member. *Architectural practice specialising in conversion, restoration and building of new theatres, concert halls, auditoria and*

cinema spaces. Specialist expertise in the design of facilities for dance and ballet.

Carr and Angier. The Old Malthouse, Clarence St, Bath BA1 5NS *tel:* 01225 446664 *fax:* 01225 446654 *email:* info@carrandangier.co.uk. Peter Angier; Keith McLaren; Emma Savage. *Specialist consultants providing professional advice on feasibility, planning, equipment and management for theatres, concert halls and conference centres, both new buildings and renovations.*

Dramascope. 35 Schofield Ave, Witney, Oxon OX28 1JR *tel:* 01993 704820 *fax:* 01993 704820 *email:* dramascope@btinternet.com. Terry Powell. *Consultancy in design, decor, sound and lighting to the theatre and leisure industry.*

Jaques, Muir and Partners. 1 Purley Place, Islington, London N1 1QA *tel:* 020 7354 1315 *fax:* 020 7226 8005 *email:* john.h.muir@talk21.com. John Muir, partner. *Theatre architects involved in restoration and building of new theatres. Includes Apollo Victoria and Carling Apollo Hammersmith, London, Theatre Royal, Norwich, Theatre Royal, Margate, Theatre Royal, Brighton.*

Ken Dibble Acoustics. PO Box 541, Rugby CV21 3YJ *tel:* 01788 541133 *fax:* 01788 541314 *email:* KDAcoustic@aol.com. Ken Dibble, principal consultant. *Acoustics and noise control consultants specialising in performing and recorded arts, leisure and entertainment. Experience in event noise control and support for licensing, planning applications and appeals.*

LDN Architects. 16 Dublin St, Edinburgh EH1 3RE *tel:* 0131 556 8631 *fax:* 0131 556 8945 *email:* architects@ldne.co.uk. Colin Ross; Mark Hopton; Tom Duff; Sam Russell; Mark Sidgwick. *General architectural practice with a particular interest in the revitalisation of performing arts buildings. Also at: 29 St Leonards Rd, Forres IV36 1EN, tel: 01309 673221, fax: 01309 676397, email: architects@ldnf.co.uk.*

Lee Associates. World's End Studios, 134 Lots Rd, London SW10 0RJ *tel:* 020 7351 4333 *fax:* 020 7460 9518 *email:* leeassoc@dircon.co.uk. Denise Lee, design dir. *Award-winning architectural and interior design company providing imaginative, cost-effective design solutions. Creative use of space is the main objective, particularly for foyers, bars, retail outlets, cloakrooms and office spaces.*

Levitt Bernstein. 1 Kingsland Passage, London E8 2BB *tel:* 020 7275 7676 *fax:* 020 7275 9348 *email:* post@levittbernstein.co.uk. Axel Burrough, dir; Matthew Goulcher, dir; Gary Tidmarsh, dir. *Architects experienced in restoring and designing new theatres, auditoria, concert halls and performance spaces, also museums and galleries.*

Michael Holden Associates. 17 West Heath Drive, London NW11 7QG *tel:* 020 8455 4640 *fax:* 020 8209 1059 *email:* michaelholdenassocs@ btinternet.com. Michael Holden, partner. *Theatre consultants, specialist in feasibility studies, the design of theatre buildings and equipment. Management consultancy and architectural departments.*

Modelbox. 20 Merton Park, Jubilee Way, London SW19 3WL *tel:* 020 8254 4720 *fax:* 020 8254 4721 *email:* info@modelbox.co.uk. Bryan Raven, gen mgr; Steve Wentworth, CAD Bureau; David Howe, lighting design services; Jason Larcombe, lighting design services. *Computer aided design services to the entertainment industry for 15 yrs. The core business is the production of theatre plans with a database of over 350 theatres. Support services for designers, lighting designers and production managers range from plan printing from PC to Mac CAD files through to full show planning, documentation and support services.*

Next Stage. Judds Farm, Winsor Lane, Winsor, Southampton SO40 2HG *tel:* 023 8081 2011 *fax:* 023 8081 2213 *email:* rayjcarter@ compuserve.com. Ray Carter, theatre consultant. *Theatre consultancy.*

O'Donnell Coward Partnership Architects. 3 Gladstone Place, Summer Rd, E Molesey, Surrey KT8 9LZ *tel:* 020 8398 5678 *email:* odcarch@aol.com. Peter O'Donnell, partner. *Full architect's services in designing and altering theatres.*

Osborn Bennett Practice. Sovereign House, The Bramhall Centre, Bramhall, Cheshire SK7 1AW *tel:* 0161 440 7555 *fax:* 0161 440 7666 *email:* obparch@aol.com. Chris Bennett, architect. *Back-of-house architects and project managers for the Millennium Show at the Dome.*

Paul S Covell. Settlands, Sackmore Lane, Marnhull, Dorset DT10 1PN *tel:* 07932 772243; 01258 820248 *fax:* 01258 820248 *email:* paul.s. covell@btopenworld.com. Paul Covell. *Theatre and lighting consultancy; architectural lighting.*

Robinson & McIlwaine Architects. 1st Floor, The Warehouse, 7 James St South, Belfast BT2 8DN *tel:* 028 9024 8922 *fax:* 028 9024 2688 *email:* peter@rmi.uk.com. John Reid, partner; Peter McGuckin, partner.

Architectural practice interested in new build and theatre restoration - recent projects include Belfast Waterfront Hall and Grand Opera House, Belfast.

Sandy Brown Associates. 1 Coleridge Gardens, London NW6 3QH *tel:* 020 7644 6500 *fax:* 020 7644 6510 *email:* post@sandybrown.com. Richard Galbraith, partner; Kyri Kyriakides, partner; Laurence Haslam, partner; Stephen Stringer, partner. *Acoustics and a/v consultancy for performing arts buildings. Scottish office at South Queensferry, Edinburgh.*

Theatre Projects Consultants Ltd. 4 Apollo Studios, Charlton Kings Rd, London NW5 2SW *tel:* 020 7482 4224 *fax:* 020 7284 0636 *email:* post@tpc-lon.com. David Staples, mgr dir; Mark Stroomer, design dir; Alan Russell, dir; Jerry Godden, dir; Andy Hayles, dir; Sandy Beaunay, mkt asst. *Consultants on the planning, design, equipping and management of theatres, concert halls and performing arts facilities.*

Theatreplan. 18 Doughty St, London WC1N 2PL *tel:* 020 7269 2669 *fax:* 020 7269 2679 *email:* info@theatreplan.net. Richard Brett; John Whitaker; Roger Fox; Neil Morton; Charles Wass. *Professional design service for theatres, opera houses, concert and conference halls, flexible auditoria, studios and a/v presentation theatres. Brief writing, feasibility studies, auditoria design, space and backstage planning, stage machinery and rigging, stage and concert lighting, sound and communications, planning and specification, safety audits.*

Theatresearch. Dacre Hall, Dacre, N Yorks HG3 4ET *tel:* 01423 780497 *fax:* 01423 781957 *email:* info@theatresearch.co.uk. David Wilmore, dir; Ric Green, associate. *Theatre consultancy, specialising in the restoration of historic theatres, particularly by the famous theatre architect Frank Matcham. Also providing advice on Lottery applications and theatre consultancy services. Academic theatre research commissions. Large library of books, photographs and material relating to theatre architecture and technology.*

Tim Benton Architect. 33 Northgate, Sleaford, Lincs NG34 7BX *tel:* 01529 304524 *fax:* 01529 306981 *email:* tim.benton@btclick.com. Tim Benton, partner. *Architectural practice interested in new theatre building and restoration of performance spaces.*

Tim Foster Architects. 1 Purley Place, London N1 1QA *tel:* 020 7354 1315 *fax:* 020 7226 8005 *email:* TFA@dial.pipex.com. Tim Foster, principal; Edmund Wilson, associate. *Architects specialising in the design of buildings for the performing and visual arts. Work includes Tricycle Theatre, Gate Theatre in London, Cliffs Pavilion, Southend-on-Sea, the Broadway Theatre and Cinema, Peterborough, the Salisbury Playhouse and the award-winning Tricycle Cinema.*

Tim Smith Acoustics. 7 Swancombe, Clapton-in-Gordano, Bristol BS20 7RR *tel:* 01275 848229 *fax:* 01275 843945. T J B Smith, principal. *Consultancy and design services for building acoustics and electroacoustic systems. Surveys and investigations of noise and vibration problems. Sound studio and auditorium design.*

Tweedale. 265 Tettenhall Rd, Wolverhampton WV6 0DE *tel:* 01902 457649 *fax:* 01902 450073 *email:* enquiries@tweedale.co.uk. Terry Reynolds, mgr dir. *Architectural and town planning company interested in new theatre/arts centre buildings and restoration work.*

Van Doet Consulting Ltd. 49 Drum Brae North, Edinburgh EH4 8AT *tel:* 07971 594512 *fax:* 07971 046645 *email:* info@vandoet.com. Graeme Dott, dir.

Musician Services

Accessory Distributors

Britannia Reeds. 156 Hatfield Rd, St Albans, Herts AL1 4JA *tel:* 01727 846055 *fax:* 01727 838435 *email:* britanniamusicshop@btinternet.com. *Specialist manufacturers and sales of ob and bsn reeds, cane and accs; m/order worldwide.*

Centrepiece Music. PO Box 1601, Newport Pagnell, Bucks MK16 8PD *tel:* 01908 218003 *fax:* 01908 211828 *email:* centrepiece.music@virgin.net. Glenda Smith, partner. *Distributor of accs for w/wind and gui: cl and sax mouthpieces (Portnoy and Beechler), Winslow ligs, etc; Neotech sax and gui slings and straps.*

Impact Percussion. Unit 7, Goose Green Trading Estate, 47 East Dulwich Rd, London SE22 9BN *tel:* 020 8299 6700 *fax:* 020 8299 6704 *email:* sales@impactpercussion.com. *Importer of orch perc and accs.*

Rosetti Ltd. 4 Tamdown Way, Springwood Industrial Estate, Braintree, Essex CM7 2QL *tel:* 01376 550033 *fax:* 01376 550042 *email:* music@rosetti.co.uk. *Str, br, w/wind, guis, perc, accs.*

T W Howarth & Co Ltd. 31 Chiltern St, London W1U 7PN *tel:* 020 7935 2407 *fax:* 020 7224 2564 *email:* sales@howarth.uk.com. *Manufacturers and wholesale importers of w/wind accs.*

Accountancy and Taxation Services

Arts Services Direct. PO Box 3136, Barnet, Herts EN5 1DY *tel:* 020 8447 3862 *fax:* 020 8447 3862 *email:* jhart@voxhumana.co.uk. Jan Hart, mgr. *Book-keeping and tax for musicians and small companies.*

Bruton Charles Chartered Accountants. The Coach House, Greys Green Business Centre, Henley-on-Thames RG9 4QG *tel:* 01491 629829 *fax:* 01491 629839 *email:* jonathan@brutoncharles.co.uk. Jonathan Lawrence-Archer. *Specialists in tax planning, accounts, VAT returns and personal financial planning for those in the mus business.*

Bruton Charles Chartered Accountants. Ashland House, 20 Moxon St, Marylebone High St, London W1M 3JE *tel:* 020 7935 7872 *fax:* 020 7486 7639 *email:* info@brutoncharles.co.uk. Mark Lynskey. *Specialists in tax planning, accounts, VAT returns and personal financial planning for those in the mus business.*

Chantrey Vellacott DFK. Derngate Mews, Derngate, Northampton NN1 1UE *tel:* 01604 639257 *fax:* 01604 231460 *email:* eharris@cvdfk.com. Elliot Harris, partner. *Audit, accounting and advisory services; personal financial planning and taxation.*

David Smith & Co. 41 Welbeck St, London W1G 8HH *tel:* 020 7224 1004 *fax:* 020 7486 8705 *email:* dcsmithco@aol.com. D C Smith, practitioner; R Shah, qualified snr. *Accounts preparation and taxation advice to self-employed musicians and teachers. Clients need not be local.*

Guy Rippon Organization, Chartered Certified Accountants. 24 Pepper St, London SE1 0EB *tel:* 020 7928 9777 *fax:* 020 7928 9222. Guy Rippon, snr partner. *Chartered certified accountants. Comprehensive accountancy services to the mus industry. Also registered auditors.*

John Seeley & Co. 1 Upper St Mary's Rd, Bearwood, Warley, W Midlands B67 5JR *tel:* 0121 429 1504 *fax:* 0121 429 3121 *email:* jseeley@johnseeley.co.uk. John Seeley, principal. *Full range of accountancy and taxation services for the mus industry. Free financial guide for musicians available on request.*

Lloyd Piggott Chartered Accountants. Blackfriars House, Parsonage, Manchester M3 2JA *tel:* 0161 833 0346 *fax:* 0161 832 0045 *email:* info@lloydpiggott.co.uk. Paula Abbott, tax associate; Gary Dodds, snr partner; Sue Redmond, partner. *Accountancy and taxation services for musicians throughout the UK.*

Martin Greene Ravden. 55 Loudoun Rd, St John's Wood, London NW8 0DL *tel:* 020 7625 4545 *fax:* 020 7625 5265 *email:* mgr@mgr.co.uk. Lionel Martin, David Ravden, Steve Daniel, Ed Grossman, Paul Simnock, Ian Thomas, partners. *Business mgt, tour accounting and admin, inter-nation tax clearances, VAT, royalty examinations, litigation support and other financial services. Business mgt for independent record and publishing companies.*

Morgans Chartered Accountants. *Tel:* 01737 356562 *fax:* 01737 379376 *email:* enquiries@morgansonline.net. Richard Morgan.

Nyman Libson Paul Chartered Accountants. Regina House, 124 Finchley Rd, London NW3 5JS *tel:* 020 7433 2400 *fax:* 020 7433 2401 *email:* mail@nymanlibsonpaul.co.uk. Amin Saleh, partner (mus division). *Specialist knowledge of the entertainment and mus industry.*

Pearson & Co (Chartered Accountants). 113 Smug Oak Business Centre, Lye Lane, Bricket Wood, St Albans, Herts AL2 3UG *tel:* 01923 894404 *fax:* 01923 894990 *email:* richard@stantonpearson.co.uk. Richard Pearson, partner. *Accountancy, audits, taxation and financial mgt services.*

The Tax Doctor Organisation Ltd. PO Box 202, Burgess Hill, W Sussex RH15 8YF *tel:* 0871 424 0061 *email:* info@taxdoctor.org.uk. Patrick Hasford; Adrian Sheridan, mortgage broker. *Self assessment return calculations and submissions to the Inland Revenue. Accounts preparation, VAT and payroll services. Mortgage advice, financial advice. Provide musicians with cost effective accounting and tax return services.*

Trevor Ford & Co. 151 Mount View Rd, London N4 4JT *tel:* 020 8341 7809 *fax:* 020 8340 3522 *email:* tfordandco@aol.com.

Willott Kingston Smith. Quadrant House, Air St Entrance, 80-82 Regent St, London W1R 5PA *tel:* 020 7304 4646 *fax:* 020 7304 4647 *email:* ghowells@kingstonsmith.co.uk. Geraint Howells, partner; Darren Drake, mgr. *Financial mgt, contract reviews, litigation support, international tax, personal financial planning, audit and accounting, taxation, VAT, royalty auditing.*

Computer Systems Consultants

Artifax. 38 Waterloo Rd, Epsom, Surrey KT19 8EX *tel:* 01372 810081 *fax:* 01372 743390 *email:* admin@artifaxsoftware.com. Timothy Nathan, dir; Nina Kaye, dir; Tim Coleman, customer services dir; Ben Curthoys, tech dir; Karl Vesper, dir; Steve Pugh, dir; Peter Bowen, development. *Computer programmes: ARTIFAX Event - for venue mgt to handle bookings, technical resources and event mgt; ARTIFAX Festival - to manage festivals for performing arts; ARTIFAX Agent - designed for artists' mgrs and concert agencies to handle all admin. ARTIFAX Ticketing for box office ticket sales and internet ticket sales, OPAS to manage orch admin.*

DMT Associates. 23 Moreton Place, London SW1V 2NL *tel:* 020 7630 6329 *fax:* 020 7821 6960 *email:* dmt@compuserve.com. Dinah Molloy, mgr dir. *Custom-designed software and services for mus organisations.*

DatabaseCollection.com. Purple Hayes, Willand Rd, Halberton, Tiverton, Devon EX16 7AN *tel:* 01884 821295 *email:* bruce@dbcoll.com. Bruce Thomas, proprietor; Sue Rivett. *Accountancy software for self-employed mus teachers.*

New Notations Computer Services Ltd. 7 Duncombe Hill, London SE23 1QY *tel:* 07968 312 032 *fax:* 0870 706 4795 *email:* sales@newnotations.co.uk. *Consultancy and hardware/software sales. Mus notation. Custom-built computer workstations. M/order.*

New Notations London. 93 Wellmeadow Rd, London SE6 1HL *tel:* 020 8697 6351 *fax:* 020 8697 0038 *email:* info@newnotations.com. Steven Gibson, proprietor. *Software sales and consultancy. Mus notation, MIDI specialists. Distributors of Score mus publishing system.*

PRIAM. Old Telephone Exchange, 32-42 Albert St, Rugby CV21 2SA *tel:* 01788 558000 *fax:* 01788 558001 *email:* sales@priamsoftware.com.

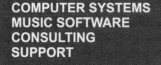

Andrew Kypri, sales dir. *Supply PRIAM business software for e-commerce, m/order, distribution and shops. Software includes sales, stock, accounts, database, mkt, rental and repairs.*

Sibelius Software Ltd. Old Toy Factory, 20-22 City North, Fonthill Rd, London N4 3HF *tel:* 020 7561 7999; 0800 458 3111 *fax:* 020 7561 7888 *email:* infoUK@sibelius.com. Jeremy Silver, chief exec offr; Ben Finn, founder and dir; Jonathan Finn, founder and dir. *Developer and distributor of mus software for professional musicians, students and educ establishments.*

Software Partners. Oak Tree House, Station Rd, Claverdon, Warks CV35 8PE *tel:* 01926 842998 *fax:* 01926 842384 *email:* info@software-partners.co.uk. Richard Blundell. *Distributors of capella mus notation software, capriccio (MIDI sequencer) tonica harmony and analysis software and capella-scan and Smartscore mus scanning software.*

Trinity Music Ltd. PO Box 3281, Nuneaton, Warks CV10 0ZT *tel:* 024 7634 4676 *fax:* 024 7638 4602 *email:* mail@trinitymusic.co.uk. Bryn Evans, mgr dir. *Mus educ software, Midi controller keyboards, mus stands, accs.*

WebProjects. Suites 5-7, Meridian House, 28 Station Rd, Redhill, Surrey RH1 1PD *tel:* 01737 768127 *email:* mark@webprojects.co.uk. Mark Walmsley, mgr dir; Ben Sauer, technical dir; Matthew Lindop, project dir; Andy Walker, creative dir. *Efficient creation, sharing and distribution of information.*

Diary and Answering Services

Bakers Diary Service. 10 Send Rd, Send, Woking, Surrey GU23 7ET *tel:* 01483 723644 *fax:* 01483 723662 *email:* bakers.diary@amserve.net. Sandy Wells, principal. *Diary mgt for professional orch and session musicians.*

Morgensterns Diary Service. PO Box 3027, S Croydon, Surrey CR2 6ZN *tel:* 020 8681 0555 *fax:* 020 8649 7464 *email:* contact@ morgensterns.com. Julian Morgenstern, mgr. *Personal mgt and booking services for orch and session musicians.*

Musicians Answering Service. Masters Yard, 180a South St, Dorking, Surrey RH4 2ES *tel:* 01306 500000 *fax:* 01306 888041 *email:* mas@maslink.co.uk. Richard Smith, mgr dir; Tania Davidson, mgr; Abbie Royston, mgr. *Established 1976; session and orch musicians; permanent or temporary; 8am-midnight, 7 days per week.*

Equipment Hire

FX Rentals Ltd. 38-40 Telford Way, London W3 7XS *tel:* 020 8746 2121 *fax:* 020 8746 4100 *email:* fx@fxrentals.co.uk. Nick Harris, mgr dir; Roger Evan, chmn. *Professional audio and inst equipment hire. Open 24 hrs every day of the yr.*

John Henry's Ltd. 16-24 Brewery Rd, London N7 9NH *tel:* 020 7609 9181 *fax:* 020 7700 7040 *email:* info@johnhenrys.com. John Henry, mgr dir. *Musical equipment and sound reinforcement rental.*

LM Productions LLP. LM House, 2 Church St, Seaford, E Sussex BN25 1HD *tel:* 01323 890752 *fax:* 01323 898311 *email:* sales@ lasermagic.com. Steve Harvey, mgr dir. *Laser display consultants; laser lighting specialists, fireworks, special effects, pyrotechnics displays, video projection, sound systems, large-format slide projection, high powered search lights.*

Whitwam Ltd. Unit 3, Chaucer Business Centre, Easton Lane, Winchester SO23 7RR *tel:* 01962 870408 *fax:* 01962 850820 *email:* service@ whitwam.ltd.uk. Michael Harding, dir; Steve Birnage, snr mgr. *Sound and vision equipment, hire and sales.*

Equipment Manufacturers

Amadeus Performance Equipment Ltd. Great Beech Barn, Kane Hythe Rd, Battle, E Sussex TN33 9QU *tel:* 01424 775867 *fax:* 01424 775866 *email:* info@amadeus-equipment.co.uk. Anne Holliday, mgr dir; John Locke, mkt dir. *Musician posture chairs, inst racks, mus stands, portable staging, acoustically-designed rehearsal rooms, customised performing arts furniture, mus folders, lights.*

Covernote. 17 Lime Ave, Alton, Hants GU34 2AD *tel:* 01420 84449 *fax:* 01420 84449 *email:* covernote.alton@virgin.net. Lindy Wiltshire. *Custom-made covers and cases for insts and related equipment.*

Discassette. Derwent House, Ferry Lane, West Row, Bury St Edmunds, Suffolk IP28 8PT *tel:* 01638 711212 *fax:* 01638 711212 *email:* info@discassette.co.uk. Ann Hack, dir. *Bespoke hand-bound mus covers and choir folders, storage folders, gold blocking, etc.*

George Veness Workshop. Stanhope Studio, Donald Way, Winchelsea, E Sussex TN36 4NH *tel:* 01797 225878. Marcus Weeks, pno tuner, technician, restorer. *Wooden mus stands.*

Hostess Furniture Ltd. Vulcan Rd, Bilston, W Midlands WV14 7JR *tel:* 01902 493681 *fax:* 01902 353185 *email:* contract.sales@ hostessfurniture.co.uk. *Range of orch seating, musicians' chairs, ergonomically designed to address the postural and health problems suffered by musicians. See also Amadeus Performance Equipment Ltd.*

John Henry's Ltd. 16-24 Brewery Rd, London N7 9NH *tel:* 020 7609 9181 *fax:* 020 7700 7040 *email:* INFO@johnhenrys.com. John Henry, mgr dir; Robert Harding, audio mgr. *Mus equipment, staging, flight cases, mus stands.*

Musisca Ltd. Piccadilly Mill, Lower St, Stroud, Glos GL5 2HT *tel:* 01453 751911 *fax:* 01453 751911 *email:* marc@musisca.co.uk. Mark Oboussier, dir. *Mus stands, cond stands, lights, desk stands, pno stools and pno wheels. Cat available on request.*

Promenade Music. 404 Marine Rd East, Morecambe, Lancs LA4 5AR *tel:* 01524 410202 *fax:* 01524 410802 *email:* sales@prom-music.co.uk. David Wood, snr partner; Keith Harris, gen mgr. *Inst and equipment discounters, professional audio installations, digital mobile recording unit, record company, press and PR.*

RAT (Music Stands) Ltd. 16 Melville Rd, London SW13 9RJ *tel:* 020 8741 4804 *fax:* 020 8741 8949 *email:* sales@ratstands.com. A C Michell, dir. *Professional mus stands, with or without lamps.*

Information Services

Allegro Training Services. 20 Langley Close, Headington, Oxford OX3 7DA *tel:* 01865 430652 *fax:* 01865 430652 *email:* ann.lee@lineone.net. Ian Ledsham, partner; Ann Lee, partner. *Provides training courses in a range of mus-related topics, such as copyright, internet use for mus, mus sources.*

Home Counties Box Office. PO Box 494, Tring, Herts HP23 4HW *tel:* 0845 225 6020 *fax:* 01442 828401 *email:* HCBoxoffice@aol.com.

Jazz Services. 1st Floor, 132 Southwark St, London SE1 0SW *tel:* 020 7928 9089 *fax:* 020 7401 6870 *email:* admin@jazzservices.org.uk. Celia Wood, information publications mgr; Chris Hodgkins, dir. *Supports the growth and development of jazz in the UK by providing services in touring, support information via website, educ, mkt and communication.*

Music Academies On Line. 78 Warwick Ave, Edgware, Middx HA8 8UJ *tel:* 020 8537 8552 *fax:* 020 8958 5206 *email:* info@ musicacademiesonline.com. M Schreider, dir; Olga Malisova, sec. *Provides information about mus academies, colleges and conservatoires worldwide, their specialisation, courses and degrees.*

The Music Information Consultancy. 1 Northend Farm Cottages, Cheriton, Alresford, Hants SO24 0PW *tel:* 01962 771719 *fax:* 01962 771719 *email:* musicinfo@clara.net. Ian Ledsham, dir. *Offers cataloguing services, mus bibliography, stock editing and advice, consultancy and research services.*

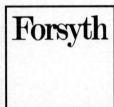

Instrument Auctioneers

Bonham's Fine Art Auctioneers 1793. 101 New Bond St, London W1S 1SR *tel:* 020 7468 8380/7629 6602 *fax:* 020 7465 0223 *email:* philip.scott@bonhams.com. Philip A Scott, dir, mus insts. *Auctions of vns, vas, vcs, bows.*

Christies. 85 Old Brompton Rd, London SW7 3LD *tel:* 020 7321 3470 *fax:* 020 7321 3321 *email:* kkeane@christies.com. Kerry Keane, dir, mus insts. *Full appraisal and sale services of fine mus insts. Four sales annually held in London and New York.*

Sotheby's. Musical Instruments Dept, 34-35 New Bond St, London W1A 2AA *tel:* 020 7293 5342 *fax:* 020 7293 5942 *email:* tim.ingles@sothebys.com. Tim Ingles, dir, mus insts.

Instrument Hire

Many **Retailers** operate schemes for the hire of student instruments. The firms and individuals listed below are concerned with the hire of professional concert instruments, generally for one concert or tour within the UK only.

Abinger Organ Hire. Little Hoe, Hoe Lane, Abinger Hammer, Dorking, Surrey RH5 6RH *tel:* 01306 730277 *fax:* 01306 731483 *email:* Liz@abinger.globalnet.co.uk. Peter Flatau; Elizabeth Matthews; Simon Flatau. *Orgs, harmoniums, hpds and elec pnos for sale and hire.*

Allen Organ Studios (London) Ltd. Trada Business Campus, Stocking Lane, Hughenden Valley, High Wycombe, Bucks HP14 4ND *tel:* 01494 563833 *fax:* 01494 563546 *email:* hires@allenorgans.co.uk. Richard Goodall, UK hire mgr; Giles Williams, UK hire mgr. *Hire of Allen classical digital computer orgs.*

Andrew Wooderson Early Keyboard Instruments. 5 Bourne Rd, Bexley, Kent DA5 1LG *tel:* 01322 558326 *fax:* 01322 525558 *email:* andrew.wooderson@btinternet.com. *Hpd hire for concerts, festivals, tours and recording. Also tuning, transport, repair and restoration. New insts hand built to order. New and second-hand insts from stock.*

Banquet of Musick. Hillview Cochno Rd, Hardgate, Clydebank, Dunbartonshire G81 6PT *tel:* 01389 875996 *email:* robert@albamusick.fsnet.co.uk. Robert Lay. *Chmbr org and hpds for hire and standby for concerts and recording. Tuning.*

Bell Percussion Ltd. 6 Greenock Rd, London W3 8DU *tel:* 020 8896 1200 *fax:* 020 8896 0100 *email:* info@bellperc.com. *Perc hire.*

Bexley Harpsichord Workshops Ltd. 5 Bourne Rd, Bexley, Kent DA5 1LG *tel:* 01322 557147 *fax:* 01322 527366. Andrew Wooderson, dir; Edmund Handy, dir. *Hpd hire for concerts, festivals, tours and recording. Also tuning, transport, repair and restoration. New insts hand built to order. New and second-hand insts from stock.*

Booth, Colin. Mount Pleasant, Westbury-sub-Mendip, Wells BA5 1HU *tel:* 01749 870516 *fax:* 01749 870516 *email:* colin@harpsichords.demon.co.uk. *Early keyboard insts. Full service for concerts and recordings.*

Cambridge Reed Organs. 18 Hill Close, Newmarket, Suffolk CB8 0NR *tel:* 01638 660531 *fax:* 01638 660531 *email:* bruce@harmonium.co.uk. Bruce Dracott, proprietor. *Harmoniums for hire.*

Deegan (Robert) Harpsichords. Tonnage Warehouse, St Georges Quay, Lancaster LA1 1RB *tel:* 01524 60186 *fax:* 01524 60186 *email:* harpsichords@hotmail.com. Robert Deegan, proprietor. *Hpd maker, hpd concert hire, transport, tuning, maintenance, restoration, repairs, spare parts, strs, etc.*

FX Rentals Ltd. 38-40 Telford Way, London W3 7XS *tel:* 020 8746 2121 *fax:* 020 8746 4100 *email:* fx@fxrentals.co.uk. Nick Harris, mgr dir; Roger Evans, chmn. *Professional audio and inst equipment hire. Open 24 hrs every day of the yr.*

Forsyth Brothers Ltd. 126 Deansgate, Manchester M3 2GR *tel:* 0161 834 3281 *fax:* 0161 834 0630 *email:* info@forsyths.co.uk. *Pno hire (digital, upright and grand) and tuning.*

Hammett, Claire. 19 Buxton Rd, E Sheen, London SW14 8SY *tel:* 020 8876 1496; 07973 659212 *fax:* 020 8876 1496 *email:* claire.hammett@ btinternet.com. *Hpds and orgs for concert and recording hire, including transport, repairs and tuning of hpds, clvds and pre-1830 f-pnos.*

Handy, Edmund. Early Keyboard Instruments, 5 Bourne Rd, Bexley, Kent DA5 1LG *tel:* 01322 527366 *fax:* 01322 527366 *email:* edmund. handy@btinternet.com. Edmund Handy, dir. *Hpd hire for concerts, festivals, tours and recording. Also tuning, transport, repair and restoration. New insts hand built to order. New and second-hand insts from stock.*

Hansford, Neil. The Bristol Violin Shop, 12 Upper Maudlin St, Bristol BS2 8DJ *tel:* 0117 925 9990 *fax:* 0117 925 0033 *email:* sales@ bristol-violin-shop.co.uk. *Inst hire, m/order and comprehensive internet cat of mus and accs.*

Harmonium Services. 6 Albert Terrace, Saltaire, Shipley, W Yorks BD18 4PS *tel:* 01274 585601; 07976 535980 *email:* phil@ harmoniumservice.demon.co.uk. Phil Fluke, proprietor. *Harmoniums for hire. Also street org on hand cart for hire.*

Harpsichord Workshop. 130 Westbourne Terrace Mews, London W2 6QG *tel:* 020 7723 9650 *fax:* 020 7723 9650 *email:* markransom@harpsichord-workshop.co.uk. Mark Ransom. *Short and long-term hire.*

Hickies, Ltd. 153 Friar St, Reading RG1 1HG *tel:* 0118 957 5771 *fax:* 0118 957 5775. *Grand and upright pnos for concert hire.*

Impact Percussion. Unit 7, Goose Green Trading Estate, 47 East Dulwich Rd, London SE22 9BN *tel:* 020 8299 6700 *fax:* 020 8299 6704 *email:* sales@impactpercussion.com. Paul Hagen. *Large perc hire fleet, worldwide delivery. Also sales and repair.*

Jaques Samuel Pianos Ltd. 142 Edgware Rd, London W2 2DZ *tel:* 020 7723 8818 *fax:* 020 7224 8692 *email:* info@jspianos.com. Daniel

Thomas, commercial hires mgr. *Pno hire, tuning, servicing, transport, practice studios.*

John Henry's Ltd. 16-24 Brewery Rd, London N7 9NH *tel:* 020 7609 9181 *fax:* 020 7700 7040 *email:* INFO@jhe.co.uk. John Henry, mgr dir. *Insts and PA.*

Ken Smith Music Services Ltd. 6 The Maltings, High St, Henlow, Beds SG16 6AQ *tel:* 01462 811244 *fax:* 01462 851801 *email:* Claviorgue@aol.com. Kenneth Smith, mgr dir; Alyda Smith, company sec. *Supplier, tuner and transporter of hpds, pipe orgs, f-pnos and harmoniums. Orch transport.*

Makin Organs Ltd. Sovereign House, 30 Manchester Rd, Shaw, Oldham, Lancs OL2 7DE *tel:* 01706 888100 *fax:* 01706 888109 *email:* davidc@makinorgans.co.uk. David Clegg, dir. *Classical orgs, MIDI expanders, nationwide hire service.*

Markson Pianos. 8 Chester Court, Albany St, London NW1 4BU *tel:* 0800 074 8980 *fax:* 020 7224 0957 *email:* sales@pianosuk.co.uk. *Pno sale, hire with option to buy, concert and recording hire, tuning and repairs, restoration, free advice. Teaching and practice studios.*

Maxima Music. 20 Wolseley Gardens, London W4 3LP *tel:* 020 8995 2757. Simon Hill. *Chmbr org.*

The Midland Organ Company. 17 Belvoir St, Melton Mowbray, Leics LE13 1QA *tel:* 01664 566348 *fax:* 01664 569208 *email:* midorgco@telinco.com. Christopher Gray, mgr dir. *Chmbr and continuo orgs for hire nationwide.*

Peter Collins Ltd. 42 Pate Rd, Melton Mowbray, Leics LE13 0DG *tel:* 01664 410555 *fax:* 01664 410535 *email:* pd_collins@lineone.net. Peter Collins, artistic dir. *Continuo org for hire.*

Pilgrim Harps. Stansted House, Tilburstow Hill Rd, South Godstone, Surrey RH9 8NA *tel:* 01342 893242 *fax:* 01342 892646 *email:* info@pilgrimharps.co.uk. *Hps for hire.*

Ransom, Mark. 130 Westbourne Terrace Mews, London W2 6QG *tel:* 020 7723 9650 *fax:* 020 7723 9650 *email:* markransom@ harpsichord-workshop.co.uk. *Hpd hire, tuning, maintenance and transport.*

Robert Morley & Co Ltd. 34 Engate St, London SE13 7HA *tel:* 020 8318 5838 *email:* jvm@morley-r.u-net.com. Julia Morley. *Long-term home rental of pnos, f-pnos, hpds, spinets, clvds, virginals, celestes.*

T W Howarth & Co Ltd. 31 Chiltern St, London W1U 7PN *tel:* 020 7935 2407 *fax:* 020 7224 2564 *email:* sales@howarth.uk.com. *Hire scheme for student w/wind insts and short-term hire of w/wind for orch concerts.*

Temple, Alex. Platt Lodge, 61 Barton Rd, Worsley, Manchester M28 2GX *tel:* 0161 794 3717 *fax:* 0870 120 8401 *email:* alextemple@supanet.com. *Hpd, clvd concert hire.*

Instrument Technicians

Those listed below offer a more specialised service than the general repairers listed in the **Retailers** section.

A Hanna & Sons. 94 Kingston Rd, Wimbledon SW19 1LA *tel:* 020 8540 5541 *fax:* 020 8540 4553 *email:* sales@hanna-pianos.co.uk. *Pno sales, tuning, repairs, reconditioning, removals, storage.*

Aitchison & Mnatzaganian. 7 Cambridge Rd, Ely, Cambs CB7 4HJ *tel:* 01353 668559 *fax:* 01353 612264 *email:* info@aitchisoncellos.com. Robin Aitchison, proprietor; Sarah Mnatzaganian, customer contact. *Vc specialists, sound adjustment, str trial service, repair and restoration, assessment and valuation. Organisers of contemporary bow exhibition 'Take a Bow'.*

Allen Organ Studios (London) Ltd. Trada Business Campus, Stocking Lane, Hughenden Valley, High Wycombe, Bucks HP14 4ND *tel:* 01494 563833 *fax:* 01494 563546 *email:* service@allenorgans.co.uk. Paul Arkwright, UK service mgr.

Andrew Wooderson Early Keyboard Instruments. 5 Bourne Rd, Bexley, Kent DA5 1LG *tel:* 01322 558326 *fax:* 01322 525558 *email:* andrew.wooderson@btinternet.com. *Tuning, maintenance, repair and restoration of early keyboard insts. Hand-built insts made to order. Insts for concerts, festivals, tours and recording. Valuations, assessments and advice. Sale of tools and accs.*

Batchelar, Timothy. 28 Colbert Drive, Leicester LE3 2JB *tel:* 0116 286 2511/289 9798; 07710 204303 *fax:* 0116 286 2511/289 9798 *email:* tim@batchelar.com. *Dealer, restorer and maker of stringed insts of the vn family. Accredited member of the Institute of Musical Instrument Technology.*

Bexley Harpsichord Workshops Ltd. 5 Bourne Rd, Bexley, Kent DA5 1LG *tel:* 01322 557147 *fax:* 01322 527366 *email:* edmund.handy@btinternet.com. Edmund Handy, dir; Andrew Wooderson, dir. *Tuning, maintenance and repair of hpds, clvds and early pnos, clvd manufacturer. Celeste maintenance and repair. Square pno restorations. Reconditioned insts for sale.*

Bishop and Son. 38 Bolton Lane, Ipswich, Suffolk IP4 2BT *tel:* 01473 255165 *fax:* 01473 255165. *Org builders, new pipe orgs, restoration, repair and tuning.*

Booth, Colin. Mount Pleasant, Westbury sub Mendip, Wells BA5 1HU *tel:* 01749 870516 *fax:* 01749 870516 *email:* colin@harpsichords.demon.co.uk. *Early keyboard insts: tuning, maintenance, repair, restoration.*

The Bridge Fiddler. Riverside House, Chapel Milton, Chapel-en-le-Frith, High Peak SK23 0QQ *tel:* 01298 813813. John Goodborn, proprietor. *Str inst and bow repairer and supplier of str insts and accs. Specialist in restoration.*

Cambridge Pianola Co & J V Pianos. The Limes, Landbeach, Cambridge CB4 8DR *tel:* 01223 861348 *fax:* 01223 441276 *email:* ftpoole@talk21.com. Tom Poole. *Pno and pianola restoration, sales and rentals. Also specialist pno removers.*

Cambridge Reed Organs. 18 Hill Close, Newmarket, Suffolk CB8 0NR *tel:* 01638 660531 *fax:* 01638 660531 *email:* bruce@harmonium.co.uk. Bruce Dracott, proprietor. *Harmonium restoration, repair, tuning and hire.*

Cavalier Music. 145 Barncroft Way, Havant, Hants PO9 3AF *tel:* 023 9247 5923. B L Boughton. *Br and w/wind repairs, specialist alterations. Insts bought and sold.*

Clive Morley Harps. Goodfellows, Filkins, nr Lechlade, Glos GL7 3JG *tel:* 01367 860493 *fax:* 01367 860659 *email:* harps@morleyharps.co.uk. *Hp servicing and repair, sales, rentals.*

Coad, Lucy. Workshop 3, Bath Rd, Wick, nr Bristol BS30 5RL *tel:* 0117 937 4949 *email:* lucy@squarepiano.co.uk. *Square pno repairs and conservation.*

David Corey Piano Tuning & Repairs. 18 Woodside Ave, Ainsdale, Southport, Merseyside PR8 3UE *tel:* 01704 574610; 07971 422601 *email:* dave@dcpianos.fsnet.co.uk. David Corey. *Member of Pianoforte Tuners' Association. Concert tuning, full re-stringing, restoration.*

Davies, Peter. The Woodwind Workshop, 37 Byram Arcade, Westgate, Huddersfield HD1 1ND *tel:* 01484 533053 *fax:* 01484 351900 *email:* online@byram92.fsnet.co.uk. Peter Davies, mgr. *Specialist repair and restoration of ob family of insts. Repairs, insurance, sales (new and second-hand), accs, mus for w/wind.*

Deegan (Robert) Harpsichords. Tonnage Warehouse, St Georges Quay, Lancaster LA1 1RB *tel:* 01524 60186 *fax:* 01524 60186 *email:* harpsichords@hotmail.com. Robert Deegan, proprietor. *Tuning, maintenance, restoration and repairs, spare parts, strs, etc.*

Derek Roberts Violins. 185 Leam Terrace, Leamington Spa, Warks CV31 1DW *tel:* 01926 428313 *fax:* 01926 428313 *email:* mail@derekroberts.co.uk. *Vn maker and restorer.*

Eric Reynolds Piano Workshop. 88 High St, Burton on Trent, Staffs DE14 1LJ *tel:* 01283 565869/086 *fax:* 01283 534922 *email:* ereynolds@used-pianos.co.uk. Ian Hewitt, sales mgr; Eric Reynolds, mgr dir; M Horsley, w/shop mgr. *Restoration of upright and grand pnos, especially polyester cabinet work.*

Forrest Pianos. 9 Ravenscar Terrace, Oakwood, Leeds, W Yorks LS8 4AU *tel:* 0113 248 4448. *Pno tuning and repairs. Concert tuning of pnos and hpds.*

Gittins, Roy. Hollebeke House, Gore End Rd, Ball Hill, Newbury, Berks RG20 0PD *tel:* 01635 253566 *fax:* 01635 253566 *email:* roygittins@beeb.net. *Br mus inst repairs and overhauls.*

Gordon Stevenson Violins. 6 Barclay Terrace, Bruntsfield, Edinburgh EH10 4HP *tel:* 0131 229 2051 *fax:* 0131 229 9298. *Maker and restorer of vns.*

Hammett, Claire. 19 Buxton Rd, E Sheen, London SW14 8SY *tel:* 020 8876 1496; 07973 659212 *fax:* 020 8876 1496 *email:* claire.hammett@btinternet.com. *Hpd tuner and technician; also clvds, chmbr orgs and pre-1830 f-pnos.*

Handy, Edmund. 5 Bourne Rd, Bexley, Kent DA5 1LG *tel:* 01322 527366 *fax:* 01322 527366 *email:* edmund.handy@btinternet.com. *Tuning, maintenance and repair of hpds, clvds and early pnos; clvd manufacturer. Celeste maintenance and repair. Square pno restorations. Reconditioned insts for sale.*

Hansford, Neil. The Bristol Violin Shop, 12 Upper Maudlin St, Bristol BS2 8DJ *tel:* 0117 925 9990 *fax:* 0117 925 0033 *email:* sales@bristol-violin-shop.co.uk. *Viols; English, French, German, Italian baroque vcs, vas and dbs.*

Harmonium Services. 6 Albert Terrace, Saltaire, Shipley, W Yorks BD18 4PS *tel:* 01274 585601; 07976 535980 *email:* phil@harmoniumservice.demon.co.uk. Phil Fluke, proprietor. *Restoration work using original materials wherever possible. Parts and reeds for sale. Insts bought and sold.*

The Harpsichord Workshop. 130 Westbourne Terrace Mews, London W2 6QG *tel:* 020 7723 9650 *fax:* 020 7723 9650 *email:* markransom@harpsichord-workshop.co.uk. Mark Ransom. *Tuning, repair, renovation, hire.*

Hibernian Violins. 67 Somers Rd, Malvern, Worcs WR14 1JA *tel:* 01684 562947 *fax:* 01684 562947. Padraig ó Dubhlaoidh, proprietor, inst conservator-restorer. *W/shop for str insts and bows. Accredited specialist conservator of str insts and bows.*

Hickies Ltd. 153 Friar St, Reading, Berks RG1 1HG *tel:* 0118 957 5771 *fax:* 0118 957 5775. *Tuning.*

Huggett, Martin. The Old Library, Stour St, Manningtree, Essex CO11 1BE *tel:* 01206 396354 *fax:* 01206 396354 *email:* martin@huggett.demon.co.uk. *Repairer, restorer, tuner of historic and modern keyboard insts. Also cabinet work.*

Impact Percussion. 7 Goose Green Trading Estate, 47 East Dulwich Rd, London SE22 9BN *tel:* 020 8299 6700 *fax:* 020 8299 6704 *email:* sales@impactpercussion.com. Paul Hagen. *Repair and custom manufacture of perc insts and stands. Also hire and sales.*

J & A Beare Ltd. 30 Queen Anne St, London W1G 8HX *tel:* 020 7307 9666 *fax:* 020 7307 9651 *email:* violins@beares.com. C Beare, dir; P Beare, dir; F Gillham, dir; D Morris, dir; S Morris, dir; S Smith, dir. *Dealers, restorers and makers of fine vns, vas and vcs.*

John Coppen Woodwind Repairs. Unit J302, Tower Bridge Business Complex, Clements Rd, London SE16 4DG *tel:* 020 7237 8989 *fax:* 020 7237 8989 *email:* Johncoppen@btinternet.com. *Hand-made keywork,* *extensions to all cls, specialising in bsn, cl and sax repairs. Sole agent for MARCA reeds. Wooden bs cl bells.*

Krattenmacher, Stefan Johann. 7 Sinclair Rd, W Kensington, London W14 0NS *tel:* 020 7602 8869 *email:* stefan@krattenmacher.co.uk. *Maker and restorer of vns, vas, vcs and dbs. Consultant; also accs, bows and small selection of fine, old insts. By appointment only.*

Lovemore Music Centre. Banbury Rd, Brackley NN13 6BA *tel:* 01280 703388 *fax:* 01280 706265. Brendon Tunley, mgr; Lance Tunley, dir. *Repairs, restorations. Br, w/wind, str insts.*

M and J Healey Violins. 12 Rosehill, Sutton, Surrey SM1 3EU *tel:* 020 8644 4700 *fax:* 020 8644 4700 *email:* malcolm@healeyviolins.f9.co.uk. *Strs. Accs, makers, repairers.*

Markson Pianos. 8 Chester Court, Albany St, London NW1 4BU *tel:* 0800 074 8980 *fax:* 020 7224 0957 *email:* sales@pianosuk.co.uk. *Pno sale, hire, restoration, repair, tuning, maintenance, transport. Concert and recording hire; hire with option to buy. Practice studios.*

Marshall McGurk Musical Services. Elm House Farm, Crosby, Maryport, Cumbria CA15 6SH *tel:* 01900 813200 *email:* 48katmos@freeuk.com; weeally@sniffout.com. Allison McGurk, partner; Steve Marshall, partner. *W/wind specialists, especially sax, cl. Also pno tuning and other insts.*

Martyn Booth Guitar Services. Unit 4, Old Brickworks, Chapel Lane, Little Cornard, Sudbury, Suffolk CO10 0PB *tel:* 01787 370192 *fax:* 01787 370192 *email:* mboothguitars@yahoo.co.uk. *Repairs and customisation of all types of gui.*

Michael Parfett Studios. Hackney City Farm, 1a Goldsmiths Row, London E2 8QA *tel:* 020 7729 4650 *fax:* 020 7729 4650 *email:* mike@michaelparfett.fsnet.co.uk. Michael Parfett, owner. *W/shop specialising in the repair, tuning and restoration of hpds, clvds, early pnos, early hps, celtic hps to modern concert hps including decoration and guilding. Pno tuning and servicing. Provide modern pno concert services at home and abroad, also technician work for hps and pnos. Happy to deal with other obscure instruments such as dulcimer, South American hps, English guis.*

The Midland Organ Company. 17 Belvoir St, Melton Mowbray, Leics LE13 1QA *tel:* 01664 566348 *fax:* 01664 569208 *email:* midorgco@telinco.com. Christopher Gray, mgr dir. *Repair,*

rebuilding and restoration of all types of pipe org; tuning service, blowing plant, humidifier service.

National Association of Musical Instrument Repairers. 10 Byron Rd, Harpenden, Herts AL5 4AB *tel:* 01582 762657 *email:* davidhinton@ouvip.com. David Hinton, sec; Gale Lawson, chmn. *Can provide contact information for members. Encourages high standard of workmanship and customer care, provides information on techniques and parts availability, technical back-up. Acts as arbitrator in the event of a dispute between repairer and customer.*

Nimblejack Ltd. 67 Old Rd, Studley, Calne, Wilts SN11 9NF *tel:* 01249 817283 *email:* alan@thewhears.freeserve.co.uk. Alan Whear. *Pno and hpd tuning, maintenance and repair. General repairs.*

Perkins, Martin. 8 Sandy Lane, Fillongley, Warks CV7 8DD *tel:* 01676 541585 *fax:* 01676 541659 *email:* mperkins@armonico.freeserve.co.uk. *Hpd and chmbr org tuner and provider.*

Peter W Salisbury Pianos Ltd. PO Box 325, 56 Gloucester Rd, Kensington, London SW7 4UB *tel:* 07092 334837; 020 8578 6741 *fax:* 020 8578 6741 *email:* info@petersalisburypianos.com. Peter Salisbury, dir. *Concert pno technician. International technical services for concert halls and festivals. Retail of new and reconditioned grand pnos. Full reconditioning services, specialist in Steinway and Bösendorfer.*

Phelps Pianos. 49-51 Fortess Rd, Kentish Town, London NW5 1AD *tel:* 0800 298 7385; 020 7485 2042 *fax:* 020 7284 1404 *email:* info@phelpsmusic.co.uk. Alister McLeod, sales mgr. *Pno specialists. Pno repairs, restoration, tuning, sales, hire and free advice. Acoustic and digital pnos (uprights and grands, new and second-hand). Also a range of mus insts and accs, practice rooms, teaching facilities.*

Ransom, Mark. 130 Westbourne Terrace Mews, London W2 6QG *tel:* 020 7723 9650 *fax:* 020 7723 9650 *email:* markransom@ harpsichord-workshop.co.uk. *Tuning, maintenance, hire, transport of hpds.*

Robert Morley & Co Ltd. 34 Engate St, London SE13 7HA *tel:* 020 8318 5838 *email:* jvm@morley-r.u-net.com. Julia Morley. *Repair, restoration and tuning of pnos, f-pnos, hpds, spinets, clvds, virginals, celestes.*

Royal National College for the Blind. College Rd, Hereford HR1 1EB *tel:* 01432 265725 *fax:* 01432 376628 *email:* info@rncb.ac.uk. Linda Wilkes, registrar and admissions offr. *Pno tuning and repairs.*

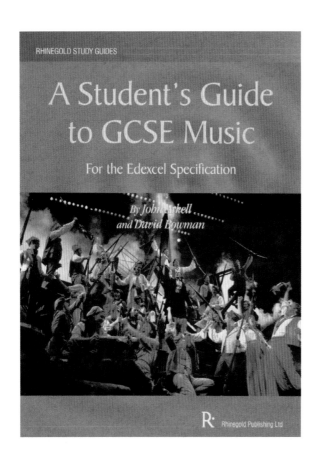
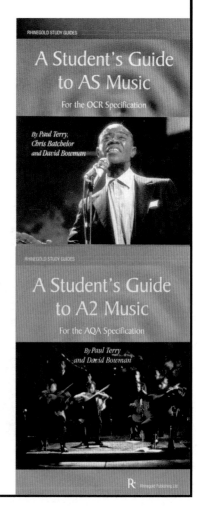

Shackell, Jeffrey. 41 Kingsfield Cres, Witney, Oxon OX28 2JB *tel:* 01993 703375; 07971 985302 *email:* info@shackellpianos.co.uk. *Concert pno technician. Specialist work to Steinway and Yamaha pnos. Sales, tuning, service work and overhauls.*

Stevens, Mike. 272 Louth Rd, Scartho, Grimsby DN33 2LF *tel:* 01472 824138 *email:* mijan.stev63@virgin.uk. *Repairs for str, w/wind, br, etc. Replacements made for any part of any inst, modifications for the disabled. Rebuilt second-hand insts for sale.*

T W Howarth & Co Ltd. 31 Chiltern St, London W1U 7PN *tel:* 020 7935 2407 *fax:* 020 7224 2564 *email:* sales@howarth.uk.com. *Specialist repair of all w/wind insts, including restoration of old and authentic insts.*

Temple, Alex. Platt Lodge, 61 Barton Rd, Worsley, Manchester M28 2GX *tel:* 0161 794 3717 *fax:* 0870 120 8401 *email:* alextemple@supanet.com. *Hpd, clvd, tuning, repairs and hire.*

Top Wind. 2 Lower Marsh, London SE1 7RJ *tel:* 020 7928 8181 *fax:* 020 7401 8788 *email:* JonD@topwind.com. Jon Dodd. *Specialist fl and picc repairs.*

Trainor, Brian. 15 Stanmore Cres, Lanark ML11 7DF *tel:* 01555 664024 *email:* brian.trainor@btinternet.com. *Br, str and w/wind inst repairs.*

Unison Strings Ltd. 113 The Custard Factory, Gibb St, Birmingham B9 4AA *tel:* 0121 693 1214 *fax:* 0121 693 1214 *email:* info@unisonstrings.co.uk. David Bruce Johnson; Francois Bignon. *Vns, vas, vcs and dbs. Also bows and accs. Vn makers and restorers. Valuations, appraisals and bow rehairing.*

Ward, Alan. St Andrews, 27 Plomer Hill, Downley, High Wycombe, Bucks HP13 5JG *tel:* 01494 523371 *email:* www.alanwardviolins.co.uk. *Vn, va, vc restorer and repairer. Also maker modern and baroque. Commissions handmade to order.*

Whittaker, Helen. Dawsons Music Ltd, 30 Pepper St, Chester CH1 1DF *tel:* 01244 348606. Helen Whittaker, repairer. *W/wind, str, br inst repairs.*

Woolrich, A P. Canal Side, Huntworth, Bridgwater, Somerset TA7 0AJ *tel:* 01278 663020 *fax:* 01278 663913 *email:* apw@ap-woolrich.co.uk. *Reproduction ironmongery for keyboard insts.*

Insurance and Financial Services

Allianz Cornhill Musical Insurance. Musical Instruments Dept, Allianz Cornhill House, 6 Vale Ave, Tunbridge Wells, Kent TN1 1EH *tel:* 0870 2400 303 *fax:* 0870 1600 304 *email:* musicalinsurance@allianzcornhill.co.uk. Dilys Killick, account developer; Wendy Hathaway, account developer. *Specialist insurers of mus insts.*

Brass Band Insurance Services. 312 High St, Harlington, Hayes, Middx UB3 5BT *tel:* 020 8759 0825 *fax:* 020 8564 9063 *email:* brassbands@bryanjames.co.uk. Mr and Mrs J Beeston, admin. *Insurers of bands, orchs, ens and individual musicians.*

E&L Insurance. Thorpe Underwood Hall, Ouseburn, York YO26 9SZ *tel:* 0870 742 3800 *fax:* 0870 742 3810 *email:* info@eandl.co.uk. Clare Bastiman, head of quotations dept. *All-risks cover for insts, br bands and equipment.*

Equity Insurance Services. 131 New London Rd, Chelmsford, Essex CM2 0QZ *tel:* 01245 357854 *fax:* 01245 491641 *email:* enquiries@equity-ins-services.com. *Motor, household and liability insurance for entertainers.*

Harrison-Beaumont (Insurance Brokers) Ltd. 2 Des Roches Square, Witney, Oxon OX8 6BE *tel:* 0870 121 7590 *fax:* 0870 121 7592 *email:* info@hbinsurance.co.uk. Jane Griffiths. *Specialists in providing injury and travel insurance to performers.*

Hibernian Violins. 67 Somers Rd, Malvern, Worcs WR14 1JA *tel:* 01684 562947 *fax:* 01684 562947. Padraigh ó Dubhlaoidh. *Advice on insuring str insts, bows. Valuations.*

Jack Hayward Harps. Harp Strings Insurance, 5 Sun Gardens, Burghfield Common, Reading RG7 3JB *tel:* 0118 983 3922 *fax:* 0118 983 3868. *All-risks insurance for all mus insts. UK to worldwide cover.*

La Playa. The Stables, Manor Farm, Milton Rd, Impington, Cambridge CB4 9NF *tel:* 01223 522411 *fax:* 01223 237942 *email:* mark.boon@laplaya.co.uk. Mark Boon, mgr dir. *Specialist*

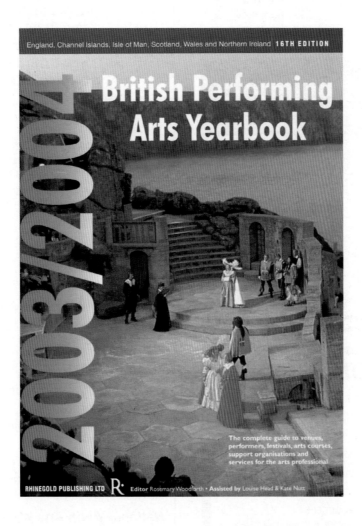

insurance for the mus and media industries. Cover includes insts, equipment, touring, cancellation, property and liabilities.

Musicians Insurance Services. 312 High St, Harlington, Hayes, Middx UB3 5BT *tel:* 020 8564 8181; 0845 345 7529 *fax:* 020 8564 9063 *email:* admin@musiciansinsurance.co.uk. Mark Prendergast, snr

underwriter; John Beeston, mkt. *Specialist insurance service for musicians. Inst insurance, liability, travel, etc.*

Shepherd Finance Ltd. 2 The Hall, Turners Green Rd, Wadhurst, E Sussex TN5 6TR *tel:* 01892 785010 *fax:* 01892 785023 *email:* branson@ shepherdfinance.co.uk. B J Branson, dir. *Specialists in finance for mus insts.*

Internet and Website Services

AA web management consultancy. 14a Graham Rd, Great Malvern, Worcs WR14 2HN *tel:* 07768 664550 *email:* andrew@ andrewaird.co.uk. *Specialist website design and mgt for the classical mus industry; academic and educ websites and online database solutions; web mgt consultancy.*

Abbey Road Interactive. Abbey Road Studios, 3 Abbey Rd, London NW8 9AY *tel:* 020 7266 7282 *fax:* 020 7266 7321 *email:* interactive@ abbeyroad.com. Trish McGregor, studio mgr. *Interactive design and digital video studio; DVD-V, DVD-A, ECD and web.*

Amazing Internet Ltd. 85 Waldegrave Park, Twickenham, Middx TW1 4TJ *tel:* 020 8607 9535 *fax:* 020 8607 9536 *email:* info@ amazinginternet.com. Andrew Skirrow, mgr dir; Ronny Adsetts, tech dir; Jesse Wilson, art dir. *Specialists in internet services to the arts. All aspects of website design and construction, internet mkt and associated IT services.*

Anne Lewis Web Design. 5 Neville Court, Grove End Rd, St John's Wood, London NW8 9DD *tel:* 020 7286 4865/5735 *fax:* 020 7266 0181 *email:* annelewis.webdesign@btinternet.com. *Individual designs, hosting services, with experienced mkt support based on broad knowledge of the mus world.*

Arts Services Direct. PO Box 3136, Barnet, Herts EN5 1DY *tel:* 020 8447 3862 *fax:* 020 8447 3862 *email:* jhart@voxhumana.co.uk. Jan Hart, mgr. *Book-keeping and tax, admin and secretarial services, basic web-design and maintenance, mkt, event promotion and mgt.*

bar-coded. 11 Fen Rd, Milton, Cambridge CB4 6AD *tel:* 07791 491198 *email:* marcus@bar-coded.co.uk. Marcus Williams. *Specialist website design, hosting and internet services.*

Cadenza. Flat D, 25 Oxford Rd, Ealing, London W5 3SP *tel:* 020 8840 1564 *fax:* 0870 056 2196 *email:* info1@cadenza.org. Keith Bramich. *Various free resources, including adverts, concert listings and directory entries, which can be set up by emailing for further details.*

Classical Artists Worldwide. 85 Waldegrave Park, Twickenham, Middx TW1 4TJ *tel:* 020 8607 9535 *fax:* 020 8607 9536 *email:* info@classical-artists.com. Andrew Skirrow, partner; Ronny Adsetts, partner. *Website design/hosting service and internet index for classical musicians and the classical mus industry. Subsidiary of Amazing Internet Ltd.*

Con Brio Web Design. 6 Munsons Lane, Feltwell, Norfolk IP26 4DE *tel:* 01482 828408; 07973 977704 *fax:* 01482 828408 *email:* info@ con-brio.com. Steve Bingham. *Web hosting, design, domain registration and e-commerce. Distinctive, personally designed websites.*

Impulse. 18 Hillfield Park, Muswell Hill, London N10 3QS *tel:* 020 8444 8587 *fax:* 020 8245 0358 *email:* impulse@impulse-music.co.uk. Geraldine Allen, mkt and PR; Sarah Rodgers, design and technical. *Impulse Classical Music Website: established 1997 to promote musicians, recordings and composer cat on the internet. Web page design, internet consultancy and copyright advice.*

MNT Design. 16 Princes St, Cheltenham, Glos GL52 6BE *tel:* 07786 753031 *fax:* 01242 234830 *email:* info@mntdesign.com. *Website design for musicians. Sites for individuals and organisations. Features include: streaming audio and video, fully updatable pages, e-commerce, flash animation.*

Orion Computer Consultants Ltd. 25 Oxford Rd, London W5 3SP *tel:* 020 8840 1564 *fax:* 0870 056 2196 *email:* enquiries@orion-arts.com. Keith Bramich, mgr dir. *Internet website design and consultancy for the arts.*

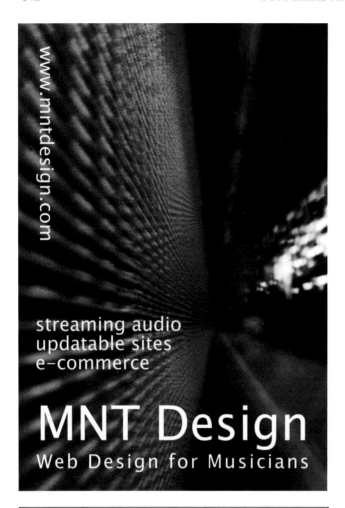

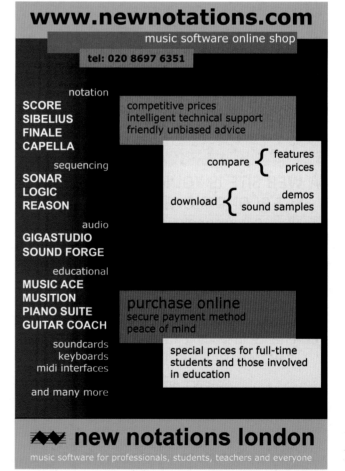

Ricardo Insua-Cao. 240 Brighton Rd, S Croydon, Surrey CR2 6AH *tel:* 020 8686 2026; 07986 605774 *email:* ricardo@rinsua.co.uk. Ricardo Insua-Cao, artist and designer. *Graphic design, website design and artwork for musicians.*

spacehoppa.com. 20 Vicarage Lane, Sandbach, Cheshire CW11 3BW *tel:* 01270 766001 *fax:* 01270 766699 *email:* info@spacehoppa.com.

Ruth Arnold. *Website design and internet consultancy for the arts.*

WebProjects. Suites 5-7, Meridian House, 28 Station Rd, Redhill, Surrey RH1 1PD *tel:* 01737 768127 *email:* mark@webprojects.co.uk. Mark Walmsley, mgr dir; Ben Sauer, technical dir; Matthew Lindop, project dir; Andy Walker, creative dir. *Efficient creation, sharing and distribution of information.*

Medical Support Organisations

Arts Psychology Consultants. 29 Argyll Mansions, Hammersmith Rd, London W14 8QQ *tel:* 020 7602 2707 *email:* info@artspsychology.com. Andy Evans, dir. *A confidential counselling and careers service for musicians and industry staff dealing with performance problems, stage fright, career guidance and personal issues. Psychologists have professional mus backgrounds. Email for details of special offers to MU and Equity members.*

British Association for Performing Arts Medicine. 196 Shaftesbury Ave, London WC2H 8JF *tel:* 020 7240 4500 (helpline)/3331 (admin); 0845 602 0235 *fax:* 020 7240 3335 *email:* bpamt@dial.pipex.com. Rosanna Preston, chief exec; Clare Hicks, admin; Yinka Fasawe O'Reilly, helpline co-ord. *Founded in 1984, BAPAM runs free diagnosis and assessment clinics run by conventional and complementary practitioners, accessed via a local Helpline, for performers with performance-related injury or illness, whether physical, psychological or emotional.*

Dorset Centre for the Alexander Technique. Vale View, Streetway Lane, Cheselbourne, Dorset DT2 7QB *tel:* 01258 839030 *email:* franalextek@btopenworld.com. Frances Robinson, dir.

Introductory groups, individual lessons and custom-made courses.

Pearson, R M. 152 Harley St, London W1G 7LH *tel:* 020 7935 0444 *fax:* 020 7354 1501 *email:* richard.pe@which.net. R M Pearson, consultant physician. *Non-NHS consultations for the medical problems of inst musicians and keyboard operators, including muscle overuse, movement disorders and rehabilitation after injuries. Also NHS via: R M Pearson, consultant physician, Harold Wood Hospital, Romford, Essex RM3 0BE.*

Performing Arts Counselling Service (PAX Northwest). Beechwood, 9 Harboro Rd, Sale, Cheshire M33 5AE *tel:* 0161 976 6992 *email:* delythw@onetel.net.uk. Delyth Wilkinson, counsellor, voice consultant. *UKRC Reg Ind Counsellor, BAPAM trained. Welcomes mus and/or voice-related psychological concerns. Private practice and NHS.*

Westminster Alexander Centre. 8 Hop Gardens, off St Martin's Lane, London WC2N 4EH *tel:* 020 7240 2118 *email:* wac@alextech.demon.co.uk. John Hunter, co-ord; Paola Corteen, teacher. *Introductory courses, private lessons, refresher classes in the Alexander Technique, including application to insts, respiration, voice, performance and dealing with injury.*

Music Copyists, Setters, Engravers and Printers

Acoustic Art. 2 Milton House, 25 Short St, Waterloo, London SE1 8LH *tel:* 020 7928 1216 *fax:* 020 7928 1216 *email:* jon.paxman@virgin.net. Jonathan Paxman; Andy Fisher. *Professional computerised mus copying and processing. Full production service. Transposition, orchestration and arranging services available.*

Acuta Music. Hambrook, Ledbury, Herefordshire HR8 2PX *tel:* 01531 670634 *fax:* 01531 670634. Robert Kay. *Computerised mus setting, hand-copying, proof-reading.*

Allegro Reproductions. 33 Belmont Close, Uxbridge, Middx UB8 1RF *tel:* 01895 232055 *fax:* 01895 232055. Stephen Duro, dir; Beryl Duro, dir. *Computerised mus engraving. Also editing, arranging, orchestrating, transposing, part extraction.*

Animus. 4 Rawlinson St, Dalton-in-Furness, Cumbria LA15 8AL *tel:* 01229 467432 *email:* selfmus@aol.com. Adrian and Pamela Self. *Computerised mus setting. Transposition, arranging. Choral and org mus a speciality.*

Barry Peter Ould Music Services. 6 Fairfax Cres, Aylesbury, Bucks HP20 2ES *tel:* 01296 428609 *fax:* 01296 581185 *email:* bipo@post.com. Barry Peter Ould. *Computerised mus setting, design, typesetting and photocopying service.*

Bowden, Elizabeth. 4 Pitt Court, Nymet Rowland, Crediton, Devon EX17 6AN *tel:* 01363 83515 *fax:* 01363 83936 *email:* lizbowdenmusic@talk21.com. *Mus copyist, computer setting (Sibelius).*

Caligraving Ltd. Brunel Way, Thetford, Norfolk IP24 1HP *tel:* 01842 752116 *fax:* 01842 755512. Oliver W Makings, sales and mkt dir. *Mus printing and book binding. Full studio facilities available.*

Camden Music. 85 Waldegrave Park, Twickenham, Middx TW1 4TJ *tel:* 020 8744 9005 *fax:* 020 8607 9536 *email:* info@camdenmusic.com. Andrew Skirrow, dir. *Specialist computerised mus typesetting service, media mus.*

Chalmers Enterprises. 76 Carnbee Park, Edinburgh EH16 6GH *tel:* 0131 620 2421 *fax:* 0131 620 2421 *email:* music@neilscott.net. Neil Scott. *Computerised mus typesetting using Coda Finale.*

Cowdrey, Elizabeth. Lower Grumbla Farm, Sancreed, Penzance, Cornwall TR20 8QX *tel:* 01736 788304; 07788 141381 *fax:* 01993 880453 *email:* lizcowdrey1@excite.com. *Hand transcription. Special interest in world mus, vn, fiddle mus.*

Craig-McFeely, Julia. 41 Freelands Rd, Oxford OX4 4BS *tel:* 01865 241323 *fax:* 01865 437582 *email:* julia.craig-mcfeely@music.oxford.ac.uk. Julia Craig-McFeely. *Typesetting of all types of mus, specialising in unusual notational requirements: editing includes early mus notations. Proof-reading and copy-editing.*

Crofton, Robin. 8 Wynbury Drive, Totteridge, High Wycombe, Bucks HP13 7QB *tel:* 01494 533775. *Computerised mus setting (Sibelius 7 and Sibelius).*

Da Capo Music Ltd. 26 Stanway Rd, Whitefield, Manchester M45 8EG *tel:* 0161 766 5950 *email:* colin@dacapomusic.co.uk. *Computerised mus setting and processing, CD production.*

Dale, Simon. 26 Leicester Rd, Lewes, E Sussex BN7 1SX *tel:* 01273 470092/486389 *email:* music@simondale.com. *Computer typesetting. Orchestration, arranging, pno reductions. Also website design and development, graphic design.*

Enigma Music Production Services. 44 Grove Rd, Amersham, Bucks HP6 6NE *tel:* 01494 431663 *fax:* 01494 431663 *email:* bev.enigma@virgin.net. B R Wilson. *Mus engraving (Sibelius 7), Sibelius 1.4 and Sibelius 2.1 (Applemac) using QuarkXPress, Adobe Illustrator and Adobe Acrobat when required.*

Fand Music Press. The Barony, 16 Sandringham Rd, Petersfield, Hants GU32 2AA *tel:* 01730 267341 *fax:* 01730 267341 *email:* sales@fandmusic.com. Peter Thompson, dir. *Pno, vocal, chmbr, choral, orch mus.*

Foster, Derek. 41 Gloucester Court, Kew Rd, Kew, Richmond, Surrey TW9 3EA *tel:* 020 8940 8373. *Mus typesetting using 'Score' and laser printed output.*

Frontier Music Services. 36 Riverdale Rd, Plumstead, London SE18 1NZ *tel:* 020 8473 2213. Jennifer Churches, proprietor. *Computerised typesetting service.*

Gibson, Stephen. 93 Wellmeadow Rd, London SE6 1HL *tel:* 020 8697 6351 *fax:* 020 8697 0038 *email:* stephen@gibmusic.freeserve.co.uk. *Mus typesetting, orchestration, arranging, vocal reductions.*

Ginn, Jeffrey. 11 Haycroft, Wootton, Bedford, Beds MK43 9PB *tel:* 01234 765602; 07778 896721 *fax:* 01234 765602 *email:* jeffginn@onetel.net.uk. *Mus typesetting to laser or film. Sibelius 7 recording service.*

Gordon, Christopher. 22 Ivybridge Close, Twickenham, Middx TW1 1EA *tel:* 020 8892 1833 *fax:* 0870 126 8552 *email:* coolwind.music@virgin.net. Christopher Gordon. *Mus-setting by computer. Hand copying at reasonable rates.*

Halstan & Co Ltd. 2-10 Plantation Rd, Amersham, Bucks HP6 6HJ *tel:* 01494 725525 *fax:* 01494 432305 *email:* sales@halstan.co.uk. Christopher Smith, mgr dir. *Mus process engraving, computerised mus setting, design service, mus printing and binding.*

Hinkins, Chris and Gail. The Old Rectory, Moorby, Boston, Lincs PE22 7PL *tel:* 01507 568476 *fax:* 01507 568476 *email:* cjhinkins@lineone.net. *High-quality computer mus engraving and audio realisations of scores.*

Hodson, Maud. 129 Mornington Rd, London E11 3DT *tel:* 020 8925 8477 *email:* maud@maud.co.uk. *Computerised mus typesetting (Sibelius).*

King's Music. Redcroft, Banks End, Wyton, Huntingdon, Cambs PE28 2A *tel:* 01480 52076 *fax:* 01480 450821 *email:* clifford.bartlett@

btopenworld.com. Clifford Bartlett. *Photocopying, mus and text typesetting, programme production (including writing and printing notes).*

Lancaster, Philip. Chosen Arts, 30 Brighton Rd, Redland, Bristol BS6 6NT *tel:* 0117 923 9355; 07989 197998 *email:* philip.lancaster@chosen-arts.org.uk. *Mus typesetting (Sibelius). Also programme notes and project concert promotion. British mus specialist.*

Langley, John. 18 Syon Park Gardens, Isleworth, Middx TW7 5NB *tel:* 020 8758 9422 *fax:* 020 8758 9865 *email:* kermit.whistler@virgin.net. *Computer typesetting and editing (Sibelius), transposing, transcribing, sequencing, arranging, orchestration, ms sourcing, orch librarian and trouble-shooting service.*

Laser Music Ltd. 19 Davies Drive, Devizes, Wilts SN10 2RJ *tel:* 01380 728772 *email:* lasermusic@argonet.co.uk. Gareth Bennett, principal associate. *Computerised mus setting and mus copying.*

Linda Lancaster Music Setting. 25 Far View Cres, Almondbury, Huddersfield HD5 8ER *tel:* 01484 546490 *fax:* 01484 480785 *email:* linda@linlanc.demon.co.uk. Paul Lancaster, partner. *Computerised mus and text setting.*

Lindley Studios. 18 Bishopstone Rd, Seaford, E Sussex BN25 2UB *tel:* 01323 872817 *fax:* 01323 872817 *email:* lindley.studios@virgin.net. David Hoyle, dir. *Computerised mus setting using Sibelius. All styles from complex orchestral/parts to commercial mus. Printing (A3) and binding. Transposition, arranging, transcription from ear.*

Longship Music. 'Smidskot', Fawells, Keith-Hall, Inverurie, Aberdeenshire AB51 0LN *tel:* 01651 882274 *fax:* 01651 882274. John Hearne. *Mus copying and typesetting (Sibelius 7). Full service including binding in card covers, title pages, etc. Phone for quotation.*

Meladina Press. 30 Chiltern Rd, St Albans, Herts AL4 9TB *tel:* 01727 861131 *fax:* 01727 861131 *email:* dimitrismirnov@lineone.net. Dmitri Smirnov, partner; Elena Firsova, partner. *Comprehensive computerised mus typesetting service (including Finale, Sibelius, Score, etc). Also specialist hand transcription, orchestration, arrangements, transposition, pno reduction and editing service.*

Music Maestro. Chicken Shed Theatre Company, Chase Side, Southgate, London N14 4PE *tel:* 020 8351 6161 ext 206 *fax:* 020 8292 0202 *email:* musicmaestro@spurge.demon.co.uk. Fiona Callan, admin; David

Carey. *Transcription service, providing printed sheet mus from any cassette tape, recording, from voice and pno to full orch score.*

Musicleigh Inklined. 35 Kirtle Rd, Chesham, Bucks HP5 1AD *tel:* 01494 771872 *email:* jackieleigh64@aol.com. Jackie Leigh. *Computerised mus typesetting (Sibelius, Finale), artwork productions, laser printing.*

Musography. 10 Carnaby, Kimbolton, Cambs PE28 0JB *tel:* 01480 861312 *fax:* 01480 861312 *email:* musography@cbmusic.freeserve.co.uk. Christopher Brown. *Computerised mus typesetting (SCORE), specialising in complex contemporary scores and baroque mus.*

New Notations Computer Services Ltd. 7 Duncombe Hill, London SE23 1QY *tel:* 07968 312032 *fax:* 0870 706 4795 *email:* sales@newnotations.co.uk. Stephen Ferre, mgr dir. *Advanced computerised mus typesetting, mus and text integration, etc. Specialists in large projects, fast turnaround. Consultancy and custom-built computer workstations and software sales. M/order.*

Orphean Press Ltd. 14 Albert Rd, Brightlingsea, Essex CO7 0NB *tel:* 01206 307701 *fax:* 01206 307701 *email:* info@orphean-press.demon.co.uk. Cheryl Jessop, mgr dir. *Mus engraving, typesetting, publishing and design. Preparation of performing editions.*

Parish Publications. 28 Tom Price Close, Cheltenham, Glos GL52 2LF *tel:* 01242 230455 *fax:* 01242 230455 *email:* parish@lineone.net. Ian and Janine Higginson, mgrs. *Computerised mus setting (Sibelius), composition, transposition, arranging, orchestrating, part extraction, proof-reading. Typesetting of all types of mus.*

Paul Rigby Music Processing. 29 Park Close, Wratten Rd East, Hitchin, Hertfordshire SG5 2AS *tel:* 01462 455184 *email:* paulrigby@musicprocess.com. *Advanced computer mus setting and processing (Sibelius 7, Sibelius 2). Orchestration and arrangements. Audio realisations.*

Pilkington, Michael. 268 Coulsdon Rd, Old Coulsdon, Surrey CR5 1EB *tel:* 01737 556346 *fax:* 01737 556346 *email:* mikepilkington@lineone.net. *Computerised mus copying, transposition, part extraction.*

RTS Music Partnership. 17 Bradford Rd, St John's, Wakefield, W Yorks WF1 2RF *tel:* 01924 370454 *fax:* 01924 370454 *email:* standford@rtsmusic.demon.co.uk. Patric Standford, dir. *Composition, arranging, computer copying, editing, revision and tutorial support; work for TV and concert, schools and amateurs.*

Rosewood Copying Services. Farthings, Rotten Row Hill, Bradfield, Berkshire RG7 6LL *tel:* 0118 974 4426 *email:* s.westmeath@virgin.net. Susanna Westmeath. *Computerised mus setting; full range of printing and publishing.*

SJ Music. 23 Leys Rd, Cambridge CB4 2AP *tel:* 01223 314771 *fax:* 01223 560353. Judith Rattenbury, principal. *Computerised mus typesetting and transposition.*

Silverfen. 57a St Philip's Rd, Cambridge CB1 3DA *tel:* 01223 461143 *fax:* 01223 461143 *email:* mail@silverfen.com. Timothy Argent, dir. *Mus setting, design, typesetting, website design.*

Smith, Andrew. 23 Bradbury Close, Wardley, Gateshead, Tyne and Wear NE10 8UF *tel:* 0191 495 2778. *Hand and computer transcription.*

Snell, Piers. 87 High St, Nash, Milton Keynes MK17 0EP *tel:* 01908 508760 *email:* P.snell@ntlworld.com. Piers Snell. *Advanced computerised mus engraving.*

Software Partners. Oak Tree House, Station Rd, Claverdon, Warks CV35 8PE *tel:* 01926 842998 *fax:* 01926 842384 *email:* info@software-partners.co.uk. Richard Blundell. *Distributors for capella (mus notation), capriccio (MIDI sequencer), tonica (harmony and composition), capella-scan and Smartscore (mus OCR software).*

Spartan Press Ltd. Strathmashie House, Laggan PH20 1BU *tel:* 01528 544770 *fax:* 01528 544771 *email:* mail@spartanpress.co.uk. Mark Goddard, mgr dir; Sandra Grant, sales co-ord. *Mus typesetting, laser, b/w and colour digital printing services.*

Steadman, Robert. 5 Henry Ave, Matlock DE4 3FL *tel:* 01629 56563 *email:* rob@robertsteadman.com. *Computerised mus copying and typesetting. Transposition and orchestration services available.*

Vann, Esther. Hambrook Cottage, Hambrook, Ledbury, Herefordshire HR8 2PX *tel:* 01531 670634 *fax:* 01531 670634. *Hand and computerised copying and notesetting.*

Wessex Music Services. 1000 Westbury Rd, Little Cheverell, Devizes, Wilts SN10 4JW *tel:* 01380 816338 *fax:* 01380 816467 *email:* admin@wessexmusic.co.uk. John Bickerton, proprietor. *Computerised mus typesetting, laser printing, arrangements, transposition.*

Wilson, Jenny. 10 Hogan Way, Stafford, Staffs ST16 3YN *tel:* 01785 228871 *fax:* 01785 228990 *email:* jenny.wilson@which.net. Jenny Wilson, proprietor. *Computerised mus setting and laser printing using Sibelius software (Acorn/PC).*

Musical Giftware and Novelties Manufacturers and Retailers

Beckmann Visual Publishing. Meadow Court, West St, Ramsey, Isle of Man IM8 1AE *tel:* 01624 816585 *fax:* 01624 816589 *email:* visual@beckmanndirect.com. Tim Beetham, mkt mgr; Jo White, publishing dir. *Mus tuition DVD/videos.*

Instrumental Furniture. Bridge House, 103 Station Rd, Gamlinghay, Sandy SG19 3HB *tel:* 01767 651145 *fax:* 01767 651145. John Hammond, designer, dir. *CD racks to coffee tables and chopping boards. Over 40 mus designs.*

Lindsay Music. 23 Hitchin St, Biggleswade, Beds SG18 8AX *tel:* 01767 316521 *fax:* 01767 317221 *email:* sales@lindsaymusic.co.uk. Carole Lindsay-Douglas, dir. *Tea-towels, thimbles, display plates, mus bags.*

The Music Box. 30/31 The Lanes (by the Oasis), Meadowhall, Sheffield S9 1EP *tel:* 0114 256 9089 *email:* ask@themusicbox.co.uk.

The Music Gifts Company. 7 Fleetsbridge Business Centre, Upton Rd, Poole, Dorset BH17 7AF *tel:* 01202 686368 *fax:* 01202 686363 *email:* orders@musicgifts.co.uk. David Gee, mgr dir. *The largest collection of British-made gifts, including stationery, kitchenware, textiles, bone china mugs, teapots, silk apparel, clocks, pewterware, etc. Over 600 gift ideas.*

Music Notables. 57 Amberwood, Ferndown, Dorset BH22 9JT *tel:* 01202 855955 *fax:* 01202 855955 *email:* info@musicnotables.co.uk. Edouard and Veronica Sefton, partners. *A range of exclusive British innovative mus-related giftware: tea-towels, aprons, tote bags, oven mitts, T-shirts, china mugs, bookmarks, stationery, etc.*

Musical Expressions Ltd. 106 High St, Bildeston, Suffolk IP7 7EB *tel:* 01449 741707. Kevin Bates, dir; Jackie Bates, sales. *Suppliers of*

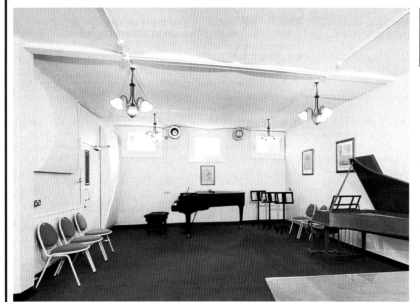

'*Musical Expressions*' *greetings cards (designs inspired by classical mus scores and insts).*

Spartan Press Music Publishers Ltd. Strathmashie House, Laggan PH20 1BU *tel:* 01528 544770 *fax:* 01528 544771 *email:* mail@ spartanpress.co.uk. Mark Goddard, mgr dir; Jonathan Kershaw, sales; Grace Haines, production; Phil Goddard, production; Sandra Grant, sales. *Greetings cards, cartoon books, ms books.*

Transformer London Ltd. Unit 34, The Cremer Business Centre, Cremer St, London E2 8HD *tel:* 020 7729 0750 *fax:* 020 7729 0752 *email:* sales@transformer-t-shirts.com. Stewart Lawman, sales dir. *Printed t-shirts and promotional garment screen printing for all bands, orchs and events.*

William Elkin Music Services. Station Rd Industrial Estate, Salhouse, Norwich NR13 6NS *tel:* 01603 721302 *fax:* 01603 721801 *email:* sales@elkinmusic.co.uk. Cindy Hazard, sales. *Giftware including jewellery, clothing, umbrellas, stationery, clocks and household goods.*

Practice Studios

Adrian Levine Studio. 27 Leicester Rd, London N2 9DY *tel:* 020 8444 5905 *fax:* 020 8444 5905 *email:* adrian@fisherlevine.plus.com. Adrian Levine, proprietor. *Rehearsal/teaching space in North London. Soundproof detached studio, 19' x 14', excellent light and acoustics, warm and private. 6' Bechstein grand pno. Refreshments. Ideal for chmbr mus or teaching. £3 per person, per hour.*

Amadeus Centre. 50 Shirland Rd, London W9 2JA *tel:* 020 7286 1686 *fax:* 020 7266 1225 *email:* info@amadeuscentre.co.uk. Amanda Mellett. *2 rehearsal halls and in-house café. Upper hall up to 55 players with grand pno; lower hall up to 25 players with pno. Ideal for auditions, rehearsals, w/shops and concerts.*

Belsize Music Rooms. 67 Belsize Lane, Hampstead, London NW3 5AX *tel:* 020 7916 0111 *fax:* 020 7916 0222 *email:* info@ belsize-music-rooms.co.uk. Clare Lange; Dawn Elizabeth Howells. *3 air-controlled and sound-proofed mus rooms with Steinway, Fazioli and Ibach pnos and a concert hpd. Quality new and second-hand upright pnos for sale. Also waiting room, outside relaxation area, refreshment facilities.*

Bromley Youth Music Centre. Southborough Lane, Bromley, Kent BR2 8AA *tel:* 020 8467 1566 *fax:* 020 8468 7595 *email:* contact@bymt.co.uk. Peter Mawson, principal. *Large hall, up to 70 players. Yamaha grand pno, 12 other rooms with uprights.*

The Clarendon Suites. 2 Stirling Rd, Edgbaston, Birmingham B16 9SB *tel:* 0121 454 2918 *fax:* 0121 455 0859 *email:* info@ clarendon-suites.co.uk. Martin Robinson, snr mgr. *9 rooms suitable for rehearsals of any kind; plus 9 for vocalists.*

Craxton Studios. 14 Kidderpore Ave, London NW3 7SU *tel:* 020 7435 2965 *fax:* 020 7431 1579. Jane Craxton, dir; Kim Mathen, dir. *Rehearsals, auditions, filming, recording. Large studio: double-height, wood-panelled, sprung maple floor, 2 concert grand pnos, up to 30 (orch) or 50 (choir). 2nd studio: grand pno, up to 7 players. Refreshment facilities, quiet secluded garden relaxation area.*

John Henry's Ltd. 16-24 Brewery Rd, London N7 9NH *tel:* 020 7609 9181 *fax:* 020 7700 7040 *email:* info@johnhenrys.com. John Henry, mgr dir; Phil Burns, sales. *Rehearsal studios; equipment sales; backline and audio rental; flightcase manufacturer; transport; storage.*

Markson Pianos. 8 Chester Court, Albany St, London NW1 4BU *tel:* 0800 074 8980 *fax:* 020 7224 0957 *email:* sales@pianosuk.co.uk. *Practice studios.*

Music Dynamics Ltd. Bishops Leys Business Park, Butts Lane, Woodmancote, Cheltenham GL52 9ZP *tel:* 01242 679379 *fax:* 01242 663992 *email:* music@musicdynamics.co.uk. Sue Silverthorne. *ChoraLine range of high-tech SATB rehearsal CDs and cassettes for choral singers. Fast personal score supply service. Short-run audio and data CD duplication. The Miller Keys scale and key signature learning kit.*

The Music Room. 49 Great Ormond St, London WC1N 3HZ *tel:* 020 7405 9848. Alec Forshaw.

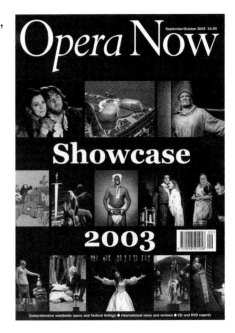
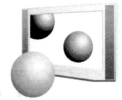

The Music Studios. 29 Marylebone Lane, London W1U 2NQ *tel:* 020 7486 0025 *fax:* 020 7935 8454. Nigel Brown, gen mgr; Kevin Bias, studio mgr. *Studios available from a half hour minimum. Popular teaching venue. Telephone bookings advised. Open 10am-9pm (closed Mon am, Sat 6pm, all day Sun). Acoustic only. Excellent grands in all rooms.*

Terminal 24 Rehearsal Ltd. 4-10 Lamb Walk, London Bridge, London SE1 3TT *tel:* 020 7403 3050 *fax:* 020 7407 6123 *email:* info@ terminal.co.uk. Charlie Barrett, dir. *Large Turbosound-equipped studios, central London. Comprehensive equipment hire on site, showcase and production rooms. Café and production office. Storage cages.*

The Warehouse. 13 Theed St, London SE1 8ST *tel:* 020 7928 9251 *fax:* 020 7928 9252 *email:* lara@lfo.co.uk. Lara Bellini, booking mgr. *2 rehearsal halls; Studio 1 up to 70 players, Studio 2 up to 32 players. Steinway and Röenisch grand pnos, orch chairs and mus stands.*

The Wathen Hall. St Paul's School, Lonsdale Rd, Barnes, London SW13 9JT *tel:* 020 8748 8874 *fax:* 020 8748 4048 *email:* manager@ wathenhall.com. Angela Parry, mgr. *Rehearsals, auditions, filming, recording; large hall (316 seats), 2 Steinway pnos ('D' and 'AS'); solo work and chmbr groups; also suitable for up to 25 (orch) or 60 (choir).*

Programme and Sleeve Notes

Ades, David. Stone Gables, Upton Lane, Seavington St Michael, Ilminster, Somerset TA19 0PZ *tel:* 01460 242226 *fax:* 01460 242226 *email:* david@rfsoc.freeserve.co.uk. *Compiler and sleeve note writer.*

Avis, Peter Graham. 91 Cambridge Rd, New Malden, Surrey KT3 3QP *tel:* 020 8336 1656 *fax:* 020 8336 1742 *email:* peteravis@waitrose.com. *Programme and CD booklet notes, more anecdotal than technical. Also available for pre-concert talks.*

Barfoot, Terry. 25 Mulberry Lane, Cosham, Portsmouth PO6 2QU *tel:* 023 9238 3356 *fax:* 023 9238 3356 *email:* terry.barfoot@talk21.com. *Programme and sleeve notes.*

Barker, Duncan. 210 Hainault Rd, London E11 1EP *tel:* 020 8558 9040 *email:* duncanbarker@beeb.net. *Programme notes for orchs, agents and concerts, also sleeve notes for CDs.*

Bartlett, Clifford. Redcroft, Banks End, Wyton, Huntingdon, Cambs PE28 2AA *tel:* 01480 52076 *fax:* 01480 450821 *email:* clifford. bartlett@btopenworld.com. *Programme and sleeve notes.*

The Basil Ramsey Programme Note Library. 604 Rayleigh Rd, Eastwood, Leigh-on-Sea, Essex SS9 5HU *tel:* 01702 524305 *fax:* 01702 526142 *email:* basilmusic@freeserve.co.uk. Basil Ramsey, dir. *Library of classical mus programme notes. Works can be requested by phone or email.*

Bryant, Michael. 61 Oak Hill, Surbiton, Surrey KT6 6DY *tel:* 020 8390 3236 *email:* michael@bryant14.demon.co.uk. *Specialising in Czech and Slovak mus and all chmbr and wind repertoire.*

Bullamore, Tim. The Priory, 54 Lyncombe Hill, Bath BA2 4PJ *tel:* 01225 330037; 07836 617030 *fax:* 01225 446627 *email:* TBullamore@ aol.com. *Programme notes for concerts, festivals, recordings, etc. Author of Fifty Festivals, the history of the Bath Festival.*

Burton, Anthony. 19 Capel Rd, E Barnet, Herts EN4 8JD *tel:* 020 8440 4380 *email:* agburton@btinternet.com. *Programme and CD notes.*

Butterworth, Neil. The Lodge, East High St, Greenlaw, Berwickshire TD10 6UF *tel:* 01361 810408. *Programme and sleeve notes, any level/length.*

Carroll, Brendan G. 2 Southbank Rd, Grassendale, Liverpool L19 9AR *tel:* 0151 427 1181 *fax:* 0151 494 3589 *email:* brendangcarroll@ aol.com. *Programme notes, sleeve notes, reviews of recordings and books. Specialises in early 20th C mus, especially opera, film mus and Korngold.*

Carson, Ian. Yew Trees, Comeytrowe Rise, Taunton TA1 5JA *tel:* 01823 272764 *fax:* 01823 272764 *email:* carson@beeb.net. *Programme and liner notes, extensive library, reviews and articles.*

Clampin, Fiona. 14 Ernsborough Court, Fairpark Rd, Exeter, Devon EX2 4HL *tel:* 01392 424399 *fax:* 07899 932620 *email:* fionaclampin@yahoo.com. *Programme and sleeve notes.*

Conway, Joe. 22 Brook Court, Harrow Rd, London E11 3PP *tel:* 01522 546876 *email:* joe.conway@ntlworld.co.uk. *Programme and sleeve notes. Also reviews, interviews, in-depth pieces. Opinionated snappy copy always available at short notice.*

Fligg, David. Leeds College of Music, 3 Quarry Hill, Leeds LS2 7PD *tel:* 0113 222 3423 *email:* d.fligg@lcm.ac.uk. *Programme and sleeve notes.*

Frontier Music Services. 36 Riverdale Rd, Plumstead, London SE18 1NZ *tel:* 020 8473 2213. Jennifer Churches, proprietor. *Copy-writing, sleeve notes and part-writing.*

Fuller, Rachel. Flat 2, 2 Colville Square, London W11 2BD *tel:* 020 7243 4971 *fax:* c/o 020 8723 6357 *email:* rachfuller@tinyworld.co.uk. Rachel Fuller.

George, Alan. 10 Bootham Terrace, York YO30 7DH *tel:* 01904 332071 *fax:* 01904 658189 *email:* FitzQtet@aol.com. *Any classical, romantic, early 20th C repertoire, str quartets, Shostakovich.*

Green OBE, Christopher. 25 The Avenue, Braintree, Essex CM7 3HY *tel:* 01376 324079 *fax:* 01376 324079 *email:* cjcgreen@apu.ac.uk. *Programme and sleeve notes.*

Holman, Peter. 119 Maldon Rd, Colchester, Essex CO3 3AX *tel:* 01206 543417 *fax:* 01206 562072 *email:* peter@parley.org.uk;

p.k.holman@leeds.ac.uk. *Specialist in pre-1800 mus.*

Humphreys, Garry. 69 Park Ave, Palmers Green, London N13 5PH *tel:* 020 8882 2106. *Specialist in British mus.*

Humphries, John. 24 Aragon Ave, East Ewell, Epsom, Surrey KT17 2QG *tel:* 020 8393 6067 *fax:* 020 8393 6067 *email:* j.humphries@ church-schools.com. *Informed notes on orch, chmbr, choral and early mus. Specialist in br and wind mus.*

Joseph, Jeffrey. 15 Selsdon Rd, London SE27 0PQ *tel:* 020 8766 6668 *email:* jjoseph@tcm.ac.uk. *Programme and sleeve notes.*

Kennedy, Paula. 37 Swainstone Rd, Reading RG2 0DX *tel:* 0118 975 0981 *fax:* 0118 975 0981 *email:* kennedy@paula57.fsnet.co.uk. *Programme and sleeve notes. Specialises in Czech and Hungarian mus.*

Lancaster, Philip. Chosen Arts, 30 Brighton Rd, Redland, Bristol BS6 6NT *tel:* 0117 923 9355; 07989 197998 *email:* philip. lancaster@chosen-arts.org.uk. *Programme notes. British mus specialist. Also mus typesetting services and project concert promotion.*

Lawrence, Richard. 15 Hugh St, London SW1V 1QJ *tel:* 020 7834 9846 *fax:* 020 7834 9846. *Programme and sleeve notes.*

Lillystone, Simon. 24 Fairfield Rd, London N8 9HG *tel:* 020 8347 9655 *email:* simon.lillystone@britishlibrary.net. *Programme and sleeve notes; mus transcription and typesettting (Finale).*

Manly, Ann. 8 Alma Square, London NW8 9QD *tel:* 020 7286 3944 *fax:* 020 7289 9081 *email:* annmanly.protheroe@btinternet.com. *Programme notes, liner notes, editorial services.*

Morley, Christopher. 16 Melbourne Rd, Halesowen B63 3NB *tel:* 0121 550 4482 *fax:* 0121 550 4482 *email:* cfmorley47@aol.com. *Programme and sleeve notes.*

The Neil Williams Classical Collection. 22 Avon, Hockley, Tamworth, Staffs B77 5QA *tel:* 01827 286086 *fax:* 01827 286086 *email:* neil@classicalcollection.co.uk. Neil Williams, owner/proprietor. *Programme and sleeve notes, especially for composers, conds and musicians; also classical mus picture archive. Specialises in classical mus research.*

Ng, Kah-Ming. 33 Binswood Ave, Oxford OX3 8NY *tel:* 01865 751928 *fax:* 01865 751928 *email:* Kah-MingNg@charivari.co.uk.

Notes in Edge-Wise. 38 Heyes Lane, Alderley Edge, Cheshire SK9 7JY *tel:* 01625 585378 *fax:* 01625 590175 *email:* edgewise@dircon.co.uk. Lynne Walker. *Arts programme or liner material, copy-writing and editing consultancy.*

Perkins, Martin. 8 Sandy Lane, Fillongley, Warks CV7 8DD *tel:* 01676 541585 *fax:* 01676 541659 *email:* mperkins@armonico.freeserve.co.uk. *Programme notes for Warwick & Leamington Spa Festival, Stratford English Music Festival, Cambridge Summer Recitals, Birmingham Conservatoire.*

Pott, Francis. Thurlows, Main Rd, Littleton, Winchester, Hants SO22 6PS *tel:* 01962 885874 *email:* fpott@argonet.co.uk. *Regular contributor of concert programme notes and liner notes to major concert venues and CD companies.*

Purkiss, Anthony. 35 Fonthill Rd, Hove, E Sussex BN3 6HB *tel:* 01273 774730 *email:* tonypurkiss@supanet.com. *Programme notes and record sleeves.*

Rayner, Roger. Flat 3, 66 Unthank Rd, Norwich, Norfolk NR2 2RN *tel:* 01603 219209 *fax:* 01603 610443 *email:* rrayner1827@ hotmail.com. *Programme and liner notes; CD and book reviews. Special interests: organ and pno mus, historic performances.*

SHP (Sara Hindley Promotions). 59 Brook St, Chester, Cheshire CH1 3DZ *tel:* 0870 066 0069 *fax:* 01244 315662 *email:* sh.promotions@classicfm.net. Maria King, writer; Rebecca Perez, mkt. *Programme notes, sleeve notes, press releases.*

Saba, Thérèse Wassily. 9 Methuen Park, Muswell Hill, London N10 2JR *tel:* 020 8442 1489 *fax:* 020 8442 1489 *email:* 106665.3500@ compuserve.com. *Programme and sleeve notes, especially Arabic, Spanish and Latin-American mus, gui mus. News ed of Classical Guitar magazine.*

Steadman, Robert. 5 Henry Ave, Matlock DE4 3FL *tel:* 01629 56563 *fax:* 01629 56563 *email:* rob@robertsteadman.com. *Con Moto, Piccolo, TVS, Vanderbeek. Concert, theatre, educ, dance.*

Stewart, Andrew. 46 Schoolbell Mews, Arbery Rd, London E3 5BZ *tel:* 020 8983 0011 *fax:* 020 8983 0011 *email:* AndrewStewart1@compuserve.com. *Specialist in choral, song and early mus. Essays supplied for festival programme books, recordings, videos, etc. Extensive resource of existing notes available.*

Stowell, Robin. 43 Woodvale Ave, Cyncoed, Cardiff CF23 6SP *tel:* 029 2075 2001 *fax:* 029 2087 4379 *email:* stowell@cardiff.ac.uk. *Programme and sleeve notes, especially mus for strs.*

Taylor, Philip. 112 Main Rd, Wilby, Northants NN8 2UE *tel:* 01933 223301 *fax:* 01933 223301 *email:* philip-taylor@beeb.net. *Specialist in Russian mus.*

Theo, Tatty. 60 South View Rd, Crouch End, London N8 7LT *tel:* 020 8348 0671; 07957 335694 *fax:* 020 8348 0671 *email:* tatty@easynet.co.uk. *Programme and sleeve notes, proof-reading. All periods of mus, but specialist in Handel and 18th C mus. Notes for festivals, reviews of recordings/books, articles and features of 18th C mus. Previously editor of 'Early Music News'.*

Ward Russell, Gillian. 10 New St, Maldon, Essex CM9 6AQ *tel:* 01621 853237 *email:* DrWardRussell@aol.com. *Programme and sleeve notes.*

Wheeler, Mike. 12 Swinscoe House, Rosengrave St, Derby DE1 1PS *tel:* 01332 362194 *fax:* 01332 362194 *email:* mike@musicadd.fsnet.co.uk. *Programme and CD notes. Also proof-reading, copy-editing and writing for publicity brochures.*

words4music. MBM Box 17, Manor Lane, Rochester, Kent ME1 3HS *tel:* 01634 829112; 07939 194952 *email:* words4.music@virgin.net. Ms R M Wendel. *English and German programme and sleeve notes; editorial services.*

Solicitors

Howell-Jones Partnership. Flint House, 52 High St, Leatherhead, Surrey KT22 8AJ *tel:* 01372 860650 *fax:* 01372 860659 *email:* peter.scott@hjplaw.co.uk. Peter Scott, partner. *Solicitors with 30 years' experience in the mus industry.*

Marshall Hatchick Solicitors. 17 Bentinck St, London W1U 2ES *tel:* 020 7935 3272 *fax:* 020 7224 1592 *email:* solicitors@marshallhatchick.co.uk. Keith Hatchick, partner; Nicholas Marshall, partner; Michael Sparrow, partner. *Regional office: The Ancient House, Church St, Woodbridge, Suffolk IP12 1DH. General arts law advice, particularly contracts, sponsorship and Lottery applications.*

Tods Murray WS. 66 Queen St, Edinburgh EH2 4NE *tel:* 0131 226 4771 *fax:* 0131 300 2202 *email:* richard.findlay@todsmurray.com. Richard Findlay, entertainment law partner; David Smith, entertainment lawyer. *Specialist entertainment and media lawyers.*

Tour and Travel Companies

abc, Arts Bureau for the Continents. 20 Tuckett Rd, Woodhouse Eaves, Leics LE12 8SE *tel:* 01509 891101 *fax:* 01509 891151 *email:* artsman@onetel.com. Sir Anthony Goodchild, UK representative. *Performing tours, exchanges, festivals worldwide for choirs, bands and orchs. Specialises in USA and Canada.*

ACFEA Tour Consultants. 12-15 Hanger Green, London W5 3EL *tel:* 020 8799 8360 *fax:* 020 8998 7965 *email:* acfea@stlon.com. Tricia George, operations dir; Richard Savage, mgr dir Europe. *Organises tailor-made concert tours and travel arrangements for amateur choirs, bands and orchestras to UK, Europe, S Africa, USA, Latin America, Mexico, Asia, New Zealand and Australia.*

Aircraft Chartering Services Ltd. 7 High St, Ewell, Epsom, Surrey KT17 1SG *tel:* 020 8394 2795 *fax:* 020 8393 6154 *email:* sales@aircraft-chartering.co.uk. Mark Hugo, mgr dir; Ian Browne, touring mgr; Andrew Richley, touring mgr. *Charter of aircraft for touring orchs, choirs and ballet companies.*

Albion Service. 17 Cleevelands Ave, Cheltenham, Glos GL50 4PY *tel:* 01242 254771 *fax:* 01242 527728 *email:* albionservice@btopenworld.com. Ian Bird, mgr; Linda Hack, sales. *Specialist in handling all accommodation requirements including hotels, self-catering, B&Bs and guest houses for all types and sizes of touring groups. Long-term lets arranged. Group and individual bookings. Also private bookings catered for. Loyalty scheme in operation. Book ferries to and from mainland UK.*

Casterbridge Concert Tours. Salcombe House, Long St, Sherborne, Dorset DT9 3BU *tel:* 01935 810810 *fax:* 01935 815815 *email:* tourops@casterbridge-tours.co.uk. Sue Rickards, concert tours mgr, UK; Ron Blake, concert tour co-ord, US. *Custom-designed European and worldwide performing tours for mus ens.*

Club Europe Concert Tours. Fairway House, 53 Dartmouth Rd, London SE23 3HN *tel:* 020 8699 7788 *fax:* 020 8699 7770 *email:* music@club-europe.co.uk. Lucy Szymonski, mkt mgr. *Tailor-made concert tours and festivals throughout Europe for all types and standard of youth and school group.*

Edwin Doran Music Travel. 63 Holly Rd, Twickenham, Middx TW1 4EA *tel:* 0870 8877 693 *fax:* 0870 8877 711. Carol Myhill. *Specialist in mus and educ tours.*

Ensemble Tours. 11 Eskview Grove, Dalkeith, Midlothian EH22 1JW *tel:* 0131 561 9513; 07811 395488 *fax:* 0131 561 9513 *email:* enquiries@ensembletours.co.uk. Chris Hutchings, gen mgr; David Chaplin, drama consultant. *Performing tours for any kind of mus group - to Scotland or throughout the UK and Europe. Can arrange participation in festivals (especially Edinburgh) and customised tours.*

Gower Music International. 2 High St, Studley, Warks B80 7HJ *tel:* 01527 851414 *fax:* 01527 851417 *email:* gower@gowstrav.demon.co.uk. Peter Cook, gen mgr; Alison Bryant, sales and mkt mgr. *High quality performance tours for choirs, bands and orchs from well-established tour operator.*

H F Holidays. Imperial House, Edgware Rd, London NW9 5AL *tel:* 020 8905 9558 (reservations)/9388 (brochure line) *fax:* 020 8205 0506 *email:* info@hfholidays.co.uk. *Wide range of mus holidays including orch and choral singing weeks. Jazz w/ends as well as mus appreciation and festivals.*

Hotelink (UK) Ltd. Southpark House, Southwood Rd, Monkton, Prestwick, Ayrshire KA9 1UP *tel:* 01292 318800 *fax:* 01292 318183 *email:* hotelink@compuserve.com. Jean and John Grant-Silver, dirs. *Specialist in negotiating best quality hotel accommodation at lowest rates for orchs and other groups on tour in the UK or abroad.*

International Air Charter Plc. Quayside House, Standard Quay, Faversham, Kent ME13 7BS *tel:* 01795 590888 *fax:* 01795 590880 *email:* sales@aircraftcharter.com. Madeleine Puzey, charter sales mgr. *Worldwide aircraft charter specialists, providing aircraft for touring orchs, bands, ballet companies and choirs. Worldwide 24-hr service. Free Quotations.*

Interchange. Interchange House, 27 Stafford Rd, Croydon, Surrey CR0 4NG *tel:* 020 8681 3612 *fax:* 020 8760 0031 *email:* interchange@interchange.uk.com. Gordon Burnett, mgr dir. *Specialist in group tours worldwide catering to individual group requests.*

Jac Live. 62-64 Chancellors Rd, London W6 9RS *tel:* 020 7870 8551 *fax:* 020 8563 9141 *email:* adrian.fuller@jactravel.co.uk. Adrian Fuller, snr performing arts consultant; Julia Haycock, events and performing arts consultant; Marnic Rowe, performing arts consultant. *Performance tours in the UK and Europe. Tailor-made concert tours for choirs, bands and orchs. Mus festival and event operators, including JAC Live's own festival Bristolive! - see entry in* **UK Music Festivals***.*

Ken Graham Trucking. Orchestral Logistics, 4 Heathcote, Tadworth, Surrey KT20 5TH *tel:* 01737 373305; 07785 330608 *fax:* 01737 370813 *email:* info@kengrahamtrucking.com. *Provides symphony orch inst transportation. 25 years' touring experience Europewide with major orchs. Uses road train and step-frame semi-trailers with ramps, climate control, riding on air. All drivers experienced in handling delicate and valuable insts.*

Legato Music Tours. 8 Meadow Lane, Alvechurch, Birmingham B48 7LH *tel:* 0121 445 4938; 07789 992417 *fax:* 0121 445 4938 *email:* info@legatotours.co.uk. Paul Storer, dir; Nigel Morley, dir. *Specialist mus tours to Europe for schools, youth groups, choirs, bands and orchs. Specialists in eastern Europe.*

Liaisons Abroad Ltd. Chenil House, 181-183 King's Rd, London SW3 5EB *tel:* 020 7376 4020 *fax:* 020 7376 4442 *email:* info@liaisonsabroad.com. Massimina Caneva, mgr dir. *Advance information and ticket reservations for international venues. The combination of travel and opera available 'a la carte', with tickets, hotels and tours on an individual or group basis.*

Maestro Travel & Touring Company. Suite 307, 33 George St, Liverpool L3 9LU *tel:* 08700 727747 *fax:* 08700 717747 *email:* info@maestrotravel.com. Ken Grundy, chief exec offr; Nigel Foo, mgr; Leanne

Evans, hotel co-ord. *Tour and travel resources for the performing arts.*

Martin Randall Travel Ltd. Voysey House, Barley Mow Passage, Chiswick, London W4 4GF *tel:* 020 8742 3355 *fax:* 020 8742 7766 *email:* info@martinrandall.co.uk. Martin Randall, dir. *Special lecture tours to European festivals and opera houses. Music festivals organised on the Rhine, the Danube and in Venice.*

Media 2000. Colne House, High St, Colnbrook, Middx SL3 0LX *tel:* 01753 764058 *fax:* 01753 764059 *email:* media2000baggage@hotmail.com. Marina Mandale, supervisor. *Specialist service for passengers travelling with 'tools of their trade' to over 300 destinations worldwide. Range of low-cost air fares, plus huge savings on excess baggage costs. Special quick check-in at UK airports, and assistance with customs paperwork.*

Music and Travel Tour Consultants Ltd. 124 Village Way, Beckenham, Kent BR3 3PA *tel:* 020 8663 3037 *fax:* 020 8663 3012 *email:* info@music-and-travel.co.uk. David Horsburgh, dir. *Travel and tour arrangements specialising in Europe and N America. Tailor-made tours, festivals and exchanges.*

Musica Europa. 7a Farm Rd, Maidenhead, Berks SL6 5HX *tel:* 01628 776795 *fax:* 01628 632112 *email:* bengunner@musica-europa.com. Ben Gunner, dir. *Concert tour organisers for performers and listeners, providing comprehensive and professional organisation.*

NST Music Tours. Chiltern House, 181 Bristol Ave, Blackpool, Lancs FY2 0FA *tel:* 01253 503043 *fax:* 01253 594617 *email:* info@ nstmusic.co.uk. Scott Gilbertson, sales team leader. *Specialist tour operator offering tailor-made performance tours for bands, choirs and orchs throughout Europe and N America. Arrangements for travel and accommodation-only arrangements also available.*

Onstage, Specialist Concert Tours. Unit 8, Waterside Business Centre, Railshead Rd, Isleworth, Middx TW7 7BY *tel:* 020 8568 5486/4586 *fax:* 020 8568 8409 *email:* concerttours@onestage.co.uk. Sonia Patel, dir; Philippa Newnham, dir. *Organises tailor-made concert and travel arrangements to suit amateur choirs, bands and orchs in the UK and abroad.*

Onyx International Travel Services Ltd. 26 Woodford Close, Caversham, Reading RG4 7HN *tel:* 0118 947 2830 *fax:* 0118 946 3104 *email:* info@onyxtravel.prestel.co.uk. *Specialists in orch and choir travel including flight, hotel bookings worldwide, air charter and tailor-made tours.*

Pathfinders. 1 Bath St, Cheltenham, Glos GL50 1YE *tel:* 01242 515712/538937 *fax:* 01242 521422 *email:* hugh@stita.co.uk. Hugh

Whittaker, mgr dir. *Long-established specialist tour operator. Specialist in all types of choral, mus and performance tours, throughout the world. Long experience with school and college groups.*

Progressive Tours Ltd. 12 Porchester Place, London W2 2BS *tel:* 020 7262 1676 *fax:* 020 7724 6941 *email:* progressivetours@skola.co.uk. Dave Stacey, sales exec. *Specialist in travel to former USSR, Cuba and most European countries, for choirs, orchs, cultural groups, etc. Exchange enquiries welcome.*

Rayburn Tours Ltd. Rayburn House, Parcel Terrace, Derby DE1 1LY *tel:* 01332 347828 *fax:* 01332 371298 *email:* enquiries@ rayburntours.com. John Boyden, gen mgr; Lucy Gates, sales mgr. *Tailor-made concert tours to worldwide destinations for all types of school, youth and amateur adult bands, choirs, orchs and ens.*

St Albans Travel Service - Good to See. 30 Culver Rd, St Albans, Herts AL1 4ED *tel:* 01727 866533 *fax:* 01727 847418 *email:* stuart@goodtosee.com. Stuart Harding, mgr dir. *UK and international travel service, hotel and theatre bookings.*

School Rail - Good to See. PO Box 1, St Albans, Herts AL1 4ED *tel:* 01727 834475 *fax:* 01727 847418 *email:* sr@stalbanstravel.co.uk. Jackie Aldridge, mgr. *Educ tours, reduced rail travel, overnight accommodation, ticket bookings, lecture and tour arrangements. Theatre and mus events. London and worldwide tours for groups, choirs, orchs, etc.*

Screen and Music Travel Ltd. Colne House, High St, Colnbrook SL3 0LX *tel:* 01753 764050 *fax:* 01753 764051 *email:* groups@ screenandmusictravel.co.uk. Colin Doran, mgr special projects; Michele Griffiths, groups department; Sue Drinkwater, mgr dir. *Specialist travel consultancy to the entertainment industry. Large and small groups at very competitive prices, all over the world. Excess baggage discounts on many worldwide airlines.*

Specialised Travel Ltd. 12-15 Hanger Green, Park Royal, London W5 3EL *tel:* 020 8799 8300 *fax:* 020 8998 7965 *email:* admin@stlon.com. Richard Savage, chmn; Tricia George, operations dir; Kristina Aljinovic, mgr dir. *ABTA, IATA and CAA bonded travel consultants to the mus industry since 1955. Competitive quotes for travel to any part of the world. Quality concert tours organised to UK, Europe, USA, South Africa, Latin America, Mexico, New Zealand, Australia and Asia.*

Young Travellers Ltd. Dept Music and Leisure, 34 Station Rd, London SE20 7BQ *tel:* 020 8778 6850 *fax:* 020 8778 9754 *email:* musicleisure@young-travellers.co.uk. S Williamson, dir. *Transportation by coach and air of orchs and choirs in the UK and abroad, including accommodation arrangements if required.*

Video Companies

Colmar Video Productions. 36 Planton Way, Brightlingsea, Colchester, Essex CO7 0LB *tel:* 01206 303764. Colin Sadler, partner. *Concert and recital videos.*

Heavy Entertainment Ltd. 222 Kensal Rd, London W10 5BN *tel:* 020 8960 9001/2 *fax:* 020 8960 9003 *email:* info@heavy-entertainment.com. David Roper, company dir; Davy Nougarede, company dir. *TV and radio producers. Promotional video and audio, electronic press kits, video news releases, media training, event staging, showreels (audio and video), audio studio hire, CD mastering and duplication, TV/radio commercials, direct-mail CDs/CD-ROMs, video and audio for the internet.*

Music Mall. 1 Upper James St, London W1F 9DE *tel:* 020 7534 1444 *fax:* 020 7534 1440 *email:* info@musicmall.co.uk. Andi Baron, production mgr; Suzanne Williams, production co-ord. *Sourcing,*

tracing, clearance, duplication, programme development for mus video.

Powerline Productions Ltd. Unit 23, Winston Close, Romford, Essex RM7 8LL *tel:* 01708 724544; 0800 074 2367 *fax:* 01708 744166 *email:* info@powerlineproductions.com. Peter Walters, mgr dir. *Promotional and PR videos. Opera/concert performances. Tour videos. All kinds of mus/theatre performance and documentary production for TV and webstreaming.*

The Promotional Video Company. First Floor, 38 Russell Rd, London W14 8HT *tel:* 020 7460 1697 *email:* info@promo-video.com. Martin Phillips, dir. *Full programme production. Promotional videos, video press-releases, tour videos, demo tapes, self-observance videos, audition tapes, concert and recital videos. USA conversions, duplication to any quantity. Special rates for those in the mus profession.*

Word Processing and Editorial Services

Better English. Suite 238, The Beaux Arts Building, 10-18 Manor Gardens, Islington, London N7 6JS *tel:* 020 7561 9375 *email:* info@ better-english.net. Michael Thorne, mgr dir. *Sub-editing and proof-reading services for press releases, websites, annual reports, etc.*

Complete Secretarial Services. Milestone, St Nicholas Ave, Great Bookham, Surrey KT23 4AY *tel:* 01372 457755 *fax:* 01372 450525 *email:* maestoso@btinternet.com. Elizabeth McArthur. *Service includes typing letters, mailings, reports, theses, CV preparation, address labels for mailshots, accounts and book-keeping for artists and small businesses, the organisation of conferences, special events, travel arrangements, etc.*

Compro. 63 Charles St, Epping, Essex CM16 7AX *tel:* 01992 572805 *fax:* 01992 572805 *email:* genevieve.pearson@ntlworld.com. Genevieve Pearson, dir. *Laser address labels of concert promoters, UK*

and abroad. Complete mailshots and mailmerge.

Edgerton Publishing Services. Pett Rd, Pett, Hastings, E Sussex TN35 4HA *tel:* 01424 813003 *fax:* 01424 813301 *email:* penfold@ eps-edge.demon.co.uk. David Penfold, proprietor. *Editorial and production services for programmes, newsletters, etc. Consultancy on publications (electronic, including websites and conventional).*

SMG Secretarial Services. 39 Parkwood Ave, Esher, Surrey KT10 8DE *tel:* 020 8398 8541 *fax:* 020 8339 0625. Susan Garratt, proprietor. *Typing of general correspondence, CV preparation, reports, theses, proof-reading, laser printing, fax.*

Wessex Music Services. 1000 Westbury Rd, Little Cheverell, Devizes, Wilts SN10 4JW *tel:* 01380 816338 *fax:* 01380 816467 *email:* admin@wessexmusic.co.uk. John Bickerton, proprietor. *Word processing and typing services, especially text with mus examples.*

Classical Music Resources on the Internet

Information Resources

American Musicological Society – www.ams-net.org
201 South 34th St, Philadelphia, PA 19104-6313, USA *tel:* 00 1 215 898 8698 *fax:* 00 1 215 573 3673 *email:* ams@sas.upenn.edu. Robert Judd, exec dir. *Comprehensive list of academic mus resources on the web.*

Aria Database – www.aria-database.com
email: ariaman@aria-database.com. *Provides basic information about each aria. Includes translations for many arias and aria texts for those that are not affected by copyright restrictions. Also provides access to a collection of operatic MIDI files. Information on the complete operatic aria collections of Mozart, Verdi, Berlioz and Puccini as well as the partial collections of over 50 other composers. Currently holds 1200 arias from 160 operas by 60 composers, 320 translations, 960 aria texts, 160 sound files.*

British Academy of Composers and Songwriters – www.britishacademy.com
British Music House, 26 Berners St, London W1T 3LR *tel:* 020 7636 2929 *fax:* 020 7636 2212 *email:* julian@britishacademy.com. Julian Lancaster. *Includes directory of mus writers of all genres (all of whom are Academy members), an extensive links page, details of events, and highlights of the Academy's magazine 'The Works'.*

The British Council: Music Team Website – music.britishcouncil.org; www.britishcouncil.org
Performing Arts Dept, 10 Spring Gardens, London SW1A 2BN *tel:* 020 7389 3005 *fax:* 020 7389 3057 *email:* music@britishcouncil.org. John Daniel, mgr. *The mus team in the performing arts dept is the expert link between British mus and the Council's global network, working with overseas colleagues to plan, resource, deliver and evaluate high-impact arts projects. Website includes information on British mus and musicians, mus educ, traditional and world mus, club culture and the mus industry; news, links, contact details and information on how the British Council supports the promotion of British mus internationally.*

British Choirs of the Net – www.choirs.org.uk
35 Old Lynn Rd, Wisbech, Cambs PE14 7AJ *tel:* 07899 860351 *email:* philliptolley@colcanto.co.uk. Phillip Tolley, owner/webmaster. *Internet information resource and free listing service for British choirs and choral societies. Also provides listing for choral composers, w/shops, mus links and touring/exchange opportunities, choral jobs and programme notes. Increasing international choir presence.*

British Music Information Centre – www.bmic.co.uk
10 Stratford Place, London W1C 1BA *tel:* 020 7499 8567 *fax:* 020 7499 4795 *email:* info@bmic.co.uk. *Fully-searchable online database of scores and recordings of 20th and 21st C classical British mus, with growing unique collection of scores viewable via the database. Concert listings and score ordering information. Features on composers, including Real Audio files. Searchable digitised library online.*

Classical Music UK – www.classicalmusic.co.uk
Suites 5-7, Meridian House, 26-28 Station Rd, Redhill, Surrey RH1 1PD *tel:* 01737 768127 *email:* editor@classicalmusic.co.uk. Mark Walmsley, publishing ed. *Classical mus news, events, vacancies, links and opinion.*

English Folk Dance and Song Society – www.efdss.org
Cecil Sharp House, 2 Regent's Park Rd, London NW1 7AY *tel:* 020 7485 2206 *fax:* 020 7284 0534 *email:* info@efdss.org. *Vaughan Williams Memorial Library of traditional mus and dance.*

Euclid - UK Cultural Contact Point – www.euclid.info
46-48 Mount Pleasant, Liverpool L3 5SD *tel:* 0700 038 2543; 0151 709 2564 *fax:* 0151 709 8647 *email:* info@euclid.info. *EUCLID, founded in 1993, is provider of European and international information in the UK for the arts and cultural sector, recognised through the appointment by DCMS and the European Commission as the official UK Cultural Contact Point. Other services include the Alert e-newsletter, the Briefing e-bulletin, the DICE Dossier and Diary, and the ACRONIM database of cultural research from across the world. EUCLID also provides research and consultancy, and recent projects include studies for the European Parliament, development projects for the Council of Europe, and research for UK local authorities.*

Findmethesound.com – www.findmethesound.com
465 West Wycombe Rd, High Wycombe, Bucks HP12 4AQ *fax:* 01494 452949 *email:* info@findmethesound.com. Jeremy Foster, web admin, Melanie Foster; web admin. *UK's largest independent musicians directory. Website where you can promote skills, services and events to others, or find information on mus and musicians. 2500+ professional musicians and ens listed. Other features include Jobs; News and Events; large festivals listings covering UK and Europe.*

Impulse Classical Music Website – www.impulse-music.co.uk
18 Hillfield Park, Muswell Hill, London N10 3QS *tel:* 020 8444 8587 *fax:* 020 8245 0358 *email:* impulse@impulse-music.co.uk. *Portal to individual promotional pages for classical composers, performers, specialist publishers and independent record labels. Sound and score samples as well as online order forms. Comprehensive listings of websites worldwide.*

Jazz UK – www.jazzuk.com
tel: 020 8295 1732 *fax:* 020 8468 7648 *email:* briangreen. london@virgin.net. Brian Green. *The international directory of professional jazz musicians, agents and promoters.*

MusicWeb – www.musicweb.uk.net
95 Arnold Ave, Coventry CV3 5ND *tel:* 02476 419652 *email:* Len@musicweb.uk.net. Len Mullenger, founder. *Over 250 CDs reviewed each month. Composer profiles, news, site updated daily. Other sites: Film Music on the Web; Seen and Heard.*

National Association of Teachers of Singing, Inc (US) – www.nats.org
4745 Sutton Rark Rd, Suite 201, Jacksonville, Florida 32224, USA *tel:* 00 1 904 992 9101 *fax:* 00 1 904 992 9326 *email:* info@nats.org. William A Vessels, exec dir. *Information about the association, its publications and upcoming events.*

Opera Resource – www.r-ds.com
email: rdstenor@hotmail.com. Anne Lawson. *Verdi, Puccini; background to some popular operas; links to synopses and libretti.*

Schubertline – www.schubertline.co.uk
Enichi Music Services, 51 Northgate, Beccles, Suffolk NR34 9AU *tel:* 01502 712554 *fax:* 0870 051 4857 *email:* mail@schubertline.co.uk. Mary Nicholson, dir. *Online score service for singers. Downloadable printed copies of songs by 18th/19th C composers in any key.*

UK Theatre Web – www.uktw.co.uk
New House, High St, Fernham, Oxon SN7 7NY *tel:* 01367 820828 *fax:* 01367 820827 *email:* info@uktw.co.uk. Frances Iles. *Online UK performing arts listings and technical services.*

WebProjects – www.webprojects.co.uk
Suites 5-7, Meridian House, 28 Station Rd, Redhill, Surrey RH1 1PD *tel:* 01737 768127 *email:* mark@webprojects.co.uk. Mark Walmsley, mgr dir, Ben Sauer; technical dir, Matthew Lindop; project dir, Andy Walker; creative dir. *Efficient creation, sharing and distribution of information.*

Online Magazines

Classical Music UK – www.classicalmusic.co.uk
Suites 5-7, Meridian House, 26-28 Station Rd, Redhill, Surrey RH1 1PD *tel:* 01737 768127 *email:* editor@classicalmusic.co.uk. Mark Walmsley, publishing ed. *Classical mus news, events, vacancies, links and opinion.*

The Opera Critic – www.theoperacritic.com
PO Box 99826, Newmarket, Auckland, New Zealand *tel:* 00 64 9525 3996 *email:* michael@theoperacritic.com. Michael Sinclaire, ed. *Online opera magazine offering daily links to opera reviews and articles which are published in worldwide publications, plus other features of interest to the opera lover.*

Sound On Sound magazine – www.soundonsound.com
Media House, Trafalgar Way, Bar Hill, Cambridge CB3 8SQ *tel:* 01954 789888 *fax:* 01954 789895 *email:* sos.feedback@soundonsound.com. Dave Lockwood, publisher. *High-tech mus recording magazine.*

Etailers

Crotchet Web Store – www.crotchet.co.uk

PO Box 5435, Birmingham, W Midlands B38 8DZ *tel:* 0121 459 5566 *fax:* 0121 459 5605 *email:* info@crotchet.co.uk. Judy Letters, customer services. *Classical and mus specialists (plus jazz, world and film). Suppliers to schools, colleges, universities, libraries and individuals. Browse new releases, search online database, special offers, etc.*

Dolphin Music – www.dolphinmusic.co.uk

81 Aigburth Rd, Liverpool L17 4JT *email:* info@dolphin-online.co.uk. Rob Williams, sales, Jason Tavaria; sales mgr. *Mus retailer.*

www.fullpitcher.co.uk

9 Mallard Close, Haslemere, Surrey GU27 1QU *tel:* 01428 648854 *fax:* 0870 429 2123 *email:* info@fullpitcher.co.uk. Sue Brookes, sales mgr. *Sheet mus to view, print and play online and other resources to support creative and flexible music-making. Custom arrange and print service available.*

www.jansmusic.co.uk

PO Box 3136, Barnet, Herts EN5 1DY *tel:* 020 8447 3862 *fax:* 020 8447 3862 *email:* jan@jansmusic.co.uk. Jan Hart, dir. *Website selling select number of CDs each month based on personal recommendation. Also facility for performers to sell their own CDs online, free concert listings, online ticket booking service for performers, regular newsletter and discussion forum. Web design and hosting service for performers without their own site.*

Musicsender – www.musicsender.com

PO Box 529, Bristol BS99 3GH *tel:* 0117 963 6011 *fax:* 0117 963 6011 *email:* orders@musicsender.com. Andy Hague, mgr. *Sheet mus retailer.*

Sheet Music Hound Ltd – www.sheetmusichound.com

54 Petworth Rd, Haslemere, Surrey GU27 3AU *fax:* 01428 652880 *email:* hound@sheetmusichound.com. Michael Barnett, dir, Andy Scott; dir. *Mus by m/order. Cat searchable via the website and orders can be created and submitted online. Also exam syllabus online and free submission of 'what's on' listings for open-entry festivals, w/shops, summer schools, etc.*

tutti.co.uk Ltd – www.tutti.co.uk

18 Hillfield Park, Muswell Hill, London N10 3QS *tel:* 020 8444 8587 *fax:* 020 8245 0358 *email:* shop@tutti.co.uk. Geraldine Allen, dir, Sarah Rodgers; dir. *Webshop for online sales of CDs, sheet mus, books about mus. Features work of contemporary British composers and performers.*

Virtual Sheet Music srl – www.virtualsheetmusic.com

Via A Spinola, 9 I-16135, Genova, Itlay *fax:* 00 39 02 700 449640 *email:* virtual@virtualsheetmusic.com. Fabrizio Ferrari, site owner. *Sheet mus supplier. Available as downloadable file or email.*

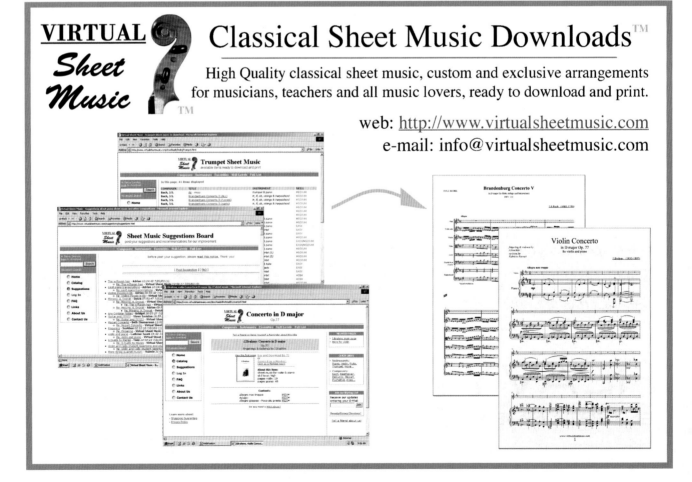

Trade Fairs

Listed below are the major international trade fairs and exhibitions that are wholly or mostly concerned with classical music. Some festivals may have an exhibition area within the festival grounds.

China

13th China International Exhibition of Pro Audio, Light Music & Technology (CALM EXPO). A1 North St, Qingnianhu, Dongcheng District, Beijing 100011, China *tel:* +86 10 64227788 ext 617; 84251210; 84251220 *fax:* +86 10 64251287/84253010 *email:* chaiyingjie@ccpitbj.org; dongsheng@biec.com.cn. Wang Dongsheng, assistant general manager; Chai Yingjie, project manager. *28-31 May 2004. Largest international exhibition of entertainment and musical instruments in Asia. The Musical Instrument Hall occupies up to 16,000 sqm, and total exhibition area is 45,000 sqm. Exhibits include professional audio systems, professional lighting equipment, musical instruments, state equipment and machines, professional and household audio-video equipment, music publications and books.*

Czech Republic

Muzika. Incheba Praha, Areal vystaviste Praha, Praha 7 - Holesovice 170 90, Czech Republic *tel:* +420 220 103 474 *fax:* +420 220 103 474 *email:* info@incheba.cz. Monika Smatova, fair admin; Pavla Bubenikova, fair realisation. *Fair of classical and electronic instruments, accessories, sound and light, stage effects, multimedia, sheet music, periodicals, literature. Workshops and concerts.*

France

MIDEM. BP 572, 11 Rue de Colonel Pierre-Avia 75726 Paris Cedex 15, France *tel:* +33 1 41 90 44 39 *fax:* +33 1 41 90 46 31 *email:* jane.garton@reedmidem.com. Jane Garton, press manager. *MidemNet (Music and Technology Forum) 24 January 2004, Midem 25-29 January 2004. Midem is a fully comprehensive market and trade show for the international music industry. It welcomes some 9000 music professionals from around the world for 5 days of deal-making, non-stop music business, networking, showcases, presentations and conferences.*

Musicora. Grande Halle de la Villette, Secession-62 Rue de Miromesnil, Paris F-75008, France *tel:* +33 1 49 53 27 00 *fax:* +33 1 49 53 27 04 *email:* secession@wanadoo.fr. Jessie Westenholz, commissaire. *6-10 May 2004 - 20th anniversary. Classical mus fair; editions, instruments, concerts, festivals, associations, admin and jazz.*

Germany

Frankfurt Book Fair. Ausstellungs und Messe GmbH, Reineckstr 3, Frankfurt am Main D-60313, Germany *tel:* +49 69 2 1020 *fax:* +49 69 2 102227/77 *email:* info@book-fair.com. Wolfgang von Schumann, marketing (for visitors); Helga Jansohn, technical director. *6-11 October 2004. Largest international book fair; also important for electronic media.*

Musikmesse. Messe Frankfurt GmbH, Postfach 15 02 10, Frankfurt am Main D-60062, Germany *tel:* +49 69 7575 5880 *fax:* +49 69 7575 6613 *email:* wolfgang.luecke@messefrankfurt.com. Wolfgang Lücke, director. *31 March-3 April 2004. International trade fair for musical instruments, musical software and hardware, sheet music and accessories.*

Prolight & Sound. Messe Frankfurt GmbH, Postfach 15 02 10, Frankfurt am Main D-60062, Germany *tel:* +49 69 7575 0 *fax:* +49 69 7575 6559 *email:* anja.kind@messefrankfurt.com. Anja Kind, assistant. *31 March-3 April 2004. International trade fair for event and communication technology, AV-production and entertainment.*

Hungary

Hungaccord Budapest International Music Fair. Nógrádi u 13/3, Budapest H-1125, Hungary *tel:* +36 1 355 7178 *fax:* +36 1 355 7178 *email:* jmeszaros@axelexo.hu. József Mészáros, director; Csaba Meszaros, secretary. *Autumn 2005 Budapest International Music Fair. Sheet music, publications, books, journals, classical instruments, electronic instruments, records, music CD-ROMs, accessories.*

Slovak Republic

Expo Music. Incheba JSC, Viedenska Cesta 3-7, Bratislava 85101, Slovak Republic *tel:* +421 2 6727 2198 *fax:* +421 2 6727 2143 *email:* kpizurova@incheba.sk; incheba@incheba.sk. Katarina Pizurova, exhibition manager. *October 2004. 11th international music fair. Expomusic is an exhibition aimed at presenting musical instruments and music holders.*

United Kingdom

Greenwich International Festival of Early Music. Early Music Shop, 38 Manningham Lane, Bradford, W Yorks BD1 3EA, UK *tel:* +44 1274 393753 *fax:* +44 1274 393516 *email:* sales@earlyms.demon.co.uk. Peter Booth, director. *Major international early music exhibition held at the Old Royal Naval College, Greenwich, London. Concerts, masterclasses, workshops, demonstration recitals.*

In the City. Deva Centre, 8 Brewery Yard, Trinity Way, Salford M3 7BB, UK *tel:* +44 161 839 3930 *fax:* +44 161 839 3940 *email:* info@inthecity.co.uk. Anthony Wilson, director; Yvette Livesey, director; Tom Clarke, co-ordinator. *Annual meeting for the UK music industry and its international partners.*

MIDEM. Reed Midem Organisation, 296 Regent St, London W1R 6AB, UK *tel:* +44 20 7528 0086 *fax:* +44 20 7895 0949 *email:* emma.dallas@reedmidem.com. Emma Dallas, UK sales manager. *25-29 January 2004. International record music publishing and video music market. Midem Classique. Classical music concerts. Also conferences.*

USA

Boston Early Music Festival and Exhibition, Inc. 262 Beacon St, Third Floor, Boston MA 02116, USA *tel:* +1 617 424 7232 *fax:* +1 617 267 6539 *email:* bemf@bemf.org. Kathleen Fay, executive director, kathy@bemf.org; Paul O'Dette, artistic director; Stephen Stubbs, artistic co-director. *Next biennial international Festival and Exhibition 13-19 June 2005.*

Record Companies

The following is a list of classical record companies. As many classical records are manufactured abroad, the importers or distributors of these are also listed, indicated by an asterisk. Membership of the **British Phonographic Industry (BPI)** (Riverside Building, County Hall, Westminster Bridge Road, London SE1 7JA *tel*: 020 7803 1300 *fax*: 020 7803 1310 *website*: www.bpi.co.uk) is indicated after each entry.

* **ARC Music.** PO Box 111, W Sussex RH19 4FZ *tel*: 01342 328567 *fax*: 01342 315958 *email*: info@arcmusic.co.uk. *World and folk mus.*

Abbey Records/SCS Music Ltd. PO Box 197, Beckley, Oxford OX3 9YJ *tel*: 01865 358282 *fax*: 0870 056 8880 *email*: steve@scsmusic.co.uk. Steve C Smith, mgr dir; Hazel Arrandale, gen mgr. *Abbey Records, SCS Music.*

Albany Records. PO Box 137, Kendal, Cumbria LA8 0XD *tel*: 01539 824008. William Lloyd, mgr dir. *Label: Albany.*

Alchemy Records and Fetish Records. PO Box 393, Maidstone, Kent ME14 5XU *tel*: 01622 729593 *email*: alchemy@crescentmoon.org.uk.

Altarus Records. Easton Dene, Bailbrook Lane, Bath BA1 7AA *tel*: 01225 852323 *fax*: 01225 852523 *email*: 100775,2716@compuserve.com; alistair_hinton@compuserve.com. Chris Rice, president; Alistair Hinton, UK office mgr. *UK Distributor: Priory Records.*

* **Amarilli Classical.** The Coach House, Blackheath Way, West Malvern, Worcs WR14 4DR *tel*: 01684 891156 *email*: office@amarilli.co.uk. Brian Capleton, production mgr. *High quality recordings of previously unrecorded early mus and contemporary mus.,*

Amon Ra Records. The Barton, Inglestone Common, Badminton, S Glos GL9 1BX *fax*: 01454 299858 *email*: Saydisc@aol.com. Gef Lucena, mgr dir. *Labels: Amon Ra, Saydisc.*

Amphion. Norton Lodge, 109 Beverley Rd, Norton-on-Derwent, Malton, N Yorks YO17 9PH *tel*: 01653 698372 *fax*: 01653 698372 *email*: amphion@btopenworld.com. Martin Monkman, proprietor. *Distributor: Priory Records.*

Apollo Sound. 32 Ellerdale Rd, London NW3 6BB *tel*: 020 7435 5255 *fax*: 020 7431 0621 *email*: info@apollosound.com. H Herschmann, mgr dir; T N Herschmann, mgr. *Label: Apollo Sound. BPI*

* **Appian Publications & Recordings (APR).** PO Box 1, Wark, Hexham, Northumberland NE48 3EW *tel*: 01434 220627 *fax*: 01434 220628. Edwin Alan, mgr. *Label: APR. Specialises in historic releases.*

* **Arembe.** 84 Filsham Rd, Hastings, E Sussex TN38 0PG *tel*: 01424 423260 *fax*: 01424 423260. Margaret Brand, mkt dir. *Label: Arembe Records.*

Athene Records. 7 Shute House, Shute, Axminster EX13 7NY *tel*: 01297 631426 *email*: athene@athenerccords.com. Joanna Leach, artistic dir; Mike Beville, technical dir. *Labels: Athene (period square pnos), Athene-Minerva (modern insts).*

Audio-B Ltd. PO Box 16797, London W3 6ZS *tel*: 020 8896 9798 *fax*: 020 8932 4836 *email*: info@audio-b.com. Malcolm Creese. *Specialist jazz label.*

BGS Records. Bath Spa University College, Newton Park, Newton St Loe, Bath BA2 9BN *tel*: 01225 875609 *fax*: 01225 875495 *email*: igf@bathspa.ac.uk. Philip Castang, label mgr. *Label is dedicated to presentation of new or rediscovered work and/or new artists.*

BMG. 69-79 Fulham High St, London SW6 3JW *tel*: 020 7384 7686 *fax*: 020 7973 0345 *email*: classics@bmg.co.uk. John Cronin, head of classics and imports. *Labels: Arte Nova, BMG Classics, Catalyst, Classic FM, Deutsche Harmonia Mundi, RCA Red Seal, Victor. BPI*

BMP Broken Music Publishing (UK) Ltd. Riverbank House, 1 Putney Bridge Approach, London SW6 3JD *tel*: 020 7371 0022 *fax*: 020 7371 0099 *email*: ripe@compuserve.com. Jurgen Dramm, mgr dir; Sharon Brooks, dir A&R. *BPI*

Bandleader Music. Modern Publicity Services Ltd, 46 High St, Rochester, Kent ME1 1LD *tel*: 01634 844433 *fax*: 01634 844455 *email*: sales@modernpublicity.co.uk.

Belltree Records. 9 Hillside Rd, Ashtead, Surrey KT21 1RZ *tel*: 01372 277703 *fax*: 01372 278406 *email*: dragonsfire@btinternet.com. Nigel Perona-Wright, partner. *Label: Belltree Records.*

* **Biddulph Recordings.** PO Box 222, Newton Abbot, Devon TQ12 4YN *tel*: 01626 873686 *fax*: 01626 873686 *email*: info@biddulphrecordings.com. Sarah Woodward. *Label is committed to restoring the great recordings of the past, and to promoting young artists.*

Bitter and Twisted Records and Productions. 22c Breakspears Rd, London SE4 1UW *tel*: 020 8691 8646 *email*: btrap@argonet.co.uk. Andrew Poppy, mgr dir; Frederick Ruby, label mgr; Grant Bardsley, mkt.

Black Mountain Ltd. 1 Squire Court, The Marina, Swansea SA1 3XB *tel*: 01792 301500 *fax*: 01792 301500. Mike Evans, dir. *Label: Black Mountain.*

Brewhouse Music. Breeds Farm, 57 High St, Wicken, Ely, Cambs CB7 5XR *tel*: 01353 720309 *fax*: 01353 723364 *email*: brewhouse@brewhousemusic.co.uk; info@brewhousemusic.co.uk. Eric and Ray Cowell, partners. *Labels: Brewhouse, Calle Classics, Home Brew.*

* **British Music Society.** 7 Tudor Gardens, Upminster, Essex RM14 3DE *tel*: 01708 224795. S C Trowell, hon treasurer. *Only distributes the society's own productions.*

* **Brittens Music Ltd.** 24 Pevensey Rd, Eastbourne, E Sussex BN21 3HP *tel*: 01323 732553 *fax*: 01323 417455 *email*: mail@seaford-music.co.uk. *Labels: Atoll, Bergen Studio, Cedille, Grappa, Kiwi-Pacific, Mediaphon, Morrison & Co Trust, NKF, Partridge, Pro-Piano, Sonpact, Tall Poppies, Vest-Norsk, Victoria.*

CRD Records Ltd. PO Box 142, Truro, Cornwall TR2 5YJ *tel*: 01872 580000 *fax*: 01872 580002 *email*: info@crdrecords.com. Graham Pauncefort, mgr dir. *Label: CRD.*

* **Cadillac Jazz Distribution.** 15 Kings Exchange, Tileyard Rd, London N7 9AH *tel*: 020 7619 9111 *fax*: 020 7619 0901 *email*: john@cadillacjazz.co.uk. John Jack, mgr dir. *Labels: Arbors, Ayler, BvHaast, Cadillac, Caprice, Chiaroscuro, Dragon, FMP, Gemini, Ogun, Phontastic, Reservior, Storyville and a large list of jazz labels. Cadillac Music and Publishing own Cadillac Dawn Club record labels.*

* **Cala Records.** 17 Shakespeare Gardens, London N2 9LJ *tel*: 020 8883 7306 *fax*: 020 8365 3388 *email*: music@calarecords.com. Geoffrey Simon, artistic dir; Daniel Schiffman, exec producer; Jeremy Swerling, mkt; Matthew Daines, mkt. *Labels: Cala Artists, Cala Cascade, Cala Records, Cala-The Edge, Cala-United.*

Campion & Cameo. 1st and 2nd Floors, 7 High St, Cheadle, Cheshire SK8 1AX *tel*: 0161 491 6655 *fax*: 0161 491 6688 *email*: dimus@aol.com. Alan Wilson, mgr dir. *Label: Campion Cameo.*

Campion Records. 1st and 2nd Floors, 7 High St, Cheadle, Cheshire SK8 1AX *tel*: 0161 491 6655 *fax*: 0161 491 6688 *email*: dimus@aol.com. Alan Wilson, mgr dir. *Label: Campion.*

Cantoris Records. Exchequer Gate, Lincoln LN2 1PZ *tel*: 01522 536981 *fax*: 01522 560550 *email*: sales@cantoris.co.uk. Paul Pinchbeck, proprietor. *Label: Cantoris. Choral orch mus of all styles.*

* **Caritas Records.** 28 Dalrymple Cres, Edinburgh EH9 2HX *tel*: 0131 667 3633 *fax*: 0131 667 3633 *email*: caritas-records@caritas-music.co.uk. Katharine Douglas, professional mgr; James Douglas, dir. *Labels: Caritas, Caritas Classics, Caritas Music Library. BPI*

Cello Classics. 38 Chandos Rd, London N2 9AP *tel*: 020 8444 6358 *fax*: 020 8883 7104 *email*: info@celloclassics.com. Sebastian Comberti, artistic dir; Nicolas Soames, admin; Peter Fallows, sales and mkt.

* **Chandos Records Ltd.** Chandos House, Commerce Way, Colchester, Essex CO2 8HQ *tel*: 01206 225200 *fax*: 01206 225201 *email*: enquiries@chandos.net. Brian Couzens, chmn; Ralph Couzens, mgr dir; Ginny Cooper, sales mgr; Paul Westcott, press offr; S Revill, finance dir. *Labels: 2for1, Bear Essentials, Brass, Chaconne, Chandos, Collect, Enchant, Flyback, Historical, Movies, New Direction, Opera in English, Television. BPI*

Choice Recordings. 7 Comiston Drive, Edinburgh EH10 5QR *tel*: 0131 446 9163 *fax*: 0131 446 9163/447 1995 *email*: electus@ukonline.co.uk. Malcolm Hobson, dir.

Clarinet Classics. 58 Crescent Rd, London E13 0LT *tel*: 020 8472 2057/8851 4220 (sales) *fax*: 020 8503 5809 *email*: enquiries@clarinetclassics.com. Victoria Soames Samek, artistic dir; Peter Fallows, sales mgr; Sheila Green, office mgr; Nicolas Soames, admin; Richard Ralph, sec.

Classical Communications. Jericho Farmhouse, Cassington, Oxon OX29 4DY *tel*: 01865 882920 *fax*: 01865 882947 *email*: mail@classicalmusicshop.com. Frances Sunderland, dir; Martin Souter, dir; Ellen Froggatt, operations mgr; Mike Williams, sales mgr. *Label: The Gift of Music.*

Claudio Records Ltd. Studio 17, The Promenade, Peacehaven, E Sussex BN10 8PU *tel*: 01273 580250 *fax*: 01273 583530 *email*: info@claudiorecords.com. Colin and William Attwell, mgr dirs. *Labels: Bohema, Claudio, Claudio Contemporary.*

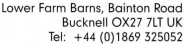
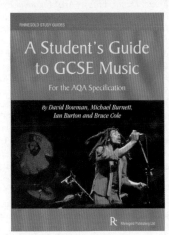

Collegium Records. PO Box 172, Whittlesford, Cambridge CB2 4QZ *tel:* 01223 832474 *fax:* 01223 836723 *email:* info@collegium.co.uk. John Rutter, mgr dir; Michael Stevens, sales/mkt offr. *Label: Collegium. BPI*

Consort Records. 34 St Mary's Grove, London W4 3LN *tel:* 020 8995 9994 *fax:* 020 8995 2115 *email:* info@tkcworld.com.

Cube Records. Onward House, 11 Uxbridge St, London W8 7TQ *tel:* 020 7221 4275 *fax:* 020 7229 6893 *email:* cube@bucksmusicgroup.co.uk. Simon Platz, chief exec; Ronen Guha, label co-ord; Laura Parks, admin.

* **DI Music (Distribution).** 1st and 2nd Floors, 7 High St, Cheadle, Cheshire SK8 1AX *tel:* 0161 491 6655 *fax:* 0161 491 6688 *email:* dimus@aol.com. Jacquiline Holmes, distribution mgr; Alan Wilson, mgr dir. *Labels: Asc, Boheme, Caffarelli, Cala, Cambria, Campion, Campion Cameo, Classico, Divine Art, DoRon, EMEC, EDA-Edition Abseit, Eres, Essay, Helicon, Karuna, Kleos, Megadisc, Melbo, Move, Newport Classics, Newport Premier, RLPO Live, Tuxedo, Walsingham, Zulus Records, ZUK Records. BPI*

Darmo Records. Arvensis, Stour Lane, Shaftesbury, Dorset SP7 0QJ *tel:* 01747 838318 *fax:* 01747 838318 *email:* kvanbarthold@aol.com. Kenneth van Barthold, proprietor.

Delphian Records Ltd. 290 Colinton Mains Rd, Edinburgh EH13 9BS *tel:* 07902 157148 *fax:* 07092 165783 *email:* info@delphianrecords.co.uk. Paul Baxter, mgr dir; Kevin Findlan, exec producer. *All genres of chmbr mus, with a special interest in scottish art mus.*

* **Delta Music PLC.** 222 Cray Ave, Orpington, Kent BR5 3PZ *tel:* 01689 888888 *fax:* 01689 888800 *email:* info@deltamusic.co.uk. L J Adams, mgr dir. *Labels: Capriccio, Delta, Delta #1, Grassmere, Lake, Laserlight, Memoir Music, Upbeat Recordings.*

* **Demon Music Group/Music Collection International (MCI).** 4th Floor, Holden House, 57 Rathbone Place, London W1T 1JU *tel:* 020 7470 8500/7396 8899 *fax:* 020 7470 6655 *email:* info@demonmusicgroup.co.uk. Neela Ebbett, gen mgr; Danny Keene, sales and mkt dir (MCI); Adrian Sear, commercial dir; Michael Neidus, head of mkt. *Labels: Decadance, Demon, e2, Edsel, Emporio, Fuego, Gallerie, Harmless, Music Club, Nascente, Nukarma, Reflection, Showtime, Startrax, Unisex, Westside.*

Deux-Elles Ltd. 63 Culver Lane, Reading RG6 1DX *tel:* 0118 901 1767 *fax:* 0118 901 2827 *email:* info@deux-elles.com. Patrick Naylor, mgr dir. *Label: Deux-Elles.*

Dinmore Records. 11 Romsley Hill Grange, Romsley, Worcs B62 0LN *tel:* 01562 710801 *fax:* 01562 710801 *email:* paul@dinmore-records.co.uk. Paul Arden-Taylor, producer/engineer. *Label: Dinmore.*

* **Disc Imports Ltd (DI Music).** 1st and 2nd Floors, 7 High St, Cheadle, Cheshire SK8 1AX *tel:* 0161 491 6655 *fax:* 0161 491 6688 *email:* dimus@aol.com. I T Wilson, chmn; A I Wilson, mgr dir; F Langton, gen mgr; J Holmes, sec, distribution mgr. *Label: Campion, Cameo. BPI*

* **Discovery Records Ltd.** Nursteed Rd, Devizes, Wilts SN10 3DY *tel:* 01380 728000 *fax:* 01380 722244 *email:* info@discovery-records.com. Mike Cox, mgr dir; Martin Cobb, commercial mgr; Bill Trythall, sales mgr. *Labels: Accord, Arcana, Assai, Cantoris, Caprice, Claves, Col Legno, Cypres, Danacord, Elan, Enchiriadis, Ensayo, Four Hands Music, Fy, Glissando, Kontrapunkt, Lammas, Lorelt, Maguelone, ODE, Ogam, Opera Tres, Ricercar, Rose Recordings, Skarbo, Solo, Solstice, Symphonia, Timpani, Verso.*

* **Divine Art Ltd.** 8 The Beeches, East Harlsey, North Allerton, N Yorks DL6 2DJ *tel:* 01609 882062 *fax:* 01609 882091 *email:* info@divine-art.com. Stephen Sutton, mgr dir. *Label: Diversions, Divine Art, Pilgrim's Star.*

Doyen Recordings Ltd. Doyen Centre, Vulcan St, Oldham, Lancs OL1 4EP *tel:* 0161 627 3500 *fax:* 0161 628 0177 *email:* doyen@doyenmobile.com. N J Childs, mgr dir; A Childs, dir.

Dunelm Records. 2 Park Close, Glossop, Derbys SK13 7RQ *tel:* 01457 855313 *fax:* 01457 855313 *email:* jim@dunelm-records.co.uk. Jim Pattison, owner; Joyce Pattison. *Label: Dunelm Records.*

EG Records. 22 Athol St, Douglas, Isle of Man IM1 1JA *tel:* 01624 622865 *fax:* 01624 661410 *email:* sam.adco@manx.net. Sam Alder, chmn. *Label: EG, Editions EG.*

EMI Classics. 27 Wrights Lane, London W8 5SW *tel:* 020 7795 7000 *fax:* 020 7795 7001. Richard Lyttelton, president, classics and jazz; Peter Alward, president, EMI classics; Theo Lap, vice-president, international mkt, classics and jazz; John King, vice-president, finance and business affairs, classics and jazz. *BPI*

Ember Records. PO Box 130, Hove, E Sussex BN3 6QU *tel:* 01273 550088 *fax:* 01273 540969 *email:* warren@tkogroup.com. Warren Heal, licensing mgr.

English Folk Dance and Song Society. Cecil Sharp House, 2 Regent's Park Rd, London NW1 7AY *tel:* 020 7485 2206 *email:* info@efdss.org. *Produces CDs of traditional dance mus and songs.*

* **Fand Music Recordings Ltd.** The Barony, 16 Sandringham Rd, Petersfield, Hants GU32 2AA *tel:* 01730 267341 *fax:* 01730 267341 *email:* sales@fandmusic.com. Peter Thompson, sales mgr.

First Night Records. 3 Warren Mews, London W1T 6AN *tel:* 020 7383 7767 *fax:* 020 7383 3020 *email:* information@first-night-records.com. *Specialists in theatrical recordings. BPI*

Flamencovision. 54 Windsor Rd, London N3 3SS *tel:* 020 8346 4500 *fax:* 020 8346 2488 *email:* hvmartin@dircon.co.uk. Helen Martin, mgr. *Label: Flamencovision.*

Fly Records. Onward House, 11 Uxbridge St, London W8 7TQ *tel:* 020 7221 4275 *fax:* 020 7229 6893 *email:* info@bucksmusicgroup.co.uk. Simon Platz, chief exec. *BPI*

* **Forsyth Brothers Ltd (Distributor).** 126 Deansgate, Manchester M3 2GR *tel:* 0161 834 3281 *fax:* 0161 834 0630 *email:* publishing@forsyths.co.uk. D R Loat, mgr dir; Jean Colter, trade mgr. *Label: Forsyth, Music Minus One, Pocket Songs.*

Four Hands Music. 15 Birchmead Close, St Albans, Herts AL3 6BS *tel:* 01727 858485 *fax:* 01727 858485 *email:* beydag@classical-artists.com. Isabel Beyer, partner; Harvey Dagul, partner. *Label: FHM.*

Gimell Records. PO Box 197, Beckley, Oxford OX3 9YJ *tel:* 01865 358282 *fax:* 0870 056 8880 *email:* info@gimell.com. Steve C Smith, mgr dir; Peter Phillips, dir. *Label: Gimell. BPI*

Grasmere Music. 59 Marlpit Lane, Coulsdon, Surrey CR5 2HF *tel:* 020 8666 0201 *fax:* 020 8667 0037. Bob Barratt, mgr dir. *Label: Grasmere Records.*

Griffin & Co Ltd. Church House, St Mary's Gate, 96 Church St, Lancaster LA1 1TD *tel:* 01524 844399 *fax:* 01524 844335 *email:* sales@griffinrecords.co.uk. John Hawkings-Byass. *Specialise in recording British Heritage mus and cathedral choirs, also all-label distributor to Heritage and cathedral market.*

Grosvenor Records. 16 Grosvenor Rd, Handsworth Wood, Birmingham B20 3NP *tel:* 0121 356 9636 *fax:* 0121 356 9636.

* **Guitar Masters Records.** 1-2 Vance Court, Trans Britannia Enterprise Park, Blaydon on Tyne NE21 5NH *tel:* 0191 414 9000 *fax:* 0191 414 9001 *email:* mail@ashleymark.co.uk.

* **Harlequin Recording.** Elgar House, Rufford, Tamworth, Staffs *tel:* 01827 53553; 07802 545726 *fax:* 01827 53553 *email:* geoff@harlequin-recording.co.uk. Geoffrey Poulton, owner and dir. *Label: Harlequin.*

* **Harmonia Mundi (UK) Ltd.** 45 Vyner St, London E2 9DQ *tel:* 020 8709 9509 *fax:* 020 8709 9501 *email:* info.uk@harmoniamundi.com. Serge Rousset, mgr dir; Simon Astridge, commercial mgr; Celia Ballantyne, press offr. *Labels: Akt/Seventh, Aeon, Andante, Apr, Arbiter, Ambroisie, Calliope, Cantaloupe, Le Chant Du Monde, Chronoscope, Dancing Rhino, Daqui, Ellipsis Arts, Emanem Evidence, FMR, Fedora, Forlane, Glossa, Harmonia Mundi, Hat (Now) Art, Hatology, Highnote, Incus, Institut Du Monde Arabe, Intuition, Iris, Jazz Point, K617, Knitting Factory, Linn Records, Long Distance, LSO Live, Mirare, Mode, Music & Arts, Navras, Nubenegra, Ocora, PSF World Arbiter, Paratactile, Paris Jazz Corner, Pearl/Opal, Pi, Playasound, Praga Digitals, Preiser, Prometheus Editions, Real Rhythm, Red Records, Satirino, Savant, Saydisc, Sketch, Soul Note, Trace, Unicorn Kanchana, Vanstory, Wergo, Winter & Winter, World Village, Zigzag Black Saint. BPI*

Heritage Recordings. 50 Bessborough Place, London SW1V 3SG *tel:* 020 7828 1055 *fax:* 020 7376 5705. Hugh MacPherson, mgr dir.

Hoxa. 4 College Rd, Clifton, Bristol BS8 3JB *tel:* 0117 974 1153 *fax:* 0117 377 5532 *email:* sound@hoxa.net. R Jeffrey-Gray, dir; S Jeffrey-Gray, admin. *Labels: Clifton Recording, Hoxa. Introduction to the Piano, And I Saw New Heaven, Psalm Songs, Gaudete, Lochrian Lollipop.*

Hyperion Records Ltd. PO Box 25, London SE9 1AX *tel:* 020 8318 1234 *fax:* 020 8463 1230 *email:* info@hyperion-records.co.uk. Mike Spring, sales mgr; Jeanette Bevan, press and promotions mgr; Simon Perry, dir; Richard Howard, production mgr. *Labels: Helios, Hyperion. BPI*

Imperial Sound. 16 Stonehill Rd, London SW14 8RW *tel:* 020 8876 3156 *email:* alanfoster@con-brio.com. *Label: Imperial.*

* **Impetus Distribution.** 10 High St, Skigersta, Ness, Isle of Lewis HS2 0TS, Outer Hebrides *tel:* 01851 810808 *fax:* 01851 810809 *email:* Impetusrecs@aol.com. *Labels: Alice, CRI, Chamber Sound, Content, Crystal, Genesis, Innova, Newtone, Nosag, Phono Suecia, Sargasso.*

* **Jammy Music.** The Beeches, 244 Anniesland Rd, Glasgow G13 1XA *tel:* 0141 954 1873 *fax:* 0141 954 6341 *email:* jammymusic@compuserve.com.

Janiculum Recordings. 4 Scarth Rd, London SW13 0ND *tel:* 020 8876 6901 *fax:* 020 8395 3919 *email:* janeclark@intune.co.uk. Jane Clark, dir.

* **Jewish Music Heritage Recordings.** Jewish Music Institute, PO Box 232, Harrow, Middx HA1 2NN *tel:* 020 8909 2445 *fax:* 020 8909 1030 *email:* jewishmusic@jmi.org.uk. Geraldine Auerbach, exec dir. *Jewish*

mus on CD and cassette including original recordings and historic re-issues.

Jonathan Wearn Productions. The Yews Cottage, Bothamsall, Retford, Notts DN22 8DT *tel:* 01623 835226 *email:* info@jonathanwearn.co.uk. Jonathan R Wearn. *Labels: CBS, Carlton, EMI Angel, EMI Capital, Guild, IMP, Philips, Pickwick, Vox Cum Laude.*

Just Accord Music. PO Box 224, Tadworth, Surrey KT20 5YJ *tel:* 01737 371631 *email:* information@justaccordmusic.com. Philip Machin, mgr dir.

* **K B Productions.** 72 Waverley Rd, Rayners Lane, Harrow, Middx HA2 9RD *tel:* 020 8866 4158 *fax:* 020 8866 4158. Keith S Bance. *Labels: Hortus (Paris).*

Keyboard Records. 418 Brockley Rd, Brockley, London SE4 2DH *tel:* 020 8699 2549. Gilbert Rowland, mgr dir. *Label: Keyboard.*

* **Kingsway Music.** 26-28 Lottbridge Drove, Eastbourne, E Sussex BN23 6NT *tel:* 01323 437700 *fax:* 01323 411970 *email:* music@kingsway.co.uk. Caroline Bonnett, A&R; Les Moir, Survivor A&R.

Lammas Records. 118 The Mount, York YO24 1AS *tel:* 01904 624132 *fax:* 01904 624132 *email:* enquiries@lammas.co.uk. *Label: Lammas Records.*

Lematt Music. White House Farm, Shropshire TF9 4HA *tel:* 01630 647374 *fax:* 01630 647612. Xavier Lee, producer; Tanya Woof, A&R; Katherine Lee, international A&R. *Label: Check.*

Libra Records Ltd. 9 Willingale Close, Woodford Green, Essex IG8 7HD *tel:* 020 8505 3813 *fax:* 020 8505 3813. A Ben-Ayad, dir.

* **Linn Records.** Floors Rd, Waterfoot, Glasgow G76 0EP *tel:* 0141 303 5027/9 *fax:* 0141 303 5007 *email:* records@linn.co.uk. Philip Hobbs, exec engineer and A&R; Caroline Dooley, head of Linn Records; Cathy Jeffries, sales & mkt; Kenny Morris, press. *Label: Linn. BPI*

* **Lismor Recordings Ltd.** 27-29 Carnoustie Place, Scotland St, Glasgow G5 8PH *tel:* 0141 420 1881 *fax:* 0141 420 1892 *email:* lismor@lismor.com. Ronnie Simpson, dir.

London Independent Records. PO Box 3136, Barnet, Herts EN5 1DY *tel:* 020 8447 3862 *fax:* 020 8447 3862 *email:* info@london-independent.co.uk. Jan Hart, dir. *Record label created to give recording opportunities to young unrecorded artists with access to funding.*

Longman Records. West House, Forthaven, Shoreham by Sea, W Sussex BN43 5HY *tel:* 01273 453422 *fax:* 01273 452914 *email:* marketing@longman-records.com. Richard Durrant, dir; Louise Brattle, promotional mgr; Michael Munday, designer. *Label: Longman. Longman is an acoustic mus label covering a variety of genres including classical.*

Lorelt (Lontano Records Ltd). 39h Hatherley Mews, Walthamstow, London E17 4QP *tel:* 020 8521 8075 *fax:* 020 8521 8075. Odaline de la Martinez, mgr dir. *Label: Lorelt.*

Lowri Records. Warwick House, 34 Warwick Rd, Coulsdon, Surrey CR5 2EE *tel:* 020 8660 7877 *fax:* 0870 135 2900 *email:* sales@lowrirecords.com. Lowri Blake, dir.

Lyric Production. 41 Arkwright Rd, Sanderstead, Surrey CR2 0LP *tel:* 020 8657 5840 *fax:* 020 8657 5840. H T Hope, mgr dir; Norma Dyer, exec producer. *Label: Lyric.*

Lyrita Recorded Edition. PO Box 998, Slough SL1 8YS. A R Itter, proprietor. *Label: Lyrita. BPI*

MPS Music and Video. Rosegarth, Hetton Rd, Houghton-le-Spring, Durham DH5 8JN *tel:* 0191 584 4141 *fax:* 0191 584 4141 *email:* carey@cnutman.freeserve.net. C Nutman, studio mgr; G Nossiter, webmaster. *Contemporary mus, especially electroacoustic and experimental mus.*

Meridian Records. PO Box 317, Eltham, London SE9 4SF *tel:* 020 8857 3213 *fax:* 020 8857 0731 *email:* mail@meridian-records.co.uk. John Shuttleworth, mgr dir; Richard Hughes, mgr/engineer. *Labels: Duo, Meridian.*

Metier Sound & Vision Ltd. 127 Stanford Cottages, Semley, Shaftesbury, Dorset SP7 9AT *tel:* 01747 830979 *fax:* 01747 830979 *email:* info@metierrecords.co.uk. David Lefeber, mgr dir. *Label: Metier (specialising in contemporary mus). Distributor: Albany (US), Liebermann (Germany), Priory Records (UK), Verge (Canada).*

* **Metronome Distribution Ltd.** Singleton Court, Wonastow Rd, Monmouth NP25 5JA *tel:* 01600 716911 *fax:* 01600 775396 *email:* info@metronome.co.uk. Sue Howell, admin. *Labels: Atma, Aura, Boston Skyline, Budapest Music Centre, Delos, Dorian, DTR, Dux, Ermitage, GM Great Opera Performances, Haenissler, Hungaraton, Marquis, Malandro, Metronome, Mondo Musica, Musica Sancta, Nuova Era, Ongaku, Opus Kura, Oxingale, Real Sound, Robert Parker, Scribendum, Soundalive, Sterndale, Summit Records. BPI*

* **Metronome Recordings Ltd.** Carrick Business Centre, Beacon House, Commercial Rd, Penryn, Cornwall TR10 8AR *tel:* 01326 377738/8737 *fax:* 01326 378643 *email:* info@metronome.co.uk. Tim Smithies, mgr dir. *Label: Metronome, Soundalive. BPI*

Minstral Records. 3-5 Bridge St, Hadleigh, Ipswich, Suffolk IP7 6BY *tel:* 01473 822596 *fax:* 01473 824175 *email:* Thomas.McIntosh@minstrelmusic.demon.co.uk. T L McIntosh, mgr dir; S Sowman, asst. *Label: Minstral.*

Montague Music. Stable Cottage, Southwick Hall, Peterborough PE8 5BL *tel:* 01832 274790 *email:* sandymacdonald@lineone.net.

Music Collection International *see* **Demon Music Group Ltd.**

Music Masters Ltd. Orchard End, Upper Oddington, Moreton-in-Marsh, Glos GL56 0XH *tel:* 01451 870701 *fax:* 01451 870702. Nicholas John, mgr dir; Peter Wheeler, mgr dir.

NMC Recordings Ltd. 4th Floor, 18-20 Southwark St, London SE1 1TJ *tel:* 020 7403 9445 *fax:* 020 7403 9446 *email:* nmc@nmcrec.co.uk. Hannah Vlcek, admin; Hannah Teale, admin asst; Colin Matthews, exec producer. *Label devoted to contemporary British classical mus. BPI*

* **New Note Distribution Ltd.** Electron House, Cray Ave, Orpington, Kent BR5 3RJ *tel:* 01689 877884 *fax:* 01689 877891 *email:* mail@newnote.com. Eddie Wilkinson, joint mgr dir; Graham Griffiths, joint mgr dir. *Labels: Bel Air, ECM New Series, GB Records, Telarc Classical and various jazz labels.*

* **Nimbus Records.** Wyastone Estate Limited, Wyastone Leys, Monmouth NP25 3SR *tel:* 01600 890007 *fax:* 01600 891052 *email:* antony@wyastone.co.uk. Antony Smith, sales; Adrian Farmer, A&R and global licensing. *Labels: Nimbus, Prima Voce, World Music. BPI*

Novelbond Limited. Sovereign House, 212-224 Shaftesbury Ave, London WC2H 8HQ *tel:* 020 7240 5821 *fax:* 020 7240 5827 *email:* order@novelbond.co.uk. Peter Watts, dir. *Label: Novelbond.*

Oboe Classics. 9 Beversbrook Rd, London N19 4QG *tel:* 020 7263 4027 *email:* mail@oboeclassics.com. Jeremy Polmear, artistic dir. *Recordings to celebrate the oboe.*

Opera Omnia Productions. York House, 26 Beverley Crescent, Bedford MK40 4BY *tel:* 01234 343033 *fax:* 01234 273605 *email:* mail@operaomnia.co.uk. Patrick Allen, mgr dir. *Label: Opera Omnia.*

* **Opera Rara.** 134-146 Curtain Rd, London EC2A 3AR *tel:* 020 7613 2858 *fax:* 020 7613 2261 *email:* info@opera-rara.com. Patric Schmid, artistic dir; Stephen Revell, mgr dir. *Label: Opera Rara.*

* **OxRecs Digital.** 37 Inkerman Close, Abingdon, Oxon OX14 1NH *tel:* 01235 550589 *email:* info@oxrecs.com. Bernard Martin, mgr dir. *Label: OxRecs.*

Paradisum Records Ltd. 19 Grove Hill, South Woodford, London E18 2JB *tel:* 020 8530 5454 *fax:* 020 8491 0898 *email:* paradisum@aol.com; info@paradisum.com. Ian Hayter, dir; Fred Shone, dir. *Labels: Jongleur, Paradisum. Distributor: RGM/Universal.*

Past Perfect Vintage Music. Lower Farm Barns, Bainton Rd, Bucknell, Oxon OX27 7LT *tel:* 01869 325052 *fax:* 01869 325072 *email:* clarity@pastperfect.com.

Pavilion Records Ltd. Sparrows Green, Wadhurst, E Sussex TN5 6SJ *tel:* 01892 783591 *fax:* 01892 784156 *email:* pearl@pavilionrecords.com. John Waite, mgr dir. *Labels: Flapper (jazz, humour, nostalgia, light music), Opal (classical, documentary, historical), Pearl (classical, historical), Topaz (jazz). BPI*

* **Pentacone.** PO Box 76, Batley, W Yorks WF17 8XN *tel:* 01274 871187 *fax:* 01274 873221 *email:* peter@pentacone.freeserve.co.uk. Peter Sheehan, proprietor. *Labels: Opus3, Prophone, Proprius, Swedish Society.*

* **Pinnacle Records.** Electron House, Cray Ave, St Mary Cray, Orpington, Kent BR5 3RJ *tel:* 01689 870622 *fax:* 01689 821741. Steve Mason, chmn; Sean Sullivan, dir; Tony Powell, mgr dir; Alan King, dir of operations. *BPI*

* **Plankton Records.** PO Box 13533, London E7 0SG *tel:* 020 8534 8500 *email:* plankton.records@virgin.net. Simon Law, snr partner; Keith Dixon, mkt and A&R. *Labels: Embryo Arts, Gutta, It Stinks, Plankton, Sarepta, Sea Dream.*

Polyphonic Reproductions Ltd. PO Box 19292, London NW10 9WP *tel:* 020 8459 6194 *fax:* 020 8451 6470 *email:* polyphonic@studio-music.co.uk. Stan Kitchen, mgr dir; Paul Williams, mkt offr; Shirley Kitchen, press offr. *Label: Polyphonic. BPI*

President Records Ltd. Units 6 & 7, 11 Wyfold Rd, Fulham, London SW6 6SE *tel:* 020 7385 7700 *fax:* 020 7385 3402 *email:* hits@president-records.co.uk. David Kassner, mgr dir. *BPI*

* **Priory Records Ltd.** 3 Eden Court, Eden Way, Leighton Buzzard, Beds LU7 4FY *tel:* 01525 377566 *fax:* 01525 371477 *email:* sales@priory.org.uk. Neil V R Collier, mgr dir; Callum Ross, finance and sales mgr. *Labels: Aeolus, Albany, Altarus, Amphion, Bel Canto, Beulah, British Music Society, CBC Records, Carus, Cramer, Dynamic, Festivo, Guild, IFO, Idis, Ikon, Isis, Kevin Mayhew, Kingdom (classical), London Independent Records, Metier, Motette, New World Records, Olympia,*

Pierian, Priory, Pro Organo, Quilisma, Sanctus, Shellwood, Sterling, Tahra, Towerhill, Tring RPO International, Urania, Vai, Vista Vera.

* **RSK Entertainment Ltd.** Unit 3, Home Farm, Welford, Newbury, Berks RG20 8HR *tel:* 01488 608900 *fax:* 01488 608901 *email:* info@rskentertainment.co.uk. Rashmi Patani, joint mgr dir; Simon Carver, joint mgr dir. *Labels: Acoustic Disc, Acoustic Records, Aleph Records, Appleseed Records, Audiopharm, Bad Taste Records, Black Lion, Blue Flame, Bridge Records, Burnside Records, Century Media, Channel Classics, Collectors Choice Music, D3, DA Music, DRG Records, Delerium, Deux-Elles Classics, Empress, Escape Music, Highnote, Inside Out, MC Records, Market Square Records, MUTT Records, NMC Classics, Naim Audio, Nightingale, Persevere Records, Red House, Repertoire Records, Righteous Babe, See For Miles, Supraphon, Silva Screen, SPV, Start Records, TER, Wolf Records. BPI*

RWM Music. PO Box 166, Northwood, Middx HA6 2FL *tel:* 01923 841645 *fax:* 01923 841785 *email:* info@rwmmusic.com. Rosalind Morgan, admin mgr; Graham Watkins, educ and competition dir. *New classical artists. Label: RWM Music.*

Redcliffe Recordings. 68 Barrowgate Rd, London W4 4QU *tel:* 020 8995 1223 *fax:* 020 8995 1223 *email:* redcliffe@frouth.freeserve.co.uk. John Rushby-Smith, producer; Derek Mills, mgr. *Label: British Music Heritage.*

* **Regent Records.** PO Box 528, Wolverhampton WV3 9YW *tel:* 01902 424377 *fax:* 01902 717661 *email:* regent.records@btinternet.com. Gary Cole, producer; Pippa Cole, admin. *Label: Regent.*

Riverrun Records. PO Box 30, Potton, Beds SG19 2XH *tel:* 01767 260223 *email:* enquiries@riverrunstudios.co.uk. Leigh James, label mgr; John Mercer, producer. *Specialise in contemporary British mus and also lesser known works from pre-classical repertoire.*

Rykodisc International. 329 Latimer Rd, London W10 6RA *tel:* 020 8960 3311 *fax:* 020 8960 1177 *email:* info@rykodisc.co.uk. Colleen Theis, promotions dir; Andy Childs, sales and distributions dir. *Labels: Arena Rock, Hannibal, Ropeadope, Rykodisc, Sound Gizmo.*

S & R Cressidia. PO Box 2077, Poole, Dorset BH16 5YA *tel:* 01202 632703 *email:* s&r@cressidia.com. Toby Richards, dir; Jane Child, press offr; David Singleton, mgr dir. *Label: Cressidia Classics.*

SCS Music Ltd. PO Box 197, Beckley, Oxford OX3 9YJ *tel:* 01865 358282 *fax:* 0870 056 8880 *email:* steve@scsmusic.co.uk. S C Smith, mgr dir. *Label: Abbey Records, SCS Music.*

* **Sain (Recordiau) Cyf.** Canolfan Sain, Llandwrog, Caernarfon, Gwynedd LL54 5TG *tel:* 01286 831111 *fax:* 01286 831497 *email:* music@sain.wales.com. Rhian Eleri, copyright controller; Dafydd Iwan, mgr dir. *Labels: Cambrian, Crai, Gwynfryn, Sain, Tryfan, Welsh Teldisc.*

Sanctuary Classics. Sanctuary House, 45-53 Sinclair Rd, London W14 0NS *tel:* 020 7300 1888 *fax:* 020 7300 1306 *email:* info@sanctuarygroup.com. Pawlina Bednarczyk, A&R mgr; Richard Harrison, mgr dir; Ray Crick, living era mgr; Karen Pitchford, publicist; Chris Craker, creative and commercial dir. *Labels: ASV, Black Box, Gaudeamus, Hallé, Living Era, White Line. BPI*

Sargasso. PO Box 10565, London N1 8SR *tel:* 020 7359 7825 *fax:* 020 7704 2141 *email:* info@sargasso.com. Veronique Joly, label mgr. *Avant-garde contemporary and experimental mus including electronic, improvisation, electroacoustic, minimalism, songwriting, etc.*

Saydisc Records. The Barton, Inglestone Common, Badminton, S Glos GL9 1BX *fax:* 01454 299858 *email:* Saydisc@aol.com. Gef Lucena, mgr. *Labels: Amon Ra, Saydisc.*

* **Select Music and Video Distribution.** 3 Wells Place, Redhill, Surrey RH1 3DR *tel:* 01737 645600 *fax:* 01737 644065 *email:* cds@selectmusic.co.uk. Anthony Anderson, mgr dir. *ASV, Arthaus, BBC Legends, BBC-Opus Arte, Bis, Black Box, CPO, Collegium, Hyperion, Marco Polo, Naxos. BPI*

Signum Records. Unit 14, 21 Wadsworth Rd, Perivale, Middx UB6 7JD *tel:* 0870 710 6101 *fax:* 020 8998 5767 *email:* info@signumrecords.com. Alistair Dixon, mgr dir; Steve Long, mgr dir; Ruth Lewis, admin. *Early and contemporary mus labels.*

Silver Sounds (CD) Ltd. Unit 7, Peerglow Estate, Queensway, Ponders End, Enfield EN3 4SB *tel:* 020 8364 7711 *fax:* 020 8805 6213 *email:* info@silversounds.co.uk. Murray Allan, mgr dir; Dom Matica, sales, product mgr. *Various labels: BR Music, Collectables, Dress Circle, Magic Records, Priddis Music, etc. Worldwide imports.*

Solarise Records. PO Box 31104, London E16 4UE *tel:* 07980 453628; 07790 865199 *email:* info@solariserecords.com. *Online independent record label, independent mus from all genres.*

* **Solo Records.** 40 Osborne Rd, London N4 3SD *tel:* 020 7272 7911 *fax:* 07092 246240 *email:* mary@solorecords.com. Mary Bradbury, dir; Mark Swartzentruber, artistic dir. *Distributor: Discovery Records Ltd.*

Somm Recordings. 13 Riversdale Rd, Thames Ditton, Surrey KT7 0QL *tel:* 020 8398 1586 *fax:* 020 8339 0981 *email:* sales@somm-recordings.demon.co.uk. Siva Oke, dir; K H Oke, admin. *Label: Somm. BPI*

* **Sony Classical.** Sony Music Entertainment (UK) Ltd, 10 Great Marlborough St, London W1V 2LP *tel:* 020 7911 8251 *fax:* 020 7911 8792. Alun Taylor, gen mgr; Alex Cowan, product mgr; Johanna Knowles, press and PR mgr. *Label: Sony Classical. BPI*

* **Soundboard.** Mount Pleasant, Westbury sub Mendip, Wells BA5 1HU *tel:* 01749 870516 *fax:* 01749 870516 *email:* colin@harpsichords.demon.co.uk. Colin Booth, proprietor. *Label: Soundboard. Mus for hpd.*

Start Audio and Video Ltd. 3 Warmair House, Green Lane, Northwood, Middx HA6 2QB *tel:* 01923 841414 *fax:* 01923 842223 *email:* startav@compuserve.com. Brian Gibbon, mgr dir; Nicholas Dicker, gen mgr. *Labels: Focus, Musketeer, Parade, Platinum Collection, Start Classics.*

State Records. 6 Kenrick Place, London W1U 6HD *tel:* 020 7486 9878 *fax:* 020 7486 9934 *email:* recordings@staterecords.co.uk. *Label: State Prima.*

Statement Records Ltd. Lower Marshay, Pennymoor, Tiverton EX16 8LZ *tel:* 01363 866665 *fax:* 01363 866667 *email:* statementrecords@yahoo.co.uk. Robert Masters, dir; Kevin Bragg, dir; Shaun Reaney, sec.

* **Survivor Records.** 26-28 Lottbridge Drove, Eastbourne, E Sussex BN23 6NT *tel:* 01323 437700 *fax:* 01323 411970 *email:* survivoradmin@kingsway.co.uk. Les Moir, A&R; Caroline Bonnett, Kingsway Music A&R.

* **Symposium Records.** 110 Derwent Ave, E Barnet, Herts EN4 8LZ *tel:* 020 8368 8667 *fax:* 020 8368 8667 *email:* symposium@cwcom.net. Eliot B Levin. *Label: Symposium. BPI*

TKO Licensing Ltd. PO Box 130, Hove, E Sussex BN3 6QU *tel:* 01273 550082 *fax:* 01273 540969 *email:* warren@tkogroup.com. Warren Heal, licensing mgr.

* **TSC Enterprises.** One Day Cottage, Town End, Taddington, Derbys SK17 9UF *tel:* 01298 85534. James H Kirkwood, proprietor. *Choral mus.*

Testament Records. 14 Tootswood Rd, Bromley, Kent BR2 0PD *tel:* 020 8464 5947 *fax:* 020 8464 5352.

That's Entertainment Records Ltd/Jay Productions Ltd. 107 Kentish Town Rd, London NW1 8PB *tel:* 020 7485 9593 *fax:* 020 7485 2282. John Yap, mgr dir; Jessica Lim, gen mgr; Doug Craib, gen mgr. *Label: Ter/Jay. BPI*

Timbre Records. PO Box 3698, London NW2 6ZA *tel:* 020 7748 3003/4 *fax:* 020 7691 7632 *email:* info@timbre.co.uk. Diane M Hinds, dir.

Tremula Records. 11 Hordern Close, Haddenham, Bucks HP17 8NA *tel:* 01844 299005 *email:* tremula@lineone.net. Kenrick Dance, proprietor. *Label: Tremula.*

Unicorn Records Ltd. T/A Unicorn Kanchana Records, PO Box 33, Petworth, W Sussex GU28 0QF *tel:* 01798 867766 *fax:* 01798 867766. Nigel Brandt, dir. *Label: Unicorn-Kanchana. BPI*

* **Universal Classics and Jazz.** 22 St Peters Square, London W6 9NW *tel:* 020 8910 5000 *fax:* 020 8910 3130 *email:* catherine.mccormick@umusic.com. Bill Holland, division dir; Dickon Stainer, mkt dir; Mark Wilkinson, head of classics; Tom Lewis, label mgr, jazz. *Labels: Belart, Decca, Deutsche Grammophon, GRP, Philips, Verve, UCJ.*

Universal Jazz. 22 St Peters Square, London W6 9NW *tel:* 020 8910 5000 *fax:* 020 8910 3131 *email:* tom.lewis@umusic.com. Tom Lewis, label mgr; Julie Allison, press offr; Dionne Clarke, mkt. *BPI*

Ra **Upbeat Recordings.** PO Box 63, Wallington, Surrey SM6 9YP *tel:* 020 8773 1223 *fax:* 020 8669 6752 *email:* info@upbeat.co.uk. Liz Biddle, mgr dir; Beryl Korman, press and PR dir. *Labels: Ossia Classics, Upbeat Classics, Upbeat Jazz, Upbeat Showbiz. BPI*

Usk Recordings. 26 Caterham Rd, London SE13 5AR *tel:* 020 8318 2031 *fax:* 020 7737 0063 *email:* info@uskrecordings.com. Timothy Salter, dir. *Label: Usk Recordings.*

Utopia Records Ltd. Utopia Village, 7 Chalcot Rd, London NW1 8LH *tel:* 020 7586 3434 *fax:* 020 7586 3438. *Pop, folk, jazz.*

* **Voiceprint.** PO Box 50, Houghton-le-Spring, Tyne and Wear DH4 5YP *tel:* 0191 512 1103 *fax:* 0191 512 1104 *email:* info@voiceprint.co.uk. Rob Ayling, mgr dir. *Classic Print.*

* **Warner Classics UK.** Electric Lighting Station, 46 Kensington Court, London W8 5DA *tel:* 020 7938 5600 *fax:* 020 7368 4903 *email:* forename.surname@warnermusic.com. Matthew Cosgrove, dir; Jennifer Chilton, dept co-ord; Chris Evans, mkt and sales mgr; Lucy Bright, press mgr. *Labels: Erato, Finlandia, Nonesuch, Teldec, Warner Fonit. BPI*

York Ambisonic. PO Box 66, Lancaster LA2 6HS *tel:* 01524 823020 *fax:* 01524 824420. Brendan Hearne, mgr dir. *Label: York Ambisonic.*

* **Zyx Records.** Unit 11 Cambridge Court, 210 Shepherds Bush Rd, London W6 7NJ *tel:* 020 7371 6969 *fax:* 020 7371 6677/88 *email:* lauren.lorenzo@zyxrecords.freeserve.co.uk. Lauren Lorenzo, gen mgr.

Recording Studios

Studios are arranged by town, with Greater London listed first. Scotland and Wales can be found at the end of the section. Studios are indicated as being 8, 16, 24 track, etc, with a note of how many performers each can accommodate. Membership of the **Association of Professional Recording Services (APRS)** (PO Box 22, Totnes, Devon TQ9 7YZ *tel:* 01803 868600 *fax:* 01803 868444 *email:* info@aprs.co.uk *website:* www.aprs.co.uk), is indicated by an asterisk. **Location Recording Studios** are listed under **Recording and Sound Duplication**.

Greater London

* Abbey Road Studios. 3 Abbey Rd, London NW8 9AY *tel:* 020 7266 7000 *fax:* 020 7266 7250 *email:* bookings@abbeyroad.com. Colette Barber, studio mgr. *Studio 1: Neve VRP 72 channel with VSX multi-channel monitoring, capacity 100 orch, 120 choir, 2 isolation rooms, large client lounge, shower room, private office. Studio 2: Neve VRP 60-channel, capacity 55. Studio 3: SSL 9000 J series 96 channel mixing console. Full range 5.1 monitoring. Penthouse: Neve Capricorn Digital mixing console with CSX film panel. 2 mobile location recording units. Audio post production: mastering, re-mastering, editing, 5.1 audio preparation and restoration, CD preparation, copying. Interactive design and digital video studio.*

* Air-Edel Recording Studios Ltd. 18 Rodmarton St, London W1H 3FW *tel:* 020 7486 6466 *fax:* 020 7224 0344 *email:* trevorbest@air-edel.co.uk. Trevor Best, studio mgr. *Specialise in mus to picture and voice-over recordings. 3 recording studios; main studio capacity 25. 24 track analogue recorder, 48 channels of automation and full sync to picture facilities. ProTools HD system.*

* Air Studios. Lyndhurst Hall, Lyndhurst Rd, Hampstead, London NW3 5NG *tel:* 020 7794 0660 *fax:* 020 7794 8518 *email:* alison@airstudios.com. Alison Burton. *Lyndhurst Hall: 400sq m orch studio, capacity 100+. Neve 88R 96 channel console. Studio 1: 140sq m, capacity 40. Custom Neve console. Studio 2: mixing room with SSL 8000 G Plus console and Ultimation. Studio 3: mixing room with 4 48 input AMS Logic Two console.*

Angel Recording Studios Ltd. 311 Upper St, London N1 2TU *tel:* 020 7354 2525 *fax:* 020 7226 9624 *email:* angel@angelstudios.co.uk. Lucy Jones, studio mgr. *2 large studios, capacity up to 75. Studio 1: AMS Neve 88R60 desk with Encore and Meyer monitoring. Studio 2: Small room with Soundtracks Jade 48 channel desk and Quested monitoring. Studio 3: AMS Neve VXS 60 desk with Encore and ATC customised monitoring. All studios have facilities for recording to picture and Dolby Surround and are equipped with hard disk recording systems, eg, ProTools, Radar, etc.*

Bluestone Studio. Onward House, 11 Uxbridge St, London W8 7TQ *tel:* 020 7243 4101 *fax:* 020 7243 4131 *email:* bluestudio@aol.com. Chris Wyles. *ProTools, HD rig.*

Britannia Row Studios. 3 Bridge Studios, 318-326 Wandsworth Bridge Rd, London SW6 2TZ *tel:* 020 7371 5872 *fax:* 020 7371 8641 *email:* bookings @britanniarowstudios.co.uk. Kate Koumi, owner. *Studio 1: Neve 60-channel. Studio 2: Mackie 56-channel.*

* CTS Studios Ltd. Suite 1a, Lansdowne House, Lansdowne Rd, London W11 3LP *tel:* 020 7467 0099 *fax:* 020 7467 0098 *email:* info @cts-lansdowne.co.uk. Chris Dibble, studio mgr. *Studio services for motion picture recording.*

* Classic Sound Ltd. 5 Falcon Park, Neasden Lane, London NW10 1RZ *tel:* 020 8208 8100 *fax:* 020 8208 8111 *email:* classicsoundltd@ dial.pipex.com. Jonathan Stokes, dir/engineer; Neil Hutchinson, dir, engineer. *48 Fader Logic II console with BcW801 Nautilus Monitoring plus large projection screen. Studios and location recording service.*

* The Dairy. 43-45 Tunstall Rd, London SW9 8BZ *tel:* 020 7738 7777 *fax:* 020 7738 7007 *email:* info@thedairy.co.uk. Emily Taylor. *Studio 1: AMS Neve VR 60 Legend. Studio 2: DDA AMR. Studio 3: Amek 2500. 4 production rooms. Logic and ProTools throughout all studios.*

* Eden Studios. 20-24 Beaumont Rd, London W4 5AP *tel:* 020 8995 5432 *fax:* 020 8747 1931 *email:* eden@edenstudios.com. Natali Horton, studio mgr. *2 48 track SSL studios, 2 programming rooms, 1 Fairlight Dream DVD studio. Accommodation; catering; in-house maintenance; free on-site parking.*

* The Exchange. 42 Bruges Place, Randolph St, London NW1 0TX *tel:* 020 7485 0530 *fax:* 020 7482 4588 *email:* studio@exchangemastering.co.uk. Seren Seaborn.

* Gateway Studio. The School of Music, Kingston Hill Centre, Surrey KT2 7LB *tel:* 020 8549 0014 *fax:* 020 8547 7337 *email:* studio@gsr.org.uk. Gurjit Dhinsa, studio mgr; Steve Lowe, house engineer/producer. *1 studio, 24 track analogue and digital mastering, teaching facilities.*

Hear No Evil. 6 Lillie Yard, London SW6 1UB *tel:* 020 7385 8244 *fax:* 020 7385 0700 *email:* info@hearnoevil.net. *Large live room, capacity 40, orch, scoring, commercials. 5.1 mixing, ProTools.*

Henry Wood Hall Ltd. Trinity Church Square, London SE1 4HU *tel:* 020 7403 0118 *fax:* 020 7378 8294 *email:* bookings@hwh.co.uk. Andrew Stevens, mgr; Charles Strickland, deputy mgr. *Ens to full symphony orch. One large hall, studio only, 2 control rooms.*

* Lansdowne Recording Studios. Lansdowne House, Lansdowne Rd, London W11 3LP *tel:* 020 7727 0041/2/3 *fax:* 020 7792 8904 *email:* info@cts-lansdowne.co.uk. Chris Dibble, studio mgr; Claire Peck, booking mgr. *1 studio, 48 track, digital, analogue, Neve 72 channel VXS with flying faders; capacity 35. Video transfers for composers and digital audio post-production.*

Limor, Gilead - Music, Arts and Media. 7a The Broadway, Stanmore, Middx HA7 4DA *tel:* 020 8420 6115; 07740 423537 *email:* gilead@onetel.net.uk. Gilead Limor, producer/engineer. *High resolution stereo and multi-track digital recording. Complete CD production packages including artwork, typesetting, manufacturing and packaging available.*

Mark Angelo Recording Studios. 13 Impress House, Mansell Rd, Acton, London W3 7QH *tel:* 020 8735 0040 *fax:* 020 8735 0041 *email:* mimi@ markangelo.co.uk. Mimi Kerns, studio mgr. *Studio recording service. 24/48 track, Neve VX, Radar II multi-track, ProTools Mix Plus; capacity 35.*

Mayfair Recording Studios. 11a Sharples Hall St, London NW1 8YN *tel:* 020 7586 7746 *fax:* 020 7586 9721. Dan Mills, studio and bookings mgr. *Solid State Logic 9064K series control room (18m x 7m), studio (11m x 6m). Neve VR 60: 60 channels, control room (8m x 6m), studio (10m x 14m). Bösendorfer grand pno fitted with MIDI output. Sync to video, Umatic or Beta. Studio 3: Amek 24-channel, ProTools. Studio 4: programming with live room. Studio 5: producer's suite with kitchen/bathroom, mezzanine style design. Studio 6: with drum booth.*

Miloco. 36 Leroy St, London SE1 4SP *tel:* 020 7232 0008 *fax:* 020 7237 6109 *email:* info@milomusic.co.uk. Nick Young, studio mgr; Jessica Gerry, bookings mgr. *4 studios, ProTools, Neve VR60, Neve V3, Amek G2520, DDA QMR48.*

Olympic Studios. 117 Church Rd, Barnes, London SW13 9HL *tel:* 020 8286 8600 *fax:* 020 8286 8625 *email:* siobhan@olympicstudios.com. Siobhan Paine. *5 studios. 1 with SSL G series, 35 orch capacity; 1 with SSL K series and 60 orch capacity; 1 with SSL G 72 channels; 1 with SSL G 64 channels; 1 with AMEK 9098i 56 channels. 6 programming rooms.*

* RAK Recording Studios. 42-48 Charlbert St, London NW8 7BU *tel:* 020 7586 2012 *fax:* 020 7722 5823 *email:* trisha@rakstudios.co.uk. Trisha Wegg, studio admin. *3 studios. 2 API desks, 1 SSL 4056 (G series computer).*

RMS Studios. 43-45 Clifton Rd, London SE25 6PX *tel:* 020 8653 4965 *fax:* 020 8653 4965 *email:* studiosrms@aol.com. Andy Le Vien, studio mgr; Alan Jones, bookings mgr. *Studio 1: Sadie 5, Radar 2, Studer A80 16 track, Soundcraft 1600, grand pno, capacity 8. Studio 2: ProTools, ADAT XT, MIDI, capacity 6. Studio 3: SADIE, CD production.*

Redwood Studios. 20 Great Chapel St, London W1F 8FW *tel:* 020 7287 3799 *fax:* 020 7287 3751 *email:* andrestudios@yahoo.co.uk. André Jacquemin, studio mgr/producer. *Studio and location recording service; hard disk recording. Studio 1 for 5 musicians, Digital Mackie d8b mixing console, full outboard equipment list on request. ProTools HD, 5.1 mixing, M&K monitoring. Foley Studio for film work, ADR work and sound design.*

* Roundhouse Recording Studios. 91 Saffron Hill, London EC1N 8PT *tel:* 020 7404 3333 *fax:* 020 7404 2947 *email:* roundhouse@ stardiamond.com. Lisa Gonther, studio mgr; Maddy Clarke, studio mgr. *2 SSL rooms (with live areas). 1 ProTools HD 5.1.*

Sahara Sound. Unit 18 A/B, Farm Lane Trading Estate, 101 Farm Lane, London SW6 1QL *tel:* 020 7386 2400 *fax:* 020 7386 2401 *email:* info@saharasound.com. Dave Tyler, studio mgr. *Grant control room, 80 channel SSL K9000 XL, monitoring.*

The Sanctuary Town House Studios. 150 Goldhawk Rd, London W12 8HH *tel:* 020 8932 3200 *fax:* 020 8932 3207 *email:* nikki.affleck@ sanctuarygroup.com. Nikki Affleck, studio mgr. *Studio 1: SSL 4072 G plus ultimation. Studio 2: SSL 8072G plus ultimation and surround monitoring. Studio 4: SSL 4072E.*

* Sanctuary Westside Studios. Olaf Centre, 10 Olaf St, London W11 4BE *tel:* 020 7221 9494 *fax:* 020 7727 0008. Nikki Affleck, studio mgr; Jo Buckley, studio booker. *Studio 1: Neve VR72. Studio 2: Solid State logic 4064E with G series computer.*

Sarm Studios (West) Ltd. 8-10 Basing St, London W11 1ET *tel:* 020 7229 1229 *fax:* 020 7221 9247/3374 *email:* henri@spz.com. Henriette Cox, bookings mgr. *4 studios, SSLJ series and surround sound. Easy on-site parking, catering and apartments.*

* Snake Ranch Studio. 90 Lots Rd, London SW10 0QD *tel:* 020 7351 7888 *fax:* 020 7352 5194 *email:* gerry@snakeranch.co.uk. Gerry O'Riordan, studio mgr. *2 studios, 24 track, analogue, video sync, ProTools and 5.1 monitoring available; capacity 25.*

* Sony Music Studios. 31-37 Whitfield St, London W1T 2SF *tel:* 020 7636 3434 *fax:* 020 7323 5964. Nick Kadrnka, dir. *3 studios, capacity 90, 2, 6; 24 and 48 track.*

Sound-Suite Recording Studios Ltd. 92 Camden Mews, London NW1 9AG *tel:* 020 7485 4881 *fax:* 020 7482 2210 *email:* peter@thesound suite.co.uk. *Audio visual post-production and mus recording facility.*

Amek Hendrix desk, Mackie HDR 24/96 digital, Otari MTR90 multitrack, Tascam DA88s, all machines locked to picture Quested & Genelec monitoring. Bechstein grand pno, synths and sequencers available. Sound design and foley recording, voice-overs, CD copying.

The Warehouse. 13 Theed St, London SE1 8ST *tel:* 020 7928 9251 *fax:* 020 7928 9252 *email:* lara@thewarehouselondon.co.uk; lara@lfo.co.uk. Lara Bellini, booking mgr. *2 studios: large, capacity 60; small, capacity 35. Steinway grand pno; SADIE digital editing; Mackie 8 busdesk 32:8:2, etc.*

The Wathen Hall. St Paul's School, Lonsdale Rd, Barnes, London SW13 9JT *tel:* 020 8748 8874 *fax:* 020 8748 4048 *email:* manager@ wathenhall.com. Angela Parry, mgr. *Large studio; suitable for solo work and chmbr groups, also up to 25 (orch) or 60 (choir); 2 Steinway pnos (models 'AS' and 'D'); equipped with all necessary infrastructure for classical mus recording, including a small control room and power lines.*

England

Bedfordshire
Potton
Riverrun Studios. PO Box 30, Potton, Beds SG19 2XH *tel:* 01767 260223 *email:* enquiries@riverrunstudios.co.uk. John Mercer, producer; Noel Rafferty, engineer. *Studio offers classical musicians the hire of a professional digital recording studio.*

Berkshire
Reading
Recording Associates. October's End Studio, 34 Ryhill Way, Shinfield, Reading RG6 4AZ *tel:* 0118 986 6142; 07977 596661 *email:* g.addis@ recordingassociates.freeserve.co.uk. Geoff Addis, dir; Anthony Hodgson, producer; Kate Addis, producer. *Digital audio, video and surround-sound recording and editing, Stereo and DTS 5.1 surround sound CD production. Studio suitable for small ens and location recording.*

Sarm Hook End. Hook End Manor, Checkendon, nr Reading, Berks RG8 0UE *tel:* 01491 681000 *fax:* 01491 681926 *email:* sarmhookend@supanet.com.

Bristol, City of
Bristol
Bristol University Music Dept. Victoria Rooms, Queens Rd, Bristol BS8 1SA *tel:* 0117 954 5006 *fax:* 0117 954 5027 *email:* j.scott@bris.ac.uk. Jonathan Scott, studio mgr; Margaret Peirson, dept sec (tel: 0117 954 5028). *Control rooms have hard disk recording/editing. Other editing/post production available. MIDI gear, mics, 5 different live rooms.*

St George's Bristol. Great George St, off Park St, Bristol BS1 5RR *tel:* 0117 929 4929 *fax:* 0117 927 6537 *email:* administration@stgeorges bris-tol.co.uk. Jonathan Stracey, dir. *Converted Georgian church with recording facilities suitable for soloists, chmbr mus, small orchs, choirs. Newly refurbished, perfect acoustics, 2 Steinway 'D' pnos, fully-equipped control room including Soundcraft digital desk, Sadie digital editing facility, variety of mics.*

Sound Conception. 82-84 York Rd, Bedminster, Bristol BS3 4AL *tel:* 0117 966 2932 *fax:* 0117 963 5059. Ken Wheeler, studio mgr; Jim Whittaker, bookings. *1 studio, multi-track digital and analogue; capacity 16; vioce-overs; ISDN.*

Buckinghamshire
Buckingham
Audiolab. 3 West St, Buckingham MK18 1HL *tel:* 01280 822814; 07739 807159 *email:* office@alab.co.uk. James Masters, studio mgr. *All styles of mus and location recording.*
Milton Keynes
* Great Linford Manor. Great Linford, Milton Keynes, Bucks MK14 5AX *tel:* 01908 667432 *fax:* 01908 668164 *email:* info@greatlinford manor.com. Sue Dawson, studio mgr, bookings. *Residential recording studio in grade II listed 17th C manor house. Original ballroom studio Neve VR60 Legend and vintage Abbey Road 24-channel Neve side-car, 2 Studer A820, Quested 4-way monitoring.*

Cambridgeshire
Peterborough
B & H Sound Services Ltd. The Old School Studio, Crowland Rd, Eye, Peterborough, Cambs PE6 7TN *tel:* 01733 223535 *fax:* 01733 223545 *email:* sound@bhsound.co.uk. Nicki Seager, producer/engineer. *ProTools TDM, 64 track digital recording, RADAR, 72 channel desk. Mobile recording rigs, digital editing and mastering, CD and cassette manufacture, equipment hire.*
St Ives
* SRT Sound Recording Technology Ltd. Audio House, Edison Rd, St Ives, Cambs PE27 3LF *tel:* 01480 461880; 020 8446 3218 *fax:* 01480 496100 *email:* srt@btinternet.com. Sarah Pownall, dir; Karen Kenney, dir. *5 studios; HDCD, 1630 PCM Umatic, Exabyte, Sony SDP 1000, analogue Dolby A/SR; cassette and CD duplication, DVD authoring.*

Cheshire
Stockport
Cavalier Studios Ltd. 280 Wellington Rd South, Stockport, Cheshire SK2 6ND *tel:* 0161 480 6073 *fax:* 0161 429 8492 *email:* info@cavalier studios.co.uk. Arny Sage, studio mgr. *1 studio, 24 track, analogue, digital mastering, Cubase, capacity 10.*

Cornwall
Fowey
* Sawmills Studio. Golant, Fowey, Cornwall PL23 1LW *tel:* 01726 833338 *fax:* 01726 832015 *email:* ruth@sawmills.co.uk. Ruth Taylor, studio mgr. *Trident series 80B desk, Quested monitors, Soundscape hard disk recorder, extensive outboard.*

Dorset
Gillingham
Conversion Studios. Woolfields, Milton on Stour, Gillingham, Dorset SP8 5PX *tel:* 01747 824729 *fax:* 01747 824986 *email:* info@ conversionstudios.co.uk. Owen Thomas, mgr. *Residential recording studios. 24 track Otari Radar II, Audient ASP804, large live rooms, fully air-conditioned. Experienced engineers, producers.*
Poole
Active Music Recording Studio. 7c Bank Chambers, Penn Hill Ave, Lower Parkstone, Poole, Dorset BH14 9NB *tel:* 01202 746049 *fax:* 01202 746049 *email:* martin@active-music.co.uk. *Ampex 124.24 track, Ampex ATR 100, Raindirk series 3 desk, ATC 100A monitors, digital editing available, large selection of mics.*

East Sussex
Eastbourne
* ICC Studios. 4 Regency Mews, Silverdale Rd, Eastbourne, E Sussex BN20 7AB *tel:* 01323 726134 *fax:* 01323 649240 *email:* info@ iccstudios.co.uk. H Kaufmann, chief exec; Mary Downe, bookings. *Well equipped recording facility that combines analogue (extensive vintage mic collection/live rooms) and digital equipment (full ProTools). 2 studios, editing suite and residential facilities.*
Peacehaven
Claudio Records Ltd. Studio 17, The Promenade, Peacehaven, E Sussex BN10 8PU *tel:* 01273 580250 *fax:* 01273 583530 *email:* info@ claudiorecords.com. Colin and William Attwell, studio mgrs. *Studio recording, digital editing and CD production.*

Kent
Tonbridge
Postern Park Digital. Postern Park Oast, Tonbridge, Kent TN11 0QT *tel:* 01732 773322 *fax:* 01732 773344 *email:* posternpkdigital@aol.com. Stephen Coles. *20-24 bit recording, SADIE editing. Church and location personal recording service. Org, f-pno and pno available.*

Kingston upon Hull
Hull
Fairview Studios. Cavewood Grange Farm, Common Lane, North Cave, Brough, E Yorks HU15 2PE *tel:* 01430 425546 *fax:* 01430 425547 *email:* info@fairviewstudios.co.uk. Jackie Herd, sales and accounts; Andy Newlove, mgr. *1 studio, 48 track (24 tracks analogue and digital); capacity 10.*

Leicestershire
Leicester
Rain Studios. 1487 Melton Rd, Queniborough, Leicester LE7 3FP *tel:* 0116 260 8813 *fax:* 0116 260 8329 *email:* info@rainstudios.com. Mark du Plessis, studio mgr. *2 studios, one for 50+ players, the other for overdubs and vocals; Calrec mixing desk, ATC monitors, ProTools, Otari MX-80, plus outboard. Also location facilities.*

Liverpool, City Of

Liverpool

Parr Street Studios. 35-45 Parr St, Liverpool L1 4JN *tel:* 0151 707 1050 *fax:* 0151 707 1813 *email:* info@parrstreet.co.uk. Anne Lewis, mgr; Paul Lewis, bookings mgr. *Residential studio complex, 3 studios, located in Liverpool city centre. Tracking and mixing facilities to suit all budgets. Professional assistants and 2 f/t maintenance engineers. Orch-size studios.*

Nottinghamshire

Nottingham

Network Studios (Nohponex Ltd). 22a Forest Rd West, Nottingham NG7 4EQ *tel:* 0115 978 4714 *fax:* 0115 942 4183 *email:* network. studios@btclick.com. B Sacorafos, mgr dir; M Vaughan, studio mgr; L Davey, bookings. *1 studio, 32 digital tracks; capacity 35.*

Oxfordshire

Oxford

Rotator Studios. 74-77 Magdalen Rd, Oxford OX4 3AQ *tel:* 01865 205600 *email:* info@rotator.co.uk. Richard Cotton, owner. *Fully professional digital recording studio, ProTools core, 32 track playback, live room capacity 15 musicians.*

Staffordshire

Keele

Clock House Recording Studio. Keele University, Keele, Staffs ST5 5BG *tel:* 01782 583301 *fax:* 01782 583301 *email:* mua00@mus.keele.ac.uk. Cliff Bradbury, studio mgr. *3 studios, ProTools multi-track. Digital, analogue, digital mastering and editing, CD preparation; capacity 20.*

Rugeley

Abbey Sound Studios. The Abbey, Heron Court, Heron St, Rugeley, Staffs WS15 2DZ *tel:* 01889 579494/5909 *fax:* 01889 881462 *email:* abbeysound@yahoo.co.uk. Lee Beddow, mgr/engineer. *8 track studio with large live room.*

Stoke-on-Trent

Sub Sound Studio. 54 Oxford St, Penkull, Stoke-on-Trent ST4 7EE *tel:* 01782 416306 *email:* studio@sub-sound.co.uk. Gordon Lee. *Analogue/digital multi-track editing, mastering. Valve/computer-based multitrack studio. On-site automated CD-ROM duplication/on disc print.*

Suffolk

Saxmundham

Ninth Wave Audio Limited. Potton Hall, Westleton, Saxmundham, Suffolk IP17 3EF *tel:* 01728 648604; 07770 364467 *fax:* 01728 648807 *email:* info@ninthwaveaudio.com. Jeremy Hayes, production; Tony Wass, engineering. *In-house mus recording facililty, including Steinway model D pnos and Father and Compton pipe orgs. Studio with adjustable acoustic, available for wet and dry hire. Complete recording and editing services for CD production (including art work and short run duplication) and promotional work for artists. Highly qualified, BBC-trained production and engineering staff.*

Surrey

Farnham

* Jacobs Studios Ltd. Ridgway House, Runwick Lane, Farnham, Surrey GU10 5EE *tel:* 01252 715546 *fax:* 01252 712846 *email:* andy@ jacobs-studios.co.uk. Andy Fernbach, studio mgr. *2 studios (fully residential), 1 Neve VR and 1 SSL.*

Guildford

Performing Arts Technology Studios. University of Surrey, Guildford GU2 5XH *tel:* 01483 686500 *fax:* 01483 686501 *email:* music@surrey.ac.uk. *3 studios with control rooms, 32 channel Neve, 84 channel Sony OXF R3; 4 editing suites. Tonmeister students may be able to offer free recordings during university terms, both in our studios and on location. Studios may be available for commercial hire during vacations.*

Woldingham

The Factory. Toftrees, Church Rd, Woldingham, Surrey CR3 7JH *tel:* 01883 652386 *fax:* 01883 652457 *email:* mackay@dircon.co.uk. *1 studio, 24 track, digital; capacity 15.*

Tyne & Wear

Wallsend

Cartel Studios. 71 High St East, Wallsend, Tyne and Wear NE28 7RJ *tel:* 0191 234 5494 *fax:* 0191 234 5494 *email:* admin@ cartelstudios.com. Phil Browne, mgr; Russell Leese, engineer; Adam

Riley, engineer. *24 track studio, 32 input desk, digital/analogue mastering also separate digital suite available.*

Warwickshire

Leamington Spa

Woodbine Street Recording Studio. 1 St Marys Cres, Leamington Spa, Warks CV31 1JC *tel:* 01926 338971 *email:* jony2r@ntlworld.com. John Rivers. *ProTools HD3; large studio with live area. Audient 8024 console plus valve and discrete component input channels. Accommodation available.*

West Midlands

Birmingham

Dep International Studios. 1 Andover St, Digbeth, Birmingham B5 5RG *tel:* 0121 633 4742 *fax:* 0121 643 4904 *email:* enquiries@ub40.co.uk. Paul Hunter.

Grosvenor Recording Studios. 16 Grosvenor Rd, Birmingham B20 3NP *tel:* 0121 356 9636 *fax:* 0121 356 9636. *2 studios, 16 track; capacity 40 and 15.*

Hollick & Taylor Recording Company Ltd. 16 Grosvenor Rd, Handsworth Wood, Birmingham B20 3NP *tel:* 0121 356 9636 *fax:* 0121 356 9636. John Taylor. *2 studios; 16 track; capacity 40 and 15.*

Ninth Wave Audio Limited (Birmingham). PO Box 5517, Birmingham B13 8QW *tel:* 0121 442 2276; 07770 364464 *fax:* 0121 689 1902 *email:* ninthwave@blueyonder.com. Tony Wass, studio mgr/chief engineer; Niall Gault, emgineer. *Specialises in classical mus, BBC radio production and live concerts. Full BBC broadcast facilities and mastering including short run CD production. 24 track high resolution digital recording mobile, CD mastering and post production suite, studio facilities. Complete packages available for CD production and promotional work for artists; highly qualified, BBC-trained production and engineering staff.*

Coventry

Depot Studios. Bond St, Coventry CV1 4AH *tel:* 024 7652 5074 *fax:* 024 7663 4373 *email:* den@depotstudios.org.uk. Den Hands; Ben Campbell. *24 track digital recording studio.*

Kingswinford

Diabolus in Musica Recording Services. 21 Oakfield Ave, Kingswinford, W Midlands DY6 8HJ *tel:* 01384 295210 *email:* paul@diabolus.org. Paul Baker. *Specialist digital recording of soloists and ens in studio or on location. Mastering for CD and cassette.*

Solihull

Made To Measure Music. 21 Fernhill Rd, Olton, Solihull, W Midlands B92 9PX *tel:* 0121 706 3621 *fax:* 0121 706 3621 *email:* sparkes@sparkes93.fsnet.co.uk. Andrew Sparkes, dir. *24 track digital, 16 track analogue, live room, composition, arrangement, production, CD and tape duplication. Also tuition.*

Wiltshire

Corsham

* Real World Studios Ltd. Box Mill, Mill Lane, Box, Corsham, Wilts SN13 8PL *tel:* 01225 743188 *fax:* 01225 743787 *email:* studios@ realworld.co.uk. Owen Leech, studio mgr. *Studio 1: SSL 4080G; studio 2: SSL 4048G.*

Worcestershire

Kempsey

The Old Smithy Recording Studio. 1 Post Office Lane, Kempsey, Worcester WR5 3NS *tel:* 01905 820659 *fax:* 01905 820015 *email:* muff.murfin@virgin.net. Jan Allsopp, bookings. *3 studios, 24 tracks, digital, analogue, video production, cassette duplication, full MIDI sequencing and sampling hardware; capacity 24. Visual broadcast facilities. Accommodation. Studio and location recording service.*

York, City of

York

National Centre for Early Music. St Margaret's Church, Walmgate, York YO1 9TL *tel:* 01904 632220 *fax:* 01904 612631 *email:* info@ ncem.co.uk. Delma Tomlin, dir. *System is built around a Tascam TMD4000 digital mixing console linked to both a Tascam DA78HR 8 track multi-track machine and a Tascam DA20 MkII DAT recorder. Recordings can be made direct to DAT for accurate stereo performance recording, or 8 track recordings can be made for later post production.*

Scotland

Glasgow, City of

Glasgow

The Audiomobile. 49 Derby St, Glasgow G3 7TU *tel:* 0141 334 5099 *fax:* 0141 339 0271 *email:* helen@cavastudios.co.uk. Helen Clark, admin. *48 or 24 track continuous, fully air-conditioned. Full interface*

with all standard broadcast applications.

Ca Va Sound Workshops. 30 Bentinck St, Glasgow G3 7TU *tel:* 0141 334 5099 *fax:* 0141 339 0271 *email:* helen@cavastudios.co.uk. Helen Clark, admin. *4 studios; Neve VR Legend with flying faders plus total recall; 48 and 24 track analogue plus 24 tracks of hard disk recording on ProTools*

5.1 with Apogee A-D convertors; 24 track demo studio with 16 tracks of hard disc recording on ProTools 5.1; mastering studio, digital editing on ProTools 5.1 with Apogee track 2 A-D convertor; fully equipped radio broadcast studio with ISDN facilities; CAP 50-100 (studio 1); sync to picture facilities in studios 1, 2 and 4.

* Scotty's Sound Studio. 17-22 Newtown St, Kilsyth, Glasgow G65 0JX *tel:* 01236 823291 *fax:* 01236 826900 *email:* b.garden@wilsonandgarden.biz. Bill Garden, dir. *1 studio, 24 track and 2 track, digital, analogue.*

Lanarkshire
Bellshill
Mara Recordings. 52 Strathview Rd, Lochview Estate, Bellshill ML4 2UY *tel:* 01698 747939 *email:* duncan@dmackay.fsnet.co.uk. Duncan Mackay, production/sound engineer. *Location recording service: digital classical recording and post production 24 bit editing. CD mastering and production, specialist in classical mus.*

Wales

Denbighshire
Denbigh
Howell's Studios. Howell's School, Denbigh, N Wales LL16 3EN *tel:* 01745 813631 *fax:* 01745 814443 *email:* rlocke@cix.co.uk. Robbie Locke, dir. *Otari Radar 24-track digital recording, specialising in youth mus. Large hall for symphony orchs. Residential capacity of 250+ for youth mus organisations. Catering and admin assistance provided.*

Gwynedd
Bangor
Electroacoustic Music and Recording Studios. Main Arts Building, University of Wales, Bangor, Gwynedd LL57 2DG *tel:* 01248 382181 *fax:* 01248 370297 *email:* a.p.lewis@bangor.ac.uk. Andrew Lewis, studio dir. *4 studios, 2 concert halls, 64 tracks digital ProTools, DAT and CD mastering, digital editing, video post-production, Bösendorfer and Steinway pnos; capacity 600.*

Caernarfon
* Sain (Recordiau) Cyf. Canolfan Sain, Llandwrog, Caernarfon, Gwynedd LL54 5TG *tel:* 01286 831111 *fax:* 01286 831497 *email:* stiwdio@

sain.wales.com. Eryl Davies, studio mgr. *Digital RADAR 24 Nyquist 56 channel AMEK Rembrandt, ATC and Genelec Monitoring, capacity 30. Also digital editing, dubbing, CD pre-mastering on SADIE Artemis and Tascam DA88, ATC monitoring. Also location recording to Genex, DAT or DA88.*

Monmouthshire
Monmouth
Nimbus Performing Arts Centre Ltd. Wyastone Leys, Monmouth NP25 3SR *tel:* 01600 891090 *fax:* 01600 891052 *email:* adrian@wyastone.co.uk. Adrian Farmer, dir. *Stage, audio and video control rooms and Steinway model 'D' pno. Suitable for soloists, chmbr mus, small orch and choirs.*

* Rockfield Studios. Amberley Court, Rockfield Rd, Monmouth NP25 5ST *tel:* 01600 712449 *fax:* 01600 714421 *email:* Rockfieldstudios@compuserve.com. *Studio 1: MC1 500 series console with extra Neve 1061 and API 550 mic, amp, equaliser modules, Studer A820 tape machines. Studio 2: Neve 8128, Studer A820 and A827 tape machines.*

International

France

Record your school for the UK album charts

Each year Eighth Wonder Recording Ltd. works with hundreds of schools and colleges all over the UK, offering free, studio quality music recordings on location.

This is a unique opportunity to feature on a compilation of the best of UK School music. The CD will be available in high street music retailers. Local and national press coverage is also planned for the intended release date in April 2004.

 To feature on the double CD all your school has to do is compose an original piece of music or song, by staff or pupils, and record it with Eighth Wonder Recording. The recording day is offered free of charge with copies of the recorded CD available for purchase by staff, pupils and parents.

The piece can be in any style and the school can even make it a competition to see which composer and which group should feature on the national chart CD. It can be performed by anyone; a band, orchestra, rock or rap group, choir, a soloist or even the entire school. This is a great chance for talented youngsters to break onto a national stage and a prestigious opportunity for composers and schools to be featured on a commercial CD for the national charts.

Tracks for the national CD must be recorded on booking dates between September 2003 and March 2004 inclusive. Eighth Wonder will be working with around two hundred clients within this period, thus they can only offer the opportunity to appear on the national CD to the first forty-five bookings made, on a first-come first served basis. Please contact Ben or Katie on 01925 230656 or email eighth.wonder@ntlworld.com for more information.

Recording and Sound Duplication

Location Recording and Production Services

Some recording studios also have sound duplication facilities. Membership of the Association of Professional Recording Services is indicated by an asterisk.

* **Abbey Road Mobiles.** 3 Abbey Rd, London NW8 9AY *tel:* 020 7266 7236 *fax:* 020 7266 7250 *email:* bookings@abbeyroad.com. Colette Barber, studio mgr. *2 flight-cased mobile location units equipped with latest technology. All digital formats, B&W stereo and 5.1 monitoring; comprehensive range of mics, full communications, CCTV and GSM cellular phones as standard.*

Allen, Patrick. 26 Beverley Crescent, Bedford MK40 4BY *tel:* 01234 343033; 07989 381250 *fax:* 01234 273605 *email:* patrickallen@ operaomnia.co.uk. Patrick Allen, producer/engineer. *Location production and recording service specialising in classical mus for broadcast and CD production. Concert recordings, demo recordings. Complete packages for CD manufacture. High bit rate digital recording, editing and mastering.*

Astounding Sounds. 9 Swan Close, Ivinghoe Aston, Leighton Buzzard LU7 9DN *tel:* 0845 456 3907; 01525 222842 *fax:* 01525 222842 *email:* astounding@onet.co.uk. Jonathan Haskell, dir. *Classical mus specialists. Digital location recording of concerts, sessions and demos, editing, CD-ROM and cassette duplication and CD production. Choirs and educ institutes, special packages.*

Audiolab. 3 West St, Buckingham MK18 1HL *tel:* 01280 822814; 07739 807159 *email:* office@alab.co.uk. James Masters, studio mgr. *All styles of mus and location recording.*

B & H Sound Services Ltd. The Old School Studio, Crowland Rd, Eye, Peterborough PE6 7TN *tel:* 01733 223535 *fax:* 01733 223545 *email:* sound@bhsound.co.uk. Daniel Lock, engineer; Nicola Seager, recording mgr. *Stereo and multi-track location recording facilities, including complete classical production service; digital editing and mastering; CD and cassette manufacture; equipment hire.*

BMP Recording. The Red House, Aswardby, Spilsby, Lincs PE23 4JU *tel:* 01790 754400 *fax:* 01790 754400 *email:* info@bmp-recording.co.uk. Ken Blair, partner; Sara Blair-Manning, partner. *Location and studio recording, digital editing and mastering, CD and digital video production.*

* **CTS Studios Ltd.** Suite 1a, Lansdowne House, Lansdowne Rd, London W11 3LP *tel:* 020 7467 0099 *fax:* 020 7467 0098 *email:* claire@ cts-lansdowne.co.uk. Claire Peck, studio bookings mgr. *Studio services.*

Casmara. 16 Westpark, Mottingham, London SE9 4RQ *tel:* 020 8857 3213 *fax:* 020 8857 0731 *email:* mail@casmarared.co.uk. Richard Hughes, owner/engineer; Susanne Stanzeleit, producer. *Recording of concerts, demos, CD production service including artwork and design. Classical mus.*

Circle Sound Services. Circle House, 14 Waveney Close, Bicester, Oxon OX26 2GP *tel:* 01869 240051 *fax:* 0870 705 9679 *email:* sound@circlesound.net. John Willett, studio mgr. *Location recording unit, hard disk digital editing and mastering, CD preparation, CD-ROM recording. Specialise in classical mus, choirs, etc.*

Classical and Acoustic Recordings. 77 Burnham Rd, Leigh-on-Sea, Essex SS9 2JR *tel:* 01702 472830 *email:* jackiewilsonsays@ ifeelgood.freeserve.co.uk. Jon Webber, owner/engineer. *Location recording service for classical musicians, choirs, schools, etc. Small studio, Broadwood grand pno. Digital editing and CD-ROM production.*

The Classical Recording Co. 16-17 Wolsey Mews, London NW5 2DX *tel:* 020 7482 2303; 07850 666531 *fax:* 020 7482 2302

email: info@classicalrecording.com. Simon Weir, producer/engineer; Campbell Hughes, engineer; Morgan Roberts, engineer; Beth Punter, production mgr. *24/96-bit digital location recording and post-production. CD mastering and cassette duplication. Archive recording and broadcast production to BBC standards.*

Classical Recording Service. 11 Romsley Hill Grange, Farley Lane, Romsley, nr Halesowen, W Midlands B62 0LN *tel:* 01562 710801 *fax:* 01562 710801 *email:* paul@dinmore-records.co.uk. Paul Arden-Taylor, dir. *Location digital recording, digital editing, CD and cassette production; classical mus.*

Claudio Records Ltd. Studio 17, The Promenade, Peacehaven BN10 8PU *tel:* 01273 580250 *fax:* 01273 583530 *email:* info@claudiorecords.com. Colin and William Attwell, studio mgrs. *Classical location and studio recording, digital editing, CD production.*

Clive Cowan Recording (CCR). 27 Stirling Ave, Leigh-on-Sea, Essex SS9 3PP *tel:* 01702 460451 *pager:* 07625 397858 *email:* info@ccr.euromarques.com. Clive Cowan. *Location recording, especially for broadcast and video. Professional audio equipment sales including Steinberg Nuendo authorised dealer. Member of the Institute of Broadcast Sound.*

Clock House Recording Studio. Keele University, Keele, Staffs ST5 5BG *tel:* 01782 583301 *fax:* 01782 583301 *email:* c.bradbury@mus.keele.ac.uk. Cliff Bradbury, studio mgr. *Digital editing facilities.*

Creative Dialogue Ltd. Air Studios, Lyndhurst Rd, London NW3 5NG *tel:* 020 7794 0660 *email:* creativedialogueltd@btinternet.com. Ian Dean. *Recording production services, mastering, classical orchestral and film.*

Downstream Ltd. 44 Marsh Lane, Nantwich, Cheshire CW5 5LH *tel:* 01270 625125 *fax:* 01270 629424 *email:* sound@downstream.ltd.uk. Edward Leetham, mgr dir. *Digital location recording and CD production. All types of project undertaken, from soloists to full orch and chorus. Live concert recordings and CD recording sessions. Short-run and long-run CD duplication. Video to DVD transfer, DVD authoring and duplication.*

Dunelm Records. 2 Park Close, Glossop, Derbys SK13 7RQ *tel:* 01457 855313 *fax:* 01457 855313 *email:* info@dunelm-records.co.uk. Jim Pattison, owner; Joyce Pattison, recording asst. *Location recording service specialising in classical mus. Live concert recordings, demo*

recordings. *Complete packages for CD and cassette production. High bit rate. Digital recording, editing and finalisation. Also booklet and inlay design and printing service.*

Eighth Wonder Recording Ltd. PO Box 649, Warrington, Cheshire WA5 9YR *tel:* 01925 230656 *fax:* 01925 495920 *email:* eighth.wonder@ntlworld.com. *Location mus recording service specialising in recording bands, choirs, orchs and soloists. Also full facilities for mixing, editing and mastering, as well as artwork design and CD duplication.*

Emerson, Roy. 80 Darwin Court, Gloucester Ave, London NW1 7BQ *tel:* 020 7267 5858; 07973 517788 *fax:* 020 7284 1148 *email:* royemerson@ukonline.co.uk. Roy Emerson. *Freelance classical recording producer and TV audio dir/mus producer, with high resolution digital location recording facilities and editing to international standards.*

Emglow Records. Norton Cottage, Colchester Rd, Wivenhoe, Colchester, Essex CO7 9HT *tel:* 01206 826342 *email:* marcelg@aspects.net. Marcel Glover. *Location recording and small-scale cassette and CD production for light, classical and early mus.*

The Exchange. 42 Bruge Place, Randolph St, London NW1 0TX *tel:* 020 7482 4588 *fax:* studio@exchangemastering.co.uk. Seren Seaborn. *Vinyl and CD mastering.*

Friary Music Services. 142b Friary Rd, London SE15 5UW *tel:* 020 7277 7068 *email:* 100115.3701@compuserve.com. Richard Black, producer. *Location recording, including quality, demos with free pianist, and complete CD projects. Classical mus only.*

* **Gateway Studio.** The School of Music, Kingston Hill Centre, Kingston KT2 7LB *tel:* 020 8547 0014 *fax:* 020 8547 7337 *email:* studio@gsr.org.uk. Gurtit Dhinsa, asst engineer/bookings; Steve Lowe, house engineer/producer. *Studio and location recording service.*

Ginn, Jeffrey. 11 Haycroft, Wootton, Bedford MK43 9PB *tel:* 01234 765602; 07778 896721 *fax:* 01234 765602 *email:* jeffginn@onetel.net.uk. *Location recording service and post-production studios. Classical recording, digital editing and mastering.*

Giraffe Productions. Ground Floor, 10 Stanley Rd, Peacehaven, E Sussex BN10 7SP *tel:* 01273 589597 *fax:* 01273 589597 *email:* info@giraffe-productions.co.uk. Ben Connellan, sound engineer; Annabel Connellan, ed/producer. *Digital location recording, digital editing, mastering, production and mus copying. Specialising in classical mus.*

Green Room Productions. The Laurels, New Park Rd, Harefield, Middx UB9 6EQ *tel:* 01895 822771 *fax:* 01895 824880 *email:* tony@ greenroom2.demon.co.uk. Tony Faulkner, proprietor. *Classical mus location, high-resolution sound and video recording.*

Hazard Chase Productions. Norman House, Cambridge Place, Cambridge CB2 1NS *tel:* 01223 312400 *fax:* 01223 460827 *email:* info@hazardchase.co.uk. Patrick Allen, exec producer; Mark Barrett, exec producer; James Brown, exec producer; John Willan, exec producer. *Location recording and production, specialising in classical mus (live concerts and studio sessions) for radio broadcast, demonstration recordings, samplers, TV and film soundtracks and CD production. Complete packages for CD and DVD manufacture. CD-ROM and CD EXTRA programming and production.*

Hear No Evil. 6 Lillie Yard, London SW6 1UB *tel:* 020 7385 8244 *fax:* 020 7385 0700 *email:* info@hearnoevil.net. Steve Parr, mgr dir; Sharon Rose, mgr dir. *Hard disk editing; specialists in orch and film scoring. Surround-sound mixing.*

Herald Audio Visual Publications. 29 Alfred Rd, Farnham, Surrey GU9 8ND *tel:* 01252 727718 *fax:* 01252 735567. Brian Johnson, mgr dir. *Specialists in choral, org, early church mus and gregorian chants. Digital and analogue.*

Instant Records. 14 Moorend Cres, Cheltenham, Glos GL53 0EL *tel:* 01242 523304 *fax:* 01242 523304 *email:* martinmitchell@ instantmusic.co.uk. Martin Mitchell, mgr dir. *Mobile digital stereo recording service for orchs, choirs and small ens. Also cassette and CD manufacture. All types of mus.*

Just Music Production. 34 Steyning Grove, London SE9 4NQ *tel:* 07939 129967 *email:* mail@justmusic-production.co.uk. Gary Skyrme, producer. *Location recording. Classical recording, editing and production. Short CD runs a speciality.*

K & A Productions. 5 Wyllyotts Place, Potters Bar, Herts EN6 2HN *tel:* 01707 661200 *fax:* 01707 661400 *email:* andrew@ kaproductions.co.uk. Andrew Walton, dir. *Digital location recording, high resolution surround including production, engineering, editing, mastering and cover design. Project supervision including replication and A&R consultation. Classical mus.*

Manygate Management Ltd. Trees, Ockham Rd South, East Horsley, Surrey KT24 6QE *tel:* 01483 281300 *fax:* 01483 281811 *email:* manygate@easynet.co.uk. John Boyden, dir. *Independent classical recording production, location recording and editing; also packaging and marketing consultants.*

Mara Recordings. 52 Strathview Rd, Lochview Estate, Bellshill ML4 2UY *tel:* 01698 747939 *email:* duncan@dmackay.fsnet.co.uk. Duncan Mackay, production/sound engineer. *Location recording service: digital recording and post production 24-bit digital editing. CD mastering and production. All types of mus, specialists in classical.*

The Mobile Recording Company. 3 South Meadow, South Horrington, Wells, Somerset BA5 3DJ *tel:* 01749 676544 *fax:* 01749 676544 *email:* info@morec.demon.co.uk. David Finch, proprietor. *24-bit high definition digital location recording, editing and mastering. CD manufacture (MCPS registered member). Low-cost self-promotion/DIY CD packages available.*

Modus Music. Elmbank, 48 Waterloo Ave, Leiston, Suffolk IP16 4HE *tel:* 01728 830008 *fax:* 01728 833943 *email:* modus@ ukcomputersolutions.co.uk. Marian and Tryggvi Tryggvason, partners. *Location recording, editing, CD mastering and duplication for classical CD market.*

Musical Cocktails Ltd. 561 Kenton Lane, Harrow Weald, Middx HA3 7LB *tel:* 020 8427 5918 *email:* sales@musicalcocktails.com. Dieter Hester, mgr dir; Chris Wyles; Karen Cormican. *Classical location recording, digital editing, mastering and remastering, CD production and duplication.*

Ninth Wave Audio Limited. PO Box 5517, Birmingham B13 8QW *tel:* 0121 442 2276; 07770 364464 *fax:* 0121 689 1902 *email:* info@ ninthwaveaudio.com. Tony Wass, engineering; Jeremy Hays, production. *24 track high resolution digital recording vehicle, CD mastering and duplication, film and TV dubbing facilities, DVD production. Specialise in classical mus, BBC radio production and live concerts. Complete packages available for CD production and promotional work for artists; highly qualified, BBC-trained production and engineering staff. Also at: Potton Hall, Westleton, Saxmundham, Suffolk IP17 3EF tel: 01728 648604 fax: 01728 648804.*

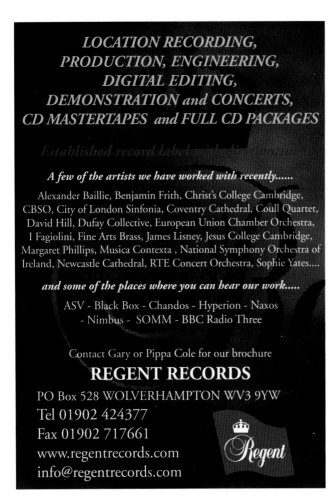

Open Play Limited. Suite 106, Hiltongrove Business Centre, Hatherley Mews, London E17 4QP *tel:* 020 8520 6644 *fax:* 020 8520 7755 *email:* info@openplay.co.uk. David Hoskins, dir. *CD and multimedia promotion company. Specialist project management service to produce compilation CDs, CD-ROM, enhanced CD and DVD for event promotion. On-site audio mastering, CD manufacturing, design and management of bespoke multimedia information systems.*

Orientis Recording Services. 54 Sycamore Rd, London SW19 4TP *tel:* 020 8286 6943 *email:* orientis-rs@blueyonder.co.uk. Simon Vout, gen mgr. *Specialists in digital location recording for classical musicians, full CD and cassette production, digital editing and mastering, artwork design and print facilities.*

OxRecs DIGITAL. 37 Inkerman Close, Abingdon, Oxon OX14 1NH *tel:* 01235 550589 *email:* info@oxrecs.com. Bernard Martin, dir. *Location classical recording specialising in orgs, chmbr orchs and choirs; digital editing, CD mastering, typesetting and design service.*

Panda Productions. 35 Norroy Rd, London SW15 1PQ *tel:* 020 8785 4250 *fax:* 020 8780 5244 *email:* amanda@pandamusic.co.uk. Amanda Hurton, producer. *Production, editing and mastering of digital location recordings. Specialist in classical orch, chmbr and inst repertoire.*

Parish Recordings. 28 Tom Price Close, Cheltenham, Glos GL52 2LF *tel:* 01242 230455 *fax:* 01242 230455 *email:* parish@lineone.net. Ian and Janine Higginson, mgrs. *Digital location recording service run by trained classical musicians. Complete packages for CD and cassette manufacture. Fully-digital recording, editing, mastering and full colour printing. Short runs of CD-ROM replication including artwork. Also live concerts and demo recordings, classical mus.*

Raymer Sound. Apsley House, Courtland Rd, Wellington, Somerset TA21 8ND *tel:* 01823 662160 *fax:* 01823 662160 *email:* neil@raymer.plus.com. Neil Raybould, recording engineer/producer. *Location recording: 8 track digital. National distribution of own-label product. Mobile recording, CD mastering and replication. Jazz, folk, choral, orch, br bands.*

Realsound on Location. 45 Scotland Rd, Nottingham NG5 1JU *tel:* 0115 978 7745 *fax:* 0115 978 7745 *email:* john@realsound.fsnet.co.uk. John Moon, owner. *All formats covered up to 24 track digital, location recording and production.*

Recording Associates. October's End Studio, 34 Ryhill Way, Shinfield, Reading RG6 4AZ *tel:* 0118 986 6142; 07977 596661 *email:* g.addis@recordingassociates.freeserve.co.uk. Geoff Addis, dir; Antony Hodgson, producer; Kate Addis, producer. *Digital audio, video and surround sound recording and editing. Stereo and DTS 5.1 surround sound CD production.*

Redbridge Recordings. 23 Bethell Ave, Cranbrook, Ilford, Essex IG1 4UX *tel:* 020 8518 3967 *fax:* 020 8518 0286 *email:* office@redbridgeclassical.co.uk. Roderick Elms, producer; David Wright, engineer. *Specialist classical location recording. Recitals, concerts, special productions, CDs, cassettes, digital editing suite, artwork preparation.*

Redwood Studios Ltd. 20 Great Chapel St, London W1F 8FW *tel:* 020 7287 3799 *fax:* 020 7287 3751 *email:* andrestudios@yahoo.co.uk. André Jacquemin, mgr. *Digital hard disk recording using ProTools HD system, film post-production suite, Dolby SR and A, large sound effects library. Tascam DA88-DA38 Mackie digital mixing console d8b, 5.1 monitoring M and K monitors. Foley Studio for film work. ADR recording and all aspects of film audio.*

Regent Records. PO Box 528, Wolverhampton WV3 9YW *tel:* 01902 424377 *fax:* 01902 717661 *email:* regent.records@btinternet.com. Gary Cole, producer/engineer. *Classical location recording (high resolution 24-bit surround sound capability) and production, post-production, digital editing. One-off and full custom CD service, demo and concert recordings.*

Simon Fox Gál. 55 Carleton Rd, London N7 0ET *tel:* 020 7609 4481 *email:* simonfox@onet.co.uk. Simon Fox Gál, producer. *Location recording, production and editing for the classical CD market. High-end equipment rig for solo, chmbr and orch work. Assistance offered in finding record labels/distribution.*

Sound Moves. The Oaks, Cross Lane, Smallfield, Surrey RH6 9SA *tel:* 01342 844190 *fax:* 01342 844290 *email:* steve@sound-moves.com. Steve Williams, owner. *Classic analogue, digital stereo or multi-track. Recording, live broadcast and post-production for all types of mus.*

Wearn, Jonathan R. The Yews Cottage, Bothamsall, Retford, Notts DN22 8DT *tel:* 01623 835226 *email:* info@jonathanwearn.co.uk.

Record Pressing, Cassett Duplication, CD Mastering

AWL Compact Disc Co Ltd. 356 Scraptoft Lane, Leicester LE5 1PB *tel:* 0116 241 3979 *fax:* 0116 243 3760. Andrew W Lipinski, mgr dir. *CD mastering and replication.*

Birnam CD. Station Rd, Birnam, Dunkeld, Perthshire PH8 0DS *tel:* 01350 727158/9 *fax:* 01350 727161 *email:* info@birnamcd.com. Martin Hadden, production; Phil Brammer, multimedia; Gavin Duncan, technical. *CD and DVD replication, audio and video cassette duplication, mastering, graphic and multimedia design.*

Cops Manufacturing. The Studio, Barnmead Rd, Beckenham, Kent BR3 1JD *tel:* 020 8778 8556 *fax:* 020 8676 9716 *email:* musicmanufacture@cops.co.uk. Jeremy Dahdi.

* **Damont Audio Ltd.** Blyth Rd, Hayes, Middx UB3 1BY *tel:* 020 8573 5122 *fax:* 020 8561 0979 *email:* mail@damontaudio.com. Chris Rose, mgr dir; Malcolm Pearce, commercial dir; Ian Ramsden, finance. *Manufacture vinyl 7 and 12 records; audio cassette duplication, mastering and printed parts.*

Docdata UK Ltd. Halesfield 14, Telford, Shropshire TF7 4QR *tel:* 01952 680131 *fax:* 01952 583501 *email:* uksales@docdata.com. Martine Tatman, sales dir. *CD, DVD and cassette manufacture.*

Downstream Ltd. 44 Marsh Lane, Nantwich, Cheshire CW5 5LH *tel:* 01270 625125 *fax:* 01270 629424 *email:* sound@downstream .ltd.uk. Edward Leetham, mgr dir. *Digital location recording and CD production. All types of project undertaken, from soloists to full orch and chorus. Live concert recordings and CD recording sessions. Short-run and long-run CD duplication. Video to DVD transfer, DVD authoring and duplication.*

Fairview Studios. Cavewood Grange Farm, Common Lane, North Cave, Brough, E Yorks HU15 2PE *tel:* 01430 425546 *fax:* 01430 425547 *email:* info@fairviewstudios.co.uk. Jackie Herd, sales and accounts; Andy Newlove, mgr. *1 studio, 48 track (24 tracks analogue and digital); capacity 10.*

Filterbond Ltd (JBS Records Division). 19 Sadlers Way, Hertford, SG14 2DZ *tel:* 01992 500101 *fax:* 01992 500101 *email:* jbsrecords.filterbond ltd@virgin.net. John B Schefel, mgr dir; David F J Reeve, dir and sec.

Finesplice Ltd. 1 Summerhouse Lane, Harmondsworth, West Drayton, Middx UB7 0AW *tel:* 020 8564 7839 *fax:* 020 8759 9629 *email:* info@finesplice.co.uk. Ben Turner, mgr dir; Julia Thomas, snr engineer. *Studios for mus editing, audio restoration, CD pre-mastering and duplication. All types of mus.*

Ginn, Jeffrey. 11 Haycroft, Wootton, Bedford MK43 9PB *tel:* 01234 765602; 07778 896721 *fax:* 01234 765602 *email:* jeffginn@onetel.net.uk. *Location recording service and post-production studios. Classical recording, digital editing and SADIE mastering. SADIE hard-disk editor, DAT, CD-ROM, Exabyte, Genex, Lexicon.*

Hiltongrove Multimedia. Hiltongrove Business Centre, Hatherley Mews, London E17 4QP *tel:* 020 8521 2424 *fax:* 020 8521 4343 *email:* info@hiltongrove.com. Guy Davis, mgr dir; David Blackman, studio mgr. *CD mastering. CD manufacture including design and print services; online quotations, bookings and tracking of all manufacturing jobs.*

* **ITD Cassettes Ltd.** Unit 21, Faraday Rd, Rabans Lane, Aylesbury, Bucks HP19 8RY *tel:* 01296 427211 *fax:* 01296 392019 *email:* itdcassets@aol.com. M A McLoughlin, mgr dir; Ray Wood, chief engineer. *Audio cassette duplication.*

Isis Duplicating Co Ltd. Unit 11, Shaftesbury Industrial Estate, The Runnings, Cheltenham, Glos GL51 9NH *tel:* 01242 571818 *fax:* 01242 700025 *email:* gevans@isisdupe.freeserve.co.uk. Glyn Ellis Evans, sales mgr. *Recording, editing, mastering, high-speed cassette duplication, CD replication.*

James Yorke Ltd. Unit M, 40-44 The Bramery, Alstone Lane, Cheltenham, Glos GL51 8HE *tel:* 01242 584222 *fax:* 01242 222445 *email:* ken@jamesyorke.co.uk. Ken Leeks, mgr dir. *Loop bin duplication for cassettes.*

K & A Productions. 5 Wyllyotts Place, Potters Bar, Herts EN6 2HN *tel:* 01707 661200 *fax:* 01707 661400 *email:* andrew@kaproductions .co.uk. Andrew Walton, dir. *Digital editing, restoration and CD and cassette mastering to Exabyte or CD-ROM. One-off CDs. Cover and inlay design and layout. Project supervision to pressing stage. Classical mus.*

Keynote Audio Services. Smoke Tree House, Tilford Rd, Farnham, Surrey GU10 2EN *tel:* 01252 794253 *fax:* 01252 792642 *email:* admin@keynoteaudio.co.uk. Tim Wheatley. *Cassette and CD-ROM duplicators and CD brokers.*

Limor, Gilead - Music, Arts and Media. 7a The Broadway, Stanmore, Middx HA7 4DA *tel:* 020 8420 6115; 07740 423537 *email:* gilead@onetel.net.uk. Gilead Limor, producer/engineer. *High resolution stereo and multi-track location recording. Soloists, chmbr ens, small-medium sized orchs. Recordings for CD production, archive, demo recordings, etc. Also artwork, typesetting and photography, CD replication and manufacturing. Complete packages available.*

The Old Smithy Recording Studio. 1 Post Office Lane, Kempsey, Worcester WR5 3NS *tel:* 01905 820659 *fax:* 01905 820015 *email:* muff.murfin@virgin.net. Janet Allsopp, booking mgr. *Cassette and CD duplication.*

Original Source CD Duplication. 3 Brookside Rd, Brislington, Bristol BS4 4JS *tel:* 0117 971 3947 *email:* info@originalsourcecds.co.uk. Mike Pitt, owner. *CD-ROM duplication specialising in short runs, from audio formats including CD, CD-ROM, DAT, minidisc, cassette, video soundtrack, vinyl. Direct-to-disc printing; production of booklet and tray insert sets; production of multi-session CDs; MP3 encoding of audio files; website design. All mus genres.*

Raymer Sound. Apsley House, Courtland Rd, Wellington, Somerset TA21 8ND *tel:* 01823 662160 *fax:* 01823 662160 *email:* neil@raymer.plus.com. Neil Raybould, recording engineer/producer. *Mobile recording, CD mastering, 8 track digital recording.*

Reflex Media Services Ltd. Unit 5, Cirrus, Glebe Rd, Huntingdon, Cambs PE29 7DL *tel:* 01480 434333 *fax:* 01480 411441 *email:* sales@reflex.media.co.uk. John Garrad, sales mgr; Roger Masterson, dir. *Editing and post-production, mastering for CD and MC, CD pressing and MC duplication. 4-colour printing/packaging and reprographics.*

Repeat Performance. 6 Grand Union Centre, West Row, London W10 5AS *tel:* 020 8960 7222 *fax:* 020 8968 1378 *email:* info@rpmuk.com. Robin Springall, mgr dir. *Mastering and duplication company with in-house graphics; short and long run duplication.*

SRT Sound Recording Technology Ltd. Audio House, Edison Rd, St Ives, Cambs PE27 3LF *tel:* 01480 461880; 020 8446 3218 *fax:* 01480 496100 *email:* srt@btinternet.com. Sarah Pownall, dir; Karen Kenny, dir. *CD manufacturer and 5 studios. Full mastering service including restoration and multi-session discs.*

* **Selecta Sound.** 52 Rockingham Ave, Hornchurch, Essex RM11 1HH *tel:* 01708 453424 *fax:* 01708 455565 *email:* select@selecta-sound.co.uk. John and Carol Smailes; Nigel Davidson, technical mgr. *Audio and video duplication; CD replication; blank tape supply. PA systems, lighting line.*

Sound Discs CD Mastering and Manufacture Ltd. Unit 5, 5 Barley Shotts Business Park, 246 Acklam Rd, London W10 5YG *tel:* 020 8968 7080; 07721 624868 *fax:* 020 8968 7475 *email:* sound.discs@virgin.net. Peter Bullick. *CD, DVD, design, duplication and manufacture.*

Sounds Good Ltd. 12 Chiltern Enterprise Centre, Station Rd, Theale, Berks RG7 4AA *tel:* 0118 930 1700 *fax:* 0118 930 1709 *email:* sales-info@sounds-good.co.uk. Martin Maynard, dir; Peter Redding, sales; Fran Martin, sales. *Cassette duplication, CD mastering and digital editing, CD pressing, inlay print. CD-ROM duplication, design and reprographics. DVD manufacture.*

Sound Recovery and Restoration

Abbey Road Studios. 3 Abbey Rd, St Johns Wood, London NW8 9AY *tel:* 020 7266 7237 *fax:* 020 7266 7250 *email:* lucy.launder@abbeyroad.com. *Audio post production: mastering, re-mastering, editing, 5.1 audio preparation and restoration, CD preparation, copying.*

Friary Music Services. 142b Friary Rd, London SE15 5UW *tel:* 020 7277 7068 *email:* 100115.3701@compuserve.com. *Highest quality transcription of all 78, 45 and 33 rpm records and analogue tape recordings. Classical mus only.*

Hiltongrove Multimedia. Hiltongrove Business Centre, Hatherley Mews, London E17 4QP *tel:* 020 8521 2424 *fax:* 020 8521 4343 *email:* info@hiltongrove.com. Guy Davis, mgr dir; David Blackman, studio mgr. *Editing and sound restoration, 5 studios. CD manufacturing including design and print services; online quotations, bookings and tracking of all manufacturing jobs.*

John R T Davies. 1 Walnut Tree Cottage, Burnham, Bucks SL1 8DH *tel:* 01628 604811. *Recovery and restoration of sound from ancient and defective recordings.*

K & A Productions. 5 Wyllyotts Place, Potters Bar, Herts EN6 2HN *tel:* 01707 661200 *fax:* 01707 661400 *email:* andrew@kaproductions.demon.co.uk. Andrew Walton, dir. *Restoration using Sonic Solutions No-Noise. Transfer off any format. Full EQ, Dynamics and Reverberation processing. Classical mus.*

Specialist Record Dealers

Many record shops carry recordings of classical music as a small proportion of their total stock. In the following list, retailers with exclusive or large sections devoted to classical music or jazz are grouped alphabetically by county. Greater London is listed first followed by the rest of the UK.

Greater London

Barbican Chimes Music. Cromwell Tower, Silk St, Barbican, London EC2Y 8DD *tel:* 020 7588 9242 *fax:* 020 7628 1080 *email:* barbican@chimesmusic.com. *Mus, CDs, inst accs, books.*

Consort Records. 34 St Mary's Grove, London W4 3LN *tel:* 020 8995 9994 *fax:* 020 8995 2115 *email:* info@tkcworld.com. *M/order early mus recordings, available for purchase online.*

Dress Circle. 57-59 Monmouth St, Upper St Martin's Lane, London WC2H 9DG *tel:* 020 7240 2227 *fax:* 020 7379 8540 *email:* info@dresscircle.co.uk. *CDs, cassettes, books, videos, DVDs; posters and merchandise associated with cabaret, musicals, theatre and nostalgia.*

English Folk Dance and Song Society. Cecil Sharp House, 2 Regent's Park Rd, London NW1 7AY *tel:* 020 7485 2206 *email:* info@efdss.org. *Produces CDs of traditional dance mus and songs. Cat available by post or online.*

HMV Shop (HMV UK Ltd). 150 Oxford St, London W1N 1DJ *tel:* 020 7631 3423. *Audio recordings (all formats), videos, computers and video games, mus merchandise and accs.*

HMV Shop. 360 Oxford St, London W1C 1AB *tel:* 020 7514 3600. *Classical, jazz, blues, br band, military, easy listening, rock and pop, soul, dance, films and shows, world mus, folk, country, new age, spoken word, games, videos.*

MDC Classic Music. Royal Festival Hall, London SE1 8XX *tel:* 020 7260 0198 *fax:* 020 7260 0197 *email:* mdc@rfh.org.uk. James Elliott, gen mgr; Matthew Grew, concerts mgr. *Classical, contemporary, jazz, world mus.*

MDC Classic Music Ltd. Mail Order Dept, 31 St Martin's Lane, London WC2N 4ER *tel:* 020 7240 0273 *fax:* 020 7379 5231 *email:* classic@mdcmusic.co.uk. *M/order classical mus dept. Classical CDs, video, DVD.*

MDC Classic Music Ltd. 437 Strand, London WC2R 0QN *tel:* 020 7240 2157 *fax:* 020 7240 5848 *email:* classic@mdcmusic.co.uk. Kevin McDermott, mgr. *Classical CDs, DVDs, plus selected musical/film soundtracks.*

MDC Opera Shop. 31 St Martin's Lane, London WC2N 4ER *tel:* 020 7240 0270 *fax:* 020 7379 5231 *email:* classic@mdcmusic.co.uk. Alan Weakley, mgr. *CDs, videos and DVDs and gifts. Books on opera, dance and ballet, opera guides and reference books, magazines. Classically trained staff.*

Mole Jazz. 311 Gray's Inn Rd, London WC1X 8PX *tel:* 020 7278 0703 *fax:* 020 7833 1029 *email:* jazz@molejazz.com. *Jazz specialists, new and second-hand CDs, LPs, books. M/order worldwide, free mailing lists, auctions of rare LPs.*

Music Discount Centre. 46 Thurloe St, London SW7 2LT *tel:* 020 7584 3338 *fax:* 020 7584 9179 *email:* classic@mdcmusic.co.uk. John Webster, mgr. *Classically trained staff. Classic CDs; films and shows; magazines.*

Ray's Jazz at Foyles. Foyles Bookshop, 113-119 Charing Cross Rd, London WC2H 0EB *tel:* 020 7440 3205 *fax:* 020 7434 1580 *email:* rays@foyles.co.uk. Paul Pace. *CDs, vinyl, 78" and DVDs (new and second-hand), jazz and world mus.*

Sound 323. 323 Archway Rd, Highgate, London N6 5AA *tel:* 020 8348 9595 *fax:* 020 8348 9595 *email:* sound323@aol.com. Mark Wastell, owner. *Experimental new mus.*

Trehantiri. 365-367 Green Lanes, London N4 1DY *tel:* 020 8802 6530 *fax:* 0870 130 8094 *email:* sales@trehantiri.com. *Specialists in Greek, Middle Eastern and Eurovision.*

Vinyl Connections. 22 Hilltop Rd, London NW6 2PY *tel:* 020 7625 8966 *fax:* 020 7625 8966 *email:* rolg1@btinternet.com. *Specialists in original 1950s-1970s classical LP records: symphony, chmbr, inst, operatic, vocal, etc. Most labels. Collections bought for cash; record cleaning service; quality vintage turntables and cartridges supplied. One off vinyl to CD transfers (also from 78s).*

Virgin Megastore. 14-19 Oxford St, London W1N 9FL *tel:* 020 7631 1234 *fax:* 020 7580 9546. *Books, records, CDs, videos, DVDs, vinyl, sheet mus.*

Rest of United Kingdom

Bath & North East Somerset
Bath

Bath Compact Discs. 11 Broad St, Bath BA1 5LJ *tel:* 01225 464766 *fax:* 01225 482275 *email:* bathcds@btinternet.com. *Classical CDs and videos/DVDs, also m/order (post free in UK).*

HMV Shop. 13-15 Stall St, Bath BA1 1QE *tel:* 01225 466681.

Belfast, City of
Belfast

HMV UK Ltd. 3,4,6 Donegall Arcade, Belfast BT1 1PT, Northern Ireland *tel:* 028 9023 8494 *fax:* 028 9023 8497.

Berkshire
Reading

Hickies Ltd. 153 Friar St, Reading RG1 1HG *tel:* 0118 957 5771 *fax:* 0118 957 5775. *Cassettes, CDs.*

HMV Shop. 13 Holy Brook Walk, The Oracle, Reading RG1 2AQ *tel:* 0118 951 2640.

Buckinghamshire
Central Milton Keynes

Chappell of Bond Street. 21 Silbury Arcade, the centre: mk, Central Milton Keynes MK9 3AG *tel:* 01908 663366 *fax:* 01908 606414 *email:* mandi_meek@chappell-bond-st.co.uk. *CDs, DVDs, mus, m/order.*

Cambridgeshire
Cambridge

MDC Classic Music. 8 Rose Crescent, Cambridge CB2 3LL *tel:* 01223 506526 *fax:* 01223 507083 *email:* classic@mdcmusic.co.uk. David Earl, mgr. *Classical CDs and DVDs. Classically trained staff.*

HMV Shop. 12-15 Lion Yard, Cambridge CB2 3NA *tel:* 01223 319090.

Cheshire
Cheadle

D I Music Direct. 1st & 2nd Floors, 7 High St, Cheadle, Cheshire SK8 1AX *tel:* 0161 491 6655 *fax:* 0161 491 6688 *email:* dimus@aol.com. *Specialist range of British and imported CDs; classical, opera.*

Devon
Exeter

Opus Classical. The Gallery, Guildhall Centre, Exeter, Devon EX4 3HW *tel:* 01392 214044 *fax:* 01392 496196 *email:* enquiries@opus-classical.com. *CDs, DVDs, books, videos.*

East Sussex
Brighton

HMV Shop. 48-50 Churchill Square Shopping Centre, Brighton BN1 2RG *tel:* 01273 749919.

Eastbourne

Brittens Music Ltd. 24 Pevensey Rd, Eastbourne, E Sussex BN21 3HP *tel:* 01323 732553 *fax:* 01323 417455 *email:* mail@seaford-music.co.uk. *Classical CDs, cassettes, videos.*

Edinburgh, City of
Edinburgh

HMV Shop. 129-130 Princes St, Edinburgh EH2 4AH *tel:* 0131 225 7008. *CDs, cassettes and videos.*

Essex
Saffron Walden
Chew & Osborne. 26 King St, Saffron Walden, Essex CB10 1ES *tel:* 01799 523728 *fax:* 01799 524597 *email:* music.saffron@chewandosborne. co.uk. *CDs, classical specialists and hi-fi.*

Glasgow, City of
Glasgow
HMV Shop. 154-160 Sauchiehall St, Glasgow G2 3DH *tel:* 0141 332 6631.
Virgin Megastore. Debenhams Bldg, 83 Argyle St, Glasgow G2 8BJ *tel:* 0141 221 2606 *fax:* 0141 221 2607 *email:* manager. glasgowarg@vriginmega.co.uk. *CDs, DVDS, videos, etc.*

Gloucestershire
Gloucester
Audiosonic (Gloucester) Ltd. 6 College St, Gloucester GL1 2NE *tel:* 01452 302280 *fax:* 01452 302202. *Cassettes, CDs, m/order. Classical mus specialists. Videos, DVDs, sheet mus; also second-hand CDs.*
Folktrax (Audio and Video) International. The Traditions Library, 16 Brunswick Square, Gloucester GL1 1UG *tel:* 01452 415110 *email:* peter@folktrax.freeserve.co.uk. Peter and Beryl Kennedy, mgrs. *CDs and videos of traditional mus and customs of the world.*

Greater Manchester
Manchester
Forsyth Bros Ltd. 126 Deansgate, Manchester M3 2GR *tel:* 0161 834 3281 *fax:* 0161 834 0630 *email:* records@forsyths.co.uk. *Classical, jazz, world, spoken word. CDs, cassettes, mus videos, DVDs, m/order.*
HMV Shop. 90-100 Market St, Manchester M1 1PD *tel:* 0161 834 8550. *CDs, cassettes, videos.*

Hampshire
Southampton
HMV Shop. 56-58 Above Bar St, Southampton SO14 7DS *tel:* 023 8033 8398. *Records, cassettes, CDs and videos, minidiscs and laser discs.*

Herefordshire
Hay-on-Wye
Hancock & Monks. 6 Broad St, Hay-on-Wye, Herefordshire HR3 5DB *tel:* 01497 821784 *fax:* 01591 610778 *email:* jerry@ hancockandmonks.co.uk. *Specialists in classical CDs, DVDs. Second-hand books on mus; sheet mus.*

Kent
Bromley
Showells Mail Order. PO Box 309, Bromley, Kent BR1 3GR *tel:* 020 8466 0649 *fax:* 020 8466 0649 *email:* showellcdvideo@aol.com. *DVDs, CDs, videos.*

Lancashire
St Annes on Sea
Squires Gate Music Centre. Rear of 13 St Andrew's Rd South, St Annes on Sea, Lancs FY8 1SX *tel:* 01253 782588 *fax:* 01253 782985 *email:* sales@lprl.demon.co.uk. *Cassettes, CDs, DVDs, videos.*

Leicestershire
Leicester
Classic Tracks. 21 East Bond St, Leicester LE1 4SX *tel:* 0116 253 7700 *fax:* 0116 251 3553 *email:* classictracks@lineone.net. *Classical mus, film soundtracks, shows and musicals, nostalgia.*
Virgin Megastore. 8 Churchgate, Leicester LE1 4AJ *tel:* 0116 242 5969 *fax:* 0116 253 0136.

Liverpool, City Of
Liverpool
HMV Shop. 22-36 Church St, Liverpool L1 3AW *tel:* 0151 709 1088. *Records, cassettes, CDs, video games.*

Norfolk
Norwich
Prelude Records. 25b St Giles Street, Norwich NR2 1JN *tel:* 01603 628319 *fax:* 01603 628319/0170 *email:* sales@prelude-records.co.uk. *CDs, DVDs, cassettes, videos, minidiscs; classical specialist.*

Northamptonshire
Northampton
Spinadisc Records. 75a Abington St, Northampton NN1 2BH *tel:* 01604 631144 *fax:* 01604 624418. *CDs, DVD, vinyl.*

Oxfordshire
Oxford
HMV Shop. 43-46 Cornmarket St, Oxford OX1 3HA *tel:* 01865 728190. *CDs, cassettes.*

Pembrokeshire
Haverfordwest
Swales Music Centre Ltd. 2-6 High St, Haverfordwest, Pembs SA61 2DJ *tel:* 01437 762059 *fax:* 01437 760872 *email:* musician@swales music.co.uk. *CDs, m/order.*

South Yorkshire
Sheffield
HMV Shop. 14-18 High St, Sheffield S1 2GE *tel:* 0114 263 4275.

Surrey
Cobham
Threshold Compact Discs. 53 High St, Cobham, Surrey KT11 3DP *tel:* 01932 865678 *fax:* 01932 865678 *email:* sales@threshold-cd.co.uk. *Classical, jazz, blues, classic soul/R&B, world, rock, pop, country, rock 'n' roll, films and shows, gospel, nostalgia.*
Godalming
Record Corner. Pound Lane, Godalming, Surrey GU7 1BX *tel:* 01483 422006 *fax:* 01483 425739 *email:* tom@therecordcorner.co.uk. *CDs, cassettes, vinyl, mus books, styli, videos, DVDs.*
Guildford
HMV Shop. 9-11 The Friary Centre, Guildford GU1 4YL *tel:* 01483 565650.
Kingston
HMV Shop. Units 11-12, 1st Floor, Bentalls Centre, Kingston KT1 1TP *tel:* 020 8974 8037.
Richmond
HMV Shop. 70-72 George St, Richmond, Surrey TW9 1HE *tel:* 020 8940 9880.

Sussex
Hailsham
Jewish Music Distribution. PO Box 67, Hailsham, Sussex BN27 4UW *tel:* 01323 832863 *fax:* 01323 832863 *email:* orders@jewishmusic-jmd.co.uk. *Retail and wholesale suppliers of Jewish recorded and printed mus. Main agent for Israel's major recording and sheet mus companies.*

Tyne & Wear
Newcastle upon Tyne
HMV Shop. 56-58 Northumberland St, Newcastle upon Tyne NE1 7DF *tel:* 0191 230 0626.

Warwickshire
Leamington Spa
Presto Classical. 11 Park St, Leamington Spa, Warks CV32 4QN *tel:* 01926 317025 *fax:* 01926 337032 *email:* info@prestoclassical.co.uk. *CDs, DVDs, large early mus, contemporary and opera sections. M/order.*

West Midlands
Birmingham
Farringdons Records. Symphony Hall, Broad St, Birmingham B1 2EA *tel:* 0121 200 2382; 0870 606 0322 (m/order) *fax:* 0121 200 2383 *email:* Farringdonsrecords@hotmail.com. *Classical jazz, world, easy, nostalgia, DVD and video.*
HMV Shop. 38 High St, Birmingham B4 7SL *tel:* 0121 643 2177. *CDs, cassettes and videos.*

West Yorkshire
Leeds
HMV Shop. 1 Victoria Walk, Headrow Centre, Leeds LS1 6JD *tel:* 0113 245 5548. *Cassettes, CDs and videos.*

Wiltshire
Devizes
Heritage Records. 39 Woodland Rd, Patney, nr Devizes, Wilts SN10 3RD *tel:* 01380 840362 *fax:* 01380 840362 *email:* heritage.records@ dial.pipex.com. *Second-hand 78s, LPs and CDs.*

York, City of
York
Banks & Sons (Music) Ltd. 18 Lendal, York YO1 8AU *tel:* 01904 658836 *fax:* 01904 629547 *email:* banksmusic@dial.pipex.com. *Classical recordings, classical sheet mus, all sheet mus, albums, tutors and studies for all insts (brass, w/wind, rcdrs, str, gui). Rental scheme on selected insts. Hi-tech dept, worldwide m/order.*

Organisations

The Queen's Household

Master of the Queen's Music. Campion Press Music Publishers, Sandon, Buntingford, Herts SG9 0QW *tel:* 01763 247287 *fax:* 01763 249984 *email:* campion_press@hotmail.com. Simon Campion. *Currently vacant. The office of Master of the Musick dates from 1626. The succession of masters in the 20th C was Elgar, Walford Davies, Bax, Bliss and Malcolm Williamson.*
Organist, Choirmaster and Composer, HM Chapels Royal: Andrew Gant. St James's Palace, London SW1A 1BG *tel:* 01865 558841 *email:* andrew.gant@btinternet.com. Nicholas Shaw, sub-org.
Organist and Choirmaster, HM Chapel Royal: Carl Jackson. Hampton Court Palace, East Molesey, Surrey KT8 9AU *tel:* 020 8781 9597 *fax:* 020 8781 9509 *email:* caj@mailbox.co.uk.

Department for Culture, Media and Sport

2-4 Cockspur St, London SW1Y 5DH *tel:* 020 7211 6200 *email:* enquiries@culture.gov.uk. Rt Hon Tessa Jowell MP, secretary of state for culture, media and sport; Rt Hon Estelle Morris MP, minister for the arts; Rt Hon Lord McIntosh MP, minister for media and heritage; Rt Hon Richard Caborn MP, minister for sport and tourism; Sue Street, permanent secretary. *The Department for Culture, Media and Sport aims to improve the quality of life for all through cultural and sporting activities, and to strengthen the creative industries. Its responsibility covers sports, National Lottery, the Millennium, libraries, museums and galleries, broadcasting, film, the creative industries (including the mus industry), press freedom and regulation, the historic environment and tourism. Most public executive functions in these fields are carried out through Non-Departmental Public Bodies (NDPBs). The department also sponsors one Executive Agency - the Royal Parks - and several public broadcasting corporations. Its direct executive responsibilities include listing buildings of special architectural or historic interest, scheduling ancient monuments, licensing the export of cultural goods and managing the Government Art Collection.*

British Council

Performing Arts Dept, 10 Spring Gardens, London SW1A 2BN *tel:* 020 7389 3005/3010 *fax:* 020 7389 3057 *email:* music@britishcouncil.org. John Kieffer, dir of performing arts, head of mus; Paul Parkinson, mus projects mgr; Jo Ross, mus projects mgr; Leah Zakss, mus projects mgr; John Daniel, information mgr; Lisa Moult, special projects co-ord; Nick Tarrant, mus projects admin. *Promotes educational, cultural and technical co-operation between Britain and other countries. The Council's work is designed to establish long-term and worldwide partnerships and to improve international understanding.*

Visiting Arts

Bloomsbury House, 74-77 Great Russell St, London WC1B 3DA *tel:* 020 7291 1600 *fax:* 020 7291 1616 *email:* information@visitingarts.org.uk. Richard Lambert, chmn; Terry Sandell OBE, dir; Nelson Fernandez, head of performing arts and training; Camilla Canellas, head of visual, media and applied arts; Adam Jeanes, asst dir resources and planning; Tim Doley, asst dir research and development; Melissa Naylor, information mgr. *Visiting Arts is a national agency which works to ensure high quality contemporary arts are brought into the UK from countries across the world and to extend dialogue between UK artists and their overseas counterparts. Through its broad range of activites and services, including information, advisory work, training and project development, Visiting Arts aims to develop greater international awareness through the arts and promote positive cultural relations. It is an independent charity funded by the British Council, the Foreign and Commonwealth Office, the four national Arts Councils of England, Scotland, Wales and Northern Ireland and the DCMS.*

Arts Council England

14 Great Peter St, London SW1P 3NQ *tel:* 020 7333 0100 *fax:* 020 7973 6590. Gerry Robinson, chmn; Peter Hewitt, chief exec. National office music staff: Hilary Boulding, mus dir; Henry Little, head of opera and mus theatre; Alan James, head of contemporary mus; Beverley Crew, CMN co-producer. *The Arts Council receives a grant-in-aid from the government, and is incorporated under Royal Charter with the following objects: (a) to develop and improve the knowledge, understanding and practice of the arts; (b) to increase the accessibility of the arts to the public and (c) to advise and co-operate with government departments, local authorities and other bodies on any matters concerned, whether directly or indirectly, with the foregoing objects. The members of the Council, who may not exceed 20 in number, are appointed by the Secretary of State for the National Heritage. Funds from the National Lottery for the Arts in England are administered by Arts Council England's National Lottery Department, which aims to give the maximum benefit to the public by supporting arts projects which make an important and lasting difference to the quality of life of people throughout England.*

Arts Council of Northern Ireland

MacNeice House, 77 Malone Rd, Belfast BT9 6AQ *tel:* 028 9038 5200 *fax:* 028 9066 1715 *email:* artsdevelopment@artscoucil-ni.org. Philip Hammond, arts development dir; Pamela Smith, arts development offr (mus); Joe Kelly, arts development offr (youth arts). *The Arts Council of Northern Ireland, funded by the Department of Culture Arts and Leisure through the Northern Ireland Assembly, has functions of subsidy and promotion similar to those of the Arts Council of England.*

Arts Council of Wales

9 Museum Place, Cardiff CF10 3NX *tel:* 029 2037 6500 *minicom:* 029 2039 0027 *fax:* 029 2022 1447 *email:* information@ccc-acw.org.uk. Peter Tyndall, chief exec; Simon Lovell-Jones, snr arts development offr, mus.

Arts Council of Wales, North Wales Office. 36 Prince's Drive, Colwyn Bay LL29 8LA *tel:* 01492 533440 *minicom:* 01492 532288 *fax:* 01492 533677 *email:* information@artswales.org.uk. Sian Tomos, dir. *Conwy, Denbighshire, Flintshire, Gwynedd, Isle of Anglesey, Wrexham.*
Arts Council of Wales, South Wales Office. 9 Museum Place, Cardiff CF10 3NX *tel:* 029 2037 6500 *fax:* 029 2022 1447 *email:* information@ccc-acw.org.uk. Simon Lovell-Jones, snr arts development offr - mus.

Scottish Arts Council

12 Manor Place, Edinburgh EH3 7DD *tel:* 0131 226 6051 *fax:* 0131 225 9833 *email:* help.desk@scottisharts.org.uk. Nod Knowles, head of mus.

Isle of Man Arts Council

10 Villa Marina Arcade, Douglas, Isle of Man IM1 2HN *tel:* 01624 611316 *fax:* 01624 615423 *email:* dawn.maddrell@iomartscouncil.dtl.gov.im. Dawn Maddrell, arts development mgr.

International Intelligence on Culture

4 Baden Place, Crosby Row, London SE1 1YW *tel:* 020 7403 6454 (mgt)/7001 (information service) *fax:* 020 7403 2009 *email:* development@intelCULTURE.org. Contact: information services. *A dynamic consultancy which brings together a highly experienced multi-national group of experts to work with and for the international culture sector. Activities include: policy intelligence, research, consultancy, training and information services. The email, journal and web-based subscriber service 'International Cultural Compass' provides up-to-date information on international developments, policies and programmes relating to culture.*

The Foundation for Sports and the Arts

PO Box 20, Liverpool L13 1HB *tel:* 0151 259 5505 *fax:* 0151 230 0664. Richard Boardley, sec designate; Karen Graham, admin. *The FSA was established in 1991 by members of the Pool Promoters' Association. Enquiries by telephone or fax.*

Music Information Centres

British Music Information Centre. 10 Stratford Place, London W1C 1BA *tel:* 020 7499 8567 *fax:* 020 7499 4795 *email:* info@bmic.co.uk. Matthew Greenall, dir; Daniel Goren, information mgr; Imogen Mitchell, production and services mgr. *Scores and recordings collection of contemporary British classical mus.*
Irish Contemporary Music Centre. 19 Fishamble St, Temple Bar, Dublin 8 *tel:* 00 353 1 673 1922 *fax:* 00 353 1 648 9100 *email:* info@cmc.ie. Eve O'Kelly, dir. *Ireland's national archive and resources centre for new mus, supporting the work of composers throughout the Republic and Northern Ireland.*
Scottish Music Information Centre. 1 Bowmont Gardens, Glasgow G12 9LR *tel:* 0141 334 6393 *fax:* 0141 337 1161 *email:* info@smic.org.uk. Andrew Logan, chief exec; Alasdair Pettinger, information mgr. *Exists to document and promote work by Scottish and Scottish-based composers of all periods. Reference, hire and audio libraries; photocopying service, scores and recordings available for sale. Promotional activities.*
Welsh Music Information Centre. Ty Cerdd, 15 Mount Stuart Square, Cardiff CF10 5DP *tel:* 029 2046 2855/5700 *fax:* 029

2046 2733 *email:* wmic@tycerdd.org. Keith Griffin, dir; Emyr Jenkins, chmn. *Re-established in June 2000. Offers information on Welsh mus and performances of contemporary mus by Welsh composers.*

Arts Council England Offices

Arts Council England, East. Eden House, 48/49 Bateman St, Cambridge CB2 1LR *tel:* 01223 454400 *fax:* 0870 242 1271 *email:* east@artscouncil.org.uk. Michael Garvey, mus offr. *Bedfordshire, Cambridgeshire, Essex, Hertfordshire (other than London borough overlap), Norfolk, Suffolk and the unitary authorities of Luton, Peterborough, Southend and Thurrock.*

Arts Council England, East Midlands. St Nicholas Court, 25-27 Castlegate, Nottingham NG1 7AR *tel:* 0115 898 7520 *fax:* 0115 950 2467 *email:* eastmidlands@artscouncil.org.uk. Laura Dyer, exec dir; Helen Flach, dir, arts and development; James Burkmar, team leader, performing arts (mus); Amanda Smith, asst offr performing arts. *Covers the counties of Derbyshire, Leicestershire, Lincolnshire (excluding N and NE Lincolnshire), Northamptonshire, Rutland and Nottinghamshire.*

Arts Council England, London. Music Unit, 2 Pear Tree Court, London EC1R 0DS *tel:* 020 7608 6198 *fax:* 020 7608 4100 *email:* samantha.reader@artscouncil.org.uk. Andrew Pinnock, head of mus; Andrew McKenzie, snr mus offr; Phil Butterworth, mus offr; Graham Carr, mus offr; Milica Robson, mus offr; Graham Knight, asst mus offr; Samantha Reader, mus admin. *London Office of Arts Council England, covers 32 London Boroughs and City of London. Chair of London Regional Council, Lady Sue Hollick.*

Arts Council England, North East. Central Square, Forth St, Newcastle upon Tyne NE1 3PJ *tel:* 0191 255 8500 *fax:* 0191 230 1020 *email:* northeast@artscouncil.org.uk. Andrew Dixon, exec dir; Mark Robinson, dir, arts and development; Mark Mulqueen, head of performing arts; Mark Monument, performing arts offr. *Durham, Northumberland, Tees Valley, Tyne and Wear.*

Arts Council England, North West. Manchester House, 22 Bridge St, Manchester M3 3AB *tel:* 0161 834 6644 *minicom:* 0161 834 9131 *fax:* 0161 834 6969 *email:* northwest@artscouncil.org.uk. Eddie Thomas, mus offr. *Cheshire, Cumbria, Lancashire and the metropolitan authorities of Bolton, Bury, Knowsley, Liverpool, Manchester, Oldham, Rochdale, St Helens, Salford, Sefton, Stockport, Tameside, Trafford.*

Arts Council England, South East. Sovereign House, Church St, Brighton, E Sussex BN1 1RA *tel:* 01273 763000 *fax:* 08702 421257 *email:* southeast@artscouncil.org.uk. Michael Craven, dir of visual arts and literature; Trevor Mason, mus offr; Felicity Harvest, regional exec dir. *Buckinghamshire, Hampshire, Oxfordshire, E and W Sussex, Kent, Surrey and the unitary authorities of Bracknell Forest, Isle of Wight, Milton Keynes, Portsmouth, Reading, Slough, Southampton, W Berkshire, Windsor, Maidenhead, Wokingham, Brighton and Hove and Medway.*

Arts Council England, South West. Bradninch Place, Gandy St, Exeter EX4 3LS *tel:* 01392 218188 *fax:* 01392 229229 *email:* southwest@artscouncil.org.uk. Nick Capaldi, regional exec dir; Michelle Hogg, exec asst; Hilary Garnham, dir, arts and development; Paul Goddard, team leader, performing arts; Moragh Brooksbank, performing arts offr, mus. *Cornwall, Devon, Dorset, Gloucestershire, Somerset, Wiltshire and the unitary authorities of Bath and N E Somerset, Bournemouth, Bristol, N Somerset, Plymouth, Poole, S Gloucestershire, Swindon and Torbay.*

Arts Council England, West Midlands. 82 Granville St, Birmingham B1 2LH *tel:* 0121 631 3121 *textphone/minicom:* 0121 643 2815 *fax:* 0121 643 7239 *email:* andrew.miller@artscouncil.org.uk. Sally Luton, regional exec dir. *Shropshire, Staffordshire, Warwickshire, Worcestershire and the metropolitan authorities of Herefordshire, Stoke-on-Trent, Telford and Wrekin.*

Arts Council England, Yorkshire. 21 Bond St, Dewsbury, W Yorks WF13 1AX *tel:* 01924 455555 *fax:* 01924 466522 *email:* info@artscouncil.org.uk. Andy Carver, chief exec; Ivor Davies, dir of performing arts; Andrew Herbert, mus offr. *S Yorkshire, W Yorkshire, N Yorkshire, N Lincolnshire, N E Lincolnshire, E Riding and Hull and York.*

National Music Council

60-62 Clapham Rd, London SW9 0JJ *tel:* 020 7820 9992 *fax:* 020 7820 9972 *email:* nationalmusiccouncil@ukonline.co.uk.

The National Music Council sits at the centre of a complex network of national mus organisations, but is the only organisation that exists to promote the interests of the mus industry as a whole. Membership is drawn from all areas of the mus business and is open to all organisations with an interest in mus and its development in the UK: professional, voluntary and amateur; subsidised and commercial; creative and educational. The council seeks to celebrate and promote the value and enjoyment of mus, which contributes, in all its forms, to the cultural, spiritual, educational, social and economic well-being of the UK.

International Music Information Centres and Organisations

The entries marked with an asterisk are members of the **International Association of Music Information Centres** (Stiftgasse 29, A-1070 Wien, Austria *tel:* +43 1 521 040 *fax:* +43 1 521 0499 *email:* office@iamic.net *website:* www.iamic.net) which is a worldwide network of organisations promoting new music. Music Information Centres are open to the public and have extensive resources: large libraries of sheet music and sound archives, and up-to-date collections of biographical and research material. Many issue publications and recordings, while all serve as a focus of musical activity.

The other organisations listed below also disseminate information about music and musical activities in their respective countries. Many take particular interest in living composers and contemporary music. These may include composers' societies, associations and national music committees of the International Music Council.

Argentina
Argentine Music Council. Sante Fe 3269 - 4B, Buenos Aires 1425, Argentina *tel:* +54 11 4822 1383 *fax:* +54 11 4822 1383 *email:* camu@aliciaterzian.com.ar. Alicia Terzian, president; Fernando Barragan, secretary.
International Encounters of Contemporary Music Foundation. Sante Fe 3269 - 4B, Buenos Aires 1425, Argentina *tel:* +54 11 4822 1383 *fax:* +54 11 4822 1383 *email:* eimc@aliciaterzian.com.ar. Carlos Berberian, president; Nidia Corrado, executive secretary; Alicia Terzian, artistic director.

Australia
* **Australian Music Centre Ltd.** PO Box N690, Grosvenor Place NSW 1220, Australia *tel:* +61 2 9247 4677 *fax:* +61 2 9241 2873 *email:* info@amcoz.com.au. John Davis, general manager; Anna Cerneaz, marketing manager; Judith Foster, music resources manager. *Street address: Level 4, The Arts Exchange, 18 Hickson Rd, The Rocks, Sydney, Australia. AMC was established to facilitate and encourage the performance and understanding of music by Australian composers throughout the world. The Music Resource Library houses 12,000 works by approx 400 composers. The collection focuses on contemporary Australian music and, in many cases, is the only source for certain works. The Library holds recordings, books and published scores, biographical files on more than 1000 Australian composers, press clippings, reviews and concert programmes, analyses, photographs and an extensive collection of programme notes. Many of these are available for hire or sale.*
Music Council of Australia. PO Box 287, Double Bay NSW 2028, Australia *tel:* +61 2 9251 3816 *fax:* +61 2 9251 3817 *email:* ozmusico@zeta.org.au. Richard Letts, executive director; Alison Cole, administrator. *Australian affiliate to UNESCO International Music Council. An advocacy and service body with a membership of 50 national music organisations and individuals. Publishes a periodical: 'Music Forum' which covers major issues in the situation of music. Also an extensive weekly email bulletin service of opportunities and news in music. Recent publication: 'Comprehensive Guide to Careers in Music'. Projects in research, policy, national and international advocacy. Forming a national music critics' circle.*
The Orchestras of Australia Network (TOAN). PO Box N690, Grosvenor Place NSW 1220, Australia *tel:* +61 2 9241 2018 *fax:* +61 2 9241 2873 *email:* info@toan.com.au. Maree Lucas, admin; Noel Cislowski, chairman.

Austria
* **IGNM - Austrian Society for Contemporary Music.** UngargAsse 11, Wien A-1030, Austria *tel:* +43 1 713 7040 *fax:* +43 1 713 7040 40 *email:* ignm@utanet.at; ignm@mica.at. Monika Fuchs. *Close co-operation with the MICA - Music Information Centre Austria.*
IAMIC - International Association of Music Information Centres. Secretariat of IAMIC, c/o mica - music information centre austria, Stiftgasse 29, Vienna A-1070, Austria *tel:* +43 1 52 1040 *fax:* +43 1 52 10499 *email:* office@iamic.net. Roland Sandberg, president; Peter Rantasa, secretary. *Worldwide network of organisations, promoting new music.*
International Music Centre Vienna. Speisinger Str 121-127, Wien A-1230, Austria *tel:* +43 1 889 0315 *fax:* +43 1 889 0315 77 *email:* office@imz.at. Henk van der Meulen, president; Franz Patay, secretary general. *International association of audio-visual producers of arts programmes with an emphasis on classical and contemporary music, jazz, world music and dance. Organises congresses, seminars, workshops and screenings on topical issues. Also organises festivals and competitions for audio-visual dance and music theatre productions. Operates a database for TV programmes and publishes a bimonthly magazine 'Music in the Media'.*
* **Music Information Centre Austria (MICA).** Stiftgasse 29, Wien A-1070, Austria *tel:* +43 1 521 040 *fax:* +43 1 521 0499 *email:* office@mica.at. Peter Rantasa, managing director. *Mica is the central communication platform for contemporary Austrian music. Provides detailed information on contemporary Austrian music. Also liaises between artists and representatives from the music business and government cultural organisations.*
Musikalische Jugend Österreichs. Lothringerstr 20, (im Konzerthausgebäude), Wien A-1037, Austria *tel:* +43 1 710 3616 *fax:* +43 1 710 3616 17 *email:* mail@jeunesse.at. Angelika Möser, general secretary; Ute Pinter, artistic management; Miriam Schreinzer, artistic management; Eleonore van der Linden, artistic management; Christoph Engel, marketing; Katrin Mackowski, press. *Promoting classical music for a young audience. Strong link with youth and music within the structure of an Austria-wide Jeunesse event network.*

Belgium
* **Centre Belge de Documentation Musicale (CeBeDeM).** Rue d'Arlon 75-77, Bruxelles B-1040, Belgium *tel:* +32 2 230 9430 *fax:* +32 2 230 9437 *email:* music-centre@cebedem.be. Alain van Kerckhoven, director. *Promotion and performance of works by Belgian contemporary composers; music sheet library, containing published and unpublished scores, biographical details, articles, press-clippings; recording library; free borrowing service; publishing and reproduction department.*
Centre of International Cultural Relations. Torenstr 13, Lokeren B-9160, Belgium *tel:* +32 9 348 8000 *fax:* +32 9 348 9974 *email:* j-p.vanavermaet@pandora.be. Jean Pierre Van Avermaet, managing director. *Operates an extended database containing musicological information, biographical data and a list of local organisers throughout Europe. Provides translations of music related texts in Russian, Bulgarian, Dutch, English, German and French.*
Jeunesse Musicales International. Palais des Beaux-Arts, 10 Rue Royale, Bruxelles B-1000, Belgium *tel:* +32 2 513 9774 *fax:* +32 2 514 4755 *email:* mail@JMI.net. Dag Franzén, secretary general. *To enable young people to develop through music across all boundaries.*
The MUSTT Foundation (Music Uplifting Society towards Transformation and Tolerance). 81 Avenue Sleecxk, Brussels 1030, Belgium *tel:* +32 2 2414990 *fax:* +32 2 2414990 *email:* musicfoundation@skynet.be. *The MUSTT has the aim to demonstrate the added values of music throughout all aspects of life and the new roles of music on society, enhancing people's awareness about the transforming, communicative, educational and healing power of music (for example music and medicine, music and business, music and therapy, etc.).*

Brazil
National Music Committee (Brazil). Rua Pres Carlos de Campos No 115 B, 2/902, Rio de Janeiro RJ, Laranjeiras 22231-080, Brazil *tel:* +55 21 2553 6222 *fax:* +55 21 2553 9963 *email:* marialuizacorker@uol.com.br. Maria-Luiza Corker-Nobre, secretary general. *Provides information about Brazilian music life and is publishing a 'Complete Guide to the Brazilian Music World' with addresses of all Brazilian institutions,*

artists, managers, orchestras, etc. The NMC participates at the IMC/UNESCO programmes, particularly the International Rostrum of Composers.

Sociedade de Cultura Artistica. Rua Nestor Pestana 196, Sao Paulo SP 01303-010 Sao Paulo SP, Brazil *tel:* +55 11 3258 3595 *fax:* +55 11 3258 3595 *email:* cultart@dialdata.com.br. Gérald Perret.

Bulgaria

Union of Bulgarian Composers. 2 Ivan Vazov Str, Sofia BG-1000, Bulgaria *tel:* +359 2 988 15 60 (secretary); +359 2 988 00 86 (co-ordinator) *fax:* +359 2 987 4378 *email:* mail@ubc-bg.com. Victor Chuchkov, president; Velislav Zaimov, secretary general; Vladimir Molle, co-ordinator. *UBC is dedicated to spread worldwide Bulgarian classical as well as contemporary music and today's Bulgarian music culture. For that purpose, UBC provides up-to-date information on Bulgarian composers and the trends in Bulgarian music life. UBC organises festivals of new Bulgarian music, workshops on traditional and contemporary Bulgarian music and celebrates anniversaries of Bulgarian composers. The Union's rich library includes archives of Bulgarian music heritage as well as records of contemporary works by Bulgarian composers.*

Canada

The Canada Council for the Arts/Conseil des Arts du Canada. PO Box 1047, 350 Albert St, Ottawa Ont K1P 5V8, Canada *tel:* +1 613 566 4414 ext 5060 *fax:* +1 613 566 4390 *email:* info@canadacouncil.ca. Micheline Lesage, director of arts division; Russell Kelley, head of music section.

* **Canadian Music Centre/Centre de Musique Canadienne (CMC).** Chalmers House, 20 St Joseph St, Toronto Ont M4Y 1J9, Canada *tel:* +1 416 961 6601 *fax:* +1 416 961 7198 *email:* info@musiccentre.ca. Elisabeth Bihl, executive director. *Collects, reproduces, promotes, records and distributes the music and recordings of Canadian contemporary music composers. Also operates a lending library of printed music, orchestra rentals and distributes independent CDs of specialised music.*

International Association of Music Libraries, Archives and Documentation Centres. National Library of New Zealand, PO Box 1467, Wellington, New Zealand *tel:* +64 4 474 3039 *fax:* +64 4 474 3035 *email:* roger.flury@natlib.govt.nz. Roger Flury, secretary general. *Encourages and promotes the activities of music librarians throughout the world; promotes co-operation, professional education and training; supports protection and presentation of musical documents and musical research.*

Croatia

Croatian Composers' Society. Berislaviceva 9, Zagreb HR 10000, Croatia *tel:* +385 1 487 2370 *fax:* +385 1 487 2372 *email:* info@hds.hr. A T Saban, secretary general; Sanda Bozic, adviser; Zrinka Lazarin, adviser. *Organises festivals of Croatian music; publishes contemporary and ancient Croatian music. Its primary aim is the further promotion of music in Croatia and the recognition of Croatian music at home and abroad. Organises festivals, publishes contemporary Croatian music.*

Culturelink Network. Institute for International Relations, Lj F Vukotinovica 2, PO Box 303, Zagreb 10000, Croatia *tel:* +385 1 482 6522 *fax:* +385 1 482 8361 *email:* clink@irmo.hr. Biserka Cvjeticanin, co-ordinator; Daniela Jelincic, researcher; Nine Obuljen, researcher; Aleksandra Uzelac, researcher. *Culturelink is an information network established by UNESCO and the Council of Europe. It is devoted to promoting research into cultural development, cultural policies and cultural and artistic co-operation. It also aims to collect, process and disseminate information. The 'Culturelink Review' is issued quarterly providing updated information on current activities and projects to its members.*

Croatian Music Information Centre. Zagreb Concert Management, Kneza Mislava 18, HR-10 000 Zagreb, Croatia *tel:* +385 1 450 1187/1188/1200 *fax:* +385 1 461 1807 *email:* mic@zg.hinet.hr; mic@mic.hr. Ivan Zivanovic, director; Jelena Vukovic, editor and database manager. *The MIC is a non-profit organisation documenting and promoting Croatian music at home and abroad. MIC mainly caters for professional musicians, as well as for those who need information, sheet music, or anything else related to Croatian music. The MIC personnel can be reached any workday from 9am to 3pm. Publication of books, sheet music, CDs, production of sheet music, distribution of music publications (books, sheet music, CDs), collection of contemporary Croatian scores which have not been published.*

Czech Republic

* **Czech Music Information Centre.** Besední 3, Praha 1 CZ-11800 Praha 1, Czech Republic *tel:* +420 257 312 422/313 717 *fax:* +420 257 317 424 *email:* his@vol.cz. Miroslav Pudlák, director; Matej Kratochvil, editor of 'Czech Music'.

Denmark

Danish Arts Council. Kunststyrelsen, KGS Nytorv 3, Box 9012, Copenhagen K DK-1022, Denmark *tel:* +45 33 744500 *fax:* +45 33 744519 *email:* musik@kunststyrelsen.dk. *Advises and assists public authorities and institutions in music-related matters. Promotes musical life in Denmark and Danish music abroad. National Committee of IMC.*

Jazzcentret/-kontakten. Borupvej 66, Ronnede DK-4683, Denmark *fax:* +45 567 11 749 *email:* jazzpar@mail.tele.dk. Arnvid Meyer, president; Cim Meyer, manager. *Jazzkontakten has been established to promote jazz music. One of the organisation's major projects, the JAZZPAR Prize, includes the world's biggest annual jazz award, a concert series, CD releases, radio and TV transmissions etc.*

Estonia

Estonian Music Council. Suur-Karja 23, Tallinn EE-10148, Estonia *tel:* +372 644 9931 *fax:* +372 644 9931 *email:* emn@kul.ee. Peep Lassmann, president. *Independent non-governmental organisation which, as the representative body of musicians, connects the musical institutions of Estonia. Composed of 47 members representing Estonian institutions and organisations in the field of music and 20 personal members. The mission of the Estonian Music Council is to propagate Estonian music in all forms, to encourage co-operation among Estonian musicians; to protect their rights and to promote and facilitate Estonian representation in international music life.*

Finland

Finland Festivals. Uudenmaankatu 36 D 21, Helsinki FIN-00120, Finland *tel:* +358 9 612 6760 *fax:* +358 9 612 67610 *email:* info@festivals.fi. Tuomo Tirkkonen, general director; Riitta Kerman, press officer. *Produces and distributes a catalogue containing dates, addresses and a short description of 69 different Finnish festivals.*

* **Finnish Music Information Centre.** Lauttasaarentie 1, Helsinki FIN-00200, Finland *tel:* +358 9 6810 1313 *fax:* +358 9 682 0770 *email:* info@mic.teosto.fi. Kai Amberla, executive director. *The Finnish MIC promotes and supplies information on Finnish composers and their music as well as Finnish music life in general. The activities cover all genres of music from classical to rock. FIMIC answers enquiries, supplies music not available in print from the music library of about 30,000 works, publishes promotional material and takes part in exhibitions and trade fairs. The extensive sound archive and the collection of press cuttings are available to the media, researchers, etc.*

Finnish Performing Music Promotion Centre (ESEK). Pieni Roobertinkatu 16, Helsinki FIN-00120, Finland *tel:* +358 9 6803 4040 *fax:* +358 9 6803 4033 *email:* esek@gramex.fi. Leena Hirvonen, secretary general. *Supports Finnish performing music projects and provides information about Finnish artists.*

France

* **Centre de Documentation de la Musique Contemporaine.** 16 Place de la Fontaine aux Lions, Paris F-75019, France *tel:* +33 1 47 15 47 15/49 86 (secretary) *fax:* +33 1 47 15 49 89 *email:* cdmc@cdmc.asso.fr. Marianne Lyon, director; Isabelle Gauchet, documentation dept. *Documentation and information on contemporary composers, works, organisations, etc. Scores, recordings, books, theses, articles, reviews of contemporary music, published and unpublished.*

National Music Committee (France) (CNM). 91 Rue Jouffroy d'Abbans, Paris F-75017, France *tel:* +33 1 42 27 07 31 *fax:* +33 1 42 27 07 31. Michel Decoust, president; Michel Bourguignon, treasurer; Edouard Labesse, secretary. *Member of International Music Council (IMC). Reports on music education, authors, publishers and performers' rights.*

Republic of Georgia

* **Georgian Music Information Centre.** 123 Agmashenebeli Ave, Tbilisi 380064, Republic of Georgia *tel:* +995 32 954861 *fax:* +995 32 968678 *email:* geomic@mail.ru. Natela Mamaladze, director; Svetlana Kervalishvili, chief editor; Nino Mamaladze, translator/interpreter; George Goglidze, computer operator. *Main aim is to promote Georgian music at home and abroad. Issue magazine 'Musical Georgia' in both Georgian and English; pamphlets about composers; Georgian music database; annual festival 'Novelty of Georgian Music'.*

Germany

Dresden Centre of Contemporary Music (DZzM). Karl-Liebknecht-Str 56, Dresden D-01109, Germany *tel:* +49 351 264620 *fax:* +49 351 264 6223 *email:* ernesti@zeitmusik.de. Udo Zimmermann, director; Marc Ernesti, PR manager. *Non-profit institution dedicated to the promotion of new music, acting as a music information centre for East Germany.*

Archives, documentation, department of musicology and Research Centre for Exiled Music. Major festival 'Dresden Days of Contemporary Music' in October.

European Music Council. Weberstr 59 A, Bonn D-53113, Germany *tel:* +49 228 96 69 96 64 *fax:* +49 228 96 69 96 65 *email:* info@european-music-council.org. *Platform for representatives of the National Music Councils and all organisations involved in the field of music education, creation, performance and heritage from all European countries.*

* **German Music Information Centre.** c/o German Music Council, Weberstr 59, Bonn D-53113, Germany *tel:* +49 228 209 1180 *fax:* +49 228 209 1280 *email:* info@miz.org. Margot Wallscheid, managing director; Joachim-Felix Leonhard, chairman of advisory committee. *Part of the German Music Council. Provides information on all aspects of music life in Germany. Includes music education and vocational training; promotional facilities; music research and documentation; music in the media, etc. Triennially publishes the 'Musik Almanach', the central reference book with facts and figures on musical life in Germany.*

Hong Kong

Hong Kong Arts Development Council. 22/F, 181 Queen's Road Central, Hong Kong *tel:* +852 2 827 8786 *fax:* +852 2 519 9301 *email:* hkadc@hkadc.org.hk. Albert Lam, chief executive. *Established to plan, promote and support the broad development of the arts and to improve the participation and education in, and knowledge, practice, appreciation, accessibility and informed criticism of the arts, with a view to improving the life of the whole community. Provides grants to arts organisations and artists in Hong Kong.*

Hungary

Hungarian Music Society. Pusztaszeri ut 30, Budapest H-1025, Hungary *tel:* +36 1 325 7313 *fax:* +36 1 325 7313. Jànos Devich, president; Ester Agghàzy, admin (+36 1 466 0543). *Aims to foster cultivation of Hungarian music, to promote the interests of musical artists, to educate young people's musical taste, and to preserve Hungarian music past and present.*

Iceland

* **Iceland Music Information Centre.** Sídumúli 34, Reykjavík IS-108 Reykjavík, Iceland *tel:* +354 568 3122 *fax:* +354 568 3124 *email:* itm@mic.is. Sigfridur Bjornsdottir, director; Ulfhildur Indridadottir, publications. *Information on Icelandic music, sound recordings and printed material. Music library with sheet music, hire material and catalogues. Information and services to the public, performers and composers. Publication of CDs and sheet music.*

India

National Music Committee (India). 12 K Dubash Marg, Bombay 400 023, India *tel:* +91 22 2284 4420/4782 *fax:* +91 22 2204 0806 *email:* bom.anparikh@lemuir.com. Arvind Parikh, co-ordinator for the Indian sub-continent IMC; (UNESCO).

Iran

National Music Committee (Iran). Iranian Music Centre, Ministry of Culture and Islamic Orientation, Av Hafez - Av Arfa, Salle Vahdat, Teheran, Iran *tel:* +98 21 672 1108 *fax:* +98 21 670 3898 *email:* iccmusic@accir.com. Ali Moradkhani, director general.

Republic Ireland

* **Irish Contemporary Music Centre.** 19 Fishamble St, Temple Bar, Dublin 8, Republic of Ireland *tel:* +353 1 673 1922 *fax:* +353 1 648 9100 *email:* info@cmc.ie. Eve O'Kelly, director. *National archive and resource centre for new music used by performers, composers, promoters and members of the public. Supports the work of composers throughout the Republic and Northern Ireland. Library and sound archive contain the only comprehensive collection in existence of music by Irish composers.*

Israel

* **Israel Music Institute.** 24 Kibbutz Galuyot Road, Tel Aviv 68166, Israel *tel:* +972 3 681 1010 *fax:* +972 3 681 6070 *email:* musicinst@bezeqint.net. Paul Landau, director. *Non-profit organisation supported by Israel Ministry of Education and Culture. Aims to publish and promote Israeli music. Information Centre has regular gatherings of composers and musicians and has ties with over 30 countries.*

National Council for Culture and the Arts. Ministry of Education, Culture and Sport, Kanfei Nesharim St 22, Jerusalem 91911, Israel *tel:* +972 2 560 1741 *fax:* +972 2 560 1568 *email:* raaya@most.gov.il. Raaya Simran, music department director. *A government institution supporting musical institutions and professional activities across the*

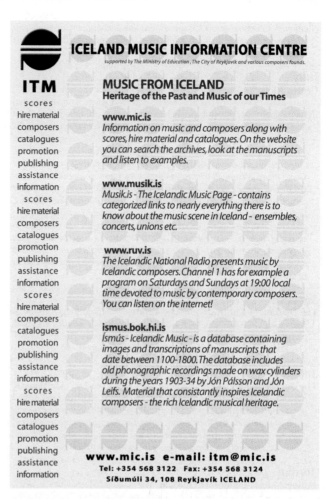
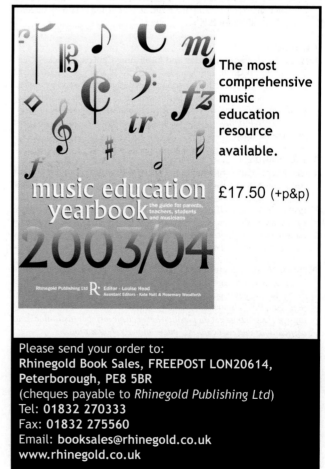

country. Commissions new compositions, encouraging the development of new projects. Also holds choir workshops and awards prizes for composers and performers.

Italy

Centro Ricerche Musicali (CRM). Via Lamarmora 18, Roma I-00185, Italy *tel:* +39 06 446 4161 *fax:* +39 06 446 7911 *email:* crm.it@usa.net. Laura Bianchini, director; Michelangelo Lupone, art director; Lorenzo Seno, scientific director. *Organiser of the yearly international forum for music, art and contemporary culture MUSICA SCIENZA; organiser of a weekly specialisation course in computer music on specific arguments, concerts, sound art installations based on planephones, holophones, sound pipes. Advanced technology centre for music research in Europe. CRM has made significant contributions to the fields of musical composition, psycho-acoustics, musicology and musical informatics, including the design and construction of original devices for analysis, synthesis and processing in real time and multiphonic sound diffusion systems such as planephones, and holophones. Collaborates with important instrumental groups and musical institutions. Realises complex electroacoustic works in concerts and workshops, conferences worldwide.*

Jamaica

The Division of Culture. Caenwood Centre, 37 Arnold Rd, Kingston 5, Jamaica *tel:* +1 876 967 4975 *fax:* +1 876 967 4975 *email:* edcultur@cwjamaica.com. Sydney Bartley, director of culture; Hillary Brown, Cariforum project; Carlinton Duncan, technical support officer.

Japan

The Japan Foundation. Performing Arts Division, 1-12-32 Akasaka, Minato-ku, Tokyo 107-6020, Japan *tel:* +81 3 5562 3530 *fax:* +81 3 5562 3500 *email:* koenka@jpf.go.jp. Atsushi Kanai, director. *Semi-government organisation designed to promote cultural exchange between Japan and the rest of the world. Awards grants towards artists' international travel costs. Occasionally organises Japanese music-related events.*

Jordan

National Music Committee (Jordan). The National Music Conservatory, PO Box 926687, Amman 11110, Jordan *tel:* +962 6 568 7620/560 5772 *fax:* +962 6 568 7621 *email:* nmc@go.com.jo. Kifah Fakhouri, director of NMC, president of IMC.

Lithuania

* **Lithuanian Music Information and Publishing Centre.** A Mickeviciaus 29, Vilnius LT-2600, Lithuania *tel:* +370 5 272 6986 *fax:* +370 5 212 0939 *email:* info@mic.lt. Daiva Parulskiene, director; Linas Paulauskis, project manager. *Documents and promotes contemporary Lithuanian music. Publishes scores, runs archives of manuscripts and recordings, provides information on Lithuanian composers and releases promotional CDs.*

Luxembourg

* **Luxembourg Music Information Centre (Luxemburger Gesellschaft für Neue Musik).** BP 828 L-2018, Luxembourg *tel:* +352 22 5821 *fax:* +352 22 5823 *email:* info@mic.lu. Marcel Wengler, director; Luc Rollinger, liaison officer. *The homepage of the Luxembourg Music Information Centre gives information about the musical life of Luxembourg and provides access to the repertoire of works by Luxembourgish composers. Music samples can also be downloaded, for listening in CD quality.*

National Music Committee (Luxembourg). 20 Montée de la Pétrusse, L-2912, Luxembourg-Grund *tel:* +352 51 99 50/4 78 66 18 *fax:* +352 29 55 51/21 86 *email:* pol.schmoetten@mcesr.lu. Alexander Mullenbach, president; Pol Schmoetten, secretary general. *Aims for the promotion of music in Luxembourg; co-operation between the member institutions and associations and associations; international co-operation.*

Union Grand-Duc Adolphe Asbl (Fédération Nationale de Musique du Grand-Duché de Luxembourg). 2 Rue Sosthène Weis, Luxembourg-Grund L-2722, Luxembourg *tel:* +352 46 25 36 1 *fax:* +352 47 14 40 *email:* direction@ugda.lu. Robert Weyland, president. *National Music Federation of Luxembourg.*

Mexico

Colegio de Compositores Latinoamericanos de Música de Arte (Mexico). Cerro de la Luz 199, Col. Romero de Terreros, Coyoacán CP 04310, Mexico, D. F. *tel:* +5255 5659 9505 *fax:* +5255 5659 9506 *email:* madeli39@prodigy.net.mx. Manuel de Elías, founder and president; Celso Garrido-Lecca, secretary; Marlos Nobre, pro-secretary.

Concerts and recordings, radio programmes, conferences (lectures) always with compositions of the members (20) of the Colegio. Activities in Mexico and the other latin-american member's countries.

Netherlands

European Association of Artists Managers. Pieter G Alferink Artists Management B. V., Herengracht 340, Amsterdam 1016 CG, Netherlands *tel:* +31 20 664 31 51 *fax:* +31 20 675 24 26 *email:* info@alferink.org. Theo van den Bogaard, managing director; Pieter G Alferlink, director; Helga Blaimschein, artist manager; Sabine Rieck, artist manager; Marion Savenije, company secretary. *Non-profit organisation which aims to protect the interests of classical music managers and their artists. Also promotes the exchange of knowledge between its members.*

European Association of Conservatoires, Academies de Musique and Musikhochschulen. ACE Office, PO Box 805, Utrecht NL-3500 AV, Netherlands *tel:* +31 30 236 1242 *fax:* +31 30 236 1290 *email:* aecinfo@aecinfo.org. Ian Horsbrugh, president; Martin Prchal, chief executive; Janneke Vrijland, office manager; Sofie Truwant, project assistant. *Represents the interests of those institutions which are concerned with training for the music profession. This is achieved by exchanges, joint activities and projects and the benefits of these activities are shared with all members. The AEC includes representatives from 190 institutions in 46 countries. The main activities include an annual Congress held in November in a different country each year.*

European Conference of Promoters of New Music. c/o Gaudeamus Foundation, Swammerdamstraat 38, Amsterdam 1091 RV, Netherlands *tel:* +31 20 694 7349 *fax:* +31 20 694 7258 *email:* info@ecpnm.com. Helmut Erdmann, president; Henk Heuvelmans, secretary. *Umbrella organisation for concert and festival organisers and music information centres in the field of contemporary music. Publishes a calendar of new music events.*

* **Gaudeamus Foundation.** Swammerdamstraat 38, Amsterdam 1091 RV, Netherlands *tel:* +31 20 694 7349 *fax:* +31 20 694 7258 *email:* info@gaudeamus.nl. Henk Heuvelmans, director. *Centre for contemporary music. Library of scores, records and CDs, periodicals. General information about contemporary music; organiser of concerts and festivals.*

International Society for Contemporary Music. Swammerdamstraat 38, Amsterdam 1091 RV, Netherlands *tel:* +31 20 694 7349 *fax:* +31 20 694 7258 *email:* info@iscm.nl. Henk Heuvelmans, secretary general. *International umbrella organisation with 49 member countries. Annual General Assembly and festival: ISCM World Music Days. Publisher of 'World New Music Magazine'.*

New Zealand

* **The Centre for New Zealand Music Ltd (SOUNZ New Zealand).** PO Box 10 042, 39 Cambridge Terrace, Wellington, New Zealand *tel:* +64 4 801 8602 *fax:* +64 4 801 8604 *email:* info@sounz.org.nz. Scilla Askew, executive director; Pascale Parenteau, information services executive. *Promotes New Zealand composers and their music. Services include: library, website, free newsletter, database (250 composers and 6000 works), catalogues, sales of scores, recordings and reference books. Study guides and workshops of New Zealand music; also promotional CDs. Funded by Creative New Zealand and APRA.*

Norway

* **Musikkinformasjonssenteret.** Tollbugata 28, Oslo N-0157, Norway *tel:* +47 22 42 90 90 *fax:* +47 22 42 90 91 *email:* info@mic.no. Morten Walderhaug, managing director; Hilde Holbaek-Hanssen, head of information; Lisbeth Risnes, head of admin; Torkild Hansen, head of production; Aslak Oppeboen, information executive, responsible for IT. *Provides information on Norwegian music; offers printing on demand from a manuscript library with 7000 works; arranges exhibitions. Resources include manuscript library, orchestral rental materials, reference library with study and listening rooms. Publishes news on Norwegian music on a daily basis at www.mic.no/english. Shares premises with the Norwegian Jazz Archives and the Norwegian Archives for Folk and Popular Song.*

Norwegian IMC Committee. Rikskonsertene, PO Box 2835 Solli, Oslo LNO-0204, Norway *tel:* +47 22 015 500 *fax:* +47 22 831 610 *email:* post@rikskonsertene.no. Einar Solbu, chief executive officer. *Responsible for the Norwegian representation in the IMC and its European branch, the EMC. Committee advises on music matters and provides information about the Norwegian music organisations that participate in international music life.*

Philippines

National Music Committee (Philippines). National Commission for Culture and the Arts, 633 General Luna St, Intramuros, Manila 1002, Philippines *tel:* +632 527 2209/2197/2192 *fax:* +632 527 2191/4/8 *email:* info@ncca.gov.ph. Ramon Santos, chairman; Corazon Dioquino, vice-chairman; Emilie Tiongco, deputy executive director. *Exists to develop and enrich the musical ability of Filipinos as creators or audience through education, performance, promoting the works of Filipino composers and researching musical traditions. Produces media and educational materials and organises promotional projects. Grants programme to assist Filipino musicians and scholars to contribute to the national cultural development thrust of the government.*

Portugal

* **Fundaçao Calouste Gulbenkian.** Ave de Berna 45 A, Lisboa 1067-001, Portugal *tel:* +351 21 782 3000 *fax:* +351 21 782 3041 *email:* musica@gulbenkian.pt. Luis Pereira Leal, director. *The foundation supports culture within Portugal and can also provide aid for Portuguese culture in other countries.*

Russia

Centre for Russian Music. Music Department, Goldsmiths College, University of London, New Cross, London SE14 6NW, UK *tel:* +44 20 7919 7646 (CRM); +44 20 7717 2275 (Alfred Schnittke Archive) *fax:* +44 20 7919 7247 *email:* a.ivashkin@gold.ac.uk. Alexander Ivashkin, centre director, curator of the Alfred Schnittke Archive; Noelle Mann, curator of the Serge Prokofiev Archive; Dmitri Smirnov; Razia Sultanova; Rosamund Bartlett. *Promotes research, publication and performance of Russian music in the West.*

Serbia

Yugoslav Music Information Centre (SOKOJ -MIC). Misarska St 12-14, Beograd 11000, Serbia *tel:* +381 11 324 5192 *fax:* +381 11 323 6168 *email:* sokojmic@eunet.yu. Marija Cvijanovic, acting manager (full time); Natasa Danilovic, advanced editor for composers' database (full time); Asja Drndic, secretary of the International Magazine for Music 'New Sound' (full time). *Music archive, library. 'New Sound', international magazine for music. Small concerts in 60-seat hall.*

Slovak Republic

* **Music Centre Slovakia.** Michalská 10, Bratislava 1 815 36, Slovak Republic *tel:* +421 2 5443 4561/4003 *fax:* +421 2 5920 4822/26; 2 5443 0379 *email:* hc@hc.sk. Ol'ga Smetanová, director. *Organises concerts and festivals; publishes sheet music and books; documentation of musical life in Slovakia.*

Spain

* **Centro de Documentación de Música y Danza INAEM.** c/o Torregalindo 10, Madrid E-28016, Spain *tel:* +34 91 353 1480/1370 *fax:* +34 91 353 1373 *email:* cdmyd@inaem.mcu.es. Antonio Álvarez Cañibano, director. *Directory and database of music and dance resources in Spain. ISMN Spanish Agency. Spanish ISMN database. Yearbook of Dance in Spain (since 1998) (4 vols and database). Musical World Premieres in Spain (since 1985) database. Musical Instruments in Spanish Collections (2 vols and database). Bibliography of Music in Spain (1991-1997) (3 vols and database).*

Sweden

Svenska Musikradet (The Swedish Music Council). c/o Jan Olof Rudén, Västerasgatan 8, Stockholm S-113 43, Sweden *tel:* +46 8 33 83 69/070 445 77 37 *email:* jan.olof.ruden@chello.se. Martin Martinsson, president; Jan Olof Rudén, secretary. *An umbrella organisation for music organisations and institutions in Sweden. It serves as the Swedish national committee of the IMC.*

* **Swedish Music Information Centre.** Box 27327, 79 Sandhamnsgatan, Stockholm S-102 54, Sweden *tel:* +46 8 783 8800 *fax:* +46 8 783 9510 *email:* swedmic@stim.se. Roland Sandberg, executive director. *Hire library and mail order service for unpublished, copyright-protected sheet music. Hire library of electroacoustic music, historical popular sheet music collection, listening room with published sheet music, commercial and tape recordings, literature about Swedish music and musical life, information service about composers and works. Own publishing house: Edition Suecia. Record society: Phono Suecia.*

Switzerland

European Festivals Association - Music, Theatre, Dance. Château de Coppet, C.P. 26, Coppet CH-1296, Switzerland *tel:* +41 22 776 8673 *fax:* +41 22 776 4275 *email:* castle.coppet@euro-festival.net. Tamas Klenjanszky, secretary general; Karine Ven, executive secretary. *Aims to promote significance of festivals through common publicity, to maintain and develop high artistic quality of festivals and emphasise their important role in international cultural co-operation.*

* **SUISA Foundation for Music.** Rue de l'Hôpital 22, Neuchatel CH-2000, Switzerland *tel:* +41 32 725 25 36 *fax:* +41 32 724 04 72 *email:* info@fondation-suisa.ch. Claude Delley, director; Claude Hübscher, artist manager; Dominique Garcin, admin manager. *Encourages the composition of all styles of Swiss music; supports projects by Swiss composers; backs the work of music publishers who encourage the musical creations of Swiss composers; publishes and distributes record anthologies containing all types of music in order to ensure the diffusion of the widest possible range of musical creation; undertakes the promotion of Swiss music both at home and abroad.*

Swiss Council of Music and Swiss Music Information Centre. Haus der Musik, Gönhardweg 32, Aarau CH-5000, Switzerland *tel:* +41 62 822 9423 *fax:* +41 62 822 9407 *email:* musikrat@aarauonline.ch. Alois Koch, president; Ursula Bally-Fahr, secretary general. *Represents the whole of Swiss musical life in its capacity as an umbrella organisation for all national organisations and associations. Four main issues: Jugend and Musik, cultural policy, music education, and co-operation with European music organisations.*

World Federation of International Music Competitions. 104 Rue de Carouge, Geneve CH-1205, Switzerland *tel:* +41 22 321 3620 *fax:* +41 22 781 1418 *email:* fmcim@iprolink.ch. Renate Ronnefeld, secretary general; Lottie Chalut, executive secretary. *Co-ordinates and promotes the activities of 112 major music competitions throughout the world, and publishes an annual calendar of competitions.*

Tunisia

National Music Committee (Tunisia). Ministry of Culture and Information, Rue du 2 Mars 1934, La Kasbah, Tunis, Tunisia *tel:* +216 71 496821 *fax:* +216 71 496821 *email:* mcu@ministeres.tu. Fehti Zghonda, secretary general.

Uruguay

National Music Committee (Uruguay) and Mercosur's Musical Documentation Centre (CEDOMM). Sarandi 450.P.4, Montevido CP 11000, Uruguay *tel:* +598 2 915 6417 *fax:* +598 2 915 5815 *email:* cedomm@adinet.com.uy. Maria Tania Siver, delegate.

USA

* **American Music Center.** 30 West 26th St, Suite 1001, New York NY 10010-2011, USA *tel:* +1 212 366 5260 *fax:* +1 212 366 5265 *email:* center@amc.net. Richard Kessler, executive director. *Promotes the creation, performance and appreciation of American contemporary music, through information services, a library of scores and recordings, a monthly on-line magazine, grant programmes, professional development workshops, catalogue of new American music for young audiences, and advocacy on behalf of American music.*

National Music Committee (USA). 425 Park St, Montclair NJ 07043, USA *tel:* +1 973 655 7974 *fax:* +1 973 655 5432 *email:* sandersd@mail.montclair.edu. David Sanders, director. *Founded in 1940 to provide a forum for the discussion of the country's national music affairs. Aims to strengthen the importance of music in American culture.*

Music Information Centres
Documenting and promoting new music worldwide

British Music Information Centre
I0 Stratford Place London W1C 1BA
tel: +44 (0)20 7499 8567 fax: +44 (0)20 7499 4795
Open to the public Mon - Fri 12 - 5pm
email: info@bmic.co.uk *web:* www.bmic.co.uk
Extensive collection: scores, recordings, composer info.
Online facilities: scores and recordings, contacts, news.
Scores to purchase. Concerts in London and nationally.

*nurturing the composition and
performance of new Irish music*

Contemporary Music Centre
19 Fishamble Street, Temple Bar, Dublin 8, Ireland
tel: +353 1 673 1922 fax: +353 1 648 9100
Open to the public Mon - Fri 10 - 5.30pm
email: info@cmc.ie *website:* www.cmc.ie
Comprehensive library and sound archive
Reference and consultancy services
CD shop, Directory of Irish composers

Welsh Music Information Centre
Tŷ Cerdd, 15 Mount Stuart Square,
Cardiff CF10 5DP

Canolfan Hysbysrwydd Cerddoriaeth Cymru
Tŷ Cerdd, 15 Sgwâr Mount Stuart,
Caerdydd CF10 5DP

Phone/Ffôn: +44(0)29 2046 2855
e-mail/e-bost: wmic@tycerdd.org Web: www.tycerdd.org

Open to the public Mon - Fri 10.00am - 6.00pm
Promoting Welsh Music through archiving, publishing and performance
Links with Welsh Music Organisations through Tŷ Cerdd (Music Centre Wales)
Moving to the new Wales Millennium Centre in Autumn 2004 where
the Welsh Music Information Centre will house a recording studio, library & IT research suite.

SCOTTISH MUSIC CENTRE

A gateway to the complete Scottish music resource, a supporter and promoter of all of Scotland's music

Online and Data Services
Retail and Hire Services
Membership Services
Education & Outreach Facilities
Music and Recordings Collection
Information & Advice & Consultancy
Promotions, Publications, Recordings & Project Management

Open to public Mon-Fri. For further details please contact :
1 Bowmont Gardens, Glasgow G12 9LR
t: +44 (0) 141 334 6393
f: +44 (0) 141 337 1161
e: info@scottishmusiccentre.com
w: www.scottishmusiccentre.com

The
International
Association
of Music
Information
Centres

a world-wide network of organisations promoting new music

www.iamic.net

Associations

This list includes musical societies devoted to a named composer or instrument. Organisations for and on behalf of people with disabilities (including organisations for the practice of music therapy) are grouped together in a separate list immediately following this section (*see* **Music and Disability**). The **Musicians' Union** regional offices are listed at the end of this section.

Access to Music. 18 York Rd, Leicester LE1 5TS *tel:* 0800 281842 *fax:* 0116 255 1938 *email:* info@access-to-music.co.uk. Alan Ramsey, mkt mgr; contact: mkt team. *A national mus training organisation and consultancy service specialising in the design of innovative training programmes which focus on rock, pop and other contemporary mus styles. Operating in 23 centres across England, offering vocational programmes which cater for musicians at all stages of their career, from basic tuition to level 4 programmes plus mus teaching qualifications (see* **Colleges of FE** *for partnership colleges).*

The Agents' Association (Great Britain). 54 Keyes House, Dolphin Square, London SW1V 3NA *tel:* 020 7834 0515 *fax:* 020 7821 0261 *email:* association@agents-uk.com. Carol Richards, admin. *Professional trade association for agents in the entertainment industry. Functions primarily for the benefit of members, but activities cover the whole entertainment business, where it provides a collective voice for negotiations with government depts, trade unions and other relevant bodies. An active part is also played in consultation with government prior to any parliamentary legislation affecting theatrical employment agencies.*

Alan Bush Music Trust. 7 Harding Way, Histon, Cambridge CB4 9JH *tel:* 01223 232659 *email:* info@alanbushtrust.org.uk. Rachel O'Higgins, hon sec; Maeve O'Higgins, chair; Paul O'Higgins, treasurer; Catherine Hinson, publicity sec; Michael Hinson, ed 'Clarion'; Julia Sanders. *Promotes the mus of Alan Bush through information resources, projects and events. Publishes annual newsletter 'Clarion' and regular e-letter.*

Alkan Society. 42 St Alban's Hill, Hemel Hempstead, Herts HP3 9NG *tel:* 01442 262895 *email:* secretary@alkansociety.org. Nicholas King, vice president, sec; Ronald Smith, president; Hugh MacDonald, vice president; Richard Shaw, vice president. *Founded in 1977. Publishes a bulletin 4 times pa, also discography.*

Arnold (Malcolm) Society. 6 Walton St, Barnsley, S Yorks S75 2PE *tel:* 01226 284116 *fax:* 01226 284116 *email:* KEITH.MASOC6@tiscali.co.uk. Keith Llewellyn, hon sec. *Exists to promote the mus of Sir Malcolm Arnold. Quarterly newsletter, concert details, reviews and details of recorded mus.*

Arts Marketing Association. 7a Clifton Court, Cambridge CB1 7BN *tel:* 01223 578078 *fax:* 01223 245862 *email:* info@a-m-a.co.uk. Pam Henderson, dir. *National body open to anyone involved in promoting the arts and cultural industries. Keeping members up-to-date with new developments and providing a network to share solutions and problems through training, events, publications, a website, and a quarterly journal.*

Arts and Business. Nutmeg House, 60 Gainsford St, Butlers Wharf, London SE1 2NY *tel:* 020 7378 8143 *fax:* 020 7407 7527 *email:* head.office@AandB.org.uk. Colin Tweedy OBE, chief exec. *Offers a range of programmes to develop partnerships between the business and arts communities. Runs programmes which place business volunteers in arts and heritage organisations. Operates New Partners, a government funded programme which invests money in partnerships between business and arts organisations. Invites businesses to become members of Arts and Business and operates regional Development Forums for arts professionals around the UK. Commisions research to explore the future developments of business and arts relationships.*

Arts & Business Cymru (North Wales Office). Room 5, 1-2 Chapel St, Llandudno LL30 2SY *tel:* 01492 574003 *email:* cymru@AandB.org.uk. Lorraine Hopkins, mgr.

Arts & Business Cymru (South Wales Office). 16 Museum Place, Cardiff CF10 3BH *tel:* 029 2030 3023 *fax:* 029 2030 3024 *email:* cymru@AandB.org.uk. Rachel Jones, dir.

Arts & Business Scotland. 6 Randolph Cres, Edinburgh EH3 7TH *tel:* 0131 220 2499 *fax:* 0131 220 2296 *email:* scotland@AandB.org.uk. Barclay Price, dir. *Provides services and advice to the business and arts communities on business sponsorship; runs Professional Development Programme, the government's New Partners programme and promotes business support of the arts.*

Associated Board of the Royal Schools of Music. 24 Portland Place, London W1B 1LU *tel:* 020 7636 5400 *fax:* 020 7637 0234 *email:* abrsm@abrsm.ac.uk. Richard Morris, chief exec; Richard Crozier, dir of professional development; Philip Mundey, dir of examinations. *The Associated Board offers a graded system of mus exams from preparatory level to professional diploma. Exams are offered in 35 insts, jazz pno, jazz ens, singing, choral singing, practical musicianship and theory. Over 600,000 candidates are examined each year in more than 90 countries. A Professional Development Course is available for inst and singing teachers, leading to the qualification of CT ABRSM.*

Association of British Choral Directors (ABCD). 15 Granville Way, Sherborne, Dorset DT9 4AS *tel:* 01935 389482 *fax:* 0870 128 4085 *email:* rachel.greaves@abcd.org.uk. Rachel Greaves, gen sec; Andrew Potter, chair. *Regional and national events including choral conducting training w/shops (beginners, intermediate, advanced), extended choral conducting courses at all levels, suitable for RCO choral conducting diploma students. M/classes, open rehearsals, discussion forums, repertoire and vocal technique seminars, residential convention. Non-members welcome. Annual Choral Directors' Convention in Exeter, 27-29 Aug 2004; fees on application; open to any age. Young Choral Conductors' Convention, Exeter, 27-29 Aug 2004; open to those aged 17-22 not earning their living from conducting.*

Association of British Jazz Musicians. 1st Floor, 132 Southwark St, London SE1 0SW *tel:* 020 7928 9089 *email:* education@jazzservices.org.uk. Adrian MacIntosh, chair. *Represents the interests of jazz musicians in the UK who are members of the Musicians' Union.*

Association of British Orchestras. 8 Gerrard St, London W1D 5PJ *tel:* 020 7287 0333 *fax:* 020 7287 0444 *email:* info@abo.org.uk. Russell Jones, dir; Adam Powell, projects mgr. *Representation of the collective interests of professional UK orchs: conferences, seminars, negotiation, training and general advocacy.*

Association of English Singers and Speakers. Paddocks, Park Lane, Ashtead, Surrey KT21 1HD *tel:* 01372 275430 *fax:* 01372 275430 *email:* NivnMiller@aol.com. Niven Miller, chmn. *Aims to encourage the communication of English words in speech and song with clarity, understanding and imagination. M/classes given, plus annual ABSS National Patricia Routledge English Song Competition (under 30; prizes of £1000, £500, £250 and accompanists prize of £250) and National Junior Competition for English Song (age 16 and under for girls, 18 and under for boys; prizes in association with the British and International Federation of Festivals of £750 scholarship and £250 scholarship).*

Association of Heads of Independent Schools. St Mary's School, Packhorse Rd, Gerrards Cross, Bucks SL0 8JQ *tel:* 01753 883370 *fax:* 01753 890966 *email:* headmistress@stmarys-gx.org. Fanny Balcombe, chmn. *Member schools, accredited by ISJC, tend to be small all-ability schools, both boarding, weekly boarding and day.*

Association of Irish Choirs. 4 Drinan St, Cork, Ireland *tel:* 00 353 21 431 2296 *fax:* 00 353 21 496 2457 *email:* info@cnc.ie. Margaret O'Sullivan, exec dir; Sonya Owers, admin; Gay Elmes, asst admin; Liz Nolan, educ and outreach offr. *Established in 1980 to promote choral mus and singing. Organises annual summer school and other courses; publishes choral mus; administers the Irish Youth Choir; issues newsletter 'In-Choir'. Library lending service. Supporting choral activity in Ireland.*

Association of Professional Music Therapists. 26 Hamlyn Rd, Glastonbury, Somerset BA6 8HT *tel:* 01458 834919 *fax:* 01458 834919 *email:* APMToffice@aol.com. Diana Asbridge, admin. *Deals with the needs of professional mus therapists in relation to standards of practice, employment career structure, training, etc.*

Association of Professional Recording Services Ltd (APRS). PO Box 22, Totnes TQ9 7YZ *tel:* 01803 868600 *fax:* 01803 868444 *email:* info@aprs.co.uk. Francesca Smith, chief admin; Peter Filleul, acting exec dir; Phil Dudderidge, chmn. *Trade association for businesses and individuals involved in professional sound recording, post production and associated fields; organises regular industry events and training initiatives.*

ASSOCIATION OF BRITISH ORCHESTRAS

Association of British Orchestras

The ABO exists to support, develop and advance the interests and activities of Orchestras. It seeks to influence aand improve the enviroment in which orchestras operate and to ensure they flourish and achieve their maximum potential

More than concert halls...

British Orchestras are unique and the envy of the world. The quality and diversity of thier work is formidable and is to be found in the world's great concert halls; festivals; recording, radio and television studios; stately homes; arenas; cathedrals and churches; parks; schools; colleges; community centers; prisons, hospitals and many more.

ABO
8 Gerrard Street
London WID 5PJ
info@abc.org.uk
www.abo.org.uk
020 7287 0333

More than concerts...

British Orchestras give amongst the finest performances of symphonic and chamber music repertoire in the world. However, beyond the concert platform orchestras undertake recordings of all kind; television programmes and documentaries; education work with school children and students; outreach projects with underprivileged secotors of the community; the elderly; people with disabilities; the business community and many more.

More than buying a ticket...

British Orchestras work continually to ensure they serve all sectors of their community. Music knows no barriers and everyone is invited to participate with the many activities of thier local orchestra.

ASSOCIATION of BRITISH ORCHESTRAS

Association of Teachers and Lecturers (ATL). 7 Northumberland St, London WC2N 5RD *tel:* 020 7930 6441 *fax:* 020 7930 1359 *email:* info@atl.org.uk. Mary Bousted, gen sec. *Provides over 150,000 members (5000 mus teachers) with full trade union services. Also curriculum development.*

Association of Teachers of Singing. Weir House, 108 Newton Rd, Burton upon Trent, Staffs DE15 0TT *tel:* 01283 542198 *fax:* 01283 542198 *email:* coralgould7@aol.com. Coral Gould, sec; Hazel Wood, chmn 2003-2004. *For qualified teachers of singing; holds annual 3-day conference in Jul in different venues; 1-day conference in Mar/Nov in London; teacher training course in Aug.*

Association of University Teachers. Egmont House, 25-31 Tavistock Place, London WC1H 9UT *tel:* 020 7670 9700 *fax:* 020 7670 9799 *email:* hq@aut.org.uk. Sally Hunt, gen sec. *Professional association and trade union which exists to maintain academic excellence and to protect the interests of its members. 46,000+ members are academic and academic-related staff in HE institutions (this includes mus conservatoires and university mus depts).*

Association of University Teachers (Scotland and Northumbria). 6 Castle St, Edinburgh EH2 3AT *tel:* 0131 226 6694 *fax:* 0131 226 2066 *email:* scotland&ne@aut.org.uk. David Bleiman, asst gen sec; Tony Axon, research offr; Lesley Little, admin offr. *Professional association for academic and related staff in universities.*

Association of Woodwind Teachers. 90 Becmead Ave, Kenton, Middx HA3 8HB *tel:* 020 8907 8428; 07730 314152 *fax:* 020 8907 8428. Angela Fussell, chmn. *Promotes and encourages high standards of w/wind teaching and gives support and practical help to w/wind teachers both specialist and general. Also encourages professional development through exchange of information and mutual support.*

Audio Engineering Society Ltd. PO Box 645, Slough SL1 8BJ *tel:* 01628 663725 *fax:* 01628 667002 *email:* uk@aes.org. Heather Lane, admin. *International society of 11,000 members in the world of audio. Over 700 members in British section.*

Australian Music Centre. 51b Dartmouth Rd, London NW2 4EP *tel:* 020 8208 1541 *fax:* 020 8208 1541 *email:* gray-dupuy@boltblue.com. Tony Gray, UK rep. *Object is to promote performance and awareness of Australian mus in Britain. Library of scores and recordings.*

Beecham (Sir Thomas) Trust. Castle House, 15 Earsham St, Bungay, Suffolk NR35 1AE *tel:* 01986 892111. Lady Shirley Beecham, trustee; A M Mackarel Davies, trustee; Christopher R Hopper MVO, chmn. *The provision of scholarships and awards at certain universities and mus institutions throughout the UK.*

Beethoven Piano Society of Europe. 28 Emperor's Gate, London SW7 4US *tel:* 020 7373 7307 *fax:* 020 7272 5440. Malcolm Troup, chmn; Maya Momcilovic Jordan, sec. *To promote performances of, and research into Beethoven's mus through competitions, w/shops, m/classes, lectures and recitals with young and established pianists alike. Publishes 'Arietta' and a quarterly newsletter.*

Benslow Music Trust. Little Benslow Hills, off Benslow Lane, Hitchin, Herts SG4 9RB *tel:* 01462 459446 *fax:* 01462 440171 *email:* info@benslow.org. David Matthews, dir of mus; Lisa Railton, chief exec. *Residential w/end, midweek and summer school courses for amateur musicians, students and teachers, aged 16+. Annual programme of over 100 different courses includes many for chmbr mus (strs, wind, pno, mixed), orchs of different standards, rcdrs, solo singing, choral, early mus, hp, big band, sax, etc. All directed and coached by leading professional musicians who, on selected courses, give public recitals in the Benslow Concerts Series. Course fees from £100. Limited amount of bursaries available for those in financial need. Brochure with full details on application or on website.*

Berkshire Young Musicians Trust. Stoneham Court, 100 Cockney Hill, Reading RG30 4EZ *tel:* 0118 901 2350 *fax:* 0118 901 2351 *email:* davidmarcou@bymt.org.uk. David Marcou, principal; Lady Solti, patron; Evelyn Glennie OBE, patron. *Provides a wide range of mus opportunities in schools, mus centres and at county level.*

Berlioz Society. 31 Doocot Rd, St Andrews, Fife KY16 8QP *tel:* 01334 474939 *email:* mmaustin@standrews.u-net.com. Michel Austin, sec; Monir Tayeb, sec; Brian Chenley, treasurer; David Cavins, chmn. *Founded in 1952. Main aims of the society: to bring together and provide a focal point for enthusiasts of the mus and writings of Berlioz; to foster a wide appreciation of Berlioz's mus and to encourage more frequent performances of it. Publishes a thrice yearly bulletin and a quarterly newsletter which are issued to individual and institutional members.*

BRITISH ARTS FESTIVALS ASSOCIATION

BAFA has a membership of over 100 Festivals, covering Music (Classical, Contemporary, Jazz, Folk, Opera), Theatre, Dance, Literature, Science, Street Arts and Multi-Discipline events.

We offer the public detailed information and advice on Festivals taking place all over the UK. We offer our members opportunities for contact and networking (through conferences, meetings, networking days, membership lists and group benefits) publicity, marketing and lobbying, research opportunities and reports, a place on the BAFA website, an annual Arts Festivals press pack, professional development courses, information and services.

If you would like to find out more about the work of the British Arts Festivals Association please check our website www.artsfestivals.co.uk,

3rd Floor, The Library, 77 Whitechapel High Street,
London, E1 7QX
Tel: 020 7247 4667 Fax: 020 7247 5010
info@artsfestivals.co.uk
www.artsfestivals.co.uk

BRITISH CHORAL INSTITUTE
Director: Dr Roy Wales

Some 2004 Choral Events

Friday, February 27 - Sunday, February 29	**CREATION (Joseph Haydn)** **Study Weekend** *In association with Emmaus Centre, West Wickham, Kent*
Friday, March 12	**AFRICAN SANCTUS (David Fanshawe)** **AFRICAN MASS (Norman Luboff)** *St John's, Smith Square* *In association with English Concert Singers*
Saturday, May 22	**GILBERT and SULLIVAN WORKSHOP** **One-day study/performance workshop on favourite choruses from G & S Operettas** **St. Nicholas Church, Brighton** **10.00 – 5.00** *In association with Brighton Festival Fringe*
Friday, June 18 - Sunday, June 20	**FRENCH CHORAL MUSIC WEEKEND** **including Duruflé 'Requiem', Fauré 'Requiem' and 'Cantique de Jean Racine', Poulenc Motets** *In association with West Dean College, Chichester*
Friday, September 17 - Sunday, September 19	**A CHILD OF OUR TIME (Michael Tippett)** **Study/performace weekend** **Alfriston, East Sussex**
Saturday, October 23	**RUTTER CHORAL MUSIC WORKSHOP** *In association with West Dean College, Chichester*

Further details of all events are available from
The Administrator, British Choral Institute
1 Bazehill Road, Rottingdean, Brighton BN2 7DB
Tel 01273 300894 Fax 01273 308394
E-mail: BritChorInst@fastnet.co.uk Website: www.BritishChoralInstitute.co.uk

The Bliss Trust. PO Box 21, Hereford HR1 3YQ *fax:* 01432 851773. Sarah Faulder, chmn. *To promote understanding and awareness of the mus of Sir Arthur Bliss through performance, recordings, research, academic writing and publication. Awards, prizes and scholarships are offered mainly through centres of learning and educ.*

Boughton (The Rutland) Music Trust. 25 Bearton Green, Hitchin, Herts SG5 1UN *tel:* 01462 434318; 07702 584152 *email:* Ianrboughton@ aol.com. Ian Boughton, admin; Vernon Handley, president; R Sherman Boughton, chmn; Michael Hurd, mus adviser. *Registered charity established in 1978 to promote the works of Rutland Boughton. Mailing list. Publicity leaflet and recordings list available on request.*

British Academy of Composers and Songwriters. British Music House, 26 Berners St, London W1T 3LR *tel:* 020 7636 2929 *fax:* 020 7636 2212 *email:* info@britishacademy.com. Julian Lancaster, head of classical relations. *Professional membership association representing the interests of mus writers of all genres. Quarterly newsletter, magazine and other printed information. Administers several major events, including the Ivor Novello Awards and the British Composer Awards.*

British Arts Festivals Association. 3rd Floor, Whitechapel Library, 77 Whitechapel High St, London E1 7QX *tel:* 020 7247 4667 *fax:* 020 7247 5010 *email:* info@artsfestivals.co.uk. Kevin Rainey, admin. *Aims to represent a full range of arts festivals. Activities include annual conference, professional development courses, arts festivals listings and website directory. Research report 'Festivals Mean Business' published 2001.*

British Association for Early Childhood Education (Early Education). 136 Cavell St, London, E1 2JA *tel:* 020 7539 5400 *fax:* 020 7539 5409 *email:* office@early-education.org.uk. Jenny Rabin, project mgr. *Promotes the right of all children to educ of the highest quality. Provides a multi-disciplinary network of support and advice for everyone concerned with the educ and care of young children from birth to age 8. Organises national conferences, seminars; publishes a termly journal and a newsletter 3 times a year, and publications on all aspects of early childhood educ and development.*

British Association of Christian Bands (Brass). Rosslyn House, 370 Bloomfield Rd, Odd Down, Bath BA2 2PD *tel:* 01225 832041 *email:* mikepriscottbath@aol.com. Mike Priscott, hon sec; Trevor Austin, hon chmn. *Brings Christian musicians together for fellowship and to learn from experienced conds. Branches in Andover, Daventry, Tyne and Wear and Faversham.*

British Association of Symphonic Bands and Wind Ensembles (BASBWE). 12 Wilshaw House, Creekside, Deptford, London SE8 4SF *tel:* 020 8469 2534 *email:* executiveofficer@basbwe.org. Martin Cope, exec offr; Alan Suttie, treasurer; Charles Hine, chmn; Sir Simon Rattle, president. *Promotes interest and activities in wind bands and ens nationwide. Quarterly publication 'Winds'. Manages the National Concert Band Festival.*

British Choral Institute. 1 Bazehill Rd, Rottingdean, Brighton BN2 7DB *tel:* 01273 300894 *fax:* 01273 308394 *email:* BritChorInst@fastnet.co.uk. Roy Wales, dir; Christine Wales, admin. *Advisory, promotional, educ and training body for choral singers, conds, administrators and organisers, with a special emphasis on developing international choral projects.*

The British Clavichord Society. 26a Church Lane, London N8 7BU *tel:* 020 8341 4700 *fax:* 020 8341 4700 *email:* JudithWardman@ compuserve.com. Judith Wardman, sec. *Encourages understanding and enjoyment of the clvd, promoting recitals and educ activities. Publishes a newsletter 3 times pa, and a directory of clvd information. M/order CDs, mus and books.*

British Copyright Council. 29-33 Berners St, London W1P 4AA *tel:* 01986 788122 *fax:* 01986 788847 *email:* copyright@bcc2.demon.co.uk. Janet Ibbotson, sec. *Liaison committee of professional associations, trade unions and collecting societies whose individual members own copyright in original literary, dramatic, musical and artistic works, together with publishers' and performers' organisations.*

British Double Reed Society. 9 Hamlyn Gardens, Church Rd, London SE19 2NX *tel:* 020 8653 3625 *email:* enquiries@bdrs.org.uk. Anthony McColl, chmn; David Moore, hon sec; Geoffrey Bridge, treasurer. *Society established to further the interests of all involved with the ob and bsn.*

British Federation of Audio. PO Box 365, Farnham GU10 2BD *tel:* 01428 714616 *fax:* 01428 717599 *email:* chrisc@british-audio.org.uk. C I C Cowan, sec. *Trade association for manufacturers and distributers of hi-fi audio equipment.*

Representing Agents in all Branches of the Entertainment Industry

The Agents' Association (Great Britain)

54 Keyes House, Dolphin Square
LONDON SW1V 3NA
Tel: 020 7834 0515
Fax: 020 7821 0261

Email: association@agents-uk.com
Website: www.agents-uk.com

British Federation of Brass Bands. 256 Longfellow Rd, Coventry, W Midlands CV2 5HJ *tel:* 024 7644 2701 *fax:* 024 7644 2701 *email:* bfbb@clara.net. Greta Russell, gen sec; Peter Parkes, president. *The national body representing the interests of br bands throughout the UK.*

British Flute Society. 41 Devon Ave, Twickenham TW2 6PN *tel:* 020 8241 7572 *email:* secretary@bfs.org.uk. Julie Wright, sec; John Rayworth, membership sec. *Promotes fl-playing from beginner to professional standard. Events held throughout the country. Quarterly journal 'Pan'.*

British Horn Society. c/o 15 Midhurst Ave, Muswell Hill, London N10 3EP *tel:* 020 8883 9645 *email:* mike@british-horn.org. Barry Tuckwell, president; Hugh Seenan, hon chmn. *Dedicated to the art, craft and fun of hn-playing. Student, amateur and professional membership. Organises festivals, w/shops and publishes 'The Horn' magazine.*

The British and International Bass Forum. PO Box 151, Aldershot, Surrey GU12 6YQ *tel:* 01252 319610 *email:* doublebass@tiscali.co.uk. David Heyes, admin and ed. *Promotes the db in all aspects of performance and educ. International membership (29 countries). 4 magazines pa. Bass-Fest and Biennial Composition Competition.*

British and International Federation of Festivals. Festivals House, 198 Park Lane, Macclesfield, Cheshire SK11 6UD *tel:* 01625 428297 *fax:* 01625 503229 *email:* info@festivals.demon.co.uk. Liz Whitehead, chief exec. *Umbrella organisation promoting the amateur mus, speech and dance festival movement. 320 member festivals and 300+ professional members.*

British Jewish Music Network *formerly* **British Society for Practitioners of Jewish Music.** 31 Primrose Hill Rd, London NW3 3DG *tel:* 020 7722 4117 *email:* julian@juliandawes.com. Julian Dawes, joint chmn; Vivienne Bellos, joint chmn. *Raises the profile of practitioners in the field of Jewish mus. Provides a practical and intellectual forum for the exchange of information, ideas and resources. Events cover a wide range of topics associated with Jewish mus. Directory of members is available to members.*

British Kodály Academy. 13 Midmoor Rd, London SW19 4JD *tel:* 020 8971 2062 *fax:* 020 8946 6561 *email:* BKAhelp@aol.com. Celia Cviic, treasurer and courses sec. *Offers teacher training according to the Kodály concept in mus educ through w/shops and INSET courses throughout the UK. Also w/end courses, diploma and certificate courses and an annual summer school.*

British Music Information Centre. 10 Stratford Place, London W1C 1BA *tel:* 020 7499 8567 *fax:* 020 7499 4795 *email:* info@bmic.co.uk. Matthew Greenall, dir; Daniel Goren, information mgr; Imogen Mitchell, production and services mgr. *Scores and recordings collection of contemporary British mus: reading and listening facilities available. Free admission; open Mon-Fri, noon-5pm. Concerts at the Warehouse, Waterloo.*

British Music Rights Ltd. British Music House, 26 Berners St, London W1T 3LR *tel:* 020 7306 4446 *fax:* 020 7306 4449 *email:* britishmusic@bmr.org. Henri Yoxall, gen mgr. *Promoting the interests of British mus composers, songwriters and publishers through lobbying to UK government and EU institutions, educ, PR and events. Members: BACS, MPA and the MCPS-PRS Alliance.*

British Music Society. 30 Chester Rd, Watford, Herts WD18 0RQ *tel:* 01923 230111 *email:* david.burkett@btinternet.com. David Burkett, hon sec; Stephen Trowell, membership enquiries, orders (7 Tudor Gardens, Upminster, Essex RM14 3DE, tel: 01708 224795). *Concentrates particularly on promoting an interest in neglected British composers through learned publications, professionally produced recordings and live concerts.*

British Association for Performing Arts Medicine. 196 Shaftesbury Ave, London WC2H 8JF *tel:* 020 7240 4500 (helpline)/3331 (admin) *fax:* 020 7240 3335 *email:* bpamt@dial.pipex.com. Rosanna Preston, chief exec; Clare Hicks, admin; Yinka Fasawe O'Reilly, helpline co-ord. *Founded in 1984, BAPAM holds free diagnosis and assessment clinics run by conventional and complementary practitioners, accessed via a local call Helpline, for performers with performance-related injury or illness, whether physical, psychological or emotional.*

The British Phonographic Industry Ltd. Riverside Building, County Hall, Westminster Bridge Rd, London SE1 7JA *tel:* 020 7803 1300 *fax:* 020 7803 1310 *email:* forname.surname@bpi.co.uk. Andrew Yeates, dir gen. *Trade association for British record companies.*

British Piano Duo Association (EPTA UK). 64 Birdwood Rd, Cambridge CB1 3TE *tel:* 01223 240418 *fax:* 01223 240418; 01279 870991 *email:* anne.applin@btinternet.com. Anne Applin, dir; Geoffrey Pratley. *Encourages the study and performance of the pno duo repertoire on one and two pnos.*

British Recording Media Association. Orbital House, 85 Croydon Rd, Caterham, Surrey CR3 6PD *tel:* 01883 334495 *fax:* 01883 334490 *email:* brma@admin.co.uk. Elaine Cole, sec. *Representative organisation for manufacturers of blank audio and video tape and other recording media.*

British Society for Music Therapy. 61 Church Hill Rd, E Barnet, Herts EN4 8SY *tel:* 020 8441 6226 *fax:* 020 8441 4118 *email:* info@bsmt.org. Denize Christophers, admin. *Promotes the use of mus therapy in the treatment and rehabilitation of children and adults suffering from emotional, physical or mental handicap. Holds meetings and conferences, publishes papers and a journal for members, displays and sells books on mus therapy and related subjects. Membership is open to all interested in mus therapy.*

British Suzuki Institute. 39 High St, Wheathampstead, Herts AL4 8BB *tel:* 01582 832424 *fax:* 01582 834488 *email:* bsi@ suzukimusic.force9.co.uk. Landa Melrose, chief exec offr. *Suzuki teacher training in vn, pno, vc, va, fl and rcdr. P/t courses lead to Diploma of European Suzuki Association. The institute, currently with 2000 members in the UK, trains Suzuki teachers and promotes the Suzuki philiosophy. Large selection of summer courses and workshops. Introductory courses in Jun and Nov and observation opportunities throughout the year.*

British Trombone Society. 1 Broomfield Rd, Coventry, W Midlands CV5 6JW *tel:* 024 7671 1900 *fax:* 024 7671 2550 *email:* membership@ trombone-society.org.uk. Steven Greenall, membership sec; Anthony Parsons, ed of 'The Trombonist' magazine. *Open to all ages and abilities, amateurs and professionals. Promotes the trb and its repertoire in all mus styles.*

British Violin Making Association. 13 Washington Rd, Maldon, Essex CM9 6BL *tel:* 01621 854357 *email:* secretary@bvma.org.uk. Kai-Thomas Roth, chmn; Paul Collins, sec; Colin Garrett, treasurer. *Aims to promote all aspects of the craft of vn and bow making in the British Isles.*

British Voice Association. Institute of Laryngology and Otology, 330 Grays Inn Rd, London WC1X 8EE *tel:* 020 7713 0064 *fax:* 020 7915 1388 *email:* bva@dircon.co.uk. Jackie Ellis, admin. *The BVA is a charitable organisation established in 1986. Its remit is the encouragement of a healthy voice, vocal skills and communication in such areas as the performing arts, business and industry, medicine and educ. Recognises the human voice as an essential element of communication and well-being; devoted to people with voice problems, ranging from severe pathology and cancer to subtle difficulties of artistic performance; dedicated to supporting, informing and encouraging members of all professions who work with these individuals.*

Cambridge Society of Musicians. MMI House, 8 Quarry St, Shawforth, Lancs OL12 8HD *tel:* 01706 853664 *fax:* 01706 852282 *email:* CSMatMMILTD@aol.com. Lord Taylor of Blackburn, president; Lee Longden, chief exec; Ian Roche, deputy chief exec. *A learned society that elects practising musicians to membership, and eligible musicians to the higher grades of associateship and fellowship. The society also elects members of support industries allied to mus to affiliate membership or fellowship. Members and non-members may be awarded the Companion, or the society medal for substantive contribution to mus. Distinguished musicians may be awarded Honorary Fellowship of the Society, and members of support industries may be awarded Honorary Membership.*

Careers Research and Advisory Centre (CRAC Ltd). Sheraton House, Castle Park, Cambridge, CB3 0AX *tel:* 01223 460277 *fax:* 01223 311708 *email:* enquiries@crac.org.uk. David Thomas, chief exec; Richard Ogdon, development dir and deputy chief exec. *CRAC promotes lifelong career development. Holds conferences on current career-related issues; organises learning programmes for teachers, students and young managers; creates customised development programmes; develops learning materials and undertakes guidance research and consultancy projects.*

Carreras (José), Friends of. 89 Gordon Rd, Corringham, Essex SS17 7QZ *tel:* 01375 678788 *fax:* 01375 678788. Joan Sheppard, chmn. *Appreciation society; career information. Leukaemia Foundation fundraising. 1000+ members worldwide.*

Cathedral Music, Friends of. Aeron House, Llangeitho, Tregaron, Ceredigion SY25 6SU *tel:* 01974 821614 *email:* joycooke@aol.com. Michael Cooke, hon sec; Peter Toyne, chmn. *To assist cathedrals financially in maintaining their mus and to increase public awareness of the unique heritage of cathedral mus.*

Cathedral Organists' Association. Royal School of Church Music, Cleveland Lodge, Westhumble, Dorking, Surrey RH5 6BW *tel:* 01306 872800 *fax:* 01306 887260 *email:* coa@rscm.com. John Harper, sec. *Association of present and former organists and dirs of mus at cathedrals and comparable choral foundations. 2 conferences pa.*

Catholic Stage Guild. Corpus Christi, 1 Maiden Lane, London WC2E 7NB *tel:* 020 7240 1221. Molly Steele, hon sec. *For Catholics engaged in the theatre, films, TV, radio and allied arts including actors, dirs, writers, performers, musicians and technicians.*

Cavatina Chamber Music Trust. 52d Maresfield Gardens, London NW3 5RX *tel:* 020 7435 8479 *fax:* 020 7431 2737 *email:* majaro@ cavatina.net. Simon Majaro, trustee; Pamela Majaro, trustee. *Aims to preserve the tradition of chmbr mus for young people by performances in schools and private venues. Also offers a subsidised ticket scheme for selected concerts in major arts venues.*

Cello Club. 41 Rochester Rd, London NW1 9JJ *tel:* 020 7482 4118 *fax:* 020 7482 4118 *email:* will@bctalk.net. William Bruce, dir; Christopher Bunting, president. *A non-profit making national club for young cellists. Members receive 3 magazines and 3 newsletters each year on everything to do with the vc world, the opportunity to participate in special vc events and discounts on vc supplies.*

Central Composers' Alliance. 21 Kingsway Rd, Leicester LE5 5TL *tel:* 0116 273 6257 *fax:* 0116 273 6257 *email:* pncrump@dircon.co.uk. Sir Richard Rodney Bennett, patron; Andrew Downes, president; David Fisher, chmn; Rosemary Duxbury, treasurer; Peter Crump, sec. *An alliance of composers resident in the Midlands and neighbouring counties, or with Midlands connections to promote their mus through performance, recording and other means and to stimulate mutual support among members. Open to bona fide composers.*

Centre for Creative Communities. Ground Floor, 118 Commercial St, London E1 6NF *tel:* 020 7247 5385 *fax:* 020 7247 5256 *email:* info@ creativecommunities.org.uk. Jennifer Williams, exec dir. *Organisation devoted to community development through the arts and educ; does not run programmes or give funds.*

Centre for Russian Music. Music Dept, Goldsmiths College, University of London, London SE14 6NW *tel:* 020 7919 7646 *fax:* 020 7919 7247 *email:* a.ivashkin@gold.ac.uk. Alexander Ivashkin, dir; Noelle Mann, curator, Sergei Prokofiev Archive. *Promotes research, publication and performance of Russian mus.*

CFC Trust. 5 Summerfield Rd, Ealing, London W5 1ND *tel:* 020 8997 5831 *email:* chanceoffice@talk21.com. Helen Ranger, arts development mgr. *Mus w/shops for vulnerable children and young people. Young people's training and mentoring programme. Professionals training (CPD).*

Chard Foundation of Women in Music. 3 Howards Row, Chard, Somerset TA20 1PH *tel:* 01460 66115 *fax:* 01460 66048 *email:* admin@chardfestival.org.uk. Angela Willes, artistic dir.

Children's Classic Concerts. 46a Fortrose St, Glasgow G11 5LP *tel:* 0141 334 8500 *fax:* 0141 334 6100 *email:* info@childrensclassicconcerts.co.uk. Jane Gordon, gen mgr; Christopher Bell, artistic dir; Emily Sawyer, educ mgr. *Organises and promotes Children's Classic Concerts, the award-winning series of concerts specially designed for primary age children and their families. Educ w/shops in conjunction with performances arranged for schools, community groups, etc.*

Choir Schools' Association. The Minster School, Deangate, York YO1 7JA *tel:* 01904 624900 *fax:* 01904 557232 *email:* info@choirschools.org.uk. Mrs W A Jackson, admin; Jane Capon, information offr. *Membership includes over 40 schools which educate boy and girl choristers for cathedrals, churches and collegiate chapels. Also administers a Bursary Trust Fund, which aims to ensure that no chorister is denied a place at choir school on financial grounds.*

Christian Copyright Licensing (Europe) Ltd. PO Box 1339, Eastbourne, E Sussex BN21 1AD *tel:* 01323 436103 *fax:* 01323 436112 *email:* sales@ccli.co.uk. *Issues licences concerning songs and hymns photocopying within churches. Also acts as agent to the Performing Right Society, Copyright Licensing Agency, Mechanical Copyright Protection Society, Phonographic Performance Licence and the Christian Video Licence Europe.*

Church Music Society. 17 Fulneck, Pudsey, W Yorks LS28 8NT *tel:* 0113 255 6143 *fax:* 0113 255 6143 *email:* cms@simonlindley.org.uk. Simon Lindley, hon sec; The Archbishop of York, president; Ian Curror, chmn. *Leading publisher of all kinds of church mus in association with OUP mus dept. Annual lecture and other events.*

Clarinet Heritage Society. 47 Hambalt Rd, London SW4 9EQ *tel:* 020 8675 3877 *email:* chs@chello.se. Stephen Bennett, hon sec. *Publishes and records new and rare cl mus and promotes the image of the cl.*

Clarinet and Saxophone Society of Great Britain. 8 Garden Close, Hampton, Middx TW12 3EG *tel:* 020 8979 6064 *email:* membership@ clarinetandsaxophone.co.uk. Susan Moss, membership sec. *Advice and consultancy service; library, discount insurance, quarterly journal, cl congress, sax congress, cl choir convention, regional events.*

The Clarsach Society. 22 Durham Rd South, Edinburgh EH15 3PD *tel:* 0131 669 8972 *fax:* 0131 620 0904 *email:* arco@globalnet.co.uk.

DALCROZE SOCIETY

Dalcroze Eurhythmics

offers a unique approach to improving performance through movement of the whole body

It is an effective and established creative approach to musical training, in which elements such as pulse, tempo, rhythm, phrasing, duration and structure are all experienced through movement.

It develops a greater awareness and enjoyment of music and is suitable for all ages.

The method consists of three disciplines Rhythmics, Aural Training & Improvisation.

For information about workshop courses and summer schools please contact:

The Dalcroze Society UK Inc:
100 Elborough Street, London SW18 5DL
Tel & Fax 020 8870 1986
Email admin@dalcroze.org.uk
www.dalcroze.org.uk

All Equity Singers get:

* Singers' Agreements
* Singers' Rates Card
* Advice on Contracts - UK & Overseas
* Public liability insurance to £5million
* 24 hours accident insurance cover
* Free welfare benefits advice
* Free legal help to chase unpaid fees
* Section on the Job Information Service
    and all from only £5 per month!

Not yet a member? Call:
London & South East: 020 7379 6000
South West & Wales: 029 20397 971
Scotland & N.Ireland: 0141 248 2472
North East: 01142 305 294
North West: 0161 832 3183
Midlands: 01926 408 638

Web: www.equity.org.uk
Email: info@equity.org.uk

Founded in 1951 at the suggestion of Sir Adrian Boult, The Elgar Society is the largest UK composer society, with nine regional branches and a world-wide membership.

Its objective is to promote knowledge of the composer Sir Edward Elgar, his music and his life. This it does through the sponsorship of recordings, including EMI's 9-CD *Elgar Edition* of Elgar conducting his own music and the world première recording of *King Olaf*; the promotion and encouragement of Elgar performances and broadcasts around the world, including the first broadcast on Chinese radio of *The Dream of Gerontius*; its website, which has now attracted over 15% of the Society's current membership, many from abroad; the publication three times a year of a journal and newsletter, and the publishing and recording activities of the Society's own imprint, Elgar Editions.

In June 2000, the Society committed itself to its biggest challenge so far: the completion of **a** uniform edition of all of Elgar's published works. The *Elgar Complete Edition* was launched by Novello in 1981 but abandoned some twelve years later while still less than half complete. It is this project which the Society now aims to take forward to completion as the *Elgar Society Edition* over the next 10-15 years. The Edition was relaunched at St James' Palace in October 2001 with the publication of volume 25, containing The *Wand of Youth* Suites and *Dream Children*. The next volume, *The Crown of India*, is scheduled for publication in early 2004.

If you wish to join or receive further details about **The Elgar Society**, or are interested in purchasing or otherwise supporting **The Elgar Society Edition**, please visit the Society's website (www.elgar.org) or contact:

The Membership Secretary, 31 Queen's Road, Marlow, Bucks SL7 2PS
e-mail: membership@elgar.org; tel: 01628 475897

The Elgar Society and Elgar Society Edition are Registered Charities
(No.298062) (No.1086576)

Alistair Cockburn, admin. *Promotes the teaching and playing of the celtic hp; organises the Edinburgh International Harp Festival and publishes mus for celtic hp. 11 area branches throughout the UK. Full mus cat available.*

Club for Acts and Actors (*incorporating* **The Concert Artistes' Association**). 20 Bedford St, London WC2E 9HP *tel:* 020 7836 3172 *fax:* 020 7836 3172. Barbara Daniels, sec. *Private Members' Club for artists in all branches of entertainment with opportunities to perform and meet with other professionals. Concert hall may be hired for rehearsals, auditions, etc. Membership is also open to those with a strong interest in the performing arts.*

Composers of Wales/Cyfansoddwyr Cymru. Ty Cerdd, 15 Mount Stuart Square, Cardiff CF10 5DP *tel:* 029 2046 5700 *fax:* 029 2046 2733 *email:* composers@tycerdd.org. Enid Luff, sec; Keith Griffin, chmn. *The professional guild of Welsh composers.*

Confraternity of Polish Artists in Great Britain. 34 Denmark Rd, London W13 8RG *tel:* 020 8567 1565. Marisa Morganti-Stachów, sec.

The Contemporary Music Centre Ireland. 19 Fishamble St, Temple Bar, Dublin 8, Ireland *tel:* 00 353 1 673 1922 *fax:* 00 353 1 648 9100 *email:* info@cmc.ie. Eve O'Kelly, dir. *Nurtures the composition and performance of new Irish mus.*

Contemporary Music-Making for Amateurs (COMA). Toynbee Studios, 28 Commercial St, London E1 6AB *tel:* 020 7247 7736 *fax:* 020 7247 7732 *email:* coma@coma.org. Chris Shurety, dir. *Provides ens and educ opportunities for amateurs of all abilities to take part in contemporary mus-making. Developing a high-quality contemporary repertoire for amateur ens through commissions, calls for pieces and research.*

Critics' Circle. c/o 69 Marylebone Lane, London W1U 2PH *tel:* 020 7224 1410. Catherine Cooper, admin; Charles Hedges, hon sec. *Organisation for critics of the performing arts. Membership by invitation only.*

Crotch (William) Society. 46 Doods Rd, Reigate, Surrey RH2 0NL *tel:* 01737 244604 *fax:* 01737 244604 *email:* jonathanrennert@ hotmail.com. Jonathan Rennert, hon sec. *Provides information to performers and scholars on the life and mus of the composer, teacher, painter and infant prodigy, Dr William Crotch (1775-1847). No membership.*

Dalcroze Society UK (Inc). 100 Elborough St, London SW18 5DL *tel:* 020 8870 1986 *fax:* 020 8870 1986 *email:* admin@dalcroze.org.uk. J Rivers, admin. *Mus educ through movement. Rhythmics, inst, improvisation, ear training for all age groups.*

Delius Trust. 16 Ogle St, London W1W 6JA *tel:* 020 7436 4816 *fax:* 020 7637 4307 *email:* delius_trust@compuserve.com. David Lloyd-Jones, chmn; Marjorie Dickinson, sec. *Promotes only the mus of Frederick Delius by giving help towards the cost of performances, recordings and publications.*

Dvořák Society for Czech and Slovak Music. 69 Grasmere Rd, London N10 2DH *tel:* 020 8883 7362 *fax:* 020 8245 5591 *email:* graham.m-m@ virgin.net. Graham Melville-Mason, chmn. *Czech and Slovak mus. Journal, newsletters, lectures, concerts, record service, library, yearbook, international reciprocal memberships.*

Early Music Network. 31 Abdale Rd, London W12 7ER *tel:* 020 8743 0302 *fax:* 020 8743 0996 *email:* glyn@earlymusicnet.demon.co.uk. Glyn Russ, admin. *Generates development of early mus through the promotion of live performances, educ and the dissemination of information. Runs biennial competition and showcases for young musicians; produces monthly listings newsletter and annual directory of performers.*

Eastern Orchestral Board. 10 Stratford Place, London W1C 1BA *tel:* 020 7629 9601 *fax:* 020 7495 4710 *email:* info@eob.org.uk. David Richardson, dir; Stuart Bruce, educ mgr; Jan Ford, mkt mgr; Nancy Buchanan, admin; Julia Ient, funding development mgr. *A development agency for professional orch mus working with local authorities, orchs and other agencies. Supports concerts, community and educ projects and audience development initiatives.*

Educational Centres Association (ECA). 21 Ebbisham Drive, Norwich NR4 6HQ *tel:* 0870 161 0302 *fax:* 01603 469292 *email:* info@e-c-a.ac.uk. Bernard Godding, chmn. *National adult educ network concerned with furthering the development of adult educ locally, nationally and internationally.*

Educational Institute of Scotland. 46 Moray Place, Edinburgh EH3 6BH *tel:* 0131 225 6244 *fax:* 0131 220 3151 *email:* enquiries@eis.org.uk. Ronald A Smith, gen sec. *Scottish teachers' union. Publishes 'Scottish Educational Journal', min 5 pa, free to members.*

Elgar Foundation. The Elgar Birthplace Museum, Crown East Lane,

Lower Broadheath, Worcester WR2 6RH *tel:* 01905 333224 *fax:* 01905 333426 *email:* birthplace@elgarmuseum.org. Catherine Sloan, museum dir; Margaret Sanders, archivist. *Charitable foundation which is trustee of the Elgar Birthplace Trust, and manages the Elgar Birthplace Museum, comprising the country cottage where Elgar was born and the Elgar Centre. Large collection of mss, letters, scores, programmes, photographs and memorabilia.*

The Elgar Society. 29 Van Diemens Close, Chinnor, Oxon OX39 4QE *tel:* 01844 354096 *fax:* 01844 354459 *email:* hon.sec@elgar.org. Wendy Hillary, hon sec. *The society exists to foster and encourage a lively interest in and enthusiasm for Elgar's mus, as well as to stimulate research into his life and works and to honour his memory.*

English Folk Dance and Song Society. Cecil Sharp House, 2 Regents Park Rd, London NW1 7AY *tel:* 020 7485 2206 *fax:* 020 7284 0534 *email:* info@efdss.org. Diana Jewitt, national educ mgr; Malcolm Taylor, librarian; Hazel Miller, chief offr. *Information service; school supply cat, project packs; library including tapes, CDs and videos. Dance courses.*

English National Opera, Friends of. London Coliseum, St Martin's Lane, London WC2N 4ES *tel:* 020 7845 9420 *fax:* 020 7845 9272 *email:* friends@eno.org. Deborah Henry-Pollard, Friends mgr. *Provides vital financial support for new productions and enjoys a wide range of opportunities to become closely involved with ENO.*

English Poetry and Song Society. 76 Lower Oldfield Park, Bath, Somerset BA2 3HP *tel:* 01225 313531 *fax:* 01225 464333 *email:* epss@members.v21.co.uk. Richard Carder, chmn. *EPSS is dedicated to the performance, publication and recording of English Art Songs; newsletter and song lists by living composers; competitions.*

English Sinfonia Friends Association. 1 Wedgwood Court, Stevenage, Herts SG1 4QR *tel:* 01438 350990 *fax:* 01438 350930 *email:* friends@englishsinfonia.org.uk. Julia Turner. *Supporters of the English Sinfonia receive regular newsletters, attend rehearsals, hold social events and periodically receive other benefits, including discounts on recordings.*

Enterprise Music Scotland. 37 Dee St, Aberdeen AB11 6DY *tel:* 01224 574422 *fax:* 01224 572315 *email:* info@emusicscotland.co.uk. Ronnie Rae, exec dir. *Established to take over from the Scottish Arts Council the admin of funding, tours co-ordination and development of mus clubs and arts guilds in Scotland.*

Equity. Guild House, Upper St Martin's Lane, London WC2H 9EG *tel:* 020 7379 6000 *fax:* 020 7379 7001 *email:* info@equity.org.uk. Ian McGarry, gen sec. *The union representing British actors, singers, dancers, variety artists, stage mgrs, theatre dirs and designers, broadcasters and others in the entertainment business.*

European Conference of Promoters of New Music. c/o Gaudeamus Foundation, Swammerdamstraat 38, Amsterdam 1091 RV *tel:* 00 31 20 694 7349 *fax:* 00 31 20 694 7258 *email:* info@ecpnm.com. H Heuvelmans, sec; H W Erdmann, president. *The European union of organisations concerned with the promotion of 20th C mus, festivals and concert organisers.*

European Guitar Teachers' Association (UK). 29 Longfield Rd, Tring, Herts HP23 4DG. Sarah Clarke, sec; John Williams, president. *Aims to improve the standard of classical gui educ and the inst's place in the mainstream mus world.*

European Piano Teachers' Association (UK) Ltd (EPTA UK). Archpool House, High St, Handcross, W Sussex RH17 6BJ *tel:* 01444 400852 *fax:* 01444 401443 *email:* eptauk@hotmail.com. Sally Course, admin; Frank Martin, chmn. *EPTA UK has 30 regional centres promoting excellence in pno teaching and performance in the UK.*

European String Teachers' Association (ESTA). 105 Perryfield Way, Richmond, Surrey TW10 7SN *tel:* 020 8940 4640 *fax:* 020 8940 4300 *email:* marionseymour@compuserve.com. Marion Seymour, admin; Derek Pedder, membership sec. *Aims to raise the standard of str playing and teaching, provide an international forum for the exchange of ideas, promote w/shops, lectures, discussions and sponsor publications.*

Faculty of Church Music. 27 Sutton Park, Blunsdon, Swindon, Wilts SN26 7BB *tel:* 020 8675 0180 *fax:* 020 8675 0180. Revd G Gleed, registrar. *Promotion of high standards in Church mus through graded exams. Tuition provided in theoretical subjects and for external mus degrees. Examinations for the grade of Associate, Licentiate and Fellow open to church musicians of any denomination.*

Farnon (Robert) Society. Stone Gables, Upton Lane, Seavington St Michael, Ilminster, Somerset TA19 0PZ *tel:* 01460 242226 *fax:* 01460 242226 *email:* david@rfsoc.freeserve.co.uk. David Ades, sec. *RFS supports work of Robert Farnon and leading musicians and composers in the light orch and film mus fields.*

Federation of British Conservatoires. c/o Birmingham Conservatoire, Paradise Place, Birmingham B3 3HG *tel:* 0121 331 5910 *fax:* 0121 331 7201 *email:* george.caird@uce.ac.uk. George Caird, sec. *The federation has a membership of the major independent conservatoires of mus in the UK.*

Federation of Music Services. 6 Berwick Courtyard, Berwick St Leonard, Salisbury, Wilts SP3 5SN *tel:* 01747 820042 *fax:* 01747 820043 *email:* fms@musiced.fsnet.co.uk. Colin Brackley Jones, chief exec; John Witchell, chmn. *Aims to offer support and advice to mus services in the provision and development of high-quality specialist mus educ to schools and the wider community; to help mus services to maintain and develop access and opportunity; and to promote the work of mus services.*

Federation of Recorded Music Societies. 2 Fulmar Place, Meir Park, Stoke-on-Trent ST3 7QF *tel:* 01782 399291 *email:* frms.sec@virgin.net. Tony Baines, sec; John Davies, chmn. *National body set up to provide help and assistance to groups wishing to listen to mus in public locations. Provides discounted PRS and PPL cover and insurance facilities; publishes a free magazine; organises a mus weekend for members. Also technical advice on sound equipment.*

Fellowship of Makers and Researchers of Historical Instruments. London Guildhall University, 41-71 Commercial Rd, London E1 1LA *tel:* 020 7320 1841 *fax:* 020 7320 1830 *email:* l.jones@londonmet.ac.uk. Lewis Jones, hon sec; David Armitage, hon ed of FoMRHI Quarterly. *Promotes the study and making of historical mus insts, and authenticity in their reconstruction and use.*

The Finzi Friends. 4 The Close, Lichfield WS13 7LD *tel:* 01543 306277 *fax:* 01543 306278 *email:* PAUL@paulspicer. Paul Spicer, chmn. *Formed in 1982 to link admirers of Gerald Finzi's mus. Aims to encourage a wider knowledge of his mus. Annual subscription £10.*

The Finzi Trust. Hillcroft, Shucknall Hill, Hereford HR1 3SL *fax:* 01432 851773. Elizabeth Pooley, admin. *Aims to advance 20th C British mus through assisting and promoting festivals, recordings and performances. Limited number of small grants offered to young musicians for training but not for diplomas, degrees or p/grad study.*

Flutewise. 8/9 Beaconsfield Rd, Portslade, E Sussex BN41 1XA *tel:* 01273 702367 *fax:* 01273 888864 *email:* mail@flutewise.com. Sir James Galway, president; Liz Goodwin, ed and dir. *International organisation for all flautists, especially the young. Quarterly magazine with competitions and prizes. Regular events and courses. Supported by the National Foundation for Youth Music.*

The Friends of Robert Stolz. Red Lion Court, Stalbridge, Sturminster Newton, Dorset DT10 2LR *tel:* 01963 362999 *email:* rowe3@supanet.com. Frau Einzi Stolz, president; Annelise Rothenberger, Nigel Douglas, hon patrons; Elaine Keys, acting sec. *Exists to increase knowledge of the last of the great waltz kings and to support performances of his mus.*

Galpin Society. 37 Townsend Drive, St Albans, Herts AL3 5RF *email:* administrator@galpinsociety.org. Maggie Kilbey, admin. *Founded in 1946 for the publication of original research into the history, construction, development and use of mus insts.*

Gilbert and Sullivan Society. Flat 7, 20 Hampden Gurney St, London W1H 5AX. Valerie Colin-Russ, hon sec. *Aims to encourage an interest in the Gilbert and Sullivan operas. Magazine 3 times pa. Research and library facilities.*

Girls' Day School Trust. 100 Rochester Row, London SW1P 1JP *tel:* 020 7393 6666 *fax:* 020 7393 6789 *email:* info@wes.gdst.net. Barbara Harrison, chief exec. *GDST is at the forefront of educ for girls, offering a distinctive educational experience with a broad, inclusive curriculum and a culture of high expectation.*

Girls' Schools Association. 130 Regent Rd, Leicester LE1 7PG *tel:* 0116 254 1619 *fax:* 0116 255 3792 *email:* office@gsa.uk.com. Ms S Cooper, gen sec; Miss S Massey, admin.

Grainger (Percy) Society. 6 Fairfax Cres, Aylesbury, Bucks HP20 2ES *tel:* 01296 428609 *fax:* 01296 581185 *email:* info@percygrainger.org.uk. Barry P Ould, sec and mus archivist. *Promotes interest in the life and works of the composer Percy Aldridge Grainger (1882-1961).*

The Gregorian Association. 26 The Grove, Ealing, London W5 5LH *tel:* 020 8840 5832 *fax:* 0870 055 3684 *email:* pjsw@beaufort.demon.co.uk. Grey Macartney, chmn; Peter Wilson, mus dir.

Grieg Society of Great Britain. 25 Belgrave Square, London SW1X 8QD *tel:* 01707 643366 *fax:* 01707 643366 *email:* audrey@pipersend.freeserve.co.uk. Jackie Etheridge, sec; Beryl Foster, chmn; Audrey Banker, membership. *Promotes interest in Grieg and other Norwegian composers amongst performers and audiences in Britain. Lecture and educ programmes arranged.*

Guild of Musicians and Singers. 8 Clave St, Wapping, London E1W 3XQ *tel:* 020 7488 3650 *email:* davidbell@connectfree.co.uk. David Bell, master; Christopher Shoebridge, sec gen (tel: 020 8751 6155). *An organisation of professional and amateur instrumentalists and singers founded in 1993. Meetings in London: lectures, concerts, recitals; bi-annual newsletter; membership on 3 levels by election.*

The Incorporated Society of Musicians

As the UK's professional body for musicians, the ISM has three prime objectives: to represent and protect the interest of everyone who works with music; to raise practical and ethical standards within the profession; and to provide our members with the best possible range and quality of advice and services. We are delighted to offer a uniquely comprehensive range of benefits to our Full members.

Full Membership Benefits

Free

- Public liability insurance to £10 million
- Individual legal advice in professional disputes
- Legal representation in courts & tribunals
- Legal expenses insurance to £100K
- Inland Revenue inquiry insurance to £100K
- 24-hour Legal Helpline
- 24-hour Tax & National Insurance Helpline
- 24-hour Counselling Helpline
- Individual advice on all professional matters
- Individual financial planning advice
- Information Sheets on professional issues
- Monthly ISM Music Journal*
- ISM Diary, Yearbook & Specialist Registers*
- Individual careers advice*

Eligibility for

- Specialist Section membership
- Specialist Register listings
- Committees and Council
- Facilities at New Cavendish Club, London W1
- ISM teachers Yellow Pages advertising

Discounted

- Tax return completion service
- Will writing service
- Conveyancing service
- Membership of Royal Over-Seas League

Discounts on

- Musical instrument insurance*
- Motor, household & travel insurance*
- Private health insurance*
- Music technology*
- Website design & hosting*
- Instruments, sheet music, CDs and more*

Also

- ISM publications & merchandise*
- ISM credit card*
- Network of 46 regional Centres*
- Professional conferences & seminars*
- Voting rights in ISM elections
- Help from ISM Members Fund
- Concessionary subscriptions for long service

Students & Associates receive benefits marked*

Membership

Various types of membership are available to individuals. **Full membership** provides comprehensive professional support for musicians throughout their careers. For music students, **Student membership** is the best way to keep up to date with the profession; Student members receive most publications free, and careers advice may be available. Amateurs, music-lovers and supporters can enrol as **Associate members**, to receive the Society's publications and join its networks.

Contact

The Incorporated Society of Musicians
10 Stratford Place
London W1C 1AA
Tel: 020 7629 4413
Fax: 020 7408 1538
Email: membership@ism.org
Website: www.ism.org

Guild of Church Musicians. St Katharine Cree, 86 Leadenhall St, London EC3A 3DH *tel:* 01883 741854 *fax:* 01883 740570 *email:* JohnMusicsure@aol.com. John Ewington OBE, gen sec. *Examining body to Archbishops of Canterbury, Wales and Westminster: Archbishop's Certificate in Church Music. Fully ecumenical.*

The Guild of International Songwriters and Composers. Sovereign House, 12 Trewartha Rd, Praa Sands, Penzance, Cornwall TR20 9ST *tel:* 01736 762826 *fax:* 01736 763328 *email:* songmag@aol.com. Carole Jones, gen sec, membership. *Mus industry organisation representing songwriters, composers, lyricists, publishers, artists, bands, management companies, record companies, producers, and anyone working in the mus industry on an international basis. Publishers of Songwriting and Composing magazine.*

Handbell Ringers of Great Britain. 87 The Woodfields, Sanderstead, S Croydon, Surrey CR2 0HJ *tel:* 020 8651 2663 *fax:* 020 8651 2663 *email:* info@hrgb.org.uk. Sandra Winter, hon sec. *National association for handbell, handchime and belleplate tune ringers.*

Havergal Brian Society. 5 Eastbury Rd, Watford WD19 4PT *tel:* 01923 224607 *fax:* 01923 250506 *email:* hbs@havergal.demon.co.uk. Alan Marshall, admin sec. *To further public knowledge of Brian's work by supporting and sponsoring its publication, performance and recording.*

Haydn Society of Great Britain. 2 Aldcliffe Mews, Aldcliffe, Lancaster LA1 5BT *tel:* 01524 61553 *fax:* 01524 61553 *email:* d.mccaldin@ lancaster.ac.uk. Denis McCaldin, dir. *Promotes the mus of Joseph Haydn and his circle in the form of concerts, recordings and the publication of an annual journal.*

The Headmasters' and Headmistresses' Conference. 130 Regent Rd, Leicester LE1 7PG *tel:* 0116 285 4810 *fax:* 0116 247 1167 *email:* hmc@hmc.org.uk. Geoff Lucas, sec; Roger Peel, membership sec. *Association of heads of independent boys' and co-ed schools; 244 members. Publishes private members bulletin, professional papers and books, services sub-committees, provides professional training. Divided into 11 geographical divisions; each division meets regularly to exchange ideas and concerns.*

Headteachers Association of Scotland. University of Strathclyde, Jordanhill Campus, Southbrae Drive, Glasgow G13 1PP *tel:* 0141 950 3298 *fax:* 0141 950 3434 *email:* head.teachers@strath.ac.uk. George S Ross, gen sec. *Exists to promote educ, particularly secondary educ in Scotland and to safeguard and promote the interests of headteachers, deputy heads and asst heads.*

House of Commons Culture, Media and Sport Committee. Committee Office, 7 Millbank, London SW1P 3JA *tel:* 020 7219 6120/5739/6924/6188 *fax:* 020 7219 2031 *email:* cmscom@ parliament.uk. Fergus Reid, clerk of the committee; Olivia Davidson, second clerk of the committee. *The committee examines the work of the Department for Culture, Media and Sport and of associated public bodies.*

Howells (Herbert) Society. 32 Barleycroft Rd, Welwyn Garden City, Herts AL8 6JU *tel:* 01707 335315 *email:* andrew.millinger@virgin.net. Andrew Millinger, sec. *Promotes interest in publication, performances and recordings of the mus of Herbert Howells.*

The Hurdy-gurdy Society. The Old Mill, Duntish, Dorchester, Dorset DT2 7DR *tel:* 01300 345412 *fax:* 01300 345412 *email:* mmuskett@beeb.net. Michael Muskett, sec.

Hymn Society of Great Britain and Ireland. 7 Paganel Rd, Minehead, Somerset TA24 5ET *tel:* 01643 703530 *fax:* 01643 703530 *email:* g.wrayford@breathemail.net. Revd Geoffrey Wrayford, sec. *Society for those interested in the study and application of hymnody.*

Incorporated Association of Organists. 17 Woodland Rd, Northfield, Birmingham B31 2HU *tel:* 0121 475 4408 *fax:* 0121 475 4408 *email:* w.j.stormont@btinternet.com. John Stormont, hon gen sec; Peter Page, mkt mgr. *Dedicated to improving org-playing at all levels; has over 6000 members worldwide. Publishes 'Organists' Review' quarterly.*

Incorporated Association of Preparatory Schools. 11 Waterloo Place, Leamington Spa, Warks CV32 5LA *tel:* 01926 887833 *fax:* 01926 888014 *email:* hq@iaps.org.uk. J H Morris, gen sec. *The main professional association for headteachers of independent preparatory and jnr schools throughout the UK and overseas.*

Incorporated Society of Musicians. 10 Stratford Place, London W1C 1AA *tel:* 020 7629 4413 *fax:* 020 7408 1538 *email:* membership@ism.org. Neil Hoyle, chief exec. *Professional body for all musicians. Legal, financial and professional services; conferences, seminars and publications. Full, associate, student and corporate categories.*

Incorporated Society of Organ Builders. Smithy Steads, Cragg Vale, Hebden Bridge HX7 5SQ *tel:* 01422 885846 *fax:* 0870 139 3645 *email:* admin@isob.co.uk. Ruth Sinclair, sec.

Independent Schools Association. Boys' British School, East St, Saffron Walden, Essex CB10 1LS *tel:* 01799 523619 *fax:* 01799 524892 *email:* isa@dial.pipex.com. T M Ham, gen sec.

Independent Schools Careers Organisation. 12a Princess Way, Camberley, Surrey GU15 3SP *tel:* 01276 21188 *fax:* 01276 691833 *email:* info@isco.org.uk. John Stuart, national dir; Katherine Skinner, national information mgr. *Provides advice to students, parents and member schools concerning all aspects of HE and careers. Jobseekers' scheme for those about to graduate. Support and training is provided for school staff.*

Independent Schools Council Information Service (ISCis). Grosvenor Gardens House, 35-37 Grosvenor Gardens, London SW1W 0BS *tel:* 020 7798 1500 *fax:* 020 7798 1501 *email:* info@iscis.uk.net. D J Woodhead, dir. *Information for parents about independent schools, including specialist mus and choir schools and mus scholarships.*

Institute of Contemporary Arts. The Mall, London SW1Y 5AH *tel:* 020 7766 1465 *fax:* 020 7306 0122 *email:* info@ica.uk.net. Vivienne Gaskin, head of performing arts; Alexis Johnson, head of educ; Jamie Eastman, mus programmer.

Institute of Entertainment and Arts Management. 17 Drake Close, Horsham, W Sussex RH12 5UB *tel:* 0870 241 7248 *fax:* 0870 241 7248 *email:* admin@ieam.co.uk. Shirley Carpenter, admin. *Professional institute for those who work in the management and admin of the performing arts and entertainment industry, providing social and welfare facilities, a monthly newsletter and regular seminars.*

Institute of Leisure and Amenity Management (ILAM). ILAM House, Lower Basildon, Reading RG8 9NE *tel:* 01491 874800 *fax:* 01491 874801 *email:* info@ilam.co.uk. Andy Worthington, chief exec. *Professional body representing over 6000 mgrs throughout the leisure industry. ILAM represents its members both nationally and regionally, offering its own qualification system and a wide range of benefits to members, including educ and training seminars, dissemination of information, publications and conferences.*

International Artist Managers' Association (IAMA). 23 Garrick St, Covent Garden, London WC2E 9BN *tel:* 020 7379 7336 *fax:* 020 7379 7338 *email:* info@iamaworld.com. Atholl Swainston-Harrison, exec dir; Melanie Crompton, admin mgr. *International professional association for classical mus artist mgrs and concert agents.*

International Association of Music Libraries (UK and Ireland Branch). Archives and Documentation Centres, c/o Edinburgh City Libraries, 9 George IV Bridge, Edinburgh EH1 1EG *tel:* 0131 242 8050 *fax:* 0131 242 8009 *email:* pbbaxter@hotmail.com. Peter Baxter, gen sec. *Interest in any issues regarding/affecting mus librarians in any sphere. Careers information and special students' subscriptions available to those working in, or with interest in, mus librarianship.*

International Federation of the Phonographic Industry (IFPI). IFPI Secretariat, 54 Regent St, London W1R 5PJ *tel:* 020 7878 7900 *fax:* 020 7878 7950 *email:* info@ifpi.org. Jason Berman, chair, chief exec. *IFPI promotes the interests of the international recording industry.*

International Society for Contemporary Music (ISCM). British Section, c/o spnm, 4th Floor, 18-20 Southwark St, London SE1 1TJ *tel:* 020 7407 1640 *fax:* 020 7403 7652 *email:* spnm@spnm.org.uk. Abigail Pogson, exec dir. *Selects new British works to be forwarded to the ISCM International Jury. Organises events to promote new British mus internationally.*

International Society for Music Education (ISME). ISME International Office, PO Box 909, Nedlands, WA 6909, Australia *tel:* 00 61 8 8386 2654 *fax:* 00 61 8 8386 2658 *email:* isme@isme.org. Judy Thönell, sec gen; Jo-anne Todd, admin. *To build and maintain a worldwide community of mus educators; to foster international and intercultural understanding and co-operation; and to nurture, advocate and promote mus educ and educ through mus in all parts of the world. Membership information and details of the next world conference are available from the above address.*

International Society for the Study of Tension in Performance. c/o 28 Emperor's Gate, London SW7 4HS *tel:* 020 7373 7307 *fax:* 020 7373 5440 *email:* carogrindea@yahoo.com. Carola Grindea, chmn; Gordana Petrovic, sec. *Charitable organisation committed to helping musicians afflicted by physical and psychological problems at ISSTIP/London College of Music 'Performing Arts Clinic'. Publishes ISSTIP journal. Organises w/shops, seminars and courses on health and the performing arts, and music medicine therapists.*

International Trombone Association. 1 Broomfield Rd, Coventry CV5 6JW *tel:* 024 7671 1900 *fax:* 024 7671 2550 *email:* steven@trombone.net. Steven Greenall, exec dir. *The world's largest association for trb players with over 4500 members from across the globe. Members receive reductions at specialist retailers, free ITA CD and the quarterly magazine, 'ITA Journal'.*

Ireland (John) Trust. 35 St Mary's Mansions, St Mary's Terrace, London W2 1SQ *tel:* 020 7723 6376 *fax:* 020 7724 8362. Mrs M Taylor, hon sec.

Ivor Gurney Society. 4 Myton Rd, London SE21 8EB *tel:* 020 8761 3180

email: jp_hay@beeb.net. William Marshall, sec; Ian Venables, chmn. *Exists to promote the performance, publication and study of Ivor Gurney's poetry and mus, his life and context.*

UK-Japan Music Society. 27 Heron Close, Great Glen, Leicester LE8 9DZ *tel:* 0116 259 3891 *fax:* 0116 259 3891. *UK Japan choir meets in London and Leicester. Performances with orch.*

Jazz Services. 1st Floor, 132 Southwark St, London, SE1 0SW *tel:* 020 7928 9089 *fax:* 020 7401 6870 *email:* admin@jazzservices.org.uk. Chris Hodgkins, dir; Celia Wood, publications mgr. *Supports the growth and development of jazz in the UK by providing services in touring support, information via website, educ, mkt and communication.*

Jewish Music Institute. SOAS, University of London, PO Box 232, Harrow, Middx HA1 2NN *tel:* 020 8909 2445 *fax:* 020 8909 1030 *email:* jewishmusic@jmi.org.uk. Geraldine Auerbach MBE, dir. *Leading promoter of Jewish mus in Britain, dedicated to the celebration, preservation and development of the living heritage of Jewish mus for the benefit of all. Programmes and summer schools cover educ, performance and information. Library, archive and resource centre open by appointment. SOAS dept of mus runs grad and p/grad courses in Jewish mus; conferences and seminars; biennial London International Jewish Music Festival and other special events. Forums such as JMI International Forum for Suppressed Music.*

The John Curwen Society. 5 Bigbury Close, Coventry CV3 5AJ *tel:* 024 7641 3010 *fax:* 024 7641 3010; 024 7641 3564 *email:* john.curwensociety@ dial.pipex.com. John Dowding, chmn; Yvonne Lawton, hon sec. *Promotes the New Curwen Method which encourages children to listen attentively to mus, to recognise pitch, rhythm and phrasing, develop a mus memory, and sing at sight with confidence. The Sing and Sign Sol-fa series is recommended for use in primary schools.*

The José Carreras Society. 8 Kingfisher Drive, Winsford, Cheshire CW7 1PF *tel:* 01606 557303 *fax:* 01606 559993 *email:* patricia. chantler@tinyworld.co.uk; josecarrerassociety@tinyworld.co.uk. Patricia Chantler, organiser. *Artistic appreciation society and support group for the José Carreras International Leukaemia Foundation. Worldwide membership.*

Kapustin Society. 20 Sutherland Drive, Guildford, Surrey GU4 7YJ *tel:* 01483 457377 *fax:* 01483 457377 *email:* kapustin_soc@btinternet.com. Jan Hoare, sec. *The Society, through its publications and holding of events such as recitals, m/classes and soirées, exists to promote interest in and appreciation of the works of Kapustin.*

Karg-Elert Archive. 38 Lyndhurst Ave, Twickenham, Middx TW2 6BX *tel:* 020 8894 6859 *fax:* 020 8894 6859 *email:* anthony@ caldicott247.fslife.co.uk. Anthony Caldicott, chmn; Graham Barber, president. *Promotion of the composer and organist Sigfrid Karg-Elert through encouraging research and dissemination of information.*

Kato Havas Association for the New Approach (KHANA). 3 Beacon View, Marple, Stockport SK6 6PX *tel:* 0161 449 7347 *email:* MGBbeaconview@compuserve.com. Gloria Bakhshayesh, personal rep to Kato Havas OBE. *Kato Havas vn teaching method. KHANA holds w/shops on the alleviation and prevention of physical tensions and anxiety in str playing. 2 journals pa.*

King (Reginald) Trust. 6 Fairfax Cres, Aylesbury, Bucks HP20 2ES *tel:* 01296 428609 *fax:* 01296 581185 *email:* rktrust@bardic-music.com. Barry Peter Ould, archivist. *Promotes interest in the life and mus of Reginald King (1904-1991). Mus and sound archives maintained.*

Klavar Music Foundation of Great Britain. Flat C, 12 Pennsylvania Rd, Exeter EX4 6BH *tel:* 00 852 2982 1177 *fax:* 00 852 2982 2731 *email:* Director@klavarmusic.org. Peter Jackson, dir; Sir Colin Davis, patron; Cy Grant, patron; Malcolm Binns, patron. *Easy to read notation system. Educ Trust. Klavar system correspondence courses for pno, org and pno-accordion. Klavar notation printed mus supplies. Free lessons from website.*

The Kodály Centre of London. 52 Highland Rd, Northwood Hills, Middx HA6 1JU *tel:* 01923 821526 *fax:* 01923 821526 *email:* david@ vinden.freeserve.co.uk. David Vinden, dir; Yuko Vinden, dir. *Kodály musicianship and teacher training classes comprising solfège musicianship, classroom techniques and methodology, choral direction and folk song analysis. For class teachers, inst teachers and singers. 3 levels of training are available. Publications include: Harmonic Foundations, the Modes, rhythm flip cards and flash cards.*

The Kodály Institute of Britain. 133 Queen's Gate, London SW7 5LE *tel:* 020 7823 7371 *fax:* 020 7584 7691. Mary Skone-Roberts, admin; Cecilia Vajda, dir. *Adult educ; 1-year p/t courses in musicianship according to the Kodály Principles at 3 levels: elementary, intermediate, advanced. Begins late Sep in London and is credit bearing for Trinity College LTCL (Mus Ed) Cert and Dip. Courses acknowledged by the Liszt Academy of Music, Budapest. Publications include books, video and audio cassettes.*

LSO Discovery. London Symphony Orchestra, Barbican Centre, London EC2Y 8DS *tel:* 020 7588 1116 *fax:* 020 7374 0127 *email:* discovery@ lso.co.uk. Andrew Burke, head of LSO Discovery; Richard McNicol, mus animateur. *Educ and community programme of the London Symphony Orchestra. Offers access to classical mus and encourages people of all ages to take part in mus-making through daytime concerts, creative mus w/shops, teacher training days, adult study days, informal recitals and other educ events. Since Dec 2002, LSO Discovery has been based in a new state-of-the-art venue - LSO St Luke's, Old St, Islington (contact details remain as above).*

Lake District Summer Music Education Outreach Programme. Stricklandgate House, 92 Stricklandgate, Kendal, Cumbria LA9 4PU *tel:* 0845 644 2505 *fax:* 0845 644 2506 *email:* info@ldsm.org.uk. Andrew Lucas, admin. *'Moving Mountains to Make Music', Lake District Summer Music's new educ outreach programme, offers a broad range of creative educ opportunities. Running throughout the year, the programme consists of a variety of w/shops, m/classes and community projects in schools and community centres.*

Leighton (Kenneth) Trust. 38 McLaren Rd, Edinburgh EH9 2BN *tel:* 0131 667 3113 *email:* joleighton@ukgateway.net. Mrs J A Leighton, sec. *Promotes British mus in general and Leighton's mus in particular by providing financial assistance for performances (especially by younger performers), recordings and commissions.*

Light Music Society. Lancaster Farm, Chipping Lane, Longridge, Preston, Lancs PR3 2NB *tel:* 01772 783646 *fax:* 01772 786026. Ernest Tomlinson, chmn; Hilary Ashton, sec. *Backing group for Library of Light-Orchestral Music. Promotes interest in light mus. Regular newsletter.*

Liszt Society. 20 Sutherland Drive, Guildford, Surrey GU4 7YJ *tel:* 01483 457377 *fax:* 01483 457377 *email:* liszt_soc@btinternet.com. Jan Hoare, sec. *The Society, through its publications and holding of events such as recitals, m/classes and soirées, exists to promote interest in and appreciation of the works of Franz Liszt.*

Live Music Now! 4 Lower Belgrave St, London SW1W 0LJ *tel:* 020 7730 2205 *email:* enquiries@livemusicnow.org. Sarah Derbyshire, exec dir; Alice Wilkinson, London dir. *Charity founded by Yehudi Menuhin, which aims to make live mus of the highest quality accessible to people without access to the arts, particularly those with special needs, while at the same time giving performance opportunities to some of the finest young professional classical, jazz, folk and world mus artists in the UK. Organises 3000 concerts and w/shops annually; 8 branches throughout the UK.*

London ArtsFest. PO Box 34904, London SW6 6GX *tel:* 020 7751 0898 *fax:* 020 7731 8009 *email:* info@londonartsfest.org.uk. Lana Lopusina Bezanov, chmn; Carola Grindea, vice-chmn; Peter Feuchtwanger, vice-chmn; Maya Jordan, sec. *A registered charity under the presidency of Sir Colin Davis CH CBE, with the aim to advance the educ of the public in, and to foster and promote the performance of, mus and arts. Internationally oriented and committed to supporting young musicians. Annual awards and Young Musicians' concert series for talented young musicians (for application see **Scholarships and Grants** section). Other events include lecture-recitals, concerts, w/shops, talks, m/classes and tours. International Festival 'Bridging Cultures' held in London in Nov/Dec. Members receive regular newsletters, journal, priority booking for London ArtsFest events, ticket discounts, free entry to lunchtime concerts and priority booking for major international events (opera, ballet, concerts, exhibitions). Membership by application.*

London Suzuki Group. 96 Farm Lane, London SW6 1QH *tel:* 020 7386 8006 *fax:* 020 7386 8006 *email:* lsg@suzukimusic.net. Nicholas Pullinger, admin. *Charitable organisation of teachers, parents and children committed to the Suzuki approach to mus educ for children aged 3-18 learning vn, va, vc and pno.*

Lowland and Border Pipers' Society. 6 Garrioch Cres, Maryhill, Glasgow G20 8RR *tel:* 0141 946 8624. Rona MacDonald, sec; Julian Goodacre, chmn. *Aims to provide a focus for everyone interested in Scottish bellows-blown pipes through meetings, concerts, sessions, newsletters and a twice-yearly magazine.*

Lute Society. Southside Cottage, Brook Hill, Albury, Guildford GU5 9DJ *tel:* 01483 202159 *fax:* 01483 203088 *email:* lutesoc@aol.com. Christopher Goodwin, sec. *Holds 4 meetings pa in central London with lectures and recitals on all aspects of the lute and related insts and their repertoire. Publishes annual journal 'The Lute', quarterly newsletter 'Lute News', performing editions, working drawings of lutes. Holds occasional 1-day w/shops. Lutes available for hire.*

The Mahler Society. 15 David Ave, Wickford, Essex SS11 7BG *tel:* 07802 700626 *fax:* 01268 560833 *email:* info@mahlersociety.org. J J Pritchard, chmn. *A charity dedicated to the appreciation and study of Gustav Mahler's life and mus.*

Making Music *formerly* **National Federation of Music Societies.** 7-15 Rosebery Ave, London EC1R 4SP *tel:* 0870 903 3780 *fax:* 0870 903 3785 *email:* info@makingmusic.org.uk. Robin Osterley, chief exec. *Provides legal, financial, artistic, training, advocacy and lobbying services for over 2000 voluntary member mus societies. See also* **Competitions for Young Performers** *section.*

Mayr + Donizetti Collaboration. 8 Cosway Mansions, Cosway St, London NW1 6UE *tel:* 020 7258 1798 *fax:* 020 7258 1798 *email:* caddy@tiscali.co.uk. Ian Caddy, founder; John Stewart Allitt, founder. *Promotes the work of the 2 composers, co-ordinates scholarship and performing material; biographies and editions for sale.*

The Mendelssohn Society. JMI, SOAS, University of London, Thornhaugh St, Russel Square, London WC1H 0XG *tel:* 020 8909 2445 *fax:* 020 8909 1030 *email:* mendelssohn@jmi.org.uk. Kurt Masur, president; Jackie Rosenfeld OBE, chmn; Malcom Troup, co-ord; Geraldine Auerbach MBE, co-ord. *Aims to promote knowledge of, and interest in, the life and works of Felix Mendelssohn and to raise funds for the Mendelssohn Scholarship Foundation in the UK which awards scholarships to young composers and to support the educational programmes of JMI.*

Metier. Glyde House, Glydegate, Bradford, W Yorks BD5 0BQ *tel:* 01274 738800 *fax:* 01274 391566 *email:* mags@metier.org.uk. Mags Roche, mkt dir; Jane Fear, head of research. *Research and development agency for the cultural industries. Part of Metier's work concentrates on improving vocational educ and tackling social inclusion. Vocational educ projects are aimed at improving the quality of training and professional development for those working in the cultural industries.*

Music Education Council. 54 Elm Rd, Hale, Altrincham, Cheshire WA15 9QP *tel:* 0161 928 3085 *fax:* 0161 929 9648 *email:* ahassan@easynet.co.uk. Anna Hassan, admin. *The major forum for those involved in mus educ and training in the UK.*

Music Industries Association. Ivy Cottage Offices, Finch's Yard, Eastwick Rd, Great Bookham, Surrey KT23 4BA *tel:* 01372 750600 *fax:* 01372 750515 *email:* office@mia.org.uk. Paul McManus, gen mgr; Lizzie Evans, membership sec; Claire Sayers, finance and systems mgr; Jill Shevlin, mkt mgr; Nick Lobley, mkt mgr. *Trade association representing manufacturers, distributors and retailers of mus insts and*

accs. Sponsors UK trade and public exhibitions and promotes British involvement in appropriate overseas trade fairs. Publishers of 'The Fourth R', 'The Brief Guide to Music in the National Curriculum' and 'Signposts to Success' magazine.

Music Masters' and Mistresses' Association (MMA). Wayfaring, Smithers Lane, E Peckham, Tonbridge, Kent TN12 5HT *tel:* 01622 872758 *fax:* 01622 872758 *email:* mma.admin@ntlworld.com. Katharine Le Page, admin; Carol Hawkins, membership sec (tel: 01227 475600). *Furthers all aspects of mus in schools. Membership open to those teaching mus in schools, and those wishing to support the development of mus in schools. Regular regional meetings, courses and an annual conference are held. Termly journal, annual yearbook and mus scholarship guide.*

Music, Mind and Movement. Flat 2, 35 Bush Lane, London EC4R 0AW *tel:* 020 7626 0183; 07850 912006 *fax:* 020 7626 0183 *email:* musicmindmovement@btinternet.com. Lucinda Mackworth-Young, dir; Nicola Gaines, dir; Karin Greenhead, dir. *Devoted to enhancing the performance, teaching and learning of mus and dance through an integrated approach. Courses run for performers, teachers and students in the practical application of psychology, physiology, eurhythmics, dance through the ages, improvisation and other disciplines related to the performance, teaching and learning of mus and dance. Freelance lectures and w/shops. Private consultations.*

Music Producers Guild. PO Box 32, Harrow, Middx HA2 7ZX *tel:* 020 7371 8888 *email:* office@mpg.org.uk. Penny Ganz, company sec; Andrew East, chmn. *Provides and represents all individuals in the mus production and recording professions. Embodies collective and individual creative contributions to the production and recording of all genres of mus and media related activities.*

Music Publishers Association Ltd. 3rd Floor, Strandgate, 20 York Buildings, London WC2N 6JU *tel:* 020 7839 7779 *fax:* 020 7839 7776 *email:* info@mpaonline.org.uk. Sarah Faulder, chief exec; Jenny Goodwin, asst chief exec. *Exists to safeguard the interests of mus publishers and the writers signed to them. Provides members with a forum and a collective voice, and aims to inform and to educate the wider public in the importance and the value of copyright.*

Musicians Against Nuclear Arms (MANA). 71 Greenfield Gardens,

name
NATIONAL ASSOCIATION OF MUSIC EDUCATORS

A Forum for Professional Debate
A National Voice for Music Education
A Regional Network for Training and Support

**Class Teacher?   Instrumental Teacher?   Adviser?
Lecturer?   Inspector?   Independent Consultant?
Administrator?**

*NAME can provide you with the individual professional
support you need*

The National Association of Music Educators exists to assist
its members, through its network of professional support, in
the development of music education of the highest quality
which is accessible to all, by

■ contributing to the creation of a strong and unified voice for
music education nationally
■ providing a forum for professional exchange through local,
national and regional events
■ promoting the professional development of members
■ nforming members of current developments by publications,
newsletters and a website
■ collaborating with other appropriate organisations

*Why not join us and let NAME provide you with the professional
support you need*

For further details or an informal chat about NAME,
please contact: Helen Fraser, NAME Administrator
Gordon Lodge, Snitterton Road,
Matlock, Derbyshire DE4 3LZ
Tel/Fax: 01629 760791
e-mail:musiceducation@name.org.uk
website:www.name.org.uk

THE NATIONAL ASSOCIATION
OF YOUTH ORCHESTRAS

**25th FESTIVAL OF BRITISH YOUTH ORCHESTRAS
& YOUTH CHOIRS**
Saturday 14 August – Sunday 5 September 2004
Central Hall, West Tollcross, Edinburgh
& Academy Concert Hall, RSAMD, Glasgow
EUROPEAN YOUTH MUSIC WEEK
July – August 2004
**ALLIANZ CORNHILL MUSICAL INSURANCE
YOUTH ORCHESTRA AWARDS**
ALLIANZ CORNHILL MUSICAL INSURANCE CONDUCTING PRIZE/SEMINAR
January 2004
**SCHOTT MUSIK INTERNATIONAL
YOUTH ORCHESTRA / YOUTH CHOIR AWARD**

The Marion Semple Weir Library of Chamber Music
Newsletter 'Full Orchestra'
Directory of Youth & Student Orchestras
Youth Orchestra Tours Guide
Student Email Newsletter
European Association of Youth Orchestras
Website – www.nayo.org.uk - updated monthly

THE NATIONAL ASSOCIATION
OF YOUTH ORCHESTRAS

Central Hall, West Tollcross, Edinburgh EH3 9BP,
t: 0131 221 1927 f: 0131 229 2921
e:admin@nayo.org.uk
President: Sir Simon Rattle CBE Chairman: Sir John Manduell CBE
*Serving 125,000 young musicians
in 1,800 youth orchestras and ensembles throughout the UK*

Registered Charity No 281493

Tune in to Youth Music!

Youth Music is bringing music-making to those children
and young people who would otherwise not have the
opportunity.

Supporting music of all styles and all cultures, Youth
Music is funding diverse projects and initiatives that will
motivate children and young people to become involved
in their communities through music.

For more information about these or other Youth Music initiatives
and an online application form for our funding programmes, go to
www.youthmusic.org.uk or call 020 7902 1060

YOUTH MUSIC

... putting children and young people
at the heart of regeneration

Youth Music is funded by
the National Lottery through Arts Council England

The
Nordoff-Robbins
Music Therapy Centre

**Director and Head of Training: Pauline Etkin
2 Lissenden Gardens, London NW5 1PP**

**In addition to being a Clinic where children and
adults can receive Music Therapy, the Centre offers
a two year full-time training course in music therapy
for professional musicians, leading to a Master of
Music Therapy degree validated by The City
University, London. The course is designed to equip
graduate therapists to work with children, young
people and adults with a variety of needs. These
include people with autism, learning and physical
disabilities, emotional and mental health problems
and ill health. The focus of Year 1 is on work with
children and adolescents whilst Year 2 concentrates
on clinical work with adults.**

**Short informative conferences are arranged at the
Centre.**

**Visitors are welcome to visit the Centre by
arrangement.**

**All enquiries to:
The Administrator,
The Nordoff-Robbins Music Therapy Centre,
2 Lissenden Gardens, London NW5 1PP
tel: 020 7267 4496 fax: 020 7267 4369
email: admin@nordoff-robbins.org.uk**

London NW2 1HU *tel:* 020 8455 1030 *fax:* 020 8455 1030 *email:* mana_admin@onetel.net.uk. John Williams, president; Tony Lamb, chair; Laurence Bielby, treasurer; Joan R Horrocks, admin. *Organises concerts to assist the peace movement. Professionals, amateurs and non-performing mus lovers welcome, as well as affiliations from mus bodies. Quarterly newsletter, free to members. Annual subscription £7.50 (unwaged £2, affiliations £15).*

Musicians Benevolent Fund. 16 Ogle St, London W1W 6JA *tel:* 020 7636 4481 *fax:* 020 7637 4307 *email:* info@mbf.org.uk. Helen Faulkner, sec; Christopher Yates, chmn. *Largest charity in the UK providing help and support to musicians and those in related occupations in any area of mus, who are in need. Runs various award schemes for young musicians and maintains an online database detailing some 200 mus awards and scholarships (see website).*

Musicians Benevolent Fund, Friends of the. 16 Ogle St, London W1W 6JA *tel:* 020 7636 4481 *fax:* 020 7637 4307 *email:* info@mbf.org.uk. Michael White, admin of public affairs. *Supports the* **Musicians Benevolent Fund** *(above).*

Musicians in Focus. 1 Poets Rd, London N5 2SL *tel:* 020 7354 2050 *fax:* 020 7359 7535 *email:* info@musiciansinfocus.org. Jacqueline Clifton, dir; Daniel de Azevedo, dir. *Founded in response to a demand for access to mus tech by visually-impaired musicians. Organises w/shops and demonstrations. Advises at all levels of educ on access to coursework and exams.*

Musicians' Social and Benevolent Council. 100a Weston Park, Crouch End, London N8 9PP *tel:* 020 8348 9358 *fax:* 020 8348 9358. Harry Gold, chmn; Richard Watson, hon treasurer; Andrew Wickens, vice chmn; Geraldine Chalmers, hon sec; Maurice Jennings, hon trustee; Peter Cameron, hon trustee; John Edney, hon trustee. Leslie Evans, John Dankworth OBE, John Williams, patrons. *Assists London-based professional musicians in times of sickness and distress. Mainly funded by contributions from London orch and theatre musicians. All donations gratefully received. Not connected to the Musicians Benevolent Fund or the Musicians' Union.*

Musicians' Union National Office. 60-62 Clapham Rd, London SW9 0JJ *tel:* 020 7582 5566 *fax:* 020 7582 9805 *email:* info@musiciansunion.org.uk. John Smith, gen sec; Howard Evans, asst gen sec - media; David Ashley, asst gen sec - admin; Horace Trubridge, asst gen sec - live. *The Musicians' Union was established in 1893 and represents over 31,000 musicians working in all sectors of the mus business, including writers and teachers. As well as negotiating on its member's behalf with all the major employers in the industry, the MU offers a range of services tailored for the self-employed by providing assistance for full-time professional, semi-pro and student mus of all ages.*

Musicworld. 23 Hitchin St, Biggleswade, Beds SG18 8AX *tel:* 01767 316521 *fax:* 01767 317221 *email:* musicworld@lindsaymusic.co.uk. Douglas Coombes, mus dir; Rose Miles, membership sec; Carole Lindsay-Douglas, ed. *Termly resource magazine for primary and middle-school teachers. Membership includes right to photocopy for use within own school. (Formerly known as National Junior Music Club of Great Britain).*

NUS Ents. 45 Underwood St, London N1 7LG *tel:* 020 7490 0946 *fax:* 020 7490 1026 *email:* info@nus-ents.co.uk. Steve Hoyland, development mgr. *National representative body of over 600 student unions providing advice, training and publications to student entertainment depts. Co-ordinate events, tours, student media and promotions.*

National Association for Gifted Children. Suite 14, Challenge House, Sherwood Drive, Bletchley, Milton Keynes MK3 6DP *tel:* 0870 770 3217 *fax:* 0870 770 3219 *email:* amazingchildren@nagcbritain.org.uk. Stephen Tommis, dir. *A national charity helping able and talented children to achieve fulfilment, and advising those involved in their upbringing and educ, including the DFES.*

National Association for Music in Higher Education (NAMHE). School of Sport and Performing Arts, University of Wolverhampton, Gorway Rd, Walsall WS1 3BD *tel:* 01902 323209 *fax:* 01902 323148 *email:* a.bayley@wlv.ac.uk. Amanda Bayley, sec. *Professional subject association for mus in HE. Membership is institutional. Forum for debate and exchange of information about all matters relating to mus in HE including teaching, research and general admin concerns.*

National Association for Primary Education (NAPE). Moulton College, Moulton, Northampton NN3 7RR *tel:* 01604 647646 *fax:* 01604 647660 *email:* nationaloffice@nape.org.uk. John Coe, national sec. *Membership includes parents, teachers, governors, school communities and others who share concern for children's educ from 0-13. National Festival of Children's Voices held annually in London, regional festivals held in Oxford and Luton.*

The National Association for Special Education Needs. NASEN House, 4-5 Amber Business Village, Amber Close, Amington, Tamworth B77 4RP *tel:* 01827 311500 *fax:* 01827 313005 *email:* welcome@nasen.org.uk. Beverley Walters, office mgr. *Promotes the development of children and young people with special educ needs, wherever they are located, offering support to those who work with them.*

National Association of Careers and Guidance Teachers. 9 Lawrence Leys, Bloxham, Banbury OX15 4NU *tel:* 01295 720809 *fax:* 01295 720809 *email:* nacgt@freeuk.com. A Vincent, gen sec. *Professional association for careers teachers and others involved in careers educ and guidance.*

National Association of Music Educators. Gordon Lodge, Snitterton Rd, Matlock, Derbys DE4 3LZ *tel:* 01629 760791 *fax:* 01629 760791 *email:* musiceducation@name.org.uk. Helen Fraser, admin. *Represents all those involved in mus educ - advisers, inspectors, teachers; lecturers in schools, FE, conservatoires and teacher educ; publishers and the educ industry; specialist organisations and freelance mus educ consultants. Network of professional support provides national and regional conferences, training days, meetings, w/shops and subject support and advice for teachers and inspectors. Also provides information for parents, governors, headteachers, politicians and the mus industry. Various publications on application as well as quarterly newsletter and biannual magazine.*

National Association of Musical Instrument Repairers. 48 Gallants Farm Rd, E Barnet, Herts EN4 8ES *tel:* 020 8368 4296. G Lawson, chmn; David Hinton, sec; Phil Foulger, membership sec. *Individual repairers dedicated to maintaining standards of quality in a particular inst. Enables enquirers to contact a local repairer of the appropriate specialism. See website for list of all repairers throughout the British Isles that are members of NAMIR.*

National Association of Percussion Teachers. 11 Mallard Close, Kempshott, Basingstoke RG22 5JP *tel:* 01256 329009 *fax:* 01256 329009 *email:* wendy.harding@bigfoot.com. Wendy A Harding, sec. *Aims to further the knowledge of perc playing and teaching and ensure the highest standards are maintained.*

(NASUWT) National Association of Schoolmasters Union of Women Teachers. Hillscourt Education Centre, Rose Hill, Rednal, Birmingham B45 8RS *tel:* 0121 453 6150 *fax:* 0121 457 6208 *email:* nasuwt@mail.nasuwt.org.uk. Eamonn O'Kane, gen sec; Christine Keates, deputy gen sec.

National Association of Youth Orchestras. Central Hall, West Tollcross, Edinburgh EH3 9BP *tel:* 0131 221 1927 *fax:* 0131 229 2921 *email:* admin@nayo.org.uk. Carol Main, dir. *National association for youth orchs throughout UK. Activities include annual Festival of British Youth Orchestras in Edinburgh and Glasgow, European Youth Music Week, Allianz Cornhill Musical Insurance Conducting Prize/Seminar (biennial), Allianz Cornhill Musical Insurance Youth Orchestra Awards (annual - entry limited to members), Schott Musik International Youth Orchestra Award. Newsletter 'Full Orchestra' published 3 times pa, free to members. Marion Semple Weir library of chmbr mus, (no hire charges to members). Directory of Youth and Student Orchestras, free to members. Youth Orchestras Tour Guide, free to members. For information on the European Association of Youth Orchestras contact Anneke van Nes, Otterswijk 13, NL-7701 PC Dedemsvaart, The Netherlands tel: 00 31 5236 38435.*

National Campaign for the Arts. Pegasus House, 37-43 Sackville St, London W1S 3EH *tel:* 020 7333 0375 *fax:* 020 7333 0660 *email:* nca@artscampaign.org.uk. Victoria Todd, dir; Anna Leatherdale, deputy dir. *NCA is the only independent lobbying organisation that represents all the arts. The campaign is funded entirely by its members to ensure its independence. It gives a voice for the arts world in all its diversity. The NCA meets, lobbies and influences decision makers - ministers, shadow ministers, officials, council leaders, peers, journalists and influential back benchers. It discusses policy and proposals in detail with major arts funders on a regular basis. Produces 'Arts News' (4 pa) and 'Arts Care' (10 pa) plus occasional papers.*

National Early Music Association (NEMA). 137 Preston Rd, Wembley HA9 8NW *tel:* 020 8904 1076 *fax:* 020 8723 7787 *email:* mwindi4108@aol.com. Mark Windisch, treasurer, admin. *Publishes the 'Early Music Yearbook' incorporating the 'Register of Early Music' and a twice yearly magazine 'Early Music Performer'.*

National Harmonica League. 112 Hag Hill Rise, Taplow, Maidenhead, Berks SL6 0LT *tel:* 01628 604069 *email:* nhl@harmonica.co.uk. *Roger Trobridge, chmn; Paul Jones, president. For harmonica enthusiasts; newsletter, events and national festival.*

National Institute of Adult Continuing Education (NIACE). 21 De Montfort St, Leicester LE1 7GE *tel:* 0116 204 4200 *fax:* 0116 285 4514 *email:* enquiries@niace.org.uk. Helen Kruse, librarian. *National organisation for adult learning.*

National Music Council. 60-62 Clapham Rd, London SW9 0JJ *tel:* 020

7820 9992 *fax:* 020 7820 9972 *email:* nationalmusiccouncil@ukonline.co.uk. Robin Osterley, chmn; Fiona Penny, admin. *Forum for mus organisations concerned to further the interests of mus and musicians in the UK. The National Music Council seeks to celebrate and promote the value and enjoyment of mus, which contributes, in all its forms, to the cultural, spiritual, educ, social and economic well-being of the UK.*

National Operatic and Dramatic Association (NODA). NODA House, 58-60 Lincoln Rd, Peterborough PE1 2RZ *tel:* 0870 770 2480 *fax:* 0870 770 2490 *email:* everyone@noda.org.uk. Mark Pemberton, chief exec; Jo Rowell, summer school admin, PA to chief exec; Brian Bell, pantomimes mgr; Richard Westbrook, IT/membership; Kathy Lewis, sales mgr; Elaine Buckley, finance mgr. *Umbrella body for the amateur theatre. Services include discounted sales of mus, scripts, make-up, insurance, etc to members. Also summer school and conferences.*

National Union of Teachers. Hamilton House, Mabledon Place, London WC1H 9BD *tel:* 020 7388 6191 *fax:* 020 7387 8458. Doug McAvoy, gen sec; Steve Sinnott, deputy gen sec.

National Youth Jazz Association (NYJA). 11 Victor Rd, Harrow, Middx HA2 6PT *tel:* 020 8863 2717 *fax:* 020 8863 8685 *email:* bill.ashton@virgin.net. William Ashton, chmn. *Organises 2 Sat clinics by the National Youth Jazz Orchestra and w/shops throughout Britain usually in conjunction with a concert by NYJO.*

North West Composers' Association. 26 Stanway Rd, Whitefield, Manchester M45 8EG *tel:* 0161 766 5950 *email:* colin@dacapomusic.co.uk. David Ellis, press and publicity offr; Colin Bayliss, sec. *Association comprises NW-based composers who promote concerts, organise educ w/shops, produce CD recordings and help to raise the awareness of contemporary mus.*

Northumbrian Pipers' Society. 7 Halton Drive, Wideopen, Northumberland NE13 6AA *tel:* 0191 236 5724 *email:* seumas@richmond77.freeserve.co.uk; Julia.Say@nspipes.co.uk. J Richmond, hon sec. *Supports the playing and making of Northumbrian pipes, and the composition of traditional Northumbrian mus.*

Notelink. PO Box 50, Sleaford, Lincs NG34 8XJ *tel:* 01400 262363 *fax:* 01400 262363 *email:* admin@notelink.org. Malcolm Goodman MBE, dir. *Registered charity supporting mus in the community.*

Opera and Music Theatre Forum. 54 Astonville St, London SW18 5AJ *tel:* 020 8516 6313 *email:* info@omtf.org.uk. Caroline Anderson, mgr. *Promotes the production, accessibility, understanding and enjoyment of opera and mus theatre. Represents and publicises the work of its members to promoters, funders and public bodies.*

The Operetta Foundation. 27 Cheetham Fold Rd, Hyde, Cheshire SK14 5DU *tel:* 0161 366 1971. Jeffrey Lomas, chmn; Joan Pancott-Lomas, development; Helen Thompson, finance controller. *Promotes and sponsors operetta.*

Orff Society (UK). 7 Rothesay Ave, Richmond, Surrey TW10 5EB *tel:* 020 8876 1944 *fax:* 020 8876 1944 *email:* orffsocuk@talk21.com. Margaret Murray, hon sec. *Through teachers' courses it promotes Orff's creative approach to mus educ, stressing improvisation and using voices, movement and perc insts.*

The Organ Club. 48 Cloudesley Mansions, Cloudesley Place, London N1 0ED *tel:* 020 7278 0801 *email:* steve.dunk@btinternet.com. Steve Dunk, membership sec. *A worldwide society for friends of the org. Monthly visits to hear new and historic insts. Annual longer tour alternately in the UK and abroad. Newsletter 6 times a year and journal 3 times a year. Large library housed at RAM, London. Prospectus with further details available from Steve Dunk, details above.*

Organists' Benevolent League. 10 Stratford Place, London W1C 1BA. Martin Neary, president; Richard Lyne, sec. *Charity to provide assistance for organists or their dependants in cases of need.*

PAMRA - Performing Artists' Media Rights Association. 161 Borough High St, London SE1 1HR *tel:* 020 7940 0400 *fax:* 020 7407 2008 *email:* office@pamra.org.uk. Sabine Schlag, exec dir. *Society set up by UK performers which administers the performers' right. Distributes money to performers arising from the use or public broadcast of their recordings, both in the UK and overseas. Printed information available.*

Pavel Haas Foundation UK. 7 Roma Read Close, Bessborough Rd, London SW15 4AZ *tel:* 020 8785 4772 *email:* pavelfoundation@aol.com. *Focussing on performance and holocaust education awareness for the 21st century.*

Philatelic Music Circle. 22 Bouverie Gardens, Kenton, Middx HA3 0RQ *tel:* 020 8907 2790 *fax:* 020 8907 2790 *email:* mwadem@hotmail.com. Irene Lawford, president and consultant ed; Geoffrey Datson, hon chmn. *For mus stamp collectors. Magazine 'The Baton'; holds meetings, exchanges, competitions, exhibitions. A/v programme on loan, library, worldwide membership.*

Piano Trio Society. Victoria House, The Green, Sarratt, Herts WD3 6AY *tel:* 01923 265066 *fax:* 01923 265066. *International membership*

organisation for performers, amateurs, composers, mus publishers, corporate members and mus lovers with a wide-ranging programme of events based on the pno trio medium. 3 newsletters pa.

Pianoforte Tuners' Association. 10 Reculver Rd, Herne Bay, Kent CT6 6LD *tel:* 01227 368808 *fax:* 01227 368808 *email:* secretary@pianotuner.org.uk. Mrs V M Addis, sec. *The association has country-wide membership. An examination is required for entry.*

The Pianola Institute. 111a Station Rd, W Wickham, Kent BR4 0PX *tel:* 020 8462 3384. Denis Hall, chmn; C L'Enfant, sec. *Journal, concerts, rolls and information archive.*

Piobaireachd Society. 20 Otago St, Glasgow G12 8JH *tel:* 0141 334 3587 *fax:* 0141 337 3024 *email:* info@piping.scot.net. Dugald MacNeill, sec.

Player Piano Group. 93 Evelyn Ave, Ruislip, Middx HA4 8AH *tel:* 01895 634288 *email:* anthonyaustin@lineone.net. Tony Austin, hon sec. *Concerned with the mus, mechanical and historic aspects of the player pno and the reproducing pno; organises social meetings, a quarterly bulletin and occasional public concerts.*

Polish Cultural Institute. 34 Portland Place, London W1B 1HQ *tel:* 0870 774 2900 *fax:* 020 7637 2190 *email:* pci@polishculture.org.uk. Joanna Stachyra, dir; Malgorzata Szum, deputy dir; Diana Walles, press offr. *Promotes Polish arts in Great Britain in general. Assists in arranging Polish-British contacts.*

Pro Corda Trust (National School for Young Chamber Music Players). Leiston Abbey House, Theberton Rd, Leiston, Suffolk IP16 4TB *tel:* 01728 831354 *fax:* 01728 832500 *email:* mail@procorda.fsbusiness.co.uk. Mererid Crump, admin; Sir Colin Davis, president. *Courses held during school holidays for young str players and pianists under the direction of distinguished musicians. See* **Summer Schools and Short Courses** *section.*

Professional Association of Teachers (PAT). Press Office, 2 St James' Court, Friar Gate, Derby DE1 1BT *tel:* 01332 372337 *fax:* 01332 290310 *email:* hq@pat.org.uk. Jean Gemmell, gen sec; Richard Fraser, communications offr. *Independent trade union and professional association with around 35,000 members from all parts of the UK in both the maintained and independent sectors, teaching at all levels from nursery to FE and HE. Also includes educ support staff and child carers. PAT is non-party political, has a no-strike policy and is not affiliated to the TUC. A publications list is available.*

The RVW Society. c/o Tudor Cottage, 30 Tivoli Rd, Brighton, E Sussex BN1 5BH *tel:* 01273 501118 *email:* davidbetts@tudorcottage.plus.com. David Betts, sec; Stephen Connock, chmn. *Aims to increase knowledge and appreciation of Ralph Vaughan Williams' mus and to encourage performances of lesser known works.*

RVW Trust. 16 Ogle St, London W1W 6JA *tel:* 020 7255 2590 *fax:* 020 7255 2591. Helen Faulkner, admin and sec. *Assists young British composers with premieres and second performances, and promotes works by neglected British composers of the past. Also considers applications from concert promoters and mus festivals who programme mus by young British composers.*

Rachmaninoff Society. 96 Kenilworth Rd, Coventry, W Midlands CV4 7AH *tel:* 024 7641 8789 *email:* rachmaninoff_society@hotmail.com; rachmaninoffsociety@yahoo.co.uk. Denise Beech, admin. *Promotes Rachmaninoff as a composer, pianist and cond. Publishes quarterly newsletter; annual conference in UK and North America.*

Commercial Radio Companies Association. The Radiocentre, 77 Shaftesbury Ave, London W1D 5DU *tel:* 020 7306 2603 *fax:* 020 7470 0062 *email:* info@crca.co.uk. Paul Brown, chief exec. *Trade body for UK commercial radio, representing commercial radio to government, the European institutions, Ofcom, copyright societies and other organisations involved with radio. Acts as a source of advice to members and administers the Radio Advertising Clearance Centre (RACC) - a clearing house for radio advertising.*

The Rawsthorne Trust. The Alpines, Main St, Hemingbrough, Selby, N Yorks YO8 6QF *tel:* 01757 630256 *fax:* 01757 630256. John Belcher, chair. *Promotes the mus of Rawsthorne with recordings, live concerts, publications, etc. Publishes 'The Creel' annually.*

Registry of Guitar Tutors (RGT). Registry Mews, 11-13 Wilton Rd, Bexhill, E Sussex TM40 1HY *tel:* 01424 222222 *fax:* 01422 213221 *email:* mail@RegistryofGuitarTutors.com. Chaz Hart, mkt mgr. *In association with London College of Music, organises a range of graded and diploma exams in electric, bs and classical gui. Publishes an annual directory of registered gui tutors.*

The Ronald Stevenson Society. 3 Chamberlain Rd, Edinburgh EH10 4DL *fax:* 0131 229 9298 *email:* info@rssoc.org.uk. P Hutton, chmn; C Scott-Sutherland, treasurer; Ian Colquhoun, sec. *Promotes the performance and recording of the work of Ronald Stevenson, and prints and publishes his mus: catalogue available.*

Royal College of Music, Frank Bridge Bequest *formerly* **The Frank Bridge Trust.** Royal College of Music, Prince Consort Rd, London SW7

2BS *tel:* 020 7591 4394 *fax:* 020 7589 7740 *email:* pbanks@rcm.ac.uk. Paul Banks, chmn. *Promotes the performance of the mus of Frank Bridge through support of concerts, recordings and publications.*

Royal College of Organists. 7 St Andrew Street, London EC4A 3LQ *tel:* 020 7936 3606 *fax:* 020 7353 8244 *email:* admin@rco.org.uk. Gordon Clarke, registrar; Alan Dear, snr exec; Robin Langley, librarian; Simon Williams, educ offr. *Educ charity of 3200 members for promotion of org playing and choral directing. Exams for Associateship, Fellowship diplomas, choral directing and org teaching diplomas and new certificate exam. Library and programme of lectures, seminars, short courses, overseas tours, m/classes. Also student section.*

Royal Liverpool Philharmonic. Philharmonic Hall, Hope St, Liverpool L1 9BP *tel:* 0151 210 2895 *fax:* 0151 210 2902 *email:* info@liverpoolphil.com. Gerard Schwarz, mus dir; Michael Elliot, chief exec; Sandra Parr, head of programming. *Promotes the Royal Liverpool Philharmonic Orchestra and Choir, the Merseyside Youth Orchestra and the Community Education Department as well as managing the Philharmonic Hall itself.*

Royal Musical Association (RMA). c/o Royal Academy of Music, Marylebone Rd, London NW1 5HT *fax:* 0161 861 7543 *email:* jeffrey.dean@stingrayoffice.com. Hugh Cobbe, president; Geoffrey Lawrence, hon treasurer; Jeffrey Dean, sec. *Holds meetings for the presentation of musicological papers and publishes 'The Journal of the Royal Musical Association', a research chronicle, a newsletter and a series of monographs. It hosts 1-day meetings, an annual conference and a conference for research students. Awards annually the Dent Medal, Jerome Roche Prize, and Peter le Huray Memorial Lecture.*

Royal Philharmonic Society. 10 Stratford Place, London W1C 1BA *tel:* 020 7491 8110 *fax:* 020 7493 7463 *email:* admin@royalphilharmonicsociety.org.uk. Rosemary Johnson, gen admin. *Financial support for commissions, lectures and new mus events. Administers competitions and awards for students in UK; also international Gold Medal and annual RPS Music Awards for outstanding achievement. Membership by application.*

Royal School of Church Music. Cleveland Lodge, Westhumble, Dorking RH5 6BW *tel:* 01306 872800 *fax:* 01306 887260 *email:* enquiries@rscm.com. Chris Wardle, course admin; Emily Ayres, membership co-ord. *Training, publishing and advisory organisation for the development of church mus. Membership open to all churches, with or without choirs, to schools and to individuals, with concessionary rates for students and young people.*

Royal Scottish Country Dance Society. 12 Coates Cres, Edinburgh EH3 7AF *tel:* 0131 225 3854 *fax:* 0131 225 7783 *email:* info@rscds.org. Ms E Gray, sec. *Aims to preserve and further the practice of traditional Scottish country dancing and to provide educ and instruction to this end. Has 166 branches throughout the world and more than 500 affiliated groups. Founded 1923.*

Royal Scottish Pipers' Society. 127 Rose St Lane South, Edinburgh EH2 4BB *tel:* 0131 225 4123; 01259 743017. A W McGhie, sec.

The Royal Society of Musicians of Great Britain. 10 Stratford Place, London W1C 1BA *tel:* 020 7629 6137 *fax:* 020 7629 6137. Maggie Gibb, sec. *The society exists to provide help for professional musicians and their families in need as a result of illness, accident or old age.*

St John's, Smith Square, Friends of. St John's, Smith Square, London SW1P 3HA *tel:* 020 7222 2168 *fax:* 020 7233 1618. Francesca Goddard, development offr. *Mailing list membership, priority booking, concerts (evening and lunchtime), art exhibitions, ticket discounts. Free entry to Thu lunchtime concert series.*

Schools Music Association of Great Britain (SMA). 71 Margaret Rd, New Barnet, Herts EN4 9NT *tel:* 020 8440 6919 *fax:* 020 8440 6919 *email:* maxwellpryce@educamus.free-online.co.uk. Maxwell Pryce MBE, hon sec and chief exec. *Promotes the mus educ of school pupils and students by encouraging and supporting all who work with them.*

Schubert Institute (UK). 56a Moor Lane, Sherburn-in-Elmet, Leeds LS25 6DN *tel:* 01977 682691 *email:* info@franzschubert.org.uk. Julian Rushton, chmn; Paul Reid, vice-chmn. *Aims to promote the study of Schubert's life and work and appreciation of his mus. All Schubert lovers welcomed. Affiliated to International Franz Schubert Institute, Vienna. Schubert Institute Research Centre inaugurated May 1997 at University of Leeds.*

Schubert Society of Britain. c/o The General Secretary, German YMCA, 35 Craven Terrace, London W2 3EL *tel:* 020 7723 9276 *fax:* 020 7706 2870 *email:* y-services@german-ymca.org.uk. U Bauer, sec. *The Schubert Society presents 'Schubertiades' in London monthly, Oct-May (except Dec), as a forum for young artists.*

Scottish Amateur Music Association. 18 Craigton Cres, Alva, Clackmannanshire FK12 5DS *tel:* 01259 760249 *email:* secretary@sama.org.uk. Margaret W Simpson, hon sec. *Provides national training courses to help and encourage amateur mus-making in Scotland.*

Scottish Association for Music Education. Music Dept, Fife Council, Auchterderran Centre, Woodend Rd, Cardenden KY5 0NE *tel:* 01592 414600 *fax:* 01592 414641 *email:* graeme.wilson@fife.gov.uk. Graeme Wilson, sec; M Miller, chmn. *Journals. Annual conference. Curriculum support and influence.*

Scottish Music Education Forum. Faculty of Education, University of Aberdeen, Hilton Place, Aberdeen AB24 4FA *tel:* 01224 274558 (direct)/779 (sec)/500 (gen) *fax:* 01224 283900 (gen)/877 (direct) *email:* j.p.stephens@abdn.ac.uk. Jonathan Stephens, dir of mus, head of aesthetic educ. *Acts as co-ordinating body, providing a point of contact for those involved in mus and mus educ courses, associations and societies. Membership (on an informal basis) consists of representatives from wide range of mus interests: school, HE, commerce, industry and special interest groups including Scottish traditional mus. Aims to promote diversity of mus in Scotland, maintain particular strengths, collate and disseminate information, and identify and promote good practice.*

Scottish Music Information Centre. 1 Bowmont Gardens, Glasgow G12 9LR *tel:* 0141 334 6393 *fax:* 0141 337 1161 *email:* info@smic.dircon.co.uk. Andrew Logan, chief exec; Alasdair Pettinger, information mgr; Mee-Ching Ho, admin. *Exists to document and promote Scottish mus. Reference library with over 10,000 scores of Scottish composers' works, some available for sale/hire. Also comprehensive database of Scottish musicians and organisations. Photocopying and binding facilities, promotional activities.*

Scottish Secondary Teachers' Association. 15 Dundas St, Edinburgh EH3 6QG *tel:* 0131 556 5919 *fax:* 0131 556 1419 *email:* info@ssta.org.uk. David Eaglesham, gen sec. *Professional association for secondary teachers in Scotland. Recognised at the Scottish Executive Education Dept and represented on the Scottish Negotiating Committee for Teachers. Publishes bulletins (6 pa) for members only.*

Secondary Heads Association. 130 Regent Rd, Leicester LE1 7PG *tel:* 0116 299 1122 *fax:* 0116 299 1123 *email:* info@sha.org.uk. John Dunford, gen sec. *Professional association which caters specifically for the leaders of secondary schools and colleges.*

Seeds Ltd (Christian Creative Resource Service). 30 Grasvenor Ave, Barnet, Herts EN5 2BZ *tel:* 020 8364 9652 *email:* seeds30@aol.com. Neil Ruckman, admin and educ; Chris Norris, chmn. *Provides creative arts w/shops with professional artists in schools, churches and prisons. These tackle themes such as worship, relationships, human rights and environmental issues.*

The Serge Prokofiev Association. Information Services, Goldsmiths College, University of London, London SE14 6NW *tel:* 020 7919 7558 *fax:* 020 7919 7255 *email:* n.mann@gold.ac.uk. Noëlle Mann, sec. *Promotes public awareness of the works and life of Serge Prokofiev in particular, and of 20th C Russian culture in general. Publishes a biannual journal 'Three Oranges' and organises events.*

UK Sibelius Society. 5 Fitzwilliam Rd, London SW4 0DL *tel:* 020 7627 3086; 020 7583 6357 *fax:* 020 7583 6358 *email:* edward@tallisgroup.com. E W Clark, president; A Barnett, chmn. *Promotes the works of Sibelius. Quarterly newsletter and awards for best CD and artist. Regular concerts held in London. Promotion activities with the Finnish Embassy.*

The Silvester (Victor) Appreciation Society. 1 Portland Cres, Weymouth, Dorset DT4 0NW *tel:* 01305 784379. Geoff Williams, sec. *Produces 3 newsletters pa.*

Simpson (Robert) Society. 5 Sispara Gardens, London SW18 1LG *tel:* 020 8877 1185 *email:* stokeshazell@hotmail.com. Terry Hazell, chmn/acting sec. *Promotes study, performance and recording of the mus and writings of Robert Simpson.*

The Sir George Dyson Trust. 22 Pheasants Way, Rickmansworth, Herts WD3 7ES *email:* lforeman@nildram.co.uk; impulse@impulse-music.co.uk. Lewis Foreman, admin. *Promotes all aspects of Dyson's life and mus; supports recordings and performances.*

Society for Co-operation in Russian & Soviet Studies. 320 Brixton Rd, London SW9 6AB *tel:* 020 7274 2282 *fax:* 020 7274 3230 *email:* ruslibrary@scrss.org.uk. J Rosen, hon librarian; J Cunningham, library asst. *Reference library of mus scores, encyclopedias and records pertaining to Russian and Soviet mus and composers.*

Society for Education, Music and Psychology Research (SEMPRE). c/o RNIB, 105 Judd St, London WC1H 9NE *tel:* 020 7391 2022 *fax:* 020 7391 2034 *email:* membership@sempre.org.uk. Elissa Bourne, membership sec; Graham Welch, chair; Susan Hallam, ed. *Aims to encourage the exchange of ideas and to disseminate research findings in the fields of psychology of mus and in mus educ.*

Society for Music Analysis. Royal Holloway, University of London, Egham, Surrey TW20 0EX *tel:* 01784 443534 *fax:* 01784 439441 *email:* matthew.riley@btinternet.com. Matthew Riley, treasurer, admin. *Society for the development of all aspects of mus analysis, especially research and teaching. Open to lecturers, students and all who are interested in analysis.*

Society of Assistants Teaching in Preparatory Schools - Music Broadsheet. 20 Brycedale Cres, Southgate, London N14 7EY *tel:* 020 8882 0630 *fax:* 020 8882 0630 *email:* satips@ford.anglia.ac.uk. June Keyte, ed. *The mus section of an organisation covering all subjects taught in prep schools. Publishes termly broadsheets for members and organises occasional conferences.*

Society of Headmasters and Headmistresses of Independent Schools. Celedston, Rhosesmor Rd, Halkyn, Holywell CH8 8DL *tel:* 01352 781102 *fax:* 01352 781102 *email:* gensec@shmis.org.uk. I D Cleland, gen sec. *An association of 95 heads of independent secondary schools with 6th forms. Most of the schools have boarders and almost all are wholly or partly co-educational. The society represents the smaller independent school offering a balanced educ to pupils of widely varying interests and abilities; also included are two of the specialist mus schools and two ballet schools.*

Society of Leisure and Entertainment Consultants and Publishers (SOLCAP). 1 Sandringham Close, Sandringham Park, Tarleton, Lancs PR4 6UZ *tel:* 01772 816046; 07752 722462. J B A Sharples, dir. *Represents consultants and publishers in the field of entertainment and the arts, recreation, marketing, leisure and allied interests.*

Society of Producers and Composers of Applied Music (PCAM). Birchwood Hall, Storridge, Malvern, Worcs WR13 5EZ *tel:* 01886 884204 *helpline:* 0906 895 0908 *fax:* 01886 884204 *email:* bfromer@netcomuk.co.uk. Bob Fromer, admin. *A trade association representing composers, producers and mus production companies who create mus for advertising, television programmes and other a/v applications.*

Society of Recorder Players. 15 Palliser Rd, London W14 9EB *tel:* 020 7385 7321 *email:* secretary@srp.org.uk. A Read, sec. *A national society with international membership offering rcdr players in the UK the opportunity to meet regularly and play in conducted ens. 52 groups meet nationwide, mostly on a monthly basis. Members also receive 'The Recorder Magazine' quarterly. Annual festival and other events take place throughout the year.*

Society of Schoolmasters and Schoolmistresses. SGBI Office, Queen Mary House, Manor Park Rd, Chistlehurst, Kent BR7 5PY *tel:* 020 8468 7997 *fax:* 020 8468 7200 *email:* sgbi@sgbi.freeserve.co.uk. L I Baggott, sec; Sarah Brydon, case offr and field worker. *Gives assistance to necessitous masters and mistresses of all recognised schools, independent or maintained, and their dependants, provided such persons have been continuously engaged in teaching for not less than 10 years.*

Society of Teachers of the Alexander Technique (STAT). Linton House, 39-51 Highgate Rd, London NW5 1RS *tel:* 020 7284 3338 *fax:* 020 7482 5435 *email:* enquiries@stat.org.uk. Tereza Noguiera, public enquiries. *Provides lists of teachers worldwide plus information on schools, training and affiliated societies.*

Sonic Arts Network. The Jerwood Space, 171 Union St, London SE1 0LN *tel:* 020 7928 7337 *email:* phil@sonicartsnetwork.org; darryl@sonicartsnetwork.org; helen@sonicartsnetwork.org. Phil Hallett, exec dir; Darryl Biggs, communications offr; Helen de Witt, programme dir. *UK organisation for those interested in experimental approaches to sound and the ways in which new technology is transforming the nature and practice of mus. A performance, information and educ resource with members worldwide. Aims to raise awareness and innovate new approaches to sonic art by commissioning, encouraging and promoting new and exciting work, and raise awareness to sonic art through information, opportunity and educ.*

The Sorabji Archive. Easton Dene, Bailbrook Lane, Bath BA1 7AA *tel:* 01225 852323 *fax:* 01225 852523 *email:* sorabji-archive@ lineone.net; alistair_hinton@compuserve.com. Alistair Hinton, curator and dir. *Makes available to the public the mus and literary collection of Sorabji's works. Includes published, ms and new edition scores; articles and essays; reviews of books, mus publications, concerts and recordings; correspondence and discography.*

Sound Sense. 7 Tavern St, Stowmarket, Suffolk IP14 1PJ *tel:* 01449 673990 *fax:* 01449 673994 *email:* info@soundsense.org. Kathryn Deane, dir. *The national development agency for community mus. Aims towards participatory, creative mus-making, offering support, advice and training to community musicians and groups as well as other arts and educ organisations. Information services include newsletters, publications, mus and disability advice and helplines.*

spnm - promoting new music. 4th Floor, 18-20 Southwark St, London SE1 1TJ *tel:* 020 7407 1640 *fax:* 020 7403 7652 *email:* spnm@spnm.org.uk. Abigail Pogson, exec dir; Jo-Anne Naish, admin; Shoël Stadlen,

Tŷ Cerdd

Music Centre Wales
info@tycerdd.org
www.tycerdd.org
phone: (029) 20 465 700
fax: (029) 20 462 733
Tŷ Cerdd, 15 Mount Stuart Square,
Cardiff, Cardiff CF10 5DP
Director: Keith Griffin

Tŷ Cerdd (Music Centre Wales) is a one-stop music information service network, bringing *"a world of music to Wales and the music of Wales to the world"*.

Currently housed in the historic docks area of Cardiff Bay, Tŷ Cerdd is amongst the arts organisations that will be resident in the new Wales Millennium Centre, due to be completed in 2004.

Tŷ Cerdd is a partnership between the following organisations:

Welsh Amateur Music Federation
(wamf@tycerdd.org)
provides funding and advice to nearly 400 societies throughout Wales, representing over 25,000 performers;

Welsh Music Information Centre
(wmic@tycerdd.org)
provides information, research material and advice on Welsh music;

Cyfansoddwyr Cymru/Composers of Wales
(composers@tycerdd.org)
the guild of Welsh Composers;

National Youth Arts Wales
(www.nyaw.co.uk)
a partnership between the Welsh Amateur Federation and the Welsh Joint Education Committee which embraces:
> National Youth Brass Band of Wales
> (nybbw@tycerdd.org)
> National Youth Choir of Wales
> (nycw@tycerdd.org)
> National Youth Jazz Orchestra of Wales
> (nyjow@tycerdd.org)
> National Youth Orchestra of Wales
> (nyow@nyaw.co.uk)
> National Youth Wind Orchestra of Wales
> (wamf@tycerdd.org)
> National Youth Theatre of Wales
> (nytw@nyaw.co.uk)
> National Youth Dance of Wales
> (nydw@nyaw.co.uk)

Viola da Gamba Society of Great Britain

The **VdGS** is a focus for every aspect of the viol and its music.

Our worldwide membership includes professional players, amateurs at all levels, teachers and makers of viols, musicologists, and people who simply appreciate the sound of viols and would like to know more about them.

Subscription in 2004 is a special introductory rate at £14 (students £5) for one year, the normal rate being £21 (students £10).

Details from: The Administrator
Caroline Wood
56 Hunters Way
Dringhouses
YORK YO24 1JJ
England
Tel/fax 01904 706959
e-mail: admin@vdgs.demon.co.uk
http://www.vdgs.demon.co.uk

young choirs .net

- the Charity that promotes and supports opportunities for young people throughout the UK to discover the joy of choral singing through:-

· Singing Days
· Choral Workshops
· Animation Schemes
· Interactive Website
· Schools' Singing Projects
· Professional Development
· International Singing Weeks
· Support, Advice and Consultation
.... and much more!

For further details about how **youngchoirs.net** could help you get singing off the ground contact:

youngchoirs.net,
Devonshire House, Devonshire Square,
Loughborough, Leicestershire LE11 3DW
T: 01509 211664 F: 01509 260630
Email: admin@youngchoirs.net
Website: www.youngchoirs.net

promotion and publications. *Promotes new mus by emerging composers throughout the UK. Educ work with school-aged composers and their teachers. Also publishes 'new notes' monthly magazine for members.*

Spohr Society of Great Britain. 123 Mount View Rd, Sheffield S8 8PJ *tel:* 0114 258 5420 *email:* chtutt@yahoo.co.uk. C H Tutt, sec; K Warsop, chmn. *Aims to support and promote the mus of Louis Spohr through research, publications and recordings.*

Steel Band Adviser. 60 Greenford Gardens, Greenford, Middx UB6 9LZ *tel:* 020 8578 6485; 07850 650401 *fax:* 020 8578 6485 *email:* terry.noel@btinternet.com. Terry Noel, chmn. *Provides advice on all aspects of steel bands, getting insts, tuition, upkeep of insts.*

Strauss (Johann) Society of Great Britain. Flat 12, Bishams Court, Church Hill, Caterham, Surrey CR3 6SE *tel:* 01883 349681 *fax:* 01883 349681 *email:* strauss.sec@yfi.co.uk. Mrs V E Coates, hon sec. *Promotes the performance, recording, study and deeper appreciation of the mus of the Strauss family and their Viennese contemporaries.*

Strauss (Richard) Society. 1 Homestead Mews, Grange Hill, W Kirby, Wirral, Cheshire CH48 4HR. John Shelton, sec; Nigel Coles, treasurer. *Quarterly newsletter. Meetings in central London.*

Sir Arthur Sullivan Society. 8 Westacres, Middleton St George, Darlington DL2 1LJ *tel:* 01325 332557 *fax:* 01388 603695 *email:* shturnbull@aol.com. Stephen Turnbull, sec; Martin Yates, chmn; William Parry, treasurer; Sir Charles Mackerras, president. *Aims "to advance the educ of the public in, and promote the performance of, the mus of Arthur Sullivan and other contemporary British composers by means of the presentation of publications, recordings, lectures, concerts and other activities." Regular magazines and newsletters; extensive range of CDs and booklets; annual residential events; extensive library of performing material, much of it unique.*

SWAP South West Association of Promoters. 143a East Reach, Taunton, Somerset TA1 3HN *tel:* 01823 332335 *fax:* 01823 332335 *email:* weekenderlive@btopenworld.com. Martin Brice, regional sec. *Represents the interests of south west based live contemporary music event promoters.*

The Takemitsu Society. c/o 26 Sandown Rd, W Malling, Kent ME19 6NS *tel:* 01732 870414 *email:* takemitsu@postmaster.co.uk. Junko Kobayashi, chmn; Peter Burt, vice-chmn. *Promotes the understanding of the mus of the late Tóru Takemitsu and other contemporary Japanese composers.*

The Tompkins Tate Musical Instrument Trust. 12 Manor Rd, Horwich, Bolton BL6 6AR *tel:* 01204 693187 *fax:* 01204 693187. Mrs N Clark. *The Trust lends str insts to young people who could not otherwise afford to play. Applications to be made in writing.*

Traditional Music and Song Association of Scotland. 95-97 St Leonard's St, Edinburgh EH8 9QY *tel:* 0131 667 5587 *fax:* 0131 662 9153 *email:* tmsa@tmsa.info. Caroline Smith, national office admin. *National organisation promoting the performance and awareness of trad Scottish mus and song, story-telling and dance. Organises w/shops, m/classes and school curriculum enrichment visits, festivals and concerts.*

United Kingdom Harp Association. 14 Tanza Rd, London NW3 2UB *tel:* 020 7435 6458 *fax:* 020 7435 6458 *email:* ukharpassn@aol.com. Sidonie Goossens, president; Julia Webb, membership; Helen Cole, ed. *600 members worldwide. For professional harpists, students, amateurs, hp makers and retailers. Publishes quarterly magazine and directory of members. Also annual awards for student harpists.*

Universities and Colleges Admissions Service (UCAS). Rosehill, New Barn Lane, Cheltenham, Glos GL52 3LZ *tel:* 0870 1122211 *fax:* 01242 544961 *email:* enquiries@ucas.ac.uk; T.Buttress@ucas.ac.uk. Tim Buttress, mkt mgr. *UCAS is the central admissions service through which applicants apply for all f/t u/grad first degrees and most DipHE and HND courses at universities and colleges in the UK.*

Video Performance Ltd. 1 Upper James St, London W1F 9DE *tel:* 020 7534 1400 *fax:* 020 7534 1414. Colleen Hue, head of VPL. *Administers the public performance and broadcast rights in mus videos on behalf of its 900 member companies.*

Viktor Ullmann Foundation.org.uk. 7 Roma Read Close, Bessborough Rd, London SW15 4AZ *tel:* 020 8785 4772 *email:* viktorfoundation@aol.com. *Promotes Ullmann's literary works and compositions through concerts, theatre, opera and a quarterly review titled 'Strange Passenger'.*

Viola da Gamba Society. 56 Hunters Way, Dringhouses, York YO24 1JJ *tel:* 01904 706959 *fax:* 01904 706959 *email:* admin@vdgs.demon.co.uk. Caroline Wood, admin; Alison Crum, president; Robert Thompson, ed of journal; Michael Fleming, chmn; Andrew Kerr, ed of newsletter. *Publishes annual journal and quarterly newsletter 'Music for Viols'. Meetings and conferences. Viols for hire.*

The Voices Foundation. 38 Ebury St, London SW1W 0LU *tel:* 020 7730 6677 *fax:* 020 7259 0598 *email:* vf@voices.org.uk. Susan Digby, founder and principal; Michael Stocks, dir of curriculum and training. *Educ charity specialising in mus curriculum development in primary*

schools and the professional development of primary teachers. 1-day w/shops for parents and teachers. 6-day/3-day courses for mus specialists and mus curriculum leaders.

Warlock (Peter) Society. 32a Chipperfield House, Cale St, London SW3 3SA *tel:* 020 7589 9595 *fax:* 020 7589 9595 *email:* mrudland@talk21.com. Malcolm Rudland, sec. *To increase awareness and knowledge of the composer.*

Welsh Amateur Music Federation. Ty Cerdd, 15 Mount Stuart Square, Cardiff CF10 5DP *tel:* 029 2046 5700 *fax:* 029 2046 2733 *email:* wamf@tycerdd.org. Keith Griffin, dir; Christopher Sharpe, office mgr; Adrian Evans, youth co-ord; Alexandra James, admin. *Offers financial assistance, advice and training to amateur mus organisations in Wales. It founded and now administers the National Youth Brass Band of Wales, National Youth Choir of Wales, National Youth Jazz Orchestra of Wales, National Youth Symphonic Brass Ensemble of Wales and National Youth Wind Orchestra of Wales.*

The Welsh Association of Ladies' Choirs. The Old Vicarage, Llandeloy, Haverfordwest SA62 6LG *tel:* 01348 831732 *email:* nancy.mann@which.net. N Mann, sec; V Grenfell, chmn, mus dir. *Works to develop an appreciation of female choral singing within a wider audience; provides a forum for shared experience and increases the friendship and co-operation between individuals and choirs by arranging massed choral events.*

Welsh Association of Male Choirs. 10 Heolderwen, Cimla, Neath, W Glamorgan SA11 3YS *tel:* 01639 637932 *fax:* 01639 637932 *email:* welsh.association.male.choirs@ukgateway.net. J Layton Watkins, gen sec. *Offers a legal advice service and mus and insurance at a discount to members. Also organises festival.*

Welsh Folk Dance Society. Ffynnonlwyd, Trelech, Caerfyrddin, Sir Gaerfyrddin SA33 6QZ *tel:* 01994 484496 *fax:* 01994 484496 *email:* dafydde@welshfolkdance.org.uk. Dafydd M Evans, sec. *Formed in 1949 to promote Welsh folk dancing and dance mus.*

Welsh Folk Song Society. Hafan, Cricieth, Gwynedd *tel:* 01766 522096. Buddug Lloyd Roberts, sec. *Annual magazine 'Canu Gwerin', Rhidian Griffiths, Rhiannon Ifans, eds.*

Welsh Jazz Society Ltd. 26 The Balcony, Castle Arcade, Cardiff CF10 1BY *tel:* 029 2034 0591 *fax:* 029 2066 5160 *email:* welshjazz@tiscali.co.uk. Brian Hennessey, mgr dir. *An educ charity devoted to the promotion, educ and presentation of jazz in all its varied forms.*

Welsh Music Information Centre. Ty Cerdd, 15 Mount Stuart Square, Cardiff CF10 5DP *tel:* 029 2046 2855/5700 *fax:* 029 2046 2733 *email:* wmic@tycerdd.org. Keith Griffin, dir; Emyr Jenkins, chmn. *Re-established in June 2000, the WMIC offers information on Welsh mus and performances of contemporary mus by Welsh composers.*

Welsh National Opera, Friends of. John St, Cardiff CF10 5SP *tel:* 029 2046 4666 *fax:* 029 2048 3050 *email:* friends@wno.org.uk. Andy Taylor, admin; Sally Bird, asst.

White (Ernest George) Society. 5 St Malo Court, Manor Rd, Folkestone, Kent CT20 2SA *tel:* 01303 211564 *email:* dorothy@ddouse.freeserve.co.uk. Dorothy Douse, sec. *An educ charity to promote White's voice teaching on the principles described as Sinus Tone Production.*

Whitlock (Percy) Trust. 32 Butcher Close, Staplehurst, Kent TN12 0TJ *tel:* 01580 891128 *fax:* 01580 891128. Malcolm Riley, hon sec; John Scott, trustee; Francis Jackson, OBE, patron. *Holds archive of scores, diaries, photographs, letters, etc.*

Whittaker Centenary Fund (JPP). Viking Publications, c/o Bussmurton (JMC), 31 High St, Cranbrook, Kent TN17 3EE *tel:* 01580 712213 *fax:* 01580 714496 *email:* jleste@bussmurton.co.uk. *To promote the mus of W G Whittaker (1876-1944).*

William Walton Trust. 3 Park St, Windsor SL4 1LU *tel:* 01753 714364 *email:* enquiries@waltontrust.org.uk. *The trust aims, through the mus of William Walton, both to encourage educ projects in schools, and to develop the potential in young professional musicians at the start of their careers.*

Women in Music. 7 Tavern St, Stowmarket, Suffolk IP14 1PJ *tel:* 01449 673990 *fax:* 01449 673994 *email:* clare.adams@womeninmusic.org. Clare Adams, women in mus offr. *Celebrates and raises public awareness of women's work in mus. Provides information on women's involvement in mus. Administers a commissioning fund.*

Workers' Music Association. 12 St Andrew's Square, London W11 1RH *tel:* 020 7243 0920. Ros Wood, chair; Vernon Frost, president; Mavis Cook, sec. *The association believes that mus has a bearing on social life and is a means of attaining a brighter and better society; publishes mus; annual summer school of mus; London-based choir.*

Worshipful Company of Musicians. 2 London Wall Buildings, London EC2M 5PP *tel:* 020 7496 8980 *fax:* 020 7588 3633 *email:* deputyclerk@wcom.org.uk. Col T P B Hoggarth, clerk; Margaret Alford, deputy clerk. *Livery Company of the City of London (founded 1500).*

York Early Music Foundation. National Centre for Early Music, off Walmgate, York YO1 9TL *tel:* 01904 645738 *fax:* 01904 612631 *email:* info@ncem.co.uk. Delma Tomlin, dir. *Educ charity. Manages National Centre for Early Music; sustains York Early Music Festival and promotes complementary activities both locally and nationally, including annual Christmas festival.*

youngchoirs.net (British Federation of Young Choirs). Devonshire House, Devonshire Square, Loughborough, Leics LE11 3DW *tel:* 01509 211664 *fax:* 01509 260630 *email:* admin@youngchoirs.net. Malcolm Goldring, chief exec; Eleri Bristow, admin. *Offers events, courses, training and encouragement to people of all ages involved with choral singing. Choral animateurs employed all over the UK.*

Young Persons Concert Foundation. PO Box 419, Enfield, Middx EN2 0ZB *tel:* 020 8367 0553; 01923 859388 *fax:* 020 8366 3535 *email:* BIN@ypcf.co.uk. William A J Starling, chief exec; Sally Needleman, special projects co-ord. *Presents w/shops and concerts (from individual str, w/wind, br and perc sections to full orch) by young professional players from the Foundation Philharmonic Orchestra; free to schoolchildren where sponsorship is available.*

Youth Music. 1 America St, London SE1 0NE *tel:* 020 7902 1060 *fax:* 020 7902 1061 *email:* info@youthmusic.org.uk. Gavin Henderson, chmn; Christina Coker, chief exec. *Youth Music is a funding, information and advice body providing music-making opportunities for under 18s, particularly focusing on those children and young people who would otherwise not have the chance to take part in practical music-making activities.*

Musicians Union Offices

National Office. 60-62 Clapham Rd, London SW9 0JJ *tel:* 020 7582 5566 *fax:* 020 7582 9805 *email:* info@musiciansunion.org.uk. John Smith, gen sec; Howard Evans, asst gen sec, media; Horace Trubridge, asst gen sec, live; David Ashley, asst gen sec, admin; Bill Kerr, orch organiser; Nigel McCune, mus business adviser. *The Musicians' Union represents and negotiates for over 31,000 musicians, vocalists and mus writers, of all genres, for both live and media engagements. Advice and information is freely given to members.*

London Office and Central London Branch. 60-62 Clapham Rd, London SW9 0JJ *tel:* 020 7840 5534 *fax:* 020 7840 5599 *email:* london@ musiciansunion.org.uk. Horace Trubridge, London official; Deborah Primarolo, asst. *The largest branch of the Union with almost 7000 members, including musicians working in West End theatres, opera houses and the four major London orchs.*

Midlands Office. Benson House, Lombard St, Birmingham B12 0QN *tel:* 0121 622 3870 *fax:* 0121 622 5361 *email:* midlands@ musiciansunion.org.uk. Bob Bennett, district organiser; Deidre Wilson, asst. *Also centre for the MU Jazz Section.*

North East Office. 40 Canal St, Manchester M1 3WD *tel:* 0161 236 1764 *fax:* 0161 236 0159 *email:* northeast@musiciansunion.org.uk. Elaine Rogers, North East district organiser; Hannah Rees, asst.

North West Office. 40 Canal St, Manchester M1 3WD *tel:* 0161 236 1764 *fax:* 0161 236 0159 *email:* northwest@musiciansunion.org.uk. Bill Kerr, North West district organiser; Hannah Rees, asst. *Also the centre for the MU Freelance Orchestral Section.*

Scottish Office. 11 Sandyford Place, Glasgow G3 7NB *tel:* 0141 248 3723 *fax:* 0141 204 3510 *email:* scotland@musiciansunion.org.uk. Ian Smith, Scotland/N Ireland district organiser; Stephanie Marron, asst. *Also centre for MU Folk, Roots and Traditional Music Section.*

South East Office and East District Office. 60-62 Clapham Rd, London SW9 0JJ *tel:* 020 7840 5536 *fax:* 020 7840 5599 *email:* eastsoutheast@ musiciansunion.org.uk. Alf Clarke, district organiser; Carol Lee, asst.

South West Office. 199 Newport Rd, Cardiff CF24 1AJ *tel:* 029 2045 6585 *fax:* 029 2045 1980 *email:* southwest@musiciansunion.org.uk. Paul Westwell, district organiser. *Also centre for the MU Theatre Section.*

Music and Disability

Organisations

Advisory and Inspection Services. The Mundella Centre, Green St, The Meadows, Nottingham NG2 2LA *tel:* 01159 535040 *fax:* 01159 535089 *email:* artssupport@education.nottocc.gov.uk. John Auty, head of arts support service. *Developing the use of the arts and a variety of creative work within schools.*

All Clear Designs. 3 Devonshire Mews, London W4 2HA *tel:* 020 8400 5093 *fax:* 020 8400 5094 *email:* allclear@easynet.co.uk. James Holme-Siedle, dir. *Specialises in access design and disability equality training, following a format of detailed audits on existing buildings or advice on new designs which produce working documents for the architect and designer. The disability equality training offers customised courses run by disabled trainers for design professionals and staff within a range of organisations.*

Artsline. 54 Chalton St, Camden, London NW1 1HS *tel:* 020 7388 2227 *fax:* 020 7383 2653 *email:* access@artsline.org.uk. Nicola Maamari, database mgr; Brian Vickers, snr access offr; Suzanne Bull, Attitude is Everything; David Haralambidis, Multicultural Project. *Minicom available. Information and advice service for disabled people on access to arts and entertainment, including participation in the arts in London. Open for enquiries Mon-Fri 9.30am-5.30pm. Produces access guides for theatres, cinemas, galleries and museums. Runs a multicultural project for disabled people from ethnic minority communities, an access guide to venues with a multicultural focus, Disability Equality Training for arts and entertainment venues in London, a youth project for disabled people aged 14-25 and an access audit service to make buildings more accessible. The Attitude is Everything project aims to encourage mus venues to sign up to a charter of good practice.*

Association of Professional Music Therapists. 26 Hamlyn Rd, Glastonbury, Somerset BA6 8HT *tel:* 01458 834919 *fax:* 01458 834919 *email:* APMToffice@aol.com. Diana Asbridge, admin. *Deals with the needs of professional mus therapists in relation to standards of practice, employment, career structure, training, etc.*

British Dyslexia Association. 98 London Rd, Reading, Berks RG1 5AU *tel:* 0118 966 8271 (helpline)/2677 *fax:* 0118 935 1927 *email:* info@dyslexiahelp-bda.demon.co.uk. John Westcombe, chmn, Music and Dyslexia Committee. *Provides information and advice relating to the effect of dyslexia on reading and writing mus. Also deals with individual enquiries regarding mus difficulties arising from dyslexia.*

British Society for Music Therapy (BSMT). 61 Church Hill Rd, E Barnet, Herts EN4 8SY *tel:* 020 8441 6226 *fax:* 020 8441 4118 *email:* info@bsmt.org. Claire Flower, chmn. *Promotes the use and development of mus therapy in the treatment and rehabilitation of children and adults suffering from emotional, physical or mental handicap. Membership is open to all interested in mus therapy. The Society holds meetings, w/shops and conferences. Publishes a journal (jointly with the Association of Professional Music Therapists) and a bulletin for members.*

British Wireless for the Blind Fund. Gabriel House, 34 New Rd, Chatham, Kent ME4 4QR *tel:* 01634 832501 *fax:* 01634 817485 *email:* margaret@blind.org.uk. Mrs M R Grainger, chief exec. *Provides radios, radio cassette recorders and radio cassette CD recorders on a free permanent loan basis to registered blind or partially sighted people in need in the UK.*

The Chantry Trust. 1a King's Mews, London WC1N 2JA *tel:* 020 7242 8586 *fax:* 020 7831 7914 *email:* rupertcrew@compuserve.com. Doreen Montgomery, trustee and admin; Rex Montgomery, founder. *Organisation researching therapeutic benefits of mus in educ for autistic and handicapped children. Currently establishing mus therapy pilot schemes in schools often in co-operation with Resources for Autism. Grants not available at present.*

Children Helping Children. 14 Whitehall Gardens, Acton, London W3 9RD *tel:* 020 8992 2092 *fax:* 020 8992 2092. Dona Lee Croft, dir; Vanessa Latarche, dir. *Fundraising gala concerts by talented, young violinists and pianists to benefit charities working to alleviate the plight of disabled, disadvantaged, potentially terminally ill, abused or neglected children.*

Community Music Wales. Unit 8, 24 Norbury Rd, Fairwater, Cardiff CF5 3AU *tel:* 029 2083 8060 *fax:* 029 2056 6573 *email:* admin@communitymusicwales.org.uk. Simon Dancey, development offr. *Inspired by the belief that everyone can derive pleasure and satisfaction from playing mus, and that mus projects provide a rich learning environment in which a host of other important skills can be acquired. Resources and expertise in a wide range of mus forms, including mus tech, are made available to people who are typically excluded from opportunities for creative self-expression and personal development for reasons of disability or disadvantage. Also professional training course for community musicians.*

Council for Music in Hospitals (England, Wales and Northern Ireland). 74 Queens Rd, Hersham, Surrey KT12 5LW *tel:* 01932 252809/11 *fax:* 01932 252966 *email:* info@music-in-hospitals.org.uk. Diana Greenman, dir. *Over 4000 live concerts pa given by professional musicians for adults and children in hospitals, nursing homes, hospices, day centres and special schools.*

Council for Music in Hospitals (Scotland). 10 Forth St, Edinburgh EH1 3LD *tel:* 0131 556 5848 *fax:* 0131 556 0225 *email:* info@musicinhospitalsscotland.org.uk. Alison Frazer, chief exec. *Concerts of live mus given by professional musicians selected for their communication skills. Participation encouraged. Venues include hospitals, hospices, homes for elderly people and day centres. Around 2000 concerts provided in Scotland annually.*

Healing Arts: Isle of Wight. St Mary's, Parkhurst Rd, Newport, Isle of Wight PO30 5TG *tel:* 01983 534253 *fax:* 01983 525157 *email:* healingarts@iow.nhs.uk. Guy Eades, arts dir; Margaret O'Connor, musician in healthcare. *Co-ordinates an arts programme across the spectrum of health services with particular emphasis on mus in healthcare.*

London Disability Arts Forum. Diorama Arts Centre, 34 Osnaburgh St, London NW1 3ND *tel:* 020 7916 5484 *fax:* 020 7916 5396 *email:* info@ldaf.net, dail@ldaf.net. Julie McNamara, artistic dir (LDAF); Joe McConnell, ed (DAIL Magazine). *Set up to define and promote disability arts, to provide a forum for disabled artists and performers, and to further the participation and representation of disabled people in the arts. Maintains and manages databases of disabled performers in all fields including mus. Publishes Disability Arts in London (DAIL) Magazine.*

MusicSpace Trust. St Matthias Campus (UWE), Oldbury Court Rd, Fishponds, Bristol BS16 2JP *tel:* 0117 344 4541 *fax:* 0117 344 4542 *email:* musicspace@uwe.ac.uk. Leslie Bunt, dir. *Provides mus therapy sessions for people of all ages, also w/shops and training sessions, including p/t mus therapy diploma course in conjunction with Bristol University and short introductory courses at the University of the West of England.*

National Association for Special Educational Needs (NASEN). NASEN House, 4-5 Amber Business Village, Amber Close, Amington, Tamworth B77 4RP *tel:* 01827 311500 *fax:* 01827 313005 *email:* welcome@nasen.org.uk. Beverley Walters, office mgr. *Promotes the interests of children and young people with special educ needs and supports those who work with them.*

National Disability Arts Forum. Mea House, Ellison Place, Newcastle upon Tyne NE1 8XS *tel:* 0191 261 1628 textphone: 0191 261 2273 *fax:* 0191 222 0573 *email:* ndaf@ndaf.org. Geoff Armstrong, dir; Silvie Fisch, IT offr; David Colley, finance and resources mgr. *Organisation established by disabled people to promote equality of opportunity for disabled people in all aspects of the arts. Particularly concerned with supporting the development of disability arts locally, nationally and internationally. EtCetera: Disability Arts News - once a week the Forum sends out its free email bulletin to subscribers all over the UK and the world. EtCetera features the latest news that relates to disabled people's participation in the arts, including jobs, events, reviews, funding opportunities, TV and radio listings and much more. To subscribe please send blank email to etcetera-subscribe@topica.com.*

National Music and Disability Information Service (NMDIS). Sound Sense, 7 Tavern St, Stowmarket IP14 1PJ *tel:* 01449 673990 *fax:* 01449 673994 *email:* info@soundsense.org. Sarah Bennett-Day, disability offr. *NMDIS, run by Sound Sense, gives information and advice on all aspects of mus and disability issues. Publications and quarterly journal available.*

Nordoff-Robbins Music Therapy Centre. 2 Lissenden Gardens, London NW5 1PP *tel:* 020 7267 4496 *fax:* 020 7267 4369 *email:* admin@nordoff-robbins.org.uk. Pauline Etkin, dir. *Centre houses a clinic which children and adults with a variety of needs can* attend for mus therapy. Offers a 2-yr Master of Music Therapy training validated by City University. Library holds collection of material including documentation of the work of Dr Nordoff and Dr Robbins.

Northern Ireland Music Therapy Trust. Graham House, Knockbracken Healthcare Park, Saintfield Rd, Belfast BT8 8BH *tel:* 028 9070 5854 *fax:* 028 9070 5854 *email:* nimtt.belfast@btopenworld.com. Fiona Davidson, exec dir; Karen Diamond, head therapist; Michael Swallow OBE, sec NIMTT board. *Promotes interest in, and the application of, mus therapy throughout Northern Ireland.*

Royal Association for Disability and Rehabilitation (RADAR). 12 City Forum, 250 City Rd, London EC1V 8AF *tel:* 020 7250 3222 *minicom:* 020 7250 4119 *fax:* 020 7250 0212 *email:* radar@radar.org.uk. *National pan-disability campaigning and information organisation working with and for all physically disabled people.*

Royal National Institute of the Blind (RNIB). Music Education and Employment Advisory Service, 105 Judd St, London WC1H 9NE *tel:* 020 7391 2296 *email:* emma.beamont@rnib.org.uk. Emma Beamont, mus information offr; Sally-Anne Zimmermann, mus educ and employment adviser. *Offers advice and information on all matters concerning the mus educ and employment of visually impaired children and adults.*

Shape. LVS Resource Centre, 356 Holloway Rd, London N7 6PA *tel:* 020 7619 6160/61 *minicom:* 020 7619 6161 *fax:* 020 7619 6162 *email:* info@shapearts.org.uk. Steve Mannix, chief exec. *Arts development agency working with disabled and older people for greater access and involvement in all aspects of the arts. W/shops, projects and events. Offers accredited training courses and placements in all aspects of arts mgt and practice. Deaf Arts Programme and Ticket Scheme with reduced price tickets and volunteer escorts/drivers. Artists' residencies in schools for deaf and disabled children plus advice, information and consultancy on all aspects of arts and disability.*

Visual Impairment Centre for Teaching and Research. School of Education, University of Birmingham, Edgbaston, Birmingham B15 2TT *tel:* 0121 414 6733 *fax:* 0121 414 4865 *email:* victar-enquiries@bham.ac.uk. Mike McLinden, lecturer in educ (visual impairment); Steve McCall, lecturer in educ (visual impairment); Graeme Douglas, research fellow; Sue Pavey, research associate; Jenny Whittaker, sec. *The Centre has a long history of work in the area of visual impairment concerned with teaching and research. It produces software programs for the visually impaired and has copies available of published research articles. A full software cat and publications list is available on request.*

Yorkshire Association for Music and Special Education Needs. 5 Primrose Row, Tong Park, Baildon BD17 7QQ *tel:* 01274 593999. Sue Tomassi, sec. *Open to anyone interested in exploring the role of mus with people with special needs; for pleasure, educ and communication, through courses, seminars, w/shops and concerts.*

Professional Training

The courses listed below are mainly designed for able-bodied people who wish to work with people with disabilities.

Anglia Polytechnic University. Dept of Music, East Rd, Cambridge CB1 1PT *tel:* 01223 363271 ext 2447 *email:* a.woodward@anglia.ac.uk (admin). Helen Odell-Miller, admissions tutor and course dir; Eleanor Richards, snr lecturer; Amelia Oldfield, snr lecturer. *MA and Professional Diploma in Music Therapy cover both university work and placements. Applicants should normally possess a degree or graduate diploma in mus, but graduates of other disciplines with an appropriate level of musicianship will be considered. Some practical experience needed, working with people with learning disabilities and/or mental illness. 15 places on course. 16 months f/t Sep-following Jan. Fees for diploma and MA entry: £4600 for UK and EU students, £6350 for international students (2002 entry prices).*

Bristol University. Dept of Music, Victoria Rooms, Queens Rd, Clifton, Bristol BS8 1SA *tel:* 0117 954 5032 *fax:* 0117 954 5033 *email:* john.pickard@bristol.ac.uk. John Pickard, snr lecturer in mus. *2-yr p/t diploma in mus therapy. Applicants should possess a mus degree or diploma and be aged 25+. 15 places on course. Next course Jan 2006.*

Goldsmiths, University of London. Dept of Professional and Community Education, Lewisham Way, London SE14 6NW *tel:* 020 7919 7229 *email:* pace@gold.ac.uk. *30-week introduction to mus therapy, Weds 5-7pm. Suitable for musicians, teachers and healthcare professionals considering pursuing professional training in mus therapy.*

Guildhall School of Music & Drama. Silk St, Barbican, London EC2Y 8DT *tel:* 020 7628 2571 *fax:* 020 7256 9438 *email:* shoskyns@gsmd.ac.uk. Sarah Hoskyns, head of mus therapy dept. *Diploma in Music Therapy. 12-month f/t p/grad mus therapy course approved by the Health Professions Council. Applicants must normally have had 3 yrs of f/t HE. Applications from mature professional musicians are also welcomed. Some experience with disabled, mentally or physically ill or hospitalised people is essential, as is personal therapy prior to or during the course. The course is likely to change its validation from the University of York to City University, London from Sep 2003 subject to validation requirements. It will continue as a p/grad diploma for 2003/4 and hopes to upgrade to 2-yr Masters course in due course.*

Nordoff-Robbins Music Therapy Centre. 2 Lissenden Gardens, London NW5 1PP *tel:* 020 7267 4496 *fax:* 020 7267 4369 *email:* admin@nordoff-robbins.org.uk. Pauline Etkin, dir, head of training. *Offers a 2-yr Master of Music Therapy training validated by City University. Fees: £5000. Places: max 6 pa. Also 1-day conferences for those interested in mus therapy for children and adults, a 10-week evening class on Nordoff-Robbins approach to mus therapy, and a preparatory course for training as a mus therapist.*

Postgraduate Diploma in Music Therapy (Nordoff-Robbins). Chessel's Land, Moray House School of Education, University of Edinburgh, Holyrood Rd, Edinburgh EH8 8AQ *tel:* 0131 651 6636 *email:* james.robertson@education.ed.ac.uk. James Robertson, programme co-ord. *The Postgraduate Diploma in Music Therapy (Nordoff-Robbins) is the first professional training programme for mus therapy to be offered in Scotland. It is a 1-yr, f/t programme and is based on the systematic integration of 8 modules. Students will experience the continuous interaction of theoretical instruction, the development of practical mus resources, the observation of clinical work of others and the responsibility of undertaking clinical work themselves both with individuals and groups.*

Royal Welsh College of Music and Drama. Castle Grounds, Cathays Park, Cardiff CF10 3ER *tel:* 029 2039 1363 *fax:* 029 2039 1305 *email:* music.admissions@rwcmd.ac.uk. Alison Levinge, course leader, mus therapy. *P/grad Diploma in Music Therapy (1); leads to a Diploma and State Registration, qualifying students to seek employment in different settings. The course is both challenging and thought-provoking and aims to equip students with the relevant clinical, therapeutic and mus skills needed to practise. Emphasis is placed on care in the community, and the course includes clinical placements with both children and adults. Applicants need to be musically of diploma or graduate level, with a strong emphasis on expressive ability and maturity of personality. Degrees in other related subjects can be considered, provided musical criteria are also met. Previous experience working with adults or children with difficulties may also be an advantage. As an extension of this training, an MA programme is now available.*

University of Surrey Roehampton *formerly* **Roehampton Institute London.** Dept of Music, Southlands College, 80 Roehampton Lane, London SW15 5SL *tel:* 020 8392 3423 *fax:* 020 8392 3435 *email:* artstherapies.programmes@roehampton.ac.uk. Kay Sobey, mus therapy programme convener; Tessa Watson, mus therapy programme convener. *Introduction to Music Therapy. A short course in the spring term for those in related professions or who are considering training. Graduate Diploma IMA in Music Therapy (1.5 f/t; 3 p/t, recognised by the Association of Professional Music Therapists) is designed to train musicians as therapists with the ability and flexibility to practise professionally with a wide range of clients within the NHS, educ, social services or private sector. Also research MA. Fees: Graduate Diploma in Mus Therapy, £4194 (1.5 yr f/t, home fee), £1398 (p/t, yr 1), £1398 (p/t, yr 2), £1398 (p/t, yr 3); MA Mus Therapy, £1308.*

Tonalis Music Centre. 4 Castle Farm Close, Leighterton, Glos GL8 8UY *tel:* 01666 890460 *fax:* 01666 890460 *email:* tonalis@aol.com. Michael Deason-Barrow, dir. *Offers a 2-yr p/t foundation training course in Community Musicing which includes themes of: mus as a healing art, working with special needs groups, newly-designed acoustic insts for therapy/remedial mus, voicework. Modular training with distance learning, 45 days pa contact time during school holidays and half terms.*

Activities and Courses for People with Disabilities

Artsreach. Jacksons Lane, 269a Archway Rd, London N6 5AA *tel:* 020 8340 5226 *fax:* 020 8348 2424 *email:* pat.p@jacksonslane.org.uk. Patricia Place, disability and access mgr. *Offers arts-based w/shops (including mus) to special schools and units, integration work in mainstream schools, primarily in the London Boroughs of Barnet, Camden, Islington and Haringay.*

The Bull. artsdepot, 5 Nether St, N Finchley, London N12 0GA *tel:* 020 8449 0048 *fax:* 020 8364 9037 *email:* info@artsdepot.co.uk. Ravi Malhotra, gen mgr; Clare Lewis, mkt mgr; Martin Hutchings, technical mgr; Tamsin Ace, educ offr. *Runs occasional performing arts w/shops for adults with learning difficulties. Regular programme of mus events, including rock, funk, jazz, Klezmer and world. Opening May 2004.*

Carousel. Community Base, 113 Queens Rd, Brighton BN1 3XG *tel:* 01273 234734 *fax:* 01273 234735 *email:* info@carousel.org.uk. Liz Hall, gen mgr. *Works to promote the active involvement and participation of people with learning disabilities in the arts (including mus) through w/shops, residencies, special events, performances, exhibitions, and training courses run for volunteers and staff.*

Community Music East Ltd. 189 King St, Norwich NR1 2DF *tel:* 01603 628367 *fax:* 01603 767863 *email:* enquiries@cme.org.uk. Ben Higham, dir. *CME works in community educ using the medium of mus. This activity ranges from a modular programme of public skills and performance based courses through to specific developmental initiatives with closed groups including young people who may be disadvantaged or disaffected and special needs groups including children and adults. CME intends to open a £2.5m Community Music Centre and Recording Studio for Norfolk in 2005.*

Ebony Steelband Trust. c/o Acklam Playcentre and Adventure, 6 Acklam Rd, London W10 5QZ *tel:* 020 8960 6424 *fax:* 020 8964 4624 *email:* services@ebony.org.uk. Pepe Francis, dir. *Classes and w/shops throughout London to provide relief and personal development through the provision of mus therapy. One-to-one sessions are also available. Steelpan tutors are available for all educ establishments. New scheme, Millenium Volunteers, for ages 16-24.*

English Touring Opera. 52-54 Roseberry Ave, London EC1R 4RP *tel:* 020 7833 2555 *fax:* 020 7713 8686 *email:* tim.yealland@ englishtouringopera.org.uk. Tim Yealland, outreach dir. *Extensive programme of work for people with disabilities including w/shops and signed performances and captioned performances for people who are deaf or hard of hearing, w/shops and audio-described performances for visually impaired people. Also creative opera projects in schools around the country, and talks and recitals in hospices.*

Glamorgan Summer School. University of Glamorgan, Pontypridd CF37 1DL *tel:* 01443 482828 *fax:* 01443 483393 *email:* summerschool@ glam.ac.uk. Gill Giles, events mgr. *Combined arts w/shop for people with and without learning difficulties, combining elements of mus, dance, movement, visual arts and drama (26 Jul-6 Aug 2004).*

Heart 'n Soul. The Albany, Douglas Way, Deptford, London SE8 4AG *tel:* 020 8694 1632 *fax:* 020 8694 1532 *email:* heartnsoul@ compuserve.com. Mark Williams, dir; Michael Gaunt, tour and mkt mgr; Angela McNicholl, finance and admin mgr; Rachel Walsh, production mgr; Zoë Gilmour, development mgr. *Theatrical mus company for people with learning disabilities. Touring shows and mus; organised by members within the UK and abroad. Also run Beautiful Octopus Club, providing multimedia entertainment for people with learning disabilities.*

Heart N Soul. Jacksons Lane, 269a Archway Rd, London N6 5AA *tel:* 020 8340 5226 *fax:* 020 8348 2424 *email:* pat.p@jacksonslane.org.uk. *Under Artreach's auspices, Heart n Soul, Europe's leading learning disabled mus/theatre company, run weekly workshops in mus, drama and voice. An ongoing workshop, auditions once a year. Every Wed except school holidays. Free of charge.*

Live Music Now! 4 Lower Belgrave St, London SW1W 0LJ *tel:* 020 7730 2205 *email:* enquiries@livemusicnow.org. Sarah Derbyshire, exec dir; Alice Wilkinson, London dir. *National charity with 8 offices around the UK. Key aims: to make mus of the highest quality available to people who would otherwise have limited opportunities to experience it; to help support outstanding young professional musicians at the start of their careers.*

Living Options *formerly* **CRYPT.** Kimbridge House, Kimbridge Rd, Bracklesham Bay, Chichester, W Sussex PO20 8PE *tel:* 01243 671865 *fax:* 01243 671865 *email:* livingoptions@hotmail.com. Sue Liversidge, national sec. *Opportunities for young disabled people (age 18+) to develop new interests and life skills, to experience the wider community while living in group homes with privacy, dignity, rights, choice, fulfillment and independence.*

Morley College. 61 Westminster Bridge Rd, London SE1 7HT *tel:* 020 7450 1838 *fax:* 020 7928 4074 *email:* enquiries@morleycollege.ac.uk. Robert Hanson, dir of mus; Joan Taylor, mus access co-ord; Andrea Johnson, mus sec. *Offers two specific courses: Music for People with Learning Difficulties and Music for People with Physical Disabilities. Also aims to integrate disabled people into other classes. Mus ranges from orchs to choirs, chmbr ens to jazz bands, folk, world, pop and electronic mus.*

Music and the Deaf. The Media Centre, 7 Northumberland St, Huddersfield HD1 1RL *tel:* 01484 483115 *fax:* 01484 483116 *email:* info@matd.org.uk. Paul Whittaker, artistic dir. *An organisation to help hearing-impaired people of all ages to explore the world of mus and to develop their own mus skills and interests. W/shops, lectures, residencies, signed song. Various publications available.*

Musicians in Focus. 1 Poets Rd, London N5 2SL *tel:* 020 7354 2050 *fax:* 020 7359 7535 *email:* info@musiciansinfocus.org. Jacqueline Clifton, dir; Daniel de Azevedo, dir. *Aims to research and further develop technology for visually impaired musicians. Provides advice and support as well as a permanent facility for w/shops and courses.*

Richard Attenborough Centre for Disability and the Arts. University of Leicester, PO Box 138, University Rd, Leicester LE1 9HN *tel:* 0116 252 2455 *fax:* 0116 252 5165 *email:* racentre@le.ac.uk. E Hartley, dir; Philip Herbert, organising tutor for mus. *Organises taught courses and opportunities to participate in creative arts activities, including mus w/shops. Priority is given to people with disabilities.*

SHARE MUSIC. Toynbee Studios, 28 Commercial St, London E1 6AB *tel:* 020 7247 7855 *fax:* 020 7247 7732 *email:* chris.shurety@ sharemusic.org.uk. Chris Shurety, exec dir. *Promotes inclusive courses in mus dance theatre with special facilities for people with physical disabilities or sensory impairment.*

Wheelchair Dance Association. Merlin Golf Club, Mawgan Porth, Newquay, Cornwall TR8 4DN *tel:* 01841 540222 *fax:* 01841 541031. Margaret Oliver MBE, national sec. *National body promoting wheelchair dancing. Assistance given and starter packs available with mus and scripts.*

Manufacturers, Suppliers and Retailers

Acorn (Percussion) Ltd. Unit 33, Abbey Business Centre, Ingate Place, London SW8 3NS *tel:* 020 7720 2243 (24 hrs) *fax:* 020 7627 8883 *email:* acornpercussion@btinternet.com. Richard Benson, sales dir. *Supplier of a variety of multicultural and mainstream perc insts for schools across the board, also for special needs educ and hospitals, etc.*

Echo City. 54 Falkland Rd, London NW5 2XA *tel:* 020 7424 0772 *fax:* 020 7424 0772 *email:* paul@echocity.co.uk. Paul Shearsmith, member; Giles Perring, member. *Designs, builds and installs sound playgrounds and organises inst building and mus w/shops. Office hours 10am-4pm Mon-Thu.*

www.fullpitcher.co.uk. 9 Mallard Close, Haslemere, Surrey GU27 1QU *tel:* 01428 648854 *fax:* 0870 429 2123 *email:* info@fullpitcher.co.uk. Sue Brookes, sales mgr. *Downloadable sheet mus and other resources to* *facilitate inclusive mus-making. Custom arranged parts can be added to ensembles to accommodate players with a range of disabilities.*

Music Education Supplies. 101 Banstead Rd South, Sutton, Surrey SM2 5LH *tel:* 020 8770 2866 *fax:* 020 8770 3554 *email:* music.mes@ btconnect.com. Ray Mason, dir. *Agents of Sonor school perc and suppliers of Suzuki handchimes and perc, Nordoff-Robbins reed horns, Aulos rcdrs, books, insts, etc.*

Remap (Technical Equipment for Disabled People). Hazeldene, Ightham, Sevenoaks, Kent TN15 9AD *tel:* 0845 130 0456 *fax:* 0845 130 0789 *email:* info@remap.org.uk. Mary-Ann Mitchell, national organiser. *Registered charity which designs, manufactures and supplies 'one-off' aids and adaptions that are not commercially available. Equipment is supplied free of charge to the client.*

Libraries and Museums

The following list is limited to major collections of musical interest with some special collections in larger libraries. An asterisk indicates membership of the **International Association of Music Libraries, Archives and Documentation Centres (UK and Ireland)**, c/o Music Library, Central Library, George IV Bridge, Edinburgh EH1 1EG *tel:* 0131 242 8053 *fax:* 0131 242 8009.

Libraries

National Copyright Libraries

Aberystwyth. National Library of Wales. Aberystwyth, Ceredigion SY23 3BU *tel:* 01970 632800 *fax:* 01970 615709 *email:* holi@llgc.org.uk. Rhidian Griffiths, dir of public services. *Mss dept rich in 19th C Welsh mus; large coll of printed Welsh mus; Welsh mus cat; British mus received under legal deposit since 1912; West European mus.*

Cambridge. Cambridge University Library, Music Department. West Rd, Cambridge CB3 9DR *tel:* 01223 333000/72 *fax:* 01223 333160 *email:* music@lib.cam.ac.uk. R M Andrewes, under-librarian, head of mus dept. *Over 500,000 items of printed mus. Ca 1000 mus mss of medieval and modern, vocal and inst mus. Includes Hedli Anderson coll, F T Arnold coll, F A Booth coll, Edith Coates and Harry Powell Lloyd coll, Marion Scott coll, Alfredo Campoli coll, Peter Warlock autograph mss, R J S Stevens diaries and memoirs, W H Weiss papers and diaries, Hans Keller papers, James Hook autograph mss.*

* **Edinburgh.** National Library of Scotland, Music Division. George IV Bridge, Edinburgh EH1 1EW *tel:* 0131 226 4531 *fax:* 0131 622 4803 *email:* music@nls.uk. Almut Boehme, head of mus. *Special colls including Balfour-Handel, Hopkinson-Berlioz, Hopkinson-Verdi; also Scottish mus colls and Grainger mss.*

London. British Library. 96 Euston Rd, London NW1 2DB *tel:* 020 7412 7772 *fax:* 020 7412 7751 *email:* music-collections@bl.uk. Chris Banks, head of mus colls. *Over one million items of printed mus received by copyright deposit, purchase or gift. Special colls include Hirsch Music Library, Royal Music Library (including Handel autographs). The large coll of mus mss includes autographs of Bach, Haydn, Mozart, Beethoven, Elgar, Vaughan Williams, Holst, Britten, Tippett, etc; medieval and modern vocal and inst mus, Stefan Zweig coll, Royal Philharmonic coll.*

* **Oxford.** Bodleian Library, Music Section. Broad St, Oxford OX1 3BG *tel:* 01865 277063 *fax:* 01865 277182 *email:* music@bodley.ox.ac.uk. P Ward Jones, mus librarian. *Including 10th-20th C mss; former Music School coll, Deneke-Mendelssohn coll, Wight Bequest, Bourne Bequest, Harding coll, former St Michael's College, Tenbury coll.*

British Library Document Supply Centre

* British Library Document Supply Services. Boston Spa, Wetherby, W Yorks LS23 7BQ *tel:* 01937 546060 *fax:* 01937 546333 *email:* dsc-customer-services@bl.uk. Contact: customer services. *Acts as a clearing house for inter-library loans, both nationally and internationally. In addition, it has an extensive stock of its own, including a substantial and comprehensive coll of more than 135,000 mus scores (excluding vocal and orch sets). The British Library does not lend directly to individuals, but through a network of borrowers comprised of public libraries, university and college libraries and other commercial or non-commercial organisations. It is free to join and any organisation may apply, details from the above address or on website. Individuals may apply to receive photocopies from the British Library's collection, but mus scores cannot be copied.*

Major Regional Public Libraries

These libraries have major music collections, and also act as regional and national centres for lending. Personal or institutional borrowers are welcome.

* **Birmingham.** Central Music Library. Chamberlain Square, Birmingham B3 3HQ *tel:* 0121 303 2482 *fax:* 0121 464 1177 *email:* music.library@birmingham.gov.uk; john.gough@birmingham.gov.uk. John Gough, head of mus services. *Including coll of British Institute of Organ Studies; material surrounding Birmingham Triennial Festivals including ms score of Mendelssohn's 'Elijah'; letters by Elgar, Gounod, Bruch, etc.*

Liverpool. Central Library (Music). William Brown St, Liverpool L3 8EW *tel:* 0151 233 5863 *fax:* 0151 233 5886 *email:* audiovisuallibrary@liverpool.gov.uk. *Including Carl Rosa opera library. Parts collection (3500 sets) available for loan.*

* **London.** Barbican Music Library. Barbican Centre, London EC2Y 8DS *tel:* 020 7638 0672 *fax:* 020 7638 2249 *email:* barbicanlib@corpoflondon.gov.uk. Robert Tucker, mus librarian. *Includes Music Preserved (formerly the Music Performance Research Centre).*

Westminster Music Library. 160 Buckingham Palace Rd, London SW1W 9UD *tel:* 020 7641 4292 *fax:* 020 7641 4281 *email:* musiclibrary@westminster.gov.uk. Ruth Walters, mus librarian. *Colls include Oriana Madrigal Soc.*

Manchester. Henry Watson Music Library. Central Library, St Peter's Square, Manchester M2 5PD *tel:* 0161 234 1976 *fax:* 0161 234 1963 *email:* music@libraries.manchester.gov.uk. Martin Thacker. *Including 2000 items of early printed mus and 500 mss; Newman Flower Handel coll.*

* **Wakefield.** Wakefield Library HQ. Balne Lane, Wakefield, W Yorks WF2 0DQ *tel:* 01924 302229 *fax:* 01924 302245 *email:* lib.ylimusicanddrama@wakefield.gov.uk. Steven Dowd, snr librarian. *Yorkshire Libraries and Information Music and Drama Collection: large coll of choral and orch sets available for hire throughout the UK.*

Regional Public Libraries

* **London.** Barnet Libraries. Hendon Music Library, The Burroughs, London NW4 4BQ *tel:* 020 8359 2629 *email:* tony.bralant@barnet.gov.uk. A P Bralant, mus librarian. *Includes colls of recordings of Chopin, Liszt, stage musicals and Japanese ethnic mus.*

* Ealing Public Libraries. Central Library, 102 Ealing Broadway Centre, Ealing, London W5 5JY *tel:* 020 8825 7126 *email:* ghillier@ealing.gov.uk. Glynis R Hillier, mus librarian; Jayne Price, asst librarian; Martin Sutton, asst librarian. *Printed and recorded mus; videos;*

reference works and books about mus. Vocal set coll. Wind band sets. DVD coll.

London Borough of Enfield Central Music Library. Cecil Rd, Enfield, London EN2 6TW *tel:* 020 8379 8392 *fax:* 020 8379 8401 *email:* central.library@enfield.gov.uk. *Mike Jones, snr lending librarian, based at Palmers Green. Audio specialisation includes J S Bach, jazz artists BAJ-BH, folk mus of Argentina, Bolivia, Chile, Paraguay and Uruguay.*

Fulham Music Library. 598 Fulham Rd, 598 Fulham Rd, London SW6 5NX *tel:* 020 8753 3870 *fax:* 020 7736 3741 *email:* info@haflibs.org.uk. *Sadie McGarry, librarian; Frances Bartholomew, librarian. For details of colls see Hammersmith Music Library.*

London Borough of Greenwich Libraries. Support Services, Plumstead Library, 232 Plumstead High St, London SE18 1JL *tel:* 020 8317 4466 *fax:* 020 8317 4868 *email:* john.conroy@greenwich.gov.uk. *John Conroy, librarian. Special audio colls of Ravel, Schumann, English folk mus, jazz performers.*

* Hammersmith Music Library. Shepherds Bush Rd, London W6 7AT *tel:* 020 8753 3826/7 *fax:* 020 8753 3815 *email:* ejones@lbhf.gov.uk. *Elin Jones, lending/mus librarian; Neil Hedgeland, lending/mus librarian. Cassettes, CDs, DVDs, videos, LPs, mus books, scores and magazines. Audio specialisation: Mendelssohn, Vaughan Williams, jazz artists HP-JEF, folk mus of Iran, Iraq, Jordan, Lebanon and Syria, British poetry. Colls also held at Fulham Music Library and branches.*

* Islington Library and Cultural Services. Central Library, 2 Fieldway Cres, London N5 1PF *tel:* 020 7527 6963 *fax:* 020 7527 6913 *email:* tony.brown@islington.gov.uk. *Tony Brown, customer services mgr. Audio specialisation of classical composers GM-KH (excluding Handel and J Haydn), jazz musicians SHB-SM, folk mus of SE Europe and recordings of obsolete mus insts. Loans within Greater London to personal borrowers only.*

* London Borough of Southwark Libraries. Bibliographical Services, 15 Spa Rd, London SE16 3QW *tel:* 020 7525 1578 *fax:* 020 7525 1536 *email:* stuart.woollard@southwark.gov.uk. *Stuart Woollard, snr librarian stock. CDs, videos, DVDs, scores and books. Special colls include Berlioz, Messiaen, jazz, SE Asian folk mus, and mus practice records.*

Wandsworth Music Libraries. Putney Music Library, Disraeli Rd, London SW15 2DR *tel:* 020 8871 7090 *fax:* 020 8789 6175 *email:* tday@wandsworth.gov.uk. *Terry Day, mus librarian, Putney. Encompasses Battersea, Balham and Putney mus libraries. Comprehensive stocks of CDs, videos, scores and books. Vocal score sets coll at Putney. GLASS coll (Greater London Audio Specialisation Scheme) at Putney. Wandsworth coll in this scheme comprises Prokofiev, Rachmaninoff, film soundtracks, jazz artists LEE-LZ and Scottish folk mus.*

* **Aylesbury.** Buckinghamshire County Library. County Library Headquarters, Walton St, Aylesbury, Bucks HP20 1UU *tel:* 01296 382266 *fax:* 01296 382274 *email:* mroll@buckscc.gov.uk. *Margaret Roll, asst resources mgr. Vocal sets, sheet mus.*

* **Bournemouth.** Bournemouth Music Library. 22 The Triangle, Bournemouth BH2 5RQ *tel:* 01202 454845 *fax:* 01202 454840 *email:* bournemouthmusic@bournemouthlibraries.org.uk. *Sandrey Date, mus librarian. Camm coll of (mainly 19th C) full scores, miniature scores, chmbr and inst mus. Wide range of printed mus, books, CDs and videos. Sets of choral and orch works available.*

* **Brighton.** Brighton Music Library. Vantage Point, New England St, Brighton BN1 2GW *tel:* 01273 296961/57/69 *fax:* 01273 296965/51 *email:* libraries@brighton-hove.gov.uk. *General range of scores, books, CDs, cassettes, videos and DVDs.*

* **Bristol.** Bristol Music Library. Central Library College Green, Bristol BS1 5TL *tel:* 0117 903 7219 *fax:* 0117 922 1081 *email:* music_collection@bristol-city.gov.uk. *Rebecca Amiel, mus and drama librarian. Russell coll of Victorian and Edwardian songs. Coll of books, mus and recordings by Bristol authors and musicians. Comprehensive coll of books, journals, scores, sets of choral/orch parts and recordings.*

Cambridge. Cambridge Central Library. 7 Lion Yard, Cambridge CB2 3QD *tel:* 01223 712000 *fax:* 01223 712036 *email:* cambridge.central.library@cambridgeshire.gov.uk.

* **Cardiff.** Cardiff County Library Service: Cardiff Central Library. St David's Link, Frederick St, Cardiff CF10 2DU *tel:* 029 2038 2116 *fax:* 029 2087 1599 *email:* centrallibrary@cardiff.gov.uk. *Elizabeth Pinnell, mus librarian; Sheila Basford, mus librarian. Mackworth and Aylward colls of 17th and 18th C mss and printed mus; currently on long-term loan to University College Cardiff Music Library.*

* **Chesterfield.** Chesterfield Library. County Music and Drama Library, New Beetwell St, Chesterfield, Derbys S40 1QN *tel:* 01246 209292 *fax:* 01246 209304. *Mrs M Brandram, county mus and drama librarian. General colls of single copy material, vocal sets, orch sets and playsets.*

Coke-Steele coll of books, scores and some mss (not yet catalogued but available for consultation by prior arrangement).

* **Colchester.** Colchester Central Library. Trinity Square, Colchester, Essex CO1 1JB *tel:* 01206 245918 *fax:* 01206 245901 *email:* adrian.ure@essexcc.gov.uk. *Adrian Ure, snr subject librarian, mus. Large coll of sets of vocal and orch mus, county mus coll.*

* **Cork.** Cork City Library. Grand Parade, Cork *tel:* 00 353 21 4277 110 *fax:* 00 353 21 4275 684 *email:* citylibrary@corkcity.ie. *Catherine Buckley, mus librarian. CD coll - classical, inst, vocal, choral and orch, pop, country and rock, jazz, blues, light opera, musicals, films, br and military band, Irish traditional and world mus, children's mus. Language courses, listening facilities. Scores and books.*

Devizes. Wiltshire Performing Arts Library. Sheep St, Devizes, Wilts SN10 1DL *tel:* 01380 722633 *fax:* 01380 722161. *Delaine Newton, librarian. Books, mus scores, vocal and orch sets, records, cassettes, CDs, DVDs, videos, chmbr mus sets, miniature scores.*

* **Dorking.** Dorking Surrey Performing Arts Library. Denbies Wine Estate, London Rd, Dorking, Surrey RH5 6AA *tel:* 01306 887509/875453 (enquiries) *fax:* 01306 875074 *email:* performing.arts@surreycc.gov.uk. *G Muncy, snr librarian. Large range of printed and a/v mus reference, information and lending materials. Major regional coll of choral and orch performance material. Charges for the loan of choral and orch sets.*

Dudley. Dudley Library. St James's Rd, Dudley, W Midlands DY1 1HR *tel:* 01384 815556 *fax:* 01384 815543 *email:* dudlibref.ed@dudley.gov.uk. *M R Gay, reference librarian.*

* **Edinburgh.** Edinburgh City Libraries and Information Services. Music Library, George IV Bridge, Edinburgh EH1 1EG *tel:* 0131 242 8050 *fax:* 0131 242 8009 *email:* central.music.library@edinburgh.gov.uk. *Peter Baxter, acting principal library offr, mus; Garry Gale, acting principal library offr. Loan colls of CDs, DVDs, scores, books and multiple sets. Large reference coll. Scottish mus of all periods. Local mus information.*

* **Gloucester.** Gloucester Music and Drama Library. Greyfriars, Gloucester GL1 1TS *tel:* 01452 426982 *fax:* 01452 506241 *email:* g.friars@gloscc.gov.uk. *Hannah Morgan, principal library asst. CDs, drama and mus related books, play sets, mus sets, printed mus, books. Inter-library loan. Personal borrowers only.*

* **Hatfield.** Performing Arts Library. Central Resources Library, New Barnfield, Travellers Lane, Hatfield, Herts AL10 8XG *tel:* 01438 737333 *minicom:* 01438 737599 *fax:* 01438 737334 *email:* centralresources.library@hertscc.gov.uk. *Miriam Valencia, librarian; Di Robb, snr library asst. Large coll of books, sheet mus, and a/v material; performance sets hire; internet access; listening access; listening facilities; reference coll.*

* **Leicester.** Leicester City Libraries. The Goldsmith Music & Drama Library, Central Lending Library, 54 Belvoir St, Leicester LE1 6QL *tel:* 0116 299 5435 *email:* central.lending@leicester.gov.uk. *Dave Robinson, a/v services mgr. Central mus library with colls of orch and vocal sets; mus books and scores; an extensive coll of sound recordings. Schools may have extended loan of materials on payment of annual subscription.*

* **Lincoln.** Lincolnshire County Libraries. Lincoln Central Library, Free School Lane, Lincoln LN2 1EZ *tel:* 01522 510800 *fax:* 01522 575011 *email:* lincoln.library@lincolnshire.gov.uk. *A H Mason, librarian (mus and drama). General public library mus coll with books, scores, sets of vocal and orch mus, CDs.*

Luton. Luton Central Music Library. St George's Square, Luton, Beds LU2 1NG *tel:* 01582 547414 *fax:* 01582 547461 *email:* williaab@luton.gov.uk. *Abigail Williams, community librarian. Scores, books, CDs.*

* **Maidstone.** Maidstone Kent Arts and Libraries. County Central Library, Springfield, Maidstone, Kent ME14 2LH *tel:* 01622 696511 *fax:* 01622 696494 *email:* frances.metcalfe@kent.gov.uk. *Miss F Metcalfe, mus librarian. Wide range of printed mus, books and a/v material. Major coll of performance sets available for loan (charge for societies outside Kent).*

* **Newcastle upon Tyne.** Newcastle Libraries and Information Services. City Library, Princess Square, Newcastle upon Tyne NE99 1DX *tel:* 0191 277 4100 *fax:* 0191 277 4107 *email:* city.lending@newcastle.gov.uk. *Barbara Heathcote, library and information mgr. Scores, books, small coll of vocal sets. Cat of printed mus and comprehensive directory coverage. Loan coll of CDs and audio cassettes.*

* **Nottingham.** Nottingham Music Library. Nottingham Central Library, Angel Row, Nottingham NG1 6HP *tel:* 0115 915 2832 *fax:* 0115 915 2830 *email:* music.library@nottinghamcity.gov.uk. *Malcolm Lewis, head of mus library. Eric Coates coll. Inter-library loan system.*

* **Plymouth.** Plymouth Music and Drama Library. Central Library, Drake Circus, Plymouth PL4 8AL *tel:* 01752 305914 *fax:* 01752 305914 *email:* music@plymouth.gov.uk. *Andrew Laycock, mus and drama librarian. Vocal and orch sets. Rev Sabine Baring-Gould coll of folk song*

mss. Mus scores, playscripts, playsets and books on mus and theatre for loan. Cassettes, CDs, videos. Comprehensive reference stock, including MusicMaster/Gramophone on CD-ROM, song index.

* **Preston.** Lancashire County Library. County Library Headquarters, County Hall, PO Box 61, Preston, Lancs PR1 8RJ *tel:* 01772 534051 *fax:* 01772 534880 *email:* alison.thies@lcl.lancscc.gov.uk. Alison Thies, principal librarian, cultural services. *J A Fuller-Maitland coll (The Times mus critic 1889-1911) includes books, scores, periodicals and mss with special emphasis on English folk mus, Bach and Purcell.*

* **Ruthin.** Denbighshire Library and Information Service. c/o Ruthin Library, Record St, Ruthin, Denbighshire LL15 1DS *tel:* 01824 705274 *fax:* 01824 702580. Llinos Davies, community librarian. *Special coll of Welsh mus.*

* **St Austell.** Cornwall Library - Performing Arts. 2 Carlyon Rd, St Austell, Cornwall PL25 4LD *tel:* 01726 61702 *fax:* 01726 77844 *email:* performingarts.library@cornwall.gov.uk. Jonathan L Roberts, principal library offr (arts). *Large general coll of mus scores, including performance sets (vocal and orch); CDs, videos, Cornish mus (folk, dance, carols); books on all aspects of mus for lending and reference; videos, sound effects recordings.*

* **Shrewsbury.** Shropshire Music and Drama Library. Lending Library, Castle Gates, Shrewsbury, Shropshire SY1 2AS *tel:* 01743 255341 *fax:* 01743 255309 *email:* music.library@shropshire-cc.gov.uk. Brian Rapson, librarian. *General colls including classical, pop, folk and world mus. Inter-library loan.*

Sutton. Sutton Central Library. St Nicholas Way, Sutton, Surrey SM1 1EA *tel:* 020 8770 4765 *fax:* 020 8770 4777 *email:* sutton.music@sutton.gov.uk. Leigh Allen, information mgr (recreation). *Sets of vocal*

scores, small coll of orch parts available on loan. Audio specialisation includes recordings of Bruckner, choral recitals, jazz artists GIM-HARD.

* **Telford.** Telford & Wrekin Libraries: Music and Drama Library. Wellington Library, 23 Walker St, Wellington, Telford TF1 1BD *tel:* 01952 248423 *fax:* 01952 256960 *email:* wellingtonlibrary@hotmail.com. Carol Woollard, snr librarian. *General colls including classical, pop, folk and world mus. Inter-library loan.*

Warwick. Warwickshire County Council Music & Drama Library. Barrack St, Warwick CV34 4TH *tel:* 01926 412168 *fax:* 01926 412471 *email:* kathleencollins@warwickshire.gov.uk. Kathleen Collins, mus and drama librarian. *25,000 mus scores, including vocal sets and sets of part-songs. Books on mus and some orch sets in the schools mus library.*

* **Worcester.** Worcestershire County Council, Worcester City Library. Foregate St, Worcester WR1 1DT *tel:* 01905 765312 *fax:* 01905 726664 *email:* worcestermusic@worcestershire.gov.uk. John Stafford, library mgr. *Choral sets, inst sets at Worcester City Library. Sound recordings at all branch libraries; single scores at all branches.*

* **Yeovil.** Somerset Libraries, Arts & Information. Performing Arts Library, King George St, Yeovil, Somerset BA20 1PY *tel:* 01935 472020 *fax:* 01935 429133 *email:* muslib@somerset.gov.uk. Roger Taylor, performing arts librarian. *Reference/bibliographic coll, including computerised song index. Loan coll of books, single-copy mus including chmbr mus sets and complete editions, drama scripts, for loan to library members. Performance sets of vocal and orch mus, plus reading sets of drama scripts, available for extended loan to registered representatives of societies, schools, churches, etc, within Somerset and adjoining areas. Request facilities for multiple copies, extended loan periods and reservations for future loan periods.*

Church and Cathedral Libraries

These libraries are private but are usually open to bona fide scholars. Applications for admission are advisable.

London. Lambeth Palace Library. London SE1 7JU *tel:* 020 7898 1400 *fax:* 020 7928 7932. R J Palmer, librarian and archivist. *A few mss (including early 16th C choir books) and some printed books including church mus.*

St Paul's Cathedral Library. The Chapter House, St Paul's Churchyard, London EC4M 8AE *tel:* 020 7246 8345 *fax:* 020 7248 3104 *email:* library@stpaulscathedral.org.uk. Joseph Wisdom, librarian. *17th-18th C mus part-books; a number of autograph scores of services and anthems, some by former organists, mainly 19th and 20th C.*

Westminster Abbey Library. East Cloister, London SW1P 3PA *tel:* 020 7654 4830 *fax:* 020 7654 4827 *email:* library@westminster-abbey.org. T A Trowles, librarian. *Includes 16th-19th C mss and printed mus.*

Bristol. Baptist College Library. The Promenade, Clifton Down, Clifton, Bristol BS8 3NJ *tel:* 0117 946 7050 *fax:* 0117 946 7787 *email:* library@bristol-baptist.ac.uk. Mrs S Shire, librarian. *Special coll of Baptist hymn books (mostly words only).*

Methodist Church Music Society Library. Wesley College, Henbury Rd, Westbury on Trym, Bristol BS10 7QD *tel:* 0117 959 1200 *fax:* 0117 950 1277. Janet Henderson, librarian. *Coll of hymn books, psalters, etc and books with special emphasis on hymnody and church mus, 17th-20th C.*

Canterbury. Cathedral Archives and Library. The Precincts, Canterbury CT1 2EH *tel:* 01227 865287 (library)/330 (archives) *fax:* 01227 865222 *email:* library@canterbury-cathedral.org; archives@canterbury-cathedral.org. Heather Forbes, archivist; Keith O'Sullivan, librarian. *Archives: medieval mus mss, 17th-18th C choir mus mss. Library: printed choir mus; mss and printed mus of Canterbury Catch Club.*

Durham. Chapter Library. The College, Durham DH1 3EH *tel:* 0191 386 2489 *email:* enquiries@durhamcathderal.co.uk. Wendy Stevenson. *17th-19th C cathedral choir and organists mss; 17th-19th C printed mus from Bamburgh Castle; Philip Falle coll of 17th C printed mus. 2 weeks notice needed to visit. Open Mon-Fri 2.15-5pm only, closed Aug.*

Hereford. Cathedral Library. Hereford HR1 2NG *tel:* 01432 374225/6 *fax:* 01432 374220 *email:* library@herefordcathedral.co.uk. J Williams, librarian. *Chained library. 18th-20th C printed and ms mus, including Roger North, Wesley and Elgar mss. Hereford Breviary, with mus c 1270.*

Lichfield. Cathedral Library. 19a The Close, Lichfield, Staffs *tel:* 01543 306175 *fax:* 01543 306109 *email:* enquiries@lichfield-cathedral.org. Percy M Young, hon mus librarian; P Bancroft, librarian. *Cat of 17th to early-19th C mss. Cat of 18th to early-19th C printed mus. Cat of late-19th C printed mus in preparation.*

Lincoln. Cathedral Library. Lincoln LN2 1PZ *tel:* 01522 544544 *fax:* 01522 511307 *email:* librarian@lincolncathedral.com. *Including medieval mss and early printed mus. 17th-19th C ms part books.*

Winchester. Cathedral Library. 1 The Close, Winchester, Hants SO23 9LS *tel:* 01962 857223 *fax:* 01962 857201 *email:* cathedral.office@winchester-cathedral.org.uk. John Hardacre, curator. *Coll of 18th and 19th C printed church mus.*

Windsor. St George's Chapel Archives and Chapter Library. The Vicars' Hall Undercroft, The Cloisters, Windsor Castle, Windsor, Berks SL4 1NJ *tel:* 01753 848725 *fax:* 01753 848763 *email:* archives@stgeorges_windsor.org. Eileen Scarff, librarian and archivist. *Including mss of Tallis and William Child.*

Worcester. Cathedral Music Library. The Chapter Office, 10a College Green, Worcester WR1 2LH *tel:* 01905 28854 *fax:* 01905 611139 *email:* info@worcestercathedral.org.uk. *17th-18th C part books, mss and printed church mus.*

York. York Minster Library. Dean's Park, York YO1 7JQ *tel:* 01904 625308 (library)/611118 (archive) *fax:* 01904 611119. Mrs D M Mortimer, librarian; P Young, archivist. *Mainly 16th-20th C mss and printed mus, including many rare items such as mss and printed mus by Purcell, the Minster repertoire of the choir from 16th C to present day; some medieval liturgical mus, mainly of the use of York; also coll donated by Marmaduke Fothergill.*

University and College Libraries

Primarily available to staff and students of the institution, but visiting scholars may also be admitted. Applications in writing are advisable.

* **London.** The Foyle Special Collections Library. King's College London, Chancery Lane, London WC2A 1LR *tel:* 020 7848 1843/5 *fax:* 020 7848 1843 *email:* catherine.sambrook@kcl.ac.uk. Katie Sambrook, special colls librarian. *Special colls relating to mus.*

* Goldsmiths College Library. Lewisham Way, London SE14 6NW *tel:* 020 7919 7168 *fax:* 020 7919 7165 *email:* lbs0lpm@gold.ac.uk. Peter Morris, asst librarian. *Includes the A L Lloyd coll (scores, books and offprints of folk and traditional mus, especially Eastern Europe), the Ewan MacColl/Peggy Seeger coll (books and scores, especially English and Scottish folksongs), the Alan Bush coll (scores of 20th C Eastern European mus) and the Denis Stevens coll (books and scores re Monteverdi).*

* Guildhall School of Music and Drama. Barbican, London EC2Y 8DT *tel:* 020 7382 7178 *fax:* 020 7786 9378 *email:* library@gsmd.ac.uk. Kate Eaton, snr librarian; Adrian Yardley, mus librarian. *Includes Appleby gui coll, Alkan Society coll, Harris Opera coll and Goossens ob mus coll.*

* Imperial College of Science, Technology and Medicine. Central Library, Imperial College London, South Kensington Campus, London SW7 2AZ *tel:* 020 7594 8611 *fax:* 020 7584 8876 *email:* h.kershaw@imperial.ac.uk. Helen Kershaw, business and humanities support librarian. *Haldane mus coll. Recordings, scores, books.*

Jewish Music Resource Centre. Room 521, Main Building, School of Oriental and African Studies, University of London, Thornhaugh St, Russell Square, London WC1H 0XG *tel:* 020 7898 4307 *fax:* 020 8909 1030 *email:* jewishmusic@jmi.org.uk. *Printed and recorded formats of a wide variety of Jewish mus.*

London College of Music and Media. Thames Valley University LRC, St Mary's Rd, London W5 5RF *tel:* 020 8231 2648 *fax:* 020 8231 2631 *email:* colin.steele@tvu.ac.uk. *Scores, books, journals, LPs, CDs, listening facilities, CD-ROM multimedia.*

* The Maughan Library and Information Services Centre. King's College London, Chancery Lane, London WC2A 1LR *tel:* 020 7848 2424 *fax:* 020 7848 2277 *email:* rosemary.clarke@kcl.ac.uk. Rosemary Clarke, information specialist (mus). *Coll supports u/grad and p/grad studies. Mus material is integrated with the humanities coll.*

Morley College Library. 61 Westminster Bridge Rd, London SE1 7HT *tel:* 020 7450 1828 *fax:* 020 7928 4074 *email:* liz.shaughnessy@morleycollege.ac.uk. Liz Shaughnessy, library mgr. *Scores, sheet mus, books, records, CDs, mus software.*

* Royal Academy of Music Library. Marylebone Rd, London NW1 5HT *tel:* 020 7873 7323 *fax:* 020 7873 7322 *email:* library@ram.ac.uk. Kathy Adamson, librarian. *Including Sir Henry Wood library of orch mus, Sir Arthur Sullivan archive, English Bach Society Library, R J S Stevens Library, David Munrow Library, Robert Spencer coll.*

* Royal College of Music Library. Prince Consort Rd, London SW7 2BS *tel:* 020 7591 4325 *fax:* 020 7589 7740 *email:* pthompson@rcm.ac.uk. Pam Thompson, chief librarian. *Includes libraries of Sacred Harmonic Society, Concerts of Ancient Music, Heron-Allen coll.*

Royal College of Organists. 7 St Andrew Street, London EC4A 3LQ *tel:* 020 7936 3606 (admin)/4321 (lib) *fax:* 020 7353 8244 (admin)/3966 (lib) *email:* robinlangley@rco.org.uk. Robin Langley, librarian. *Mainly org mus, recordings and books on the org; non-members for reference only, by prior appointment, during college opening hours.*

* School of Oriental and African Studies Library. University of London, Thornhaugh St, Russell Square, London WC1H 0XG *tel:* 020 7898 4172 *fax:* 020 7898 4159 *email:* yyl@soas.ac.uk. *Books, sound recordings (and video) of Asian and African mus.*

* Trinity College of Music, Jerwood Library of the Performing Arts. King Charles Court, Old Royal Naval College, Greenwich, London SE10 9JF *tel:* 020 8305 3950 *fax:* 020 8305 3999 *email:* library@tcm.ac.uk. Rosemary Firman, chief librarian. *Incorporating the Mander and Mitchenson Theatre coll. Special colls include: Lionel Tertis coll; Barbirolli coll; Charles Proctor coll; William Lovelock coll; Cherkassky coll; Almeida coll (includes Charles Munch's conducting scores); Alan Cave coll of wind mus; Filmharmonic archive of original film scores; Joseph Ortiz coll (zarzuela mus); Frank Cordell coll; British Music Society archive; Westbrook archive; Music Preserved.*

* University of London Library Music Collection. Senate House, Malet St, London WC1E 7HU *tel:* 020 7862 8436 *fax:* 020 7862 8480 *email:* ull@ull.ac.uk. Christopher Pressler, arts collections team leader.

Including Tudor church mus coll, Littleton coll, John Edmunds' Thurston Dart Memorial coll, George coll of pno mus, Pianola Roll coll.

* **Aberdeen.** Aberdeen University Library. Special Libraries and Archives, University of Aberdeen, King's College, Aberdeen AB24 3SW *tel:* 01224 274266 *fax:* 01224 273956 *email:* r.turbet@abdn.ac.uk. Richard Turbet, special colls cataloguer. *Including libraries of Gavin Greig and Forbes Leith; Stationers' Hall coll (18th-19th C printed mus obtained under copyright).*

Aberystwyth. University of Wales (Hugh Owen Library), Aberystwyth, Dyfed SY23 3DZ *tel:* 01970 622391 *fax:* 01970 622404 *email:* library@aber.ac.uk. Mike Hopkins, dir info services. *Including David de Lloyd mss; Mendelssohn letters and autographs; George Powell bequest (19th C scores and some 18th-19th C mss).*

* **Belfast.** Queen's University, Belfast BT7 1NN *tel:* 028 9033 5020 *fax:* 028 9027 3072 *email:* n.russell@qub.ac.uk. *Including Bunting mss of Irish folk mus; Hamilton Harty library.*

* **Birmingham.** Barber Music Library. University of Birmingham, Edgbaston, Birmingham B15 2TS *tel:* 0121 414 5852 *fax:* 0121 414 5853 *email:* music-library@bham.ac.uk. Emily Quinton, snr information asst. *Including Granville Bantock and Shaw-Hellier colls, Elgar diaries.*

* Birmingham Conservatoire Library. University of Central England, Paradise Place, Birmingham B3 3HG *tel:* 0121 331 5914/5 *fax:* 0121 331 5906 *email:* conservatoire.library@uce.ac.uk. Robert Allan, faculty librarian. *Birmingham Flute Society coll.*

Bristol. University of Bristol Library. Tyndall Ave, Bristol BS8 1TJ *tel:* 0117 928 9000 *fax:* 0117 925 5334 *email:* library@bris.ac.uk. Michael Leat, asst librarian.

* **Cambridge.** Anglia Polytechnic University Library. East Rd, Cambridge CB1 1PT *tel:* 01223 363271 ext 2699 *fax:* 01223 363271 ext 2311 *email:* libhelpcam@anglia.ac.uk. Jenny Cefai, academic liaison librarian; Sue Gilmurray, subject librarian. *Books, scores, CDs, LPs, videos. Loans to members of the university only; otherwise reference only.*

Cambridge University Library *see* **National Copyright Libraries.**

Clare College Archives. Queens Rd, Cambridge CB3 9AJ *tel:* 01223 333228 *fax:* 01223 765560 *email:* archives@clare.cam.ac.uk. Elizabeth Stratton, Edgar Bowing archivist. *Including mss of Cecil Sharp's folksong colls; mss of W C Denis-Browne; mss of F P Haines.*

Gonville and Caius College. Cambridge CB2 1TA *tel:* 01223 332419 *fax:* 01223 332430 *email:* library@cai.cam.ac.uk. J H Prynne, librarian. *Including mss and fragments of mus from the 10th-18th C (mostly 11th-14th C); also papers and materials relating to Charles Wood (1866-1926).*

King's College. Rowe Music Library, Cambridge CB2 1ST *tel:* 01223 331252 *fax:* 01223 331891 *email:* library@kings.cam.ac.uk. Iain Fenlon, Rowe mus librarian. *Including libraries of L T Rowe, A H Mann and A H King; also E J Dent papers.*

Magdalene College. Cambridge CB3 0AG *tel:* 01223 332100 *fax:* 01223 332187 *email:* pepyslibrary@magd.cam.ac.uk. R Luckett, Pepys librarian; Mrs A Fitzsimons, asst librarian. *Pepys Library (personal library of Samuel Pepys (1633-1703): mss, ballads, printed mus); library open during term-time (appointment for readers necessary). Catalogued in R C Latham, ed 'The Pepys Library at Magdalene College', Cambridge (11 vols), IV.*

Pembroke College. Cambridge CB2 1RF *tel:* 01223 338121 *fax:* 01223 338163 *email:* lib@pem.cam.ac.uk. T R S Allan, librarian; P A Aske, asst librarian. *Including 17th C ms part-mus; 18th C chmbr mus.*

Pendlebury Library of Music. University Music School, West Rd, Cambridge CB3 9DP *tel:* 01223 335182 *fax:* 01223 335183. *Library of the university mus faculty.*

Peterhouse. Trumpington St, Cambridge CB2 1RD *tel:* 01223 338200 *fax:* 01223 337578. R W Lovatt, Perne librarian. *Including 16th-17th C part-books (permanently deposited at University Library).*

St John's College. Cambridge CB2 1TP *tel:* 01223 338662 *fax:* 01223 337035 *email:* library@joh.cam.ac.uk. *Samuel Butler coll, Rootham compositions. St John's College Chapel Old Library.*

Trinity College. Cambridge CB2 1TQ *tel:* 01223 338488 *fax:* 01223 338532 *email:* trin-lib@lists.cam.ac.uk. D J McKitterick, librarian. *Including roll of 15th C English carols, two 15th C Greek mss with mus, lute tablatures of Bacheler, Greaves, Johnson and Taylor, autographs of Gray, Parry and Stanford; early printed mus of Byrd, Mace, Playford and Purcell.*

* **Cardiff.** Royal Welsh College of Music and Drama Library. Castle Grounds, Cathays Park, Cardiff CF10 3ER *tel:* 029 2034 2854 *fax:* 029 2039 1304 *email:* agusjm@rwcmd.ac.uk. Judith Agus, librarian.

* **Colchester.** Colchester Institute Library. Sheepen Rd, Colchester, Essex CO3 3LL *tel:* 01206 518642 *fax:* 01206 518643. Miss J Henshaw, subject librarian (mus and performing arts). *Liturgical mus, wind, br and jazz band scores, folk mus, collected works.*

Durham. University Library. Palace Green Section, Durham DH1 3RN *tel:* 0191 334 2932 *fax:* 0191 334 2942 *email:* pg.library@durham.ac.uk. Sheila Hingley, sub-librarian. *Britten correspondence and related mss, Dame Ethel Smyth mss, medieval liturgical mss, Pratt Green Collection of hymn books and hymnology. Papers of Else Headlam-Morley (1866-1950), composer.*

Edinburgh. Edinburgh University Library: Main Library. George Square, Edinburgh EH8 9LJ *tel:* 0131 650 3384 *fax:* 0131 667 9780 *email:* Library@ed.ac.uk. Sheila E Cannell, acting librarian. *Colls of scores, books, periodicals and sound recordings. Special colls include Sir Donald Tovey archive; Niecks bequest of books on the theory of mus; Weiss coll of Beethoven literature; Kenneth Leighton mss; Dallapiccola complete scores. General and special book colls include books of Scottish song; special colls include early Scottish mss (surviving leaves of 14th C Inchcolm Antiphoner, and colls of lute and pipe-tunes, etc); English madrigal books; Marjorie Kennedy-Fraser coll of Hebridean folk-song recordings and books on Highland mus and dance; archives of the Scottish Students' Song Book Committee (1901-1991) and Edinburgh Royal Choral Union (1857-).*

School of Scottish Studies Archives. Dept of Celtic and Scottish Studies, University of Edinburgh, 27 George Square, Edinburgh EH8 9LD *tel:* 0131 650 4159 *fax:* 0131 650 4163 *email:* cathlin. macaulay@ed.ac.uk. Cathlin Macaulay, archives asst. *Book colls include Scots and Gaelic song since the 18th C, folk mus and ethnomusicology of Ireland, England, N America and the world. Archives include traditional and national Scottish mus field recordings, the John Levy coll of ethnomusicological recordings (mostly oriental), the Peter Cooke coll of African mus recordings, the Will Forret coll, Gus Macdonald and Edgar Ashton colls of Scottish national, popular, folk revival mus on LP, and smaller colls (Appalachian, Chilean, Irish, Indian). Publications include: Scottish Studies Journal and Tocher.*

Egham. Royal Holloway, University of London, Music Library. Egham Hill, Egham, Surrey TW20 0EX *tel:* 01784 443560/759 *fax:* 01784 439441 *email:* m.brooke@rhul.ac.uk. Matthew Brooke. *Includes library of Dom Anselm Hughes.*

* **Exeter.** University Library. Stocker Rd, Exeter EX4 4PT *tel:* 01392 263873 *fax:* 01392 263871 *email:* library@exeter.ac.uk. Diane Workman, subject librarian, mus. *Including special coll of American mus.*

* **Glasgow.** Royal Scottish Academy of Music and Drama. 100 Renfrew St, Glasgow G2 3DB *tel:* 0141 270 8268 *fax:* 0141 270 8353 *email:* library@rsamd.ac.uk. Gordon Hunt, head of information services.

* University Library. Hillhead St, Glasgow G12 8QE *tel:* 0141 330 6797 (mus)/6704/5 (general) *fax:* 0141 330 4952 *email:* library@ lib.gla.ac.uk (general); m.mackie@lib.gla.ac.uk (mus). Morag Mackie, subject librarian, mus. *Includes Euing Music coll; Drysdale, Farmer, Lamond, McEwen, MacCunn, Zavertal colls. Incorporates Trinity College library and Mearns coll of hymnology.*

Guildford. The University Library. University of Surrey, Guildford, Surrey GU2 7XH *tel:* 01483 683361 *fax:* 01483 689500. Sally Smith, mus librarian.

Hull. Brynmor Jones Library. The University of Hull, Cottingham Rd, Hull HU6 7RX *tel:* 01482 465250 *fax:* 01482 466205 *email:* libhelp@ hull.ac.uk. Richard Heseltine, dir of academic services and university librarian.

Leeds. Brotherton Library. University of Leeds, Leeds LS2 9JT *tel:* 0113 343 5663 *fax:* 0113 343 5561 *email:* library@library.leeds.ac.uk. *Including mss and correspondence of Mendelssohn, Charles Dibdin mss, Novello (mus publishers) mss and correspondence, correspondence of Herbert Thompson (mus critic), Fiske-Platt coll of late 18th C and early 19th C English opera.*

Liverpool. The University of Liverpool Music Library. PO Box 147, 82 Bedford St South, Liverpool L69 3BX *tel:* 0151 794 3105/2684 *fax:* 0151 794 2681 *email:* C.Morgan@liverpool.ac.uk. Colin Morgan, arts librarian. *Russian mus, German mus 1830-1945, French mus 1860-1945, facsimile editions.*

* **Manchester.** John Rylands University Library of Manchester. Oxford Rd, Manchester M13 9PP *tel:* 0161 275 3751 (main library)/834 5343 (special colls) *fax:* 0161 273 7488 (main library)/834 5574 (special colls) *email:* sheila.c.padden@man.ac.uk. Sheila Padden, subject specialist for mus. *The main library has printed scores and secondary mus material. Special colls include: medieval mus mss; several 18th-19th C British mus scores; Wesley family papers; rare scores and collected editions of the works of Handel and Bach and research notes on Handel and Mahler (Arthur D Walker Music Collection); material relating to Ralph Vaughan Williams (papers of Michael Kennedy).*

* Royal Northern College of Music Library. 124 Oxford Rd, Manchester M13 9RD *tel:* 0161 907 5243 *fax:* 0161 273 7611 *email:* library@rncm.ac.uk. Anna Smart, librarian. *Including Alan Rawsthorne mss, Horenstein coll, Adolph Brodsky archive, Newmania (memorabilia of Philip Newman), Rothwell coll of wind mus, Dame Eva Turner coll, John Ogden archive, Ida Carroll archive, Thomas Pitfield archive, John Golland mss, Arthur Butterworth mss, RNCM coll of historic mus insts. Philip Jones br ens archive, Elizabeth Harwood archive.*

Norwich. University of East Anglia Library, Norwich NR4 7TJ *tel:* 01603 592425/07 *fax:* 01603 591010 *email:* librid@uea.ac.uk. Jean Steward, dir of library learning and IT services. *Alex Noel-Tod, mus librarian.*

* **Nottingham.** The Denis Arnold Music Library. The Arts Centre, University of Nottingham, University Park, Nottingham NG7 2RD *tel:* 0115 951 4596 *fax:* 0115 951 4756 *email:* Library-Arts-Enquiries@nottingham.ac.uk. Catherine Ayre, snr library asst. *Approx 24,000 books and scores, including many collected editions of composers and national mus colls. Also sheet mus and miniature scores. Over 30 current periodical subscriptions.*

* **Oxford.** Bodleian Library *see* **National Copyright Libraries**.

Christ Church Library. Oxford OX1 1DP *tel:* 01865 276169 *email:* library@christ-church.ox.ac.uk. *Includes Henry Aldrich bequest and Richard Goodson bequest.*

University Faculty of Music Library. St Aldate's, Oxford OX1 1DB *tel:* 01865 276146/8 *fax:* 01865 286260 *email:* john.wagstaff@ music.ox.ac.uk. John Wagstaff, librarian; Julie Crawley, deputy librarian. *Open Mon-Fri 9.30am-5.30pm, Sat 10am-1pm (term-time), Mon-Fri 10am-4.30pm (vacations). General u/grad and research mus coll, including sound and video recordings.*

Reading. International Centre for Research in Music Education. University of Reading, Bulmershe Court, Earley, Reading RH6 1HY *tel:* 0118 931 8821 *fax:* 0118 935 2080 *email:* g.s.a.cox@reading.ac.uk. Gordon Cox, dir. *An extensive archive of documents relating to the development of mus educ in the UK. Publications of the Music Teaching in Professional Practice Initiative. MA in Music Education dissertations. Comprehensive coll of publications and materials for primary and secondary class teaching.*

University Music Library. 35 Upper Redlands Rd, Reading RG1 5JE *tel:* 0118 378 8413 *fax:* 0118 378 8412 *email:* c.b.cipkin@reading.ac.uk. Christopher Cipkin, mus librarian; Julia Munro, librarian. *Finzi coll, Newbury String Players' coll.*

St Andrews. Library and Information Services. University Library, North Street, St Andrews, Fife KY16 9TR *tel:* 01334 462281 *fax:* 01334 462282 *email:* lis.library@st-and.ac.uk. *Includes Finzi coll of 18th C mus.*

Sheffield. University of Sheffield Music Library. 38 Taptonville Rd, Sheffield, S Yorks S10 5BR *tel:* 0114 222 7330 *fax:* 0114 266 8053 *email:* musiclib@library.shef.ac.uk. Tom McCanna, mus librarian.

* **Totnes.** Dartington College of Arts Library, Totnes, Devon TQ9 6EJ *tel:* 01803 861651 *fax:* 01803 861666 *email:* library@dartington.ac.uk. Dorothy Faulkner, dir, academic services; Richard Taylor, deputy librarian.

* **York.** University Library, Heslington, York YO10 5DD *tel:* 01904 433865 *fax:* 01904 433866 *email:* lib-enquiry@york.ac.uk. David Griffiths. *Copland coll and Delius coll.*

Libraries of Societies and Institutions

These libraries are for the use of members and staff, but reference facilities are extended to visitors. Applications in writing are advisable.

London. Arts Council England Information Department. 14 Great Peter St, London SW1P 3NQ *tel:* 0845 300 6200 *fax:* 020 7973 6590 *email:* enquiries@artscouncil.org.uk. Jennifer Perkins, snr offr. *Enquiry service provides information on the Arts Council, arts funding, policies and other related subjects; enquiry line open Mon-Fri 9am-5pm, out-of-hours answering machine. Reference library is a specialist resource for researchers and those working in arts funding.*

The BBC Music Library. Information and Archives, Unit 7, Ariel Way, London W12 7SL *tel:* 020 8576 0208 *fax:* 020 8225 9984 *email:* commercial.unit@bbc.co.uk. *Loans of mus materials for non-broadcast use are made only if no other source exists and are subject to copyright restrictions. Enquiries 9.30am-6pm Mon-Fri; visits by appointment only.*

British Film Institute National Library. 21 Stephen St, London W1T 1LN *tel:* 020 7255 1444 *fax:* 020 7436 2338 *email:* library@bfi.org.uk. Ray Templeton, head of library and educ. *Includes information about film and TV mus and composers.*

British Institute of Recorded Sound *see* British Library National Sound Archive *under* **Specialised Gramophone Record and Tape Libraries**.

British Music Information Centre. 10 Stratford Place, London W1C 1BA *tel:* 020 7499 8567 *fax:* 020 7499 4795 *email:* info@bmic.co.uk. Matthew Greenhall, dir. *Coll of contemporary British mus; visitors welcome Mon-Fri 12-5pm. Reading and listening facilities for scores; recordings, books, videos, background information on composers. Live events in London and nationally.*

* English Folk Dance and Song Society. Vaughan Williams Memorial Library, Cecil Sharp House, 2 Regent's Park Rd, London NW1 7AY *tel:* 020 7485 2206 *fax:* 020 7284 0523 *email:* library@efdss.org. Malcolm Taylor. *Includes Cecil Sharp bequest; original recordings by many leading folksong collectors.*

Gerald Coke Handel Foundation. 40 Brunswick Square, London WC1N 1AZ. *Handel coll. Temporarily housed, partly at the Hampshire Record Office, Winchester and partly at the Victoria and Albert Museum, London.*

* The Serge Prokofiev Archive. Information Services, Goldsmiths College, University of London, London SE14 6NW *tel:* 020 7919 7558 *fax:* 020 7919 7255 *email:* mua01nm@gold.ac.uk. Nolle Mann, curator. *Property of the Serge Prokofiev Foundation. The archive holds copies of published works, microfilms of mss, books, articles and reviews; sound recordings, photos, documents. Also, unique coll of Prokofiev's correspondence 1921-1935.*

Society for Co-operation in Russian and Soviet Studies. 320 Brixton Rd, London SW9 6AB *tel:* 020 7274 2282 *fax:* 020 7274 3230 *email:* ruslibrary@scrss.org.uk. Jane Rosen, hon librarian; John Cunningham, library asst. *Reference library of books on Russian/Soviet musicians, mus scores, encyclopaedias and recordings appertaining to Russian and Soviet mus and composers. Fees available on request.*

* **Aldeburgh.** Britten-Pears Library. The Red House, Golf Lane, Aldeburgh, Suffolk IP15 5PZ *tel:* 01728 452615 *fax:* 01728 453076 *email:* bpl@britten-pears.co.uk. Christopher Grogan, librarian; Nicholas Clark, curator for reader services; Andrew Plant, curator for Holst library; Judith Tydeman, archivist. *Printed book and periodical colls, specialising in British 20th C mus literature relating to Britten, Pears and their associates. Mss, printed mus and personal papers of Benjamin Britten and Peter Pears, as well as press cuttings, programmes, photographs and sound and video recordings (chiefly relating to Britten and Pears). Mss of works by other composers and literary mss. English song (16th C to present day), Aldeburgh Festival and Britten-Pears School archives, English Opera Group and English Music Theatre archives. Julian Herbage material relating to Thomas Arne. Open Mon-Fri, 10am-1pm and 2.15-5.15pm by appointment only.*

Cambridge. Dept of Manuscripts and Printed Books. Dept of Applied Arts, Fitzwilliam Museum, Trumpington St, Cambridge CB2 1RB *tel:* 01223 332900 *fax:* 01223 332923 *email:* fitzwilliam-enquiries@lists.cam.ac.uk. Stella Panayotova, asst keeper. *Admission by appointment.*

Cardiff. Ty Cerdd (Welsh Amateur Music Federation, Welsh Music Information Centre and Cyfansoddwyr Cymru/Composers of Wales). 15 Mount Stuart Square, Cardiff CF10 5DP *tel:* 029 2046 2855/5700 *fax:* 029 2046 2733 *email:* wamf@tycerdd.org. Keith Griffin, dir. *Mus of Welsh composers, published and unpublished. Choral and other scores, general performance material.*

Crowthorne. British Institute of Jazz Studies. 17 The Chase, Crowthorne, Berks RG45 6HT *tel:* 01344 775669 *fax:* 01344 780947 *email:* bijs99@hotmail.com. Graham Langley, sec. *Library of jazz and blues material: books, periodicals, ephemera, etc; visits by appointment.*

Glasgow. Scottish Music Information Centre. 1 Bowmont Gardens, Glasgow G12 9LR *tel:* 0141 334 6393 *fax:* 0141 337 1161 *email:* info@smic.org.uk. Andrew Logan, chief exec; Alasdair Pettinger, information mgr. *Exists to document and promote Scottish mus. Reference library with over 10,000 scores of Scottish composers' works, some available for sale/hire. Also comprehensive database of Scottish musicians and organisations. Photocopying and binding facilities, promotional activities.*

Loughton. National Jazz Archive. Loughton Central Library, Traps Hill, Loughton, Essex IG10 1HD *tel:* 020 8502 0181 *fax:* 020 8508 5041 *email:* david.nathan@essex.gov.uk. David Nathan, archivist. *Archive of printed material for research into jazz. Books, periodicals, concert brochures, photographs, posters, etc.*

Manchester. Chetham's Library. Long Millgate, Manchester M3 1SB *tel:* 0161 834 7961 *fax:* 0161 839 5797 *email:* librarian@chethams.org.uk. Michael Powell, librarian. *Halliwell-Phillipps coll of proclamations, broadsides, ballads and poems. Reference only.*

Preston. Library of Light-Orchestral Music. Lancaster Farm, Chipping Lane, Longridge, Preston, Lancs PR3 2NB *tel:* 01772 783646 *fax:* 01772 786026. Ernest Tomlinson, chmn; Hilary Ashton, sec. *35,000+ published sets, ms arrangements; hire and sale.*

* **Stockport.** National Library for the Blind. Far Cromwell Rd, Bredbury, Stockport, Cheshire SK6 2SG *tel:* 0161 355 2045 *fax:* 0161 355 2098 *email:* melanie.baker@nlbuk.org. Melanie Baker, mus librarian. *Large coll of braille mus on free loan; UK source for Library of Congress braille and large-print mus.*

Stratford-upon-Avon. Shakespeare Centre Library. Henley St, Stratford-upon-Avon, Warks CV37 6QW *tel:* 01789 201813 *fax:* 01789 296083 *email:* library@shakespeare.org.uk. Susan Brock, head of library and information resources; Sylvia Morris, deputy head of library and RSC librarian. *Mus connected with Shakespeare and RSC productions, including Leslie Bridgewater, Vaughan Williams, Ilona Sekacz, James Walker and Guy Woolfenden mus.*

* **Westhumble.** Royal School of Church Music. Cleveland Lodge, Westhumble, Dorking RH5 6BW *tel:* 01306 872800 *fax:* 01306 877260 *email:* library@rscm.com. *Colles Library, church mus and books. Please enquire for details of access.*

Windsor. Eton College Library. Eton College, Windsor, Berks SL4 6DB *tel:* 01753 671221 *fax:* 01753 801507 *email:* collections@etoncollege.org.uk. M C Meredith, librarian. *Includes the Eton Choir Book (c 1500), 18th C ms org books, minor mss of works by Parry, Butterworth, Quilter, Warlock, Britten, Hoddinott, etc.*

Specialised Gramophone Record and Tape Libraries

* **London.** BBC Music Library *see* **Libraries of Societies and Institutions**.

* British Library National Sound Archive. The British Library, 96 Euston Rd, London NW1 2DB *tel:* 020 7412 7676 *fax:* 020 7412 7441 *email:* sound-archive@bl.uk. Crispin Jewitt, dir; Y Yasumura, principal asst librarian; Chris Clark, head of public service. *Largest reference coll of sound recordings in the UK open to the public, free listening and viewing service, full reference library of associated literature. Information on commercial discs, history of recording, broadcasting and location of recordings around the UK. Groups from schools, universities, colleges by prior arrangement; w/shops, talks and seminars also offered by arrangement. Free newsletter. Member of the International Association of Sound and Audiovisual Archives.*

Music Preserved. Trinity College of Music, King Charles Court, Old Royal Naval College, Greenwich, London SE10 9JF *tel:* 020 8305 4425 *email:* rfirman@tcm.ac.uk. R Firman. *Archive of audio and video archive-recording of public performances given by international artists and orchestras from 1933 to present. Also recordings of interviews with artists. Also at: Barbican Music Library, Barbican Centre, Silk St, London EC2Y 8DS tel: 020 7638 0672.*

National Sound Archive *see* **British Library National Sound Archive**.

* School of Oriental and African Studies Library. University of London, Thornhaugh St, London WC1H 0XG *tel:* 020 7898 4172 *fax:* 020 7898 4159 *email:* yyl@soas.ac.uk. *Books, video and sound recordings of Oriental and African mus.*

Gloucester. folktrax.org. Central Library and Archive, Heritage House, 16 Brunswick Square, Gloucester GL1 1UG *tel:* 01452 415110 *email:* peter@folktrax.freeserve.co.uk. Peter and Beryl Kennedy, mgrs. *Traditional mus and customs in print and on studio tape, cassette, CD, film and video.*

St Annes-on-Sea. Squires Gate Music Centre Ltd. Rear 13 St Andrews Rd South, St Annes-on-Sea, Lancs FY8 1SX *tel:* 01253 782588 *fax:* 01253 782985 *email:* sales@lrpl.demon.co.uk. Carole Riches, dir; Kathleen Singleton, dir. *Commercial lending library for classical CDs and DVDs and specialist suppliers of classical CDs both in the UK and worldwide.*

Museums and Other Collections

Hours of opening may vary considerably and should be checked before a visit is organised. Some collections may be viewed only after written application to the curator.

London. Fenton House. Hampstead Grove, London NW3 *tel:* 020 7435 3471; 01494 755563 (info line) *fax:* 020 7435 3471 *email:* fentonhouse@nationaltrust.org.uk. Mimi S Waitzman, curator of insts. *Early keyboard insts, including hpds, clvds and early pnos. Demonstration tours, concert series, recordings and guide to insts available. Access to playable insts by audition with the curator.*

Handel House Museum. 25 Brook St, London W1K 4HB *tel:* 020 7495 1685 *fax:* 020 7495 1759 *email:* mail@handelhouse.org. Jacqueline Riding, dir; Caroline Churchill, operations mgr; Letty Potter, admin; Antonia Perkins, development and communications mgr. *Located at the home of G F Handel. Seeks to honour the memory of the composer by collecting, documenting and conserving objects relating to his life and works. Includes portraits, furniture, live mus and public events.*

Horniman Museum. 100 London Rd, London SE23 3PQ *tel:* 020 8699 1872 *fax:* 020 8291 5506 *email:* enquiry@horniman.ac.uk. Margaret Birley, keeper of mus insts; D W Allen, librarian. *Large coll of mus insts from all over world (8000 insts) including Adam Carse coll of historic European wind insts, Wayne coll of concertinas, Percy A Bull coll and Alice Schulmann Frank coll of world mus insts and Dolmetsch coll. A checklist of part of the coll is available on the museum's website. Library includes books on mus insts. Also educ service. Open 10.30am-5.30pm Tue-Sat, 2-5.30pm Sun.*

Museum of London. London Wall, London EC2Y 5HN *tel:* 0870 444 3852 *fax:* 0870 444 3853 *email:* info@museumoflondon.org.uk. Beverley Cook, asst curator. *Str, keyboard and wind insts; small coll only, 1950s fittings from Dobell's Jazz shop, printed ephemera on theatres and mus in London (open 7 days a week). Small number of paper rolls, vinyl discs, cylinders, c 1900-70s.*

Royal College of Music. Prince Consort Rd, London SW7 2BS *tel:* 020 7589 3643 (switchboard)/7591 4346 (museum)/7591 4340 (portraits) *fax:* 020 7589 7740 *email:* museum@rcm.ac.uk; portraits@rcm.ac.uk. Mrs E P Wells, museum curator. *Museum of insts (keyboard, str, wind, perc), including Tagore, Donaldson, Hipkins, Ridley, Hartley and Fleming colls; 700 insts and accs (600 European, 100 Asian and African) from c 1480 to present day. Dept of Portraits and Performance History: paintings, prints, photographs, concert programmes, etc.*

Theatre Museum. Russell St, Covent Garden, London WC2E 7PR *tel:* 020 7943 4700 *fax:* 020 7943 4777. C Malbon, publicity. *National Museum of Performing Arts including drama, musical theatre, mus, pop, melodrama, dance and opera. Public research facilities.*

Victoria and Albert Museum. Cromwell Rd, South Kensington, London SW7 2RL *tel:* 020 7942 2294 *fax:* 020 7942 2291 *email:* j.yorke@vam.ac.uk. James Yorke, curator. *Comprehensive exhibition coll of decorative mus insts; mus insts and mus iconography included in National Art Library at the V & A. Catalogue of Musical Instruments at the Victoria and Albert Museum; Vol 1, Keyboard Instruments by Howard Schott; Vol 2, Non-keyboard Instruments by Anthony Baines, with additions by James Yorke.*

Belfast. Ulster Museum. Botanic Gardens, Belfast BT9 5AB *tel:* 028 9038 3000 *fax:* 028 9038 3013. Mrs W Glover, curator of ethnography; Robert Heslip, curator of numismatics. *Small coll of ancient and modern mus insts. Ethnographic mus insts include 2 sets of Chimu pottery panpipes, 2 Bronze Age hns, 3 pairs of Uillean pipes, 4 hps, 2 fifes, 4 Lambeg drums.*

Bradford. Bolling Hall Museum. Bowling Hall Rd, Bradford, W Yorks BD4 7LP *tel:* 01274 723057 *fax:* 01274 726220. *Coll of mus insts dispersed among various museums in Bradford Metropolitan area. Mostly at Cliffe Castle Museum, Keighley.*

Cambridge. Fitzwilliam Museum. Trumpington St, Cambridge CB2 1RB *tel:* 01223 332900 *fax:* 01223 332923 *email:* fitzwilliam-enquiries@lists.cam.ac.uk. Stella Panayotova, asst keeper, dept of mss and printed books. *Printed and ms mus, including major colls of Handel, Macfarren, Hadley and the Fitzwilliam Virginal Book. A few guis, lutes, and keyboard insts, a pitch pipe, and small coll of unstrung hps are in the Dept of Applied arts, but not available to the public until Jul 2004.*

University Museum of Archaeology and Anthropology. Downing St, Cambridge CB2 3DZ *tel:* 01223 333516 *fax:* 01223 333517 *email:* cumaa@hermes.cam.ac.uk. David W Phillipson, dir and curator; Anita C Herle, snr asst curator; Robin B Boast, snr asst curator; Christopher R Chippindale, snr asst curator; Amiria Henare, asst curator. *Coll of insts of anthropological interest.*

Cardiff. Museum of Welsh Life (National Museums & Galleries of Wales). St Fagans, Cardiff CF5 6XB *tel:* 029 2057 3500 *fax:* 029 2057 3490 *email:* post.awc@btconnect.com. Emma Lile, asst curator. *Str, keyboard and wind insts.*

Carlisle. Tullie House. City Museum and Art Gallery, Castle St, Carlisle, Cumbria CA3 8TP *tel:* 01228 534781 *fax:* 01288 810249 *email:* enquiries@tullie-house.co.uk. Melanie Gardner, keeper of fine and decorative art. *Str and wind insts, including Andrea Amati vn of 1564 and str insts by Forster family.*

Cheltenham. Holst Birthplace Museum. 4 Clarence Rd, Pittville, Cheltenham, Glos GL52 2AY *tel:* 01242 524846 *fax:* 01242 580182 *email:* holstmuseum@btconnect.com. Melanie Armstrong, curator. *Unique coll of Holst material including printed mus, pictures, concert programmes, books, personal possessions. Open to public all yr (closed Sun-Mon), admission charge; guided tours by appointment.*

Douglas. Manx National Heritage. Manx Museum, Douglas, Isle of Man IM1 3LY *tel:* 01624 648000 *fax:* 01624 648001 *email:* enquiries@mnh.gov.im. Stephen Harrison, dir. *Str, keyboard and wind insts.*

East Clandon. Cobbe Collection Trust. Hatchlands Park, E Clandon, Surrey GU4 7RT *tel:* 01483 211474 *fax:* 01483 225922 *email:* enquiries@cobbecollection.co.uk. Alison Hoskyns. *Coll of historic keyboard insts associated with great composers, in National Trust House. Open Tue-Thu and Sun afternoons, Apr-Oct. Also concert series, tours, CDs and cat available.*

Edinburgh. Edinburgh University Collection of Historic Musical Instruments. Reid Concert Hall, Bristo Square, Edinburgh EH8 9AG *tel:* 0131 650 2422 *fax:* 0131 650 2425 *email:* euchmi@ed.ac.uk. Arnold Myers, dir. *Comprehensive display of over 1000 mus insts showing 400 yrs of history of folk and domestic mus, bands and orchs. New 'Sound Laboratory' gives hands-on approach to how mus insts work, with live sounds, physical models, computer displays and visible effects. Open Wed 3-5pm, Sat 10am-1pm (Mon-Fri 2-5pm throughout Edinburgh Festival). Closed over Christmas and New Year. Admission free.*

National War Museum of Scotland. The Castle, Edinburgh EH1 2NG *tel:* 0131 247 4409 *fax:* 0131 225 3848 *email:* e.philip@nms.ac.uk. Edith D Philip, asst curator, library/archives. *Military wind and perc insts from 18th C. Sound archives on tape of European and N American military mus (appointment necessary).*

Royal Museum & Museum of Scotland. National Museums of Scotland, Chambers St, Edinburgh EH1 1JF *tel:* 0131 225 7534 *fax:* 0131 220 4819 *email:* info@nms.ac.uk. *International and Scottish colls of str, keyboard and wind insts, including Glen and Ross bagpipe coll, coll of pipe-making tools. Jean Jenkins coll of sound recordings (ethnomusicological), also photographic slides and mus insts.*

Goudhurst. Finchcocks Living Museum of Music. Finchcocks, Goudhurst, Kent TH17 1HH *tel:* 01580 211702 *fax:* 01580 211007 *email:* katrina@finchcocks.co.uk. William Dow, curator. *Richard Burnett coll of historic keyboard insts. Open Sun and Bank Holidays Easter-Sep; Wed and Thu in Aug; other times by prior arrangement. Mus tours whenever open.*

Halifax. Shibden Hall. Listers Rd, Halifax, W Yorks HX3 6XG *tel:* 01422 352246/321455 *fax:* 01422 348440 *email:* shibden.hall@calderdale.gov.uk. Polly Salter, museums offr, social history. *General coll of mus insts, particularly 18th C chmbr. Also 19th C scores.*

Holdenby. Holdenby House, Holdenby, Northants NN6 8DJ *tel:* 01604 770074 *fax:* 01604 770962 *email:* enquiries@holdenby.com. Jim Powell, admin. *Non-player pno exhibition, old pnos including a 1790 Broadwood Grand. 11 pnos from British Piano Museum. House tours/groups by appointment, min 25.*

Huddersfield. Tolson Memorial Museum. Ravensknowle Park, Wakefield Rd, Huddersfield HD5 8DJ *tel:* 01484 223830 *fax:* 01484 223843. *Br, wind and str insts.*

Ipswich. Christchurch Mansion. Christchurch Park, Ipswich IP4 2BE *tel:* 01473 433554 *fax:* 01473 433564 *email:* christchurch.mansion@ipswich.gov.uk. Tim Heyburn, head of museums service. *Str, wind and keyboard insts.*

Ipswich Museum. High St, Ipswich IP1 3QH *tel:* 01473 433550 *fax:* 01473 433558 *email:* museums.service@ipswich.gov.uk. D L Jones, keeper, human history. *Ethnographic insts.*

Keighley. Cliffe Castle Museum, Keighley, W Yorks BD20 6LH *tel:* 01535 618230 *fax:* 01535 610536. Contact: snr keeper, history. *General coll of mus insts.*

Leicester. Charles Moore Collection of Musical Instruments. Music Dept, University of Leicester, University Rd, Leicester LE1 7RH *tel:* 0116 252 2781; 01234 360221 *fax:* 0116 252 2782 *email:* ap1@leicester.ac.uk. Stephen Weston, curator; Anthony Pither, dir of mus; Margaret Rose, admin asst. *Mainly 18th, 19th and 20th C w/wind and br.*

Liverpool. National Museums Liverpool, Decorative Art Dept. c/o PO Box 33, 127 Dale St, Liverpool L69 3LA *tel:* 0151 478 4262 *fax:* 0151 478 4693 *email:* pauline.rushton@liverpoolmuseums.org.uk. Pauline Rushton, curator of costume and textiles. *Coll of 17th-19th C insts including former Rushworth and Dreaper coll.*

Maidstone. Maidstone Museum and Bentlif Art Gallery. St Faiths Street, Maidstone, Kent ME14 1LH *tel:* 01622 602850 *fax:* 01622 685022 *email:* veronicatonge@maidstone.gov.uk. Veronica Tonge, keeper of fine and applied art. *Str, keyboard and wind insts, includes a Traeri portable clvd.*

* **Manchester.** Royal Northern College of Music. 124 Oxford Rd, Manchester M13 9RD *tel:* 0161 907 5243 *fax:* 0161 273 7611 *email:* library@rncm.ac.uk. Anna Smart, college librarian. *Including Alan Rawsthorne mss, Horenstein coll, Adolph Brodsky archive, Newmania (memorabilia of Philip Newman), Rothwell coll of wind mus, Dame Eva Turner coll, John Ogden archive, Ida Carroll archive, Philip Jones Brass Ensemble archive, Thomas Pitfield archive, John Golland mss, Arthur Butterworth mss, RNCM coll of historic mus insts, Harwood archive.*

Merthyr Tydfil. Cyfarthfa Castle Museum and Art Gallery. Merthyr Tydfil CF47 8RE *tel:* 01685 723112 *fax:* 01685 723112 *email:* museum@cyfarthfapark.freeserve.co.uk. Scott Reid, museums offr. *Mid 19th C coll of insts, ms mus, photographs and ephemera relating to the Cyfarthfa Band; also ethnographic inst coll.*

Northleach. Keith Harding's World of Mechanical Music. Oak House, High St, Northleach, Glos GL54 3ET *tel:* 01451 860181 *fax:* 01451 861133 *email:* Keith@mechanicalmusic.co.uk. Keith Harding. *Demonstrations and large stock of antique clocks, mus boxes, automata, reproducing pnos and mechanical mus insts presented as live entertainment. Restoration work done. Open Mon-Sun 10am-6pm (except Christmas and Boxing Day).*

Norwich. Strangers' Hall Museum (Norfolk Museums and Archaeology Service). Charing Cross, Norwich NR2 4AL *tel:* 01603 667229 *email:* museums@norfolk.gov.uk. Helen Rowles, asst. *Str, keyboard, perc and mechanical wind insts. Gramophones, printed and ms mus in store. Viewing by arrangement.*

Oxford. Ashmolean Museum. Beaumont St, Oxford OX1 2PH *tel:* 01865 278000 *fax:* 01865 278056 *email:* western-art@ashmus.ox.ac.uk. *Hill coll of str insts and bows (photographs and measured drawings of str insts available for research).*

Bate Collection of Musical Instruments. Oxford University Faculty of Music, St Aldate's, Oxford OX1 1DP *tel:* 01865 276139 *fax:* 01865 276128 *email:* bate.collection@music.oxford.ac.uk. H La Rue, curator; A Lamb, deputy curator. *W/wind, br, early keyboards and bow makers w/shop. Open Mon-Fri, 2-5pm, admission free. Open Sat during University full term, 10am-12pm.*

University of Oxford, Pitt Rivers Museum. Parks Rd, Oxford OX2 6PN *tel:* 01865 270927 *fax:* 01865 274725 *email:* pitt@prm.ox.ac.uk. H La Rue, university lecturer, curator. *Important worldwide coll of more than 6000 mus insts. Music Makers gallery in the Balfour Galleries: 60 Banbury Rd, Oxford Tel: 01865 274726. Includes a sound guide. Open by appointment only.*

St Albans. Organ Museum. c/o 326 Camp Rd, St Albans, Herts AL1 5PB *tel:* 01727 851557 *fax:* 01727 851557 *email:* billwalkerorgans@rdplus.net. Keith Pinner, chmn, sales offr, trustee; Peter Allen, treasurer, trustee; Colin Hartwell, sec; John Miller, publicity, trustee; Bill Walker, concert organiser, trustee. *Mechanical insts and theatre orgs; open Sun 2.15-4.30pm. Other times by arrangement.*

Shipley. Victorian Reed Organ and Harmonium Museum. Victoria Hall, Victoria Rd, Saltaire Village, Shipley, W Yorks *tel:* 01274 585601 (after 5pm); 07976 535980 *email:* phil@harmoniumservice.demon.co.uk. Phil and Pam Fluke, curators. *Private coll of about 100 reed orgs. Players encouraged to play. Also mechanical reed orgs. Open to the public Sun-Thu, 11am-4pm. Please phone beforehand.*

Worcester. The Elgar Birthplace Museum. Crown East Lane, Lower Broadheath, Worcester WR2 6RH *tel:* 01905 333224 *fax:* 01905 333426 *email:* birthplace@elgarmuseum.org. Catherine Sloan, museum dir; Margaret Sanders, archivist. *Elgar Centre and adjacent birthplace cottage, housing and displaying a unique coll of Elgarian material including mss, scores, letters, programmes, photographs and memorabilia.*

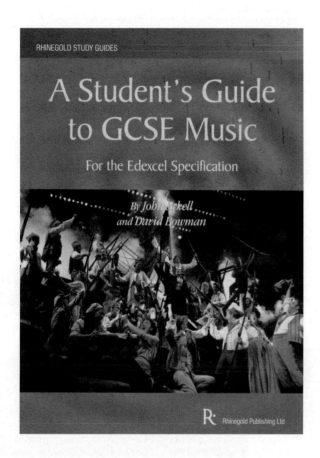

Early Music

The specialist publications are *Early Music Today, Early Music Review, Early Music,* and the *Early Music Yearbook,* details of which will be found in the **Music Periodicals** section.

Additional information can be obtained from **The Early Music Network** (31 Abdale Rd, London W12 7ER *tel:* 020 8743 0302 *fax:* 020 8743 0996 *email:* glyn@earlymusicnet.demon.co.uk *website:* www.earlymusic.org.uk), or from the **National Early Music Association** (c/o Mark Windisch, 137 Preston Rd, Wembley, Middx HA9 8NW *tel:* 020 8904 1706 *email:* mwindi4108@aol.com *website:* www.nema-uk.org).

Early Music Fora

Border Marches Early Music Forum (BMEMF). 13 Courtnay Rise, Hereford HR1 1BP *tel:* 01432 341154 *email:* hannah@thedaviesf9.co.uk. Hannah Davies, chair. *Medieval to baroque vocal and inst day w/shops held on Sat or Sun, in Herefordshire and surrounding Border Marches region. Occasional sponsoring of early mus concerts.*

Midlands Early Music Forum (MEMF). 21 Oakfield Ave, Kingswinford, W Midlands DY6 8HJ *tel:* 01384 295210 *email:* paul@diabolus.org. Paul Baker, sec. *Regular newsletter, w/shops, social events.*

North East Early Music Forum (NEEMF). 105 Bolling Rd, Ben Rhydding, Ilkley LS29 8QH *tel:* 01943 607252 *email:* stanghan@aol.com. Margaret Kurosinski, hon sec; Jillian Johnson, events co-ord. *Regular one-day w/shops in performance and interpretation, for singers and insts. Residential w/end in Sep.*

North West Early Music Forum (NWEMF). 11 Malvern Ave, Gatley, Cheadle SK8 4HT *tel:* 0161 491 2582 *email:* secretary@nwemf.org.uk. Janet Evans, sec. *W/shops and summer school for singers and instrumentalists.*

South West Early Music Forum (SWEMF). Little Hampden, Hunnacott, Landkey, Barnstaple, Devon EX32 0NW *tel:* 01271 831092 *fax:* 01271 830335 *email:* smadgwic@devon.gov.uk. Susan Madgwick, sec. *Promoting interest in early mus through w/shop performances.*

Southern Early Music Forum (SEMF). 108 Howard Drive, Allington Park, Maidstone ME16 0QB *tel:* 01622 762409 *email:* tim.samuelson@btinternet.com. Tim Samuelson, newsletter ed. *Early mus playing days. Register of contacts for musicians in the South East.*

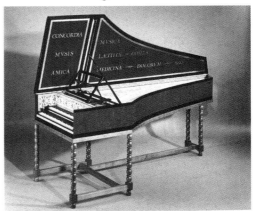

Indexes

INDEXES

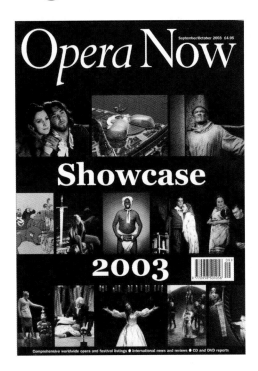

Index of Advertisers

Volume I contains pages 1 to 384 and Volume II contains pages 385 to 768. Both volumes begin with roman numeral pages and the correct volume is identified in this index by either I or II following the roman numeral page number.

Index of Advertising Artists in Volume 1

762

Index of Subjects

For your *free editorial entry* in the

British & International Music Yearbook

Complete this form or a photocopy, and return to:

British & International Music Yearbook, Books Department, Rhinegold Publishing Ltd,

PO Box 3362, Stratford-upon-Avon CV37 6ZP (*tel:* 01789 209280/1 *fax:* 01789 264009)

ORGANISATION/INSTITUTION ....

SECTION OF BOOK ....

ADDRESS ....

....

....

....

....POSTCODE...

TEL..FAX...

EMAIL..

WEBSITE ....

CONTACT ....POSITION...

OTHER PERSONNEL ....

....

....

COMPREHENSIVE DETAILS (PLEASE INCLUDE FOR ALL ENTRIES) ....

....

....

....

....

....

....

....

Performers, Ensembles, Conductors and **Composers** please use the form on the next page.
Please attach any additional details to support your entry.
Editorial entries are *free*, but are included at the discretion of the editor.

For inclusion in the 2005 edition, please return this form by end of July 2004.

PLEASE TICK HERE IF YOU WOULD BE INTERESTED IN
ADVERTISING IN THE BRITISH MUSIC YEARBOOK

Performers, Ensembles, Conductors and Composers

For your *free editorial entry* in the

British & International Music Yearbook

Complete this form or a photocopy, and return to:

British & International Music Yearbook, Books Department, Rhinegold Publishing Ltd,
PO Box 3362, Stratford-upon-Avon CV37 6ZP (*tel:* 01789 209280/1 *fax:* 01789 264009)

NAME..

VOICE/INSTRUMENT/COMPOSER/CONDUCTOR/ENSEMBLE

....

CONTACT ADDRESS ....

....

....

....POSTCODE..

TEL ....FAX..

EMAIL...

WEBSITE ....

AGENT(S) ....

COMPREHENSIVE DETAILS: Performers and conductors, please list your last six performances (including dates, venues, works performed, etc) and include a short CV. Composers, please list your publishers and details of your last six works performed or broadcast. Ensembles, also include personnel details and a description of ensemble. **Please note that no entries can be accepted without these details.**

....

....

....

....

....

....

....

Please attach any additional details to support your entry.
Editorial entries are *free*, but are included at the discretion of the editor.

For inclusion in the 2005 edition, please return this form by end of July 2004.

PLEASE TICK HERE IF YOU WOULD BE INTERESTED IN
ADVERTISING IN THE BRITISH MUSIC YEARBOOK